ANATOMY AND PHYSIOLOGY

WILLIAM F. EVANS

Associate Professor and Chairman
Department of Health Sciences
University of Arkansas, Little Rock

SECOND EDITION

anatomy and physiology

PRENTICE-HALL, INC., Englewood Cliffs, New Jersey

Library of Congress Cataloging in Publication Data

Evans, William F
  Anatomy and physiology.

  Bibliography: p.
  Includes index.
  1. Human physiology. 2. Anatomy, Human. I. Title.
[DNLM: 1. Anatomy. 2. Physiology. QS4 E93a 1976]
QP34.5.E9 1976   612   75-25845
ISBN 0-13-035196-2

ANATOMY AND PHYSIOLOGY

second edition

William F. Evans

© 1976, 1971 by PRENTICE-HALL, INC.
Englewood Cliffs, New Jersey

Current printing:

10 9 8 7 6 5 4

Illustrations by Russell Peterson

Printed in the United States of America

Prentice-Hall International, Inc., *London*

Prentice-Hall of Australia, Pty., Ltd., *Sydney*

Prentice-Hall of Canada, Ltd., *Toronto*

Prentice-Hall of India (Private) Ltd., *New Delhi*

Prentice-Hall of Japan, Inc., *Tokyo*

Prentice-Hall of Southeast Asia, *Singapore*

contents

SEVEN integration and control by the nervous system **145**

Again to Annette

preface

The second edition of this book has the same primary objective as the first edition: to provide a concise, readable, basic textbook of anatomy and physiology for students of nursing, physical education, and the health-related professions. This edition brings many changes in content and style, which, hopefully, will increase the usefulness of the book. Virtually all sections concerned with functions of the body systems have been rewritten, and the discussions of physiology relative to pure anatomy have been significantly expanded. This is in keeping with the present trend of placing emphasis on function, where it properly belongs. The chapters that are most extensively revised are Chapters 2 ("The Body Systems and Protoplasm"), 11 ("The Breathing Mechanism and Gaseous Exchange"), and 13 ("Metabolism, Foods, and Nutrition"). Other major changes include the thorough revision of the sections on the physiology of vision and hearing, portal and fetal circulation, regulation of arteriole diameter, and the tonsils and paranasal sinuses. New discussions have been added involving the thymus and pineal body and the pressure points for the control of hemorrhage. An earnest attempt has been made to clarify the anatomy and physiology of the major spinal tracts and pathways. For the convenience of the reader, the second edition contains tables that summarize the principle actions of skeletal muscles.

A completely new chapter, concerned with fluid, electrolyte, and acid-base balance, has been added, while most of the presentation of general chemistry of the first edition has been deleted. Each chapter is now concluded with a section of study questions and problems. The material concerning the body defenses against disease and injury has been incorporated into the main body of the text, and is no longer isolated as a separate chapter at the end of the book.

While the illustration concepts of the first edition have been retained, all of the figures have been redrawn in two colors on a larger scale. In addition to the figures in the text, there are now eight full color plates that depict the human anatomy.

The most gratifying aspect of laboring over a volume such as this is its acceptance by others. Without the approval of his students and peers, an author lacks strong motivation, and this is inevitably reflected in his work. The fine reception accorded the first edition of *Anatomy and Physiology* has supplied me with ample motivation to produce this second edition, with the fervent hope that it represents a significant improvement over the first.

I wish to thank my many students and everyone on the publisher's staff, whose more than diligent efforts helped to make easier the task of revision.

W.F.E.

the language of anatomy: the body as a whole

The student who wishes to acquire a working knowledge of **anatomy** (the study of body structure) and **physiology** (the study of body function) must first learn the definitions and usage of a sizeable number of words or terms and phrases, virtually all of which are unique to the subject. Like physics, chemistry, psychology, and numerous other studies, anatomy has a terminology or language all its own. For some time, the language of anatomy has been in a state of confusion, and although the situation has vastly improved, complete standardization of anatomical terms and phrases has yet to be achieved. In this book, only those terms and phrases which have met with general acceptance will be used. It is the dual purpose of this chapter to present some of the most important and frequently used anatomical terminology, and at the same time introduce the student to the subject of anatomy itself.

Anatomy is conveniently separated into two major divisions: *gross anatomy,* which includes all those body structures that can be seen with the unaided eye; and *microscopic anatomy* or *histology,* which is concerned with the microscopic study of the various tissues and their cellular components. The former will be explored at this time.

The body regions

(See Figure 1-1 and Color Plates I-VIII.) Grossly, the body can first be divided into *head and neck, trunk,* and *extremities or limbs.* The trunk is the body minus the head, neck, and extremities. The chest is known as the *thorax or thoracic region,* while that portion of the trunk below it on the front of the body is called the *abdomen or abdominal region.* The *upper back* is that portion of the back between and just below the shoulder blades or *scapulae* (sing., scapula). The *lower back* is the *lumbar region.* The front wall of the thorax, made up of the large chest muscles, breastbone and portions of the ribs, nerves, blood and lymph vessels, and connective tissue, is called the *pectoral region.* High on the sides of the thorax, where the upper extremity meets the trunk, is the armpit or *axilla,* also called the *axillary fossa* or *axillary region.* Through the axilla pass the large nerves and blood vessels supplying the upper extremity. Below the lumbar region, the large hip muscles and varying amounts of fat form two rounded prominences, usually more conspicuous in women, the *buttocks.* This portion of the body is also referred to as the *gluteal region,* and is often the target of hypodermic needles. Important vessels and nerves to the lower limb pass through or near the gluteal region, and others traverse the triangular area at the front of the trunk between the thighs, the *pubic region or groin.* The pubic region is the lowest portion of the front of the abdomen. High between the legs, the pubic region is continuous with a region called the *perineum,* which contains the *external sex organs* and *anal opening.*

THE HEAD AND NECK   The *head* is small in proportion to ·the remainder of the adult

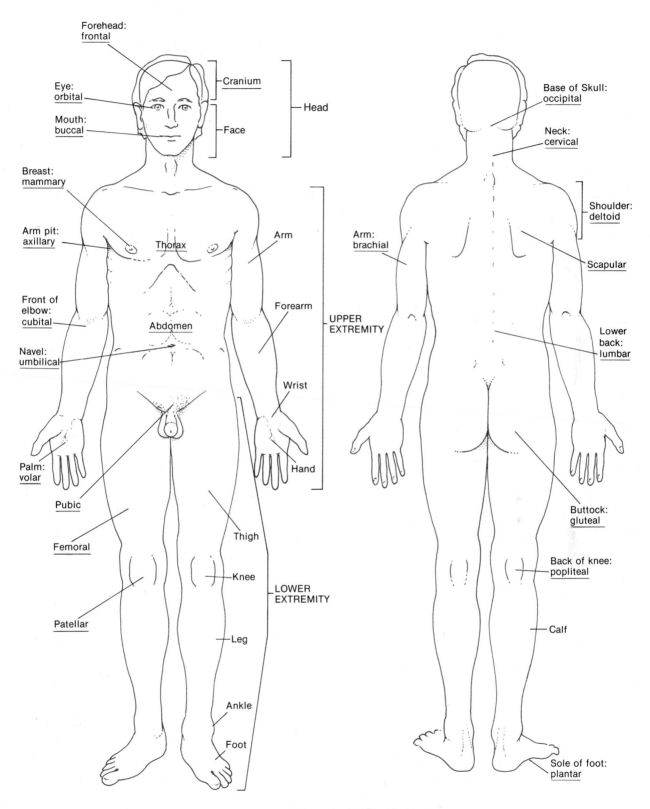

Figure 1.1 Major body regions. Some are labeled with common and scientific terms, with the latter indicated by underscores. The subject is standing in the anatomical position.

3

body, but houses such important structures as the brain, organs of special sense (eyes, ears, organs of taste and smell), and the upper portions of the respiratory and digestive tracts. The *neck* permits the head to move about and contains such structures as the *trachea* (windpipe), the *esophagus* (food tube connecting the mouth with the stomach) *large blood vessels,* the *spinal cord,* and *several nerves.* The spinal cord is in direct continuation with the *brain* and extends for most of the length of the *vertebral column* (spinal column or backbone).

THE UPPER EXTREMITY   The *upper extremity* or limb is divided anatomically into *shoulder, upper arm* or *brachium, forearm* or *antebrachium,* and *hand.* The *elbow* is the point of junction between the upper arm and forearm, and the front of the elbow is known as the *cubital fossa.* Passing through the cubital fossa on their way to the forearm and hand are nerves and blood vessels from the upper arm, and also vessels that carry blood back up the limb toward the heart. The cubital fossa is an important site for the *intravenous* (within a vein) *injection* of drugs and nutrients, and for the withdrawal of blood. The *wrist* is the region of junction between the forearm and hand.

THE LOWER EXTREMITY   That portion of the lower limb between the trunk and the knee or *genu* is known as the *thigh;* that extending from the knee to the foot is the *leg;* and below the leg is the *foot.* The junction between leg and foot is the *ankle.* Behind the knee is a region somewhat comparable to the cubital fossa of the upper limb, the *popliteal fossa.*

Terms indicating direction

Directional terms are *relative;* that is, a structure or body region is described as being in a certain position or direction as related to another structure or region. A *standard posture,* the **anatomical position** (Fig. 1-1), is always to be kept in mind when using terms of direction, and its importance cannot be overemphasized. In the anatomical position, the *body is erect, feet on floor and slightly apart* with the *head and palms facing forward.* No matter what the actual position of the body, the directional terms used are always those which would apply if the body were in the anatomical position. Some of these terms are as follows.

ANTERIOR   Anterior means *toward the front of the body or body part.* For example, the nose and eyes are on the anterior aspect or surface of the head. Another example: the toes and the palms of the hands face anteriorly. The term *ventral* is synonymous with anterior in the human, but it refers to the underside of four-footed animals (quadrupeds), such as cats and dogs (Fig. 1-2).

POSTERIOR   This term means *toward the back of the body or body part;* for example, the back of the head, the lower back, and the backs of the limbs are all posterior. Posterior is synonymous with the term *dorsal* in humans, the latter being a term used more frequently when referring to quadrupeds.

SUPERIOR   A term indicating "*upward.*" The head and neck sit on the superior end of the trunk; the nose is superior in position to the mouth; and the third rib is superior to the fourth rib.

INFERIOR   A term meaning "*downward*": the mouth is inferior in position to the nose, and so on. The terms superior and inferior are not commonly used when describing human extremities or any anatomical features of four-footed animals.

MEDIAL   When a point or structure is described as being medial to another point or structure, this means that it is *nearer an imaginary vertical midline dividing the body into right and left halves.* In the anatomical position, the little finger is on the medial side of the hand, the upper part of the nose is medial to either eye, and the big toe is on the medial side of the foot. The term *mesial* is sometimes substituted for medial.

LATERAL   This term describes the position of a body part or point on the body that is *farther away from the midline with reference to another point or part.* For example, one ear is on each lateral aspect of the head; the shoulders are located on the lateral aspects of the superior end of the trunk; and the thumbs are on the lateral sides of the hands

Labels on image:
Cranial superior
Dorsal posterior
Ventral anterior
Cranial anterior
Caudal posterior
Dorsal superior
Ventral inferior
Caudal inferior

Figure 1.2 Major directional terms, comparing human with quadruped.

(remember the rule of always mentally reverting to the anatomical position when using directional terms).

SUPERFICIAL This term means *at the surface of the body* or *nearer the surface than some other point or structure.* Loose areolar connective tissue just beneath the skin, is known as *superficial fascia.* Nerves and blood vessels of the skin are superficial in position, in relation to deeper lying counterparts. One part of a body structure is always superficial to another. *Superficial* is the opposite of *deep.*

DEEP Deep implies that *a given point or structure lies inward,* away from the surface of the body, or more inward with reference to a related structure. Beneath the superficial fascia previously mentioned is a tough, membranous covering on the muscles, the *deep fascia.* The interior of an organ, such as the kidney or lung, is deep to the outer portion, which is superficial to the deeper portions. A needle used in giving an injection *moves from superficial to deep* during insertion, and *from deep to superficial* during withdrawal. The term *central* is sometimes substituted for

deep, and *peripheral* is often used in preference to superficial. For example, the brain and spinal cord comprise the *central nervous system,* while the nerves which extend outward away from the brain and spinal cord make up the *peripheral nervous system. Internal* and *external* are still other terms sometimes substituted for superficial and deep. In the abdomen, for example, there is an *external abdominal oblique muscle* and an *internal abdominal oblique muscle.*

PROXIMAL AND DISTAL These terms indicate *nearness to* and *distance away from* the trunk, and they are usually reserved for discussions of the anatomy of the extremities. The knee, then, is proximal to the ankle; the hand is at the distal end of the upper extremity; and the nails are on the distal ends of the digits (fingers and thumbs). The terms proximal and distal are used also when referring to the relative nearness of a point on a nerve, blood vessel, urine tube (ureter or urethra), or other structure to its origin. For example, the proximal end of the ureter is the end continuous with a kidney, while the distal end attaches to the urinary bladder. Another example: the proximal end of the aorta (the largest artery in the body) has its origin (beginning) at the heart, while the distal end is far from the heart, in the abdominal region.

Sections and planes

In anatomical laboratories, bodies must be cut or sectioned in order to study deep structures in relation to each other (Fig. 1-3). A cut *from anterior to posterior,* separating the body into equal right and left halves, is a *midsagittal section,* and is made in the *median plane.* The term *parasagittal* refers to a plane or section that is parallel to a midsagittal section or plane. When the body is sectioned in a horizontal direction (remember the anatomical position!), a *cross-section* (or transverse section) has been made—in a *transverse plane.* Sectioning the body or one of its parts so that front and rear portions (*not* equal halves) are produced involves *frontal* or *coronal* planes and sections. It will be noted in Fig. 1-3 that while there are *two vertical planes* or sections, there is *only one which is horizontal.*

5

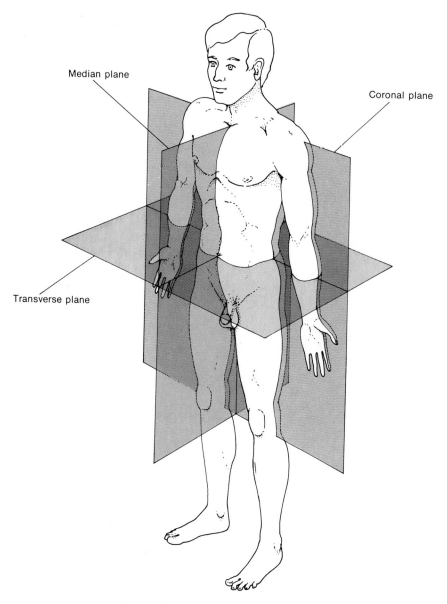

Figure 1.3 The body planes.

Median plane

Coronal plane

Transverse plane

Surface anatomy

Many points and *landmarks* can be located on the surface of the body, some by the use of imaginary lines and some by feel or *palpation*.

One example of an *anatomical landmark* is the *point of the shoulder* (Fig. 1-4), a bump caused by a bony process (projection) on the scapula or shoulder blade, the *acromion process*. As will be seen later, several blood vessels, nerves, and muscles can be located by using the acromion as a reference point. An important site of injection into the deltoid muscle can be located with reference to this point. The *suprasternal*

notch, another anatomical landmark, is easily palpated (felt) at the superior end of the *sternum* (or "breastbone"). A few centimeters below the notch is a point which protrudes slightly anteriorly, the *sternal angle.* It is formed by the junction of the *manubrium* (upper portion of the sternum) with the *body* (the largest portion) of the sternum. Deep to the sternal angle is the first part of the *aorta;* and since the *second pair of ribs* joins the sternum at this point, it is a simple matter to count ribs beginning at the sternal angle.

The *xiphisternal junction* locates the so-called pit of the stomach. Here, the cartilaginous *xiphoid process* joins the inferior end of the body of the sternum. Along either side of the inferior portion of the trunk, the *iliac crest,* or crest of the ilium, can be seen and palpated. It is formed by the upper portion of the *ilium bone.* The iliac crests are not prominent in overweight individuals. The bump at the lateral side of the ankle is known as the *lateral malleolus;* the one on the medial aspect of the ankle is the *medial malleolus.* The former is the distal portion of the *fibula bone,* while the latter represents the corresponding portion of the *tibia.* The sharp anterior border of the tibia forms a ridge commonly called the *shin.* Other bones and bony prominences, such as the *clavicle* or "collarbone" and the *mastoid process* behind the ear, can easily be seen and palpated by the student.

SPECIAL SURFACE ANATOMY OF THE ABDOMEN   The physician customarily marks off the surface of the abdomen (mentally) into *nine regions or areas* (Fig. 1-4). The upper third of the surface consists of the *right and left hypochondriac areas laterally,* and the *epigastric area medially;* the middle third is made up of the *right and left lumbar and umbilical areas,* while the *right and left iliac and hypogastric areas* constitute the lower one-third. Although the upper areas seem to be taking in a large portion of the chest, it should be pointed out that, internally, the dome-shaped *diaphragm* (Fig. 1-5) extends the abdomen far more superiorly than is commonly supposed.

The areas of the abdomen are marked off by drawing imaginary (or washable-ink) lines on the skin as follows:

1.   *One line transversely,* at the level of the ninth ribs, where they join the sternum.

2.   *One line transversely* at the anterior portion of the iliac crests.

3.   *Two lines vertically,* halfway between the midline (which passes through the *umbilicus,* or navel) and the most anterior portion of the ilium which is palpable, the *anterior superior iliac spine.*

It will be noted that each of the vertical lines passes *slightly medial to the nipple* of the breast.

Figure 1.4   Surface anatomy.

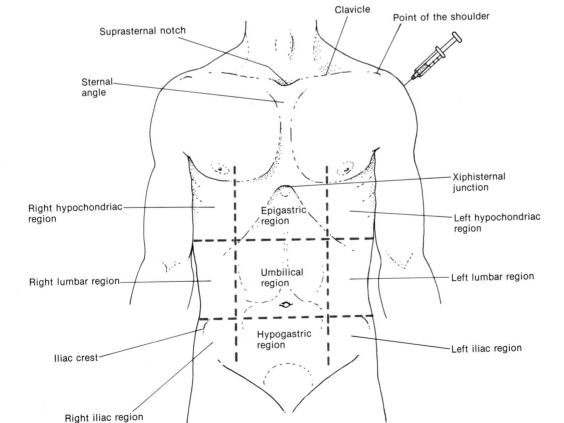

Suprasternal notch

Clavicle

Point of the shoulder

Sternal
angle

Xiphisternal
junction

Right hypochondriac
region

Epigastric
region

Left hypochondriac
region

Right lumbar region

Umbilical
region

Left lumbar region

Iliac crest

Hypogastric
region

Left iliac region

Right iliac region

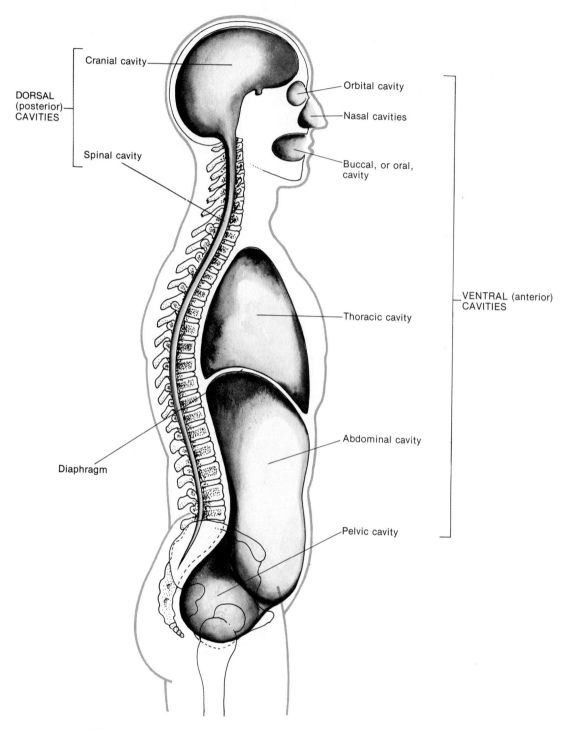

Figure 1.5 Body cavities.

Body cavities

Students often seem surprised to learn of the large number of cavities and spaces in the human body. Some idea of the positions and relative sizes of the *major body cavities* can be obtained by examining Fig. 1-5. The body cavities can be arranged into *two*

groups: those which are *posterior or dorsally placed;* and those which lie more *anterior or ventral.* The dorsal or posterior cavities include the *cranial cavity,* containing the brain, and the *spinal cavity or vertebral canal,* containing the spinal cord. As shown in the figure, the spinal and cranial cavities are continuous with one another.

The ventral or anterior cavities include the *orbital cavities* containing the eyes, the *nasal cavities* of the nose, *buccal cavity* or mouth, *thoracic or chest cavity, abdominal cavity,* and *pelvic cavity,* continuous above with the abdomen. Like the cranial and spinal cavities, the abdominal and pelvic cavities are merely different portions of one large cavity, and are sometimes spoken of together as the *abdominopelvic cavity.* The thoracic, abdominal, and pelvic cavities are often spoken of by anatomists as constituting one large cavity, the *celom.* The celom contains the *thoracic viscera* (organs) in the thoracic cavity above the diaphragm and the *abdominal and pelvic viscera* below the diaphragm.

One more outstanding body cavity should be mentioned: the cavity of the digestive tract, or *alimentary canal,* made up of the esophagus, stomach, and intestines. This arrangement constitutes a cavity-within-a-cavity, since the digestive tract opens only to the outside—at the mouth and anus—and does not communicate with the celom.

The body systems

Cells comprise the *tissues* of the body, tissues make up *organs,* and these in turn make up *organ systems.* Organ systems comprise the *human organism.* There are some ten systems in the body. Some anatomists group certain of the following into still fewer systems, while others contend they should be further subdivided into more systems. For our purposes, the following list will suffice: *skeletal, muscular, digestive, respiratory, reproductive, nervous, urinary, circulatory, endocrine,* and *integumentary* systems. Each of these systems is discussed in detail, both anatomically and physiologically, in the succeeding chapters of this book.

Ideally, dissection of a laboratory animal or human subject would proceed one system at a time. Due to the scarcity of dissection material and lack of time, this procedure is not followed when human subjects are used. Instead, dissection is carried out *regionally,* and the burden of visualizing the body as a *connected, integrated whole* falls to the student, who must avoid the pitfall of thinking of the body as a group of isolated body regions.

In this chapter, the reader has been introduced to the study of anatomy. In the next chapter, physiology will be of primary concern. In the remaining chapters, anatomy is integrated with physiology, to keep the relationship between structure and function in constant view.

**OUTLINE
SUMMARY**

1. The language of anatomy: special terminology pertaining to body structure and position
2. Divisions of anatomy
   A. Gross anatomy: concerned with those body structures visible to the unaided eye
   B. Microscopic anatomy (histology): concerned with the study of cells and tissues with the aid of a microscope
3. The major gross body regions
   A. Head and neck
   B. Extremities (limbs)
   C. Trunk (the body minus the head, neck, and extremities)
      a. Thorax (chest)
      b. Abdomen (front of trunk below the thorax)
      c. Upper back (between and just below shoulder blades)
      d. Lumbar region (lower back)
      e. Pectoral region (front wall of thorax)
      f. Axilla (armpit region)
      g. Gluteal region (buttocks)
      h. Pubic region (groin, or triangular area between thighs); continuous above with abdominal region
      i. Perineum (highest region between the thighs)
   D. The upper extremity—portions
      a. Shoulder
      b. Upper arm or brachium
      c. Elbow and a depression on the front of it, the cubital fossa
      d. Forearm or antebrachium
      e. Wrist
      f. Hand
   E. The lower extremity—portions
      a. Hip
      b. Thigh
      c. Knee and the depression behind it, the popliteal region or fossa
      d. Leg
      e. Ankle
      f. Foot

4. Terms of direction
    A. The anatomical position: a standard posture, always mentally assumed when thinking in anatomical terms
    B. Directional terms
        a. Anterior
        b. Posterior
        c. Superior
        d. Inferior
        e. Medial
        f. Lateral
        g. Superficial
        h. Deep
        i. Proximal and distal
5. Sections and planes: a section is a cut; a plane is the path taken by the knife while making the cut
6. Surface anatomy: points and landmarks that can be located either by sight, palpation (feeling), or both. Examples:
    A. Point of the shoulder
    B. Scapula and its acromion process
    C. Suprasternal notch
    D. Sternal angle
    E. Xiphisternal junction
    F. Iliac crest (crest of the ilium)
    G. Lateral malleolus of the ankle
    H. Medial malleolus of the ankle
    I. Sharp border of the tibia, or "shin"
    J. Clavicle or "collarbone"

7. Special surface anatomy of the abdomen—nine regions or areas, all important in medicine
    A. Epigastric
    B. Hypochondriac (right and left)
    C. Umbilical
    D. Lumbar (right and left)
    E. Hypogastric
    F. Iliac (right and left)
8. Body cavities
    A. Orbital (eye sockets)
    B. Nasal
    C. Buccal (mouth)
    D. Thoracic
    E. Abdominal
    F. Pelvic
    G. Cranial
    H. Spinal
9. Body systems: consist of organs which work together to perform a common function—ten systems
    A. Skeletal
    B. Muscular
    C. Digestive
    D. Respiratory
    E. Reproductive
    F. Nervous
    G. Urinary
    H. Circulatory
    I. Endocrine
    J. Integumentary

STUDY QUESTIONS AND PROBLEMS

1. Describe the anatomical position. Why is it helpful to use such a position in medicine and nursing?

2. What are the gross divisions of the body? What is gross anatomy?

3. Locate the following regions of your own body: lumbar, axillary, pectoral, thoracic, abdominal, gluteal, and pubic.

4. What contents of the axilla are vital to the movement and nourishment of the upper extremity?

5. Where is the cubital fossa? The popliteal region? The brachium?

6. An instructor of anatomy moves her hand from her abdominal region upward toward her head. Anatomically speaking, her hand is moving in what direction? Next, she moves her hand from the abdominal region of a cat to the head of the cat. Anatomically speaking, in what direction is her hand moving in this instance?

7. The term *ventral* is synonymous with what other term in the human?

8. What anatomical term means the opposite of *deep*? What is the opposite of *lateral*? *Proximal*? *Posterior*?

9. A section that divides the body into anterior and posterior portions is given a name. What is this name? What is the name given to a section that divides the body into right and left halves? Into upper and lower portions?

10. Nurse L. notes the point of the shoulder of her patient, and locates an injection site with reference to this point. What forms the point of the shoulder?

11. What bone forms the lateral malleolus at the ankle? Medial malleolus? What is the anatomical name for the collarbone?

12. Sketch and label the nine regions of the abdomen. State the three rules for marking off the lines on the skin.

13. List the anterior and posterior body cavities.

14. What is the celom?

the body systems, physiology, and protoplasm

Just as anatomy is concerned with body structure, physiology is the study of body *function*. Investigation of the physiological processes of the various organs and organ systems leads inevitably to examination of the physiology of tissues, the cells that comprise these tissues, and, ultimately, to the study of the material that comprises cells, *protoplasm*.

In this chapter, the general functions of the organ systems are considered, certain fundamentals of physiology are examined, and the most outstanding features of protoplasm—living matter—are summarized. This approach should give the reader an overview of the intricate workings of the body and its larger parts. The understanding of the material in this chapter is necessary to an understanding and working knowledge of body processes as they are presented throughout the remainder of the book.

Chief functions of the body systems

INTEGUMENTARY SYSTEM   The *integumentary system,* or *integument,* consists of the *skin* and its accessory structures, *hair* and *nails.* The skin is well supplied with blood vessels, nerves, and sweat and oil glands. The chief functions of the skin include protection, helping to maintain a constant body temperature and water content, excretion of wastes,

perception of changes in the environment (sensation), and vitamin production.

SKELETAL SYSTEM   *Bones, cartilage,* and the *ligaments* that hold bones together at joints form the *skeletal system.* This system gives the body support and protection, permits movement, provides for muscle attachment, forms blood cells, stores minerals, and removes certain poisons from the blood.

MUSCULAR SYSTEM   This body system is made up of the *skeletal muscles* and their *tendons and other attachments,* and does not include the muscle of the heart (cardiac muscle) or that found in the walls of such structures as the stomach, intestine, or blood vessels (smooth muscle). The skeletal muscles, because they are able to shorten, bring about all our body movements. The large amount of heat they produce is vital to the maintenance of body temperature, and the alternating contractions (shortening) of muscles helps the skeletal system to give the body support.

NERVOUS SYSTEM   The nervous system consists of the *brain, spinal cord,* and *nerves,* each of which is made up of nerve cells (neurons) and supporting tissues. This system keeps us apprised of changes in our environment by enabling us to see, hear, smell, taste, and experience sensations of temperature, touch, pressure, and pain. The nervous system also enables us to reason, to remember, and experience emotions. It sends impulses that cause muscles to contract and glands to secrete, and it works with all body systems to integrate all physiological processes so that normal functions can be maintained. Much of the activity of the nervous system is reflex in character; that is, it is carried out below the level of consciousness.

CIRCULATORY SYSTEM   The *heart, blood vessels,* and *blood* comprise the circulatory system. The heart pumps the blood throughout the body, transporting food, water, hormones, antibodies, oxygen, carbon dioxide, and many other substances to or from the body cells as required. Body temperature regulation is a partial responsibility of the circulatory system, since warm blood is constantly moved throughout the body.

RESPIRATORY SYSTEM   The chief organs of breathing or respiration are the *diaphragm* and *lungs.* The diaphragm is a muscular sheet that separates the thoracic from the abdominal cavity, and draws fresh air into the lungs and forces used air out. The transfer of oxygen from the air to the blood and of carbon dioxide from the blood to the atmosphere occurs in the lungs. Oxygen must be supplied to all the body cells, and carbon dioxide must be removed from them, in order for life to exist. The voice—and, therefore, all verbal communication—is largely the responsibility of the respiratory system.

DIGESTIVE SYSTEM   This organ system consists chiefly of the *tongue* and *teeth, esophagus* or *food tube, stomach, intestines, liver,* and *pancreas.* The responsibility of the digestive system is the reduction of large food particles to a size and chemical nature that can be absorbed (taken from the digestive system into the blood) and thereby utilized by the body cells for energy, growth, and tissue repair.

URINARY SYSTEM   Sometimes called the *excretory* system, the urinary apparatus consists of *two kidneys* connected by long tubes (*ureters*) to a storage device, the *bladder,* plus a third tube, (the *urethra*), which leads from the bladder to the outside. Many of the waste products of the body are filtered out of the blood as it passes through the kidneys,

and these wastes are then removed from the body in the urine.

REPRODUCTIVE SYSTEM   The functions of the reproductive system fall into two categories: *cytogenic* (cell-producing) and *endocrinic* (hormone-producing). Sex cells (*gametes*) of two differing kinds are produced by the male and female reproductive systems, and their union is essential to the production of a new individual. The male gamete is called *sperm cell;* the female, an *ovum.* The hormones produced by the reproductive system aid the nervous system in its regulatory role, and have great influence on the appearance and reproductive activities of the individual.

ENDOCRINE SYSTEM   The glands of this system (*thyroid, parathyroid, pituitary,* and *adrenal,* plus *portions of the pancreas, testes,* and *ovaries*), in conjunction with certain other hormone-producing tissues, produce powerful chemical substances—*hormones*—that exert great influence on the growth and development of the individual, and aid the nervous system in the regulation of numerous body processes.

*Fundamental concepts
in physiology*

Of the many areas of body function of great interest to the field of physiology, there are a few which are of particular importance. Among these are the mechanisms involved in the beating of the heart and circulation of the blood, the utilization of food and oxygen and the release of energy, the elimination of wastes, the contraction of muscles, the perception of changes in the environment, transmission of the nerve impulse and regulation and coordination of body processes by the nervous system and hormones, transport of materials through cell membranes, and the constancy of the internal environment. The last mentioned is perhaps the most singularly important item in the list, and merits further discussion.

HOMEOSTASIS: THE DYNAMIC BALANCE OF LIFE   The internal environment of the body consists of those fluids that bathe the body cells—*intercellular* or *tissue fluid, blood,* and *lymph.* Many years ago, it was discovered that although oxygen, foods, water, and other substances are constantly leaving the body fluids to enter cells, while carbon dioxide and other wastes are continually leaving cells and entering these fluids, the chemical composition of the fluids remains within remarkably narrow limits. **Homeostasis** was the name given to this phenomenon by the great physiologist Walter B. Cannon. By definition, homeostasis is the dynamic balance or *steady state* involving levels of salts, water, sugars, and other materials—even osmotic and acid-base relationships—in the body fluids. Homeostasis is a dynamic rather than a static (stationary) equilibrium because the composition of the body fluids is in a state of flux. What is remarkable is that, within limits, no matter what we eat, how much or how little we exercise, or what daily stresses and strains we are subjected to, we retain homeostatic equilibrium of our body fluids. The rhythm of the heart and that of breathing, the constancy of the body temperature, and the steady level of blood pressure under specific circumstances or conditions are all manifestations of homeostatic mechanisms at work within the body. Every organ system plays some role in the maintenance of homeostasis: The circulatory system keeps the body fluids well mixed, the respiratory system constantly brings in oxygen and eliminates carbon dioxide, the digestive system takes in food and water and eliminates solid wastes, the skin and kidneys eliminate watery wastes, the skeletal system forms blood cells, the nervous

system integrates the functioning of other systems, and so on.

PROTOPLASM

In his many attempts to find out just what makes living things live, man has tried to analyze protoplasm to determine what materials are in it and in what proportion. So far, man has only been able to analyze protoplasm shortly after it has stopped living, because as soon as analysis is begun, living substance dies. Through the efforts of many researchers for a great number of years, it has been determined that freshly killed protoplasm consists of a relatively large number of chemical substances, or *elements,* none of which is unique to living matter; that is, these substances are distributed also in the nonliving matter of the world. It seems to be the very special way in which they are combined that gives protoplasm the qualities of life: *the ability to respond to stimuli* (changes in external or internal environment of the body), *to conduct an impulse* (wave of excitability) once a stimulus has been received, *to grow, to reproduce,* and *to carry out the many chemical processes known collectively as metabolism.* It is known that protoplasm is colloidal in character, and can change from sol to gel and vice versa; it is also known that its reaction is neutral (neither acidic nor basic). Long ago, scientists noted that protoplasm is often translucent, and that it takes on the color of the cells in which it is found. For example, the protoplasm found in muscle cells is reddish, while that in certain cartilage is blue-gray.

**OUTLINE
SUMMARY**

1. Physiology: study of body function. The organ systems:
   A. Integumentary: protection sensation, excretion
   B. Skeletal: support, protection, blood formation
   C. Muscular: movement, heat production
   D. Nervous: conscious awareness, abstract thought, correlation and integration of body functions

   E. Circulatory: transport of materials throughout the body, distribution of body heat
   F. Respiratory: gaseous exchange
   G. Digestive: preparation of food for utilization
   H. Urinary: elimination of body wastes
   I. Reproductive: essential to production of a new individual
   J. Endocrine: helps regulate growth and

development and regulation of body processes by means of hormones

2. Fundamental concepts in physiology. Homeostasis: the dynamic balance of life
   A. The internal environment
   B. Dynamic balance (steady state) of chemical composition of internal environment
   C. Contribution of organ systems to homeostasis
3. Protoplasm
   A. Special features of living matter: the qualities of life
      a. Responsiveness or irritability
      b. Conductivity
      c. Growth
      d. Reproduction
      e. Metabolism
   B. Physical features of protoplasm
      a. Translucent: permits passage of some light
      b. Colloidal: can change from sol to gel and vice versa
      c. Reaction: neutral (neither acidic nor basic
      d. Color: takes on color of tissue in which it is found

1. List the five special qualities of living matter.
2. Define *homeostasis,* and give three examples.
3. List the major functions of each of the body systems.
4. What is meant by the "internal environment" of the body?
5. List the physical features of protoplasm.

cells and tissues

Every tissue and organ of the body is made up of structures too small to be seen with the unaided eye: cells . . . *muscle cells, nerve cells, bone cells, blood cells,* and many other kinds of cells (Fig. 3-1). There are about two thousand billion cells in the tissues of a newborn baby, and this number greatly increases as growth takes place. It should be emphasized that *only when the chemicals of protoplasm are so organized do they actually form living matter.* In certain tissues, such as heart muscle, the cells have fused together so that they can hardly be considered individual, discrete units; but these tissues are still highly cellular in character.

During the development of an infant in the mother's body, each kind of cell becomes specialized, or *differentiated,* in order that it

Figure 3.1 Various types of cells.

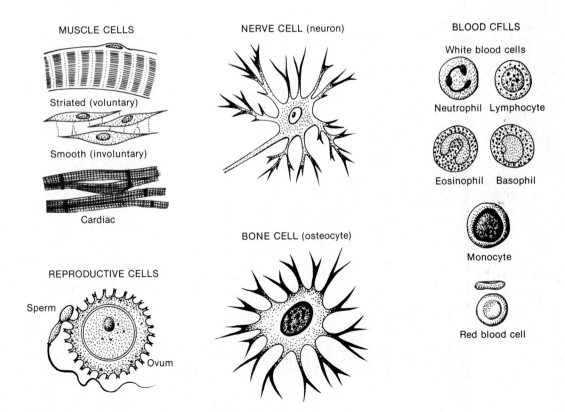

MUSCLE CELLS

Striated (voluntary)

Smooth (involuntary)

Cardiac

REPRODUCTIVE CELLS

Sperm

Ovum

NERVE CELL (neuron)

BONE CELL (osteocyte)

BLOOD CELLS

White blood cells

Neutrophil   Lymphocyte

Eosinophil   Basophil

Monocyte

Red blood cell

may help similar cells to do a particular job, as a *tissue*. The various types of cells do not look very much alike (Fig. 3-1). Skeletal-muscle cells are relatively long and cigar-shaped, while some of the cells of the intestine take the form of little cubes. This is not the only respect in which cells of different tissues are dissimilar; they are also *functionally unlike*. Muscle cells *contract* (shorten) and cause the heart to beat, the body to move, and digestive organs to mix food with digestive juices and move it along; nerve cells carry electrical-type *impulses* which enable us to see, feel, hear, learn, reason, remember, taste, and detect odors; bone and cartilage cells give our bodies necessary *support*. Still other cells form glands (Fig. 3-2) and their secretions, such as *hormones and digestive juices*. Structurally and functionally, then, *there is no such thing as a truly typical cell.*

Cell size and shape

With one exception—the *ovum,* or female reproductive cell—the cells of the human body are all of *microscopic size:* if a slice of muscle, nerve, bone, or any other tissue is examined without the aid of a microscope, individual cells of course cannot be seen. Most of them are only *a few microns in diameter* and are, therefore, far below the limit of human visibility; and even though certain nerve cells (such as those in the

sciatic nerve of the leg) are over 3 feet (ft) long, they are far too small in diameter to be seen individually. Some of the smallest cells of the body are blood cells. The most numerous of these, red blood cells, are each only about 7.5 microns (μ) in diameter, but are still bent and twisted out of shape as they pass through networks of the most minute blood vessels in the body, *capillaries*.

The ability of the eye—or an optical instrument—to separate two dots or lines placed close together is known as *resolving power*. The unaided human eye can distinguish two dots separated by a distance of about 100 μ $1/10$ mm). Another way of expressing this is to say that the eye has a resolving power of $1/254$ inch (in.). The best light microscope improves on the eye about 500 times with a resolving power of 0.2 μ (200 millimicrons or 2000 angstroms), while the electron microscope, with a resolving power of about 5 angstroms (Å), improves on the light microscope almost 400 times and on the human eye, 200,000 times. Because electrons must travel in a vacuum and will pass only through specimens that are exceedingly thin, specimens must be killed and embedded in materials that harden and permit slicing. The fact that only non-living tissue can be examined with the electron microscope limits the usefulness of the instrument to a certain extent.

The shape of an isolated cell, minus the long extensions of protoplasm characteristic of some muscle and nerve cells, varies from *spherical* to *cubelike*. The ovum, which is about 300 μ in diameter and barely visible to the unaided eye, is a good example of a spherical cell. It is not squeezed from several different directions simultaneously as are most of the cells in a body tissue. These latter cells often appear as irregularly shaped, many-sided structures in their natural environment—that is, surrounded by other cells. The function of a cell also helps to determine its shape. Just how the shape of a cell contributes to its ability to function in a particular manner will best be understood in later sections concerned with the various physiological processes in which cells take important parts.

Even though the cells of one tissue do not resemble exactly the cells of another,

Figure 3.2 Some different types of glands.

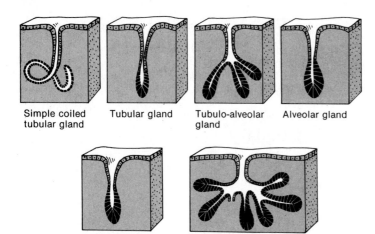

Simple coiled tubular gland   Tubular gland   Tubulo-alveolar gland   Alveolar gland

Simple gland   Compound gland

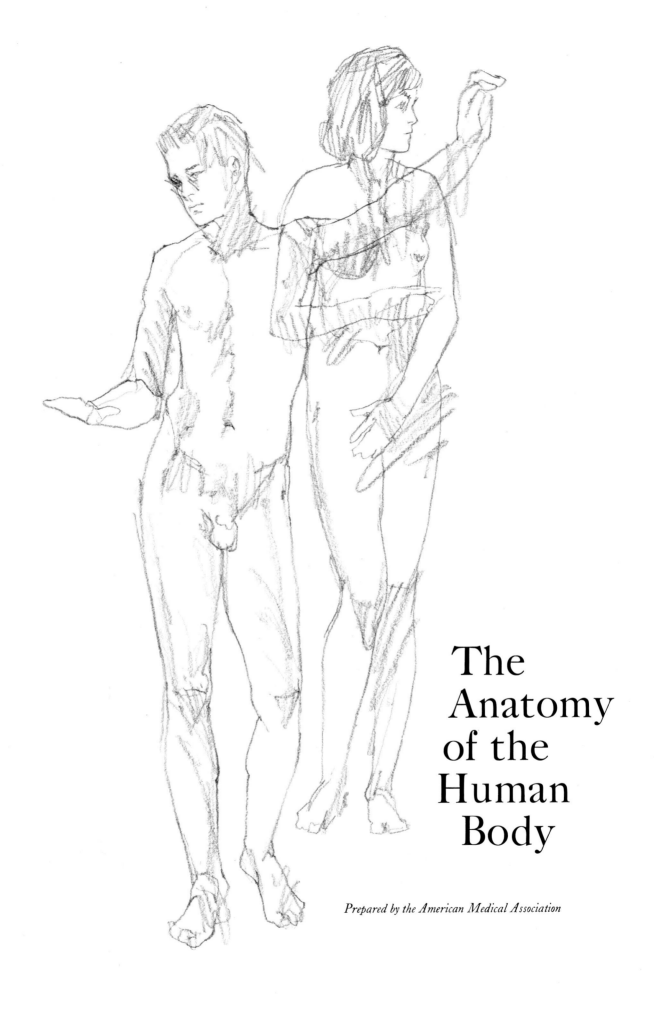

The Anatomy of the Human Body

Prepared by the American Medical Association

PLATE I

Back View

The skin of an average size adult has over 3,000 square inches of surface area, weighs about six pounds and varies in thickness from 1/50 of an inch on the eyelids to as much as 1/3 of an inch on the palms and soles. Skin is composed of three distinct layers: epidermis, dermis and subcutaneous fatty tissue.

The skin protects against the invasion of bacteria; receives and uses radiation from the sun; acts as a temperature regulator and cooling mechanism; serves as an organ of perception for the nervous system through its many specialized nerve endings; keeps blood and tissue fluids from escaping.

One-third of all blood circulating throughout the body is received by the skin.

PLATE I shows the subcutaneous layer as seen from the underside revealing some of the networks of veins. The larger veins are cut at points where they penetrate to deeper levels to join other veins returning blood to the heart.

2. Abdominal venous plexus
9. Basilic vein
23. Cephalic (upper arm) vein
37. Cubital vein
41. Epigastric artery and vein, superficial
82. Mammillary venous plexus
129. Saphenous vein, great
153. Thoracoepigastric vein

Illustrations by ERNEST W. BECK

Copyright © 1965 by the American Medical Association

All Rights Reserved.

Printed in U.S.A. by the Trans-Vision® Division, Milprint Incorporated.

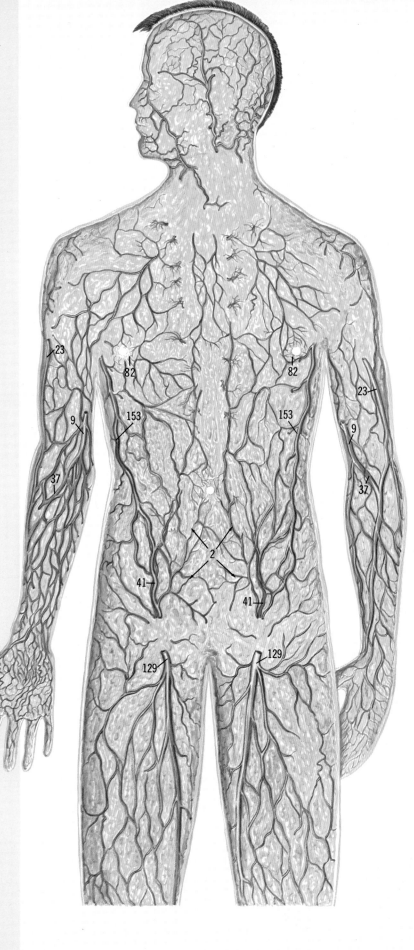

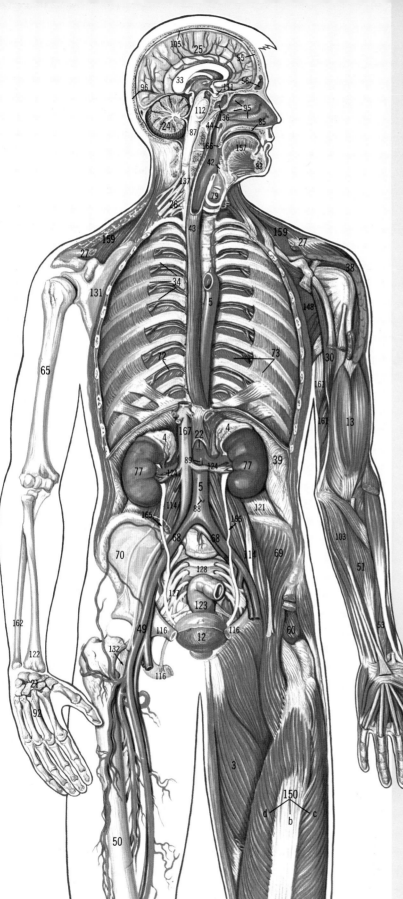

PLATE VIII

Front View

3. Adductor muscles of thigh
4. Adrenal (suprarenal) gland
5. Aorta (great artery)
12. Bladder, urinary
13. Brachialis muscle
21. Carpal (wrist) bones
22. Celiac artery
24. Cerebellum (hindbrain)
25. Cerebrum (forebrain)
26. Cervical nerves
27. Clavicle (collarbone)
30. Coracobrachialis muscle
33. Corpus callosum
34. Costae (ribs)
38. Deltoid muscle
39. Diaphragm (breathing muscle)
42. Epiglottis (windpipe valve)
43. Esophagus (gullet)
44. Eustachian tube opening
49. Femoral, artery, vein
    and nerve
50. Femur (thigh bone)
51. Flexor carpi radialis muscle
53. Flexor digitorum sublimis
    muscle (bends fingers)
55. Frontal (forehead) bone
56. Frontal sinus (airspace)
60. Gluteus medius muscle
65. Humerus (upper arm bone)
68. Iliac artery and vein, common
69. Iliacus muscle (bends thigh)
70. Ilium (hip bone)
72. Intercostal (rib) artery,
    vein and nerve
73. Intercostal (rib) muscles,
    external and internal
77. Kidney
79. Larynx (voice box)
83. Mandible (jawbone)
85. Maxilla (hard palate)
87. Medulla oblongata
88. Mesenteric artery, inferior
89. Mesenteric artery, superior
92. Metacarpal (hand) bones
95. Nasal turbinates
96. Occipital bone (skull base)
103. Palmaris longus muscle
105. Parietal bone (skull dome)
111. Pituitary ("Master") gland
112. Pons (connecting bridge)
114. Psoas muscles
116. Pubic bone
121. Quadratus lumborum muscle

122. Radius (lower arm bone)

123. Rectum
124. Renal artery and vein
127. Sacral nerve plexus
128. Sacrum
131. Scapula (shoulder
     blade)
132. Sciatic nerve
136. Sphenoid sinus
137. Spinal cord
148. Subscapularis
     muscle

150. Thigh muscle
     b. Vastus intermedius
     c. Vastus lateralis
     d. Vastus medialis
157. Tongue
159. Trapezius (neck-shoulder
     action) muscle
161. Triceps brachii muscle
162. Ulna (lower arm bone)
165. Ureter
166. Uvula
167. Vena cava (great vein),
     inferior

ERNEST W. BECK

PALMAR VIEW OF THE RIGHT HAND

BACK OF THE RIGHT HAND

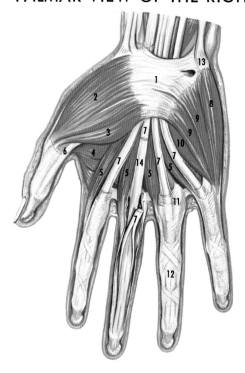
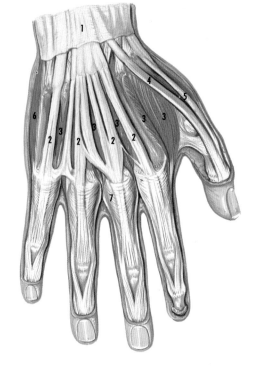

1. Transverse carpal ligament
2. Abductor pollicis brevis m.
3. Flexor pollicis brevis m.
4. Abductor pollicis m.
5. Lumbrical muscles
6. Flexor pollicis longus m.
7. Tendons of flexor digitorum sublimis m.

8. Abductor digiti V m.
9. Flexor digiti V brevis m.
10. Opponens digiti V m.
11. Digital ligaments
12. Annular ligaments
13. Pisiform bone
14. Tendon of flexor digitorum profundus muscle

1. Dorsal carpal ligament
2. Tendon of extensor digitorum communis muscle
3. Dorsal interosseus muscles
4. Tendon of extensor pollicis longus m.
5. Tendon of extensor pollicis brevis m.
6. Abductor digiti V m.
7. Digital ligaments

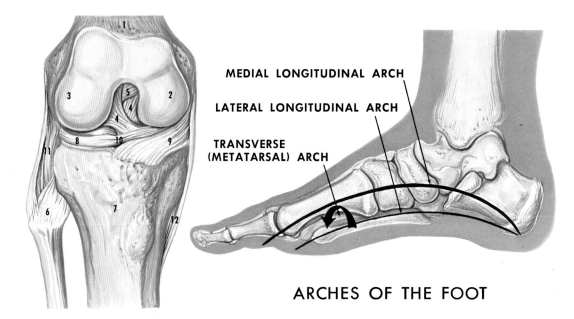

MEDIAL LONGITUDINAL ARCH

LATERAL LONGITUDINAL ARCH

TRANSVERSE (METATARSAL) ARCH

ARCHES OF THE FOOT

THE RIGHT KNEE JOINT

1. Femur
2. Medial condyle
3. Lateral condyle
4. Anterior cruciate ligament

5. Posterior cruciate ligament
6. Head of fibula and ligament
7. Tibia
8. Lateral meniscus

9. Medial meniscus
10. Transverse ligament
11. Collateral fibular ligament
12. Collateral fibular ligament

there are certain features which are common to most cells, and which can be described by constructing an *imaginary, idealized cell.*

The parts of a cell

If a cell is examined using an ordinary *light microscope,* it is usually possible to see only a few of the structures which actually lie within it. With more powerful instruments, however, such as the *phase-contrast microscope* and *electron microscope,* more parts of our "typical" cell come into view. It is noted, for example, that the contents of the cell are held intact by a flexible but tough outer covering, the *cell membrane,* or *plasma membrane* (Fig. 3-3). This membrane is barely visible on some cells with a light microscope, and invisible on others; but upon being *sectioned* (cut) by using very special laboratory techniques, the edge of this membrane when viewed with an electron microscope is seen to consist of three layers, somewhat resembling a sandwich. The *outer layer* of the sandwich has been found to be *protein,* the *middle layer* is *lipid* material, and the *inner layer,* more *protein.* In the living cell, this membrane is probably less than 100 Å thick; and the individual layers cannot be made out with an ordinary microscope. Many tiny pores perforate the cell membrane (Fig. 3-3), and the membrane is not a mere covering, such as the leather around the outside of a baseball. Within the cell can be seen a continuation of the membrane, the much-folded *endoplasmic reticulum,* or ER; and deep inside the cell, near the center, is suspended the large spherical *nucleus,* which is surrounded by a somewhat porous continuation of the endoplasmic reticulum, the *nuclear membrane.* In a sense, the cell membrane, endoplasmic reticulum, and nuclear membrane *are all different portions of the same structure.* Other structures in the cell have membranes similar to those just discussed, and these membranes may have developed from a common original structure and later have broken away. The term *unit membrane* is often used when discussing the membranous covering of any cell structure that has one. The cell membrane itself, in some ways still unknown to us, selectively regulates the passage of all materials into and out of the cell. The endoplasmic reticulum is thought to be concerned with the manufacture of hormone-type compounds called *steroids* (hormones are chemical substances that aid the nervous system in the regulation and coordination of physiological processes; see Chapter 9) and forms a series of channels which serve to transport materials from one part of the cell to the other.

THE CELL NUCLEUS   The nucleus of a cell *controls the transmission of hereditary traits* from generation to generation (see Chapter 16), *manufactures nucleic acids* to be used in the making of proteins and the hereditary material *chromatin,* and, by means of exchanging materials with the cytoplasm surrounding the nucleus (through pores in the nuclear membrane), *controls chemical activities throughout the cell.* Some cells die when their nuclei are killed or removed; others live for a time but fail to reproduce. Upon close examination of the cell nucleus, two spherical bodies, each much smaller than the nucleus itself, are seen lying within it. These are *nucleoli* (sing., *nucleolus*), and seem to be reservoirs of *ribonucleic acid* (RNA), which is transferred to the cytoplasm during protein synthesis. *Deoxyribonucleic acid* (DNA), the stuff of which chromatin is made, and *proteins* are also found in relatively small amounts in the nucleoli. The protoplasm found within the nucleus, although essentially the same as that in the cytoplasm, is given the name *nucleoplasm.*

THE NUCLEIC ACIDS   Two of the most important chemical compounds manufactured in the cell nucleus are *deoxyribonucleic acid* (DNA) and *ribonucleic acid* (RNA). They both consist of *macromolecules* or "giant" molecules, which are in turn made up of long chains of many smaller molecular units linked together. Both DNA and RNA are synthesized in the nucleus; but whereas DNA remains in the nucleus, most of the RNA moves through the nuclear membrane into the cystoplasm. The synthesis of proteins within the cell depends upon the presence of RNA; without DNA, which is the material of the genes of the chromosomes, genetic information would neither be stored in the cell

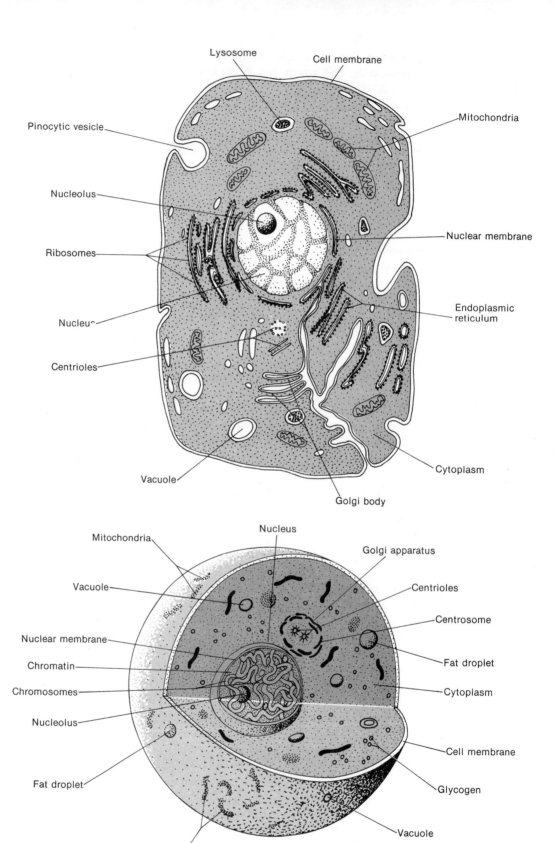

Figure 3.3 Major parts of a cell. (Top: Electron-microscopic structure. Bottom: Three-dimensional structure. Both are diagrammatic.)

20

nucleus nor transmitted from one generation to the next.

The smaller molecular units that comprise a nucleic-acid molecule are called *nucleotides*. Each nucleotide consists of a 5-carbon sugar (a *pentose*) linked to a *phosphate group* and to a *nitrogenous base*. *Ribose* is the pentose of RNA, and there are four nitrogenous bases with which it can attach: *adenine, cytosine, guanine,* and *uracil*. The bases of DNA are identical with those of RNA, except that uracil is replaced by *thymine*. Adenine and guanine are called *purines,* while cytosine, thymine, and uracil are all *pyrimidines*. (They are given these names because of their particular chemical structure, which resembles the respective compounds *purine* and *pyrimidine*.) *Deoxyribose,* the carbohydrate of DNA, has one less oxygen atom in its molecule than ribose (hence the prefix, deoxy-). Whereas the molecules of RNA each consist of one long chain of nucleotides, the DNA molecules has *two chains,* each twisting about the other in a *double helix,* somewhat like two spiral staircases which wind about the same axis (Fig. 3-4). The double helix of the DNA molecule is held together in the following manner: purines and pyrimidines extend inward at regular intervals from one helix and join weakly, by means of *hydrogen bonds,* with purines and pyrimidines extending from the opposite helix. The purines and pyrimidines are linked to deoxyribose units in DNA and to ribose units in RNA. Units consisting of bases linked to sugars are called *nucleosides*. Careful examination of Fig. 3-4 will reveal that the molecule is so constructed that the *pyrimidines* on one spiral of DNA always meet the *purines* of the other; in fact, in DNA, *adenine always links to thymine,* and *guanine to cytosine;* while in RNA, thymine is replaced by uracil. Hereditary patterns are coded by the DNA of the genes, which probably makes up the bulk of the chromosomes. Virtually *infinite arrangements of the nucleotides* in the DNA molecule are possible, which accounts for the wide variety of physical, mental, and physiological characteristics seen in people. DNA can *replicate* (duplicate) itself. In this process, each molecule *splits lengthwise* and forms a new molecule of DNA by picking up new raw materials in

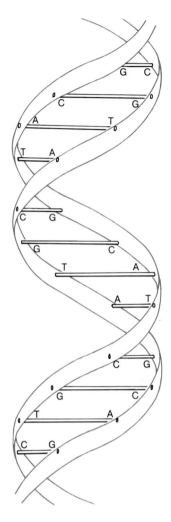

Figure 3.4 The Watson-Crick model of DNA. A = adenine; G = guanine; T = thymine; C = cytosine. The spiralling "ribbons" represent phosphate-pentose chains.

the cell nucleus. DNA also serves as a pattern for the assembly of (single-stranded) RNA molecules.

THE CYTOPLASM   The largest portion of a cell is that which surrounds the nucleus: the *cytoplasm*. It consists of the protoplasm located between the cell nucleus and cell membrane, the endoplasmic reticulum, and a number of structures known collectively as *inclusions* and *organelles*. Among the cell organelles are *mitochondria,* the *Golgi apparatus, fibrils, centrioles, lysosomes, vacuoles, tubules, cilia,* and *flagella*. Various *secretory granules, excretory granules, ribo-*

somes, microsomes, crystals, pigment granules, and *protein, carbohydrate,* and *lipid materials* make up the cell inclusions. Organelles are thought to be living structures because they are *able to reproduce themselves.* Inclusions cannot reproduce, and are regarded as nonliving cellular bodies. Mitochondria vary in general outline from sausagelike to teardrop shape, and average about 0.5 μ in diameter and 4 μ in length. The larger ones can barely be seen with a light microscope. Mitochondria have double-walled unit membranes, with infoldings known as *cristae.* In the living cell, mitochondria are in constant motion, and are sometimes clustered in those areas where activities such as *ciliary motion*—the undulating or wavelike movement of tiny hairlike extensions of cells, *cilia*—*gland secretion,* and the *movement of materials through the cell membrane* are going on. They play major roles in the *oxidation of simple proteins, carbohydrates,* and *fats* to *carbon dioxide* and *water,* or to *acids* and *alcohols.* When these oxidations take place, *energy is released* and is used in producing the *high-energy phosphate compound* ATP (adenosinetriphosphate). Enzymes necessary for the utilization of ATP during energy requiring processes (such as muscle contraction) are also found in the mitochondria. Mitochondria have been studied perhaps more than any single organelle, and have been described as the "enzyme factories," "powerhouses," and "respiratory centers" of cells. The *Golgi apparatus,* or Golgi complex as it is sometimes called, consists of a collection of membrane-bound cavities or *vesicles* often arranged as layers or stacks. The whole is surrounded by a unit membrane which is continuous with the endoplasmic reticulum. The apparatus is thought to be concerned with the transport of various substances to a position near the cell nucleus. It may also provide a surface upon which many of the chemical reactions of cell metabolism can occur. Finally, the Golgi apparatus may be important in the formation and release of enzymes by the pancreas, salivary glands, and other enzyme-producing glands. The apparatus is especially well developed in these glands.

Fibrils are long, thin, threadlike structures found mostly in the cytoplasm of muscle and nerve cells. Those in muscle cells are called *contractile fibrils* because of their ability to shorten during muscle contraction. Within the cytoplasm, lying very near the nuclear membrane, is a pair of small dotlike structures or bodies called *centrioles.* They are important during cell division. They seem to start the process by forming a series of extremely thin *filaments* between them, then stretching these filaments out into a football-shaped structure, or *spindle* (Fig. 3-10). The filaments are then called *spindle fibers,* which serve as points of attachment for rodlike bodies of genetic material called *chromosomes* during division of the cell, as described in a later section of this chapter. Seen in the cytoplasm are also a few rather spherical bodies, as large or larger than the smaller mitochondria, but having a much more granular appearance: *lysosomes.* These are bounded by a membrane, and contain enzymes which are important in the breakdown, by hydrolysis, of waste debris in the cell. Some of the larger lysosomes have been observed with mitochondria inside them. The membranes of lysosomes do not form cristae as do those of mitochondria. *Vacuoles* and *tubules* are important organelles. Vacuoles are membranous sacs that serve to store fluid and function in excretion by the cell. Tubules are, as the name implies, "little tubes." They aid in transporting materials throughout the cytoplasm, and add strength and support to the cell.

Cilia and *flagella* are important organelles which deserve more than token discussion. Both are microscopic filamentous projections of the cell cytoplasm and membrane. Both have the same basic structure, and whether they are to be called cilia or flagella depends upon their number per cell and their length in relation to the cell. If the projections on a given cell are short and numerous, they are classed as cilia (Fig. 3-5). If they are few but long and whiplike —often longer than the cell itself—they are flagella. All members of the animal kingdom except the roundworms and crustaceans such as lobsters depend upon the movements of these organelles for the performance of certain functions. In man, *cerebrospinal fluid* (commonly called "spinal fluid") is circulated within the ventricle spaces of the brain and spinal cord by cilia, and cilia on the

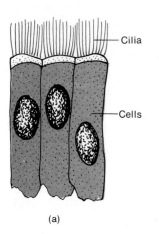

Cilia

Cells

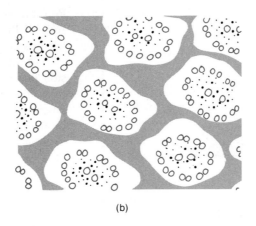

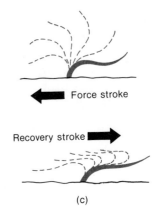

Force stroke

Recovery stroke

(a)   (b)   (c)

Figure 3.5 Cilia. (a) Ciliated columnar epithelial cells. (b) Electron-microscopic view of cilia on cross section. (c) Ciliary action.

linings of the air passageways to and within the lungs cleanse these surfaces as they wave dust and other foreign matter upward into the throat where it can be coughed out or swallowed. Ciliary action also transports the ovum from the ovary through the *uterine tubes* (oviducts) to the *uterus* or womb. Each sperm cell has a flagellum which, by means of its whiplike action, propels the sperm upward in the female reproductive tract. This is the only example of a flagellum in a human cell.

Electron-microscopic studies of cilia and flagella reveal that the slender cylindrical stalks of these organelles are made up of *hollow extensions of the cell membrane, filled with cytoplasm.* Coursing lengthwise through this cytoplasm are two single fibrils, positioned in the center of the structure, and nine groups of fibrils arranged around the periphery (Fig. 3-5). All these fibrils are extremely small in diameter. Located at the *base* of each cilium of flagellum, within the main cytoplasm of the cell, is a bulblike enlargement, the *basal body* or *basal granule,* which is often seen to be attached to long, narrow *rootlets* of a fibrous nature, which reach even further into the cell. The presence of the basal body is necessary for the organelle to act, and the cilium or flagellum will function even if contained in a small, isolated bit of cytoplasm as long as the basal body is intact.

Two phases can be recognized in the action of cilia: the *contractile* or *force stroke,* and the *recovery stroke* (Fig. 3-5). During the force stroke the cilium is functional,

doing whatever it is designed to do; the recovery stroke is passive in character, and it is during this action that the cilium is preparing for the next force stroke. In general, flagella use more undulating, whiplike strokes than do cilia.

The exact mechanism of ciliary (or flagellary) movement is not known. It is known, however, that both cilia and flagella depend upon power generated throughout the length of their fibrils, and *not* upon a pulling action or contraction of the cytoplasm in the cell proper. It is likely that ciliary action is chemically similar to muscle contraction, especially that of smooth muscle (found in the walls of certain body organs and blood vessels), which contracts in a purely involuntary, reflex manner, not under control of the will.

Ribosomes are among the most important cell inclusions. They are small, dark, dense granules; some are attached to the endoplasmic reticulum, while others are distributed throughout the cytoplasm. They are made of RNA and protein, and are probably the sites at which amino acids are linked together to form protein molecules. The more ribosomes a cell contains, it has been found, the greater is its protein output.

Cell permeability

In order for a cell to remain alive and healthy, food materials and oxygen must get into the cell, and carbon dioxide and other wastes must get out. In normal health, the

23

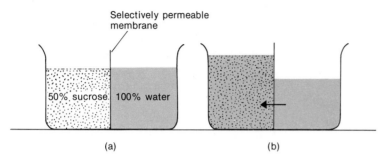

Figure 3.6 Diffusion through a selectively permeable membrane. (a) The two solutions are separated by the membrane. (b) The membrane is permeable to water molecules, but not to molecules of sucrose; therefore, net diffusion is from the water into the sucrose solution.

cell membrane somehow controls this traffic of substances into and out of the cell. The degree to which substances move through a cell membrane is referred to as the *permeability* of the membrane. Living cells are *differentially* or *selectively permeable* (old term, semipermeable), permitting certain substances to pass through their membranes and barring the passage of others. Disease can drastically alter the permeability of cells, often with serious and even fatal consequences.

Water passes through cell membranes very readily, many substances do not pass through at all, and others fall at various points between these two extremes. How is it that a cell membrane is selectively permeable? Any answer to this question is today still incomplete. Some materials seem to move through the membrane according to the laws of simple diffusion or filtration, while others do not. The *law of diffusion* states that *a substance, if it is a liquid or gas* (if it is permited to do so), *will pass from a region of greater concentration of its molecules to a region of less concentration of its molecules.* The diffusion of water or of aqueous (water) solutions through a cell membrane is called *osmosis.* Diffusion as such does not always involve a membrane; for example, solid potassium permanganate, when placed in water, slowly dissolves and diffuses throughout the water. The exact same thing happens to a lump of sugar placed in a cup of coffee.

Perfume will quickly diffuse throughout a room if the bottle is left open; so will ether left in an open container.

A familiar demonstration of the diffusion of water through a membrane involves the setup illustrated in Fig. 3-6; the container has two compartments, separated by a membrane which has been manufactured to be *permeable only to water molecules,* or to other molecules of similar size—that is, the pores of the membrane are not large enough to permit larger particles to pass through. One compartment of the container is filled to a certain level with water, the other to the same level with a 50% water solution of the sugar sucrose. Sucrose molecules are too large to pass through the membrane. Shortly after the two liquids are placed in their compartments, a curious thing happens: as the kinetic energy of the water molecules causes them to strike the membrane, *more of them pass from the pure-water side of this membrane into the side containing the sugar solution.* The level of the sugar solution rises above that of the pure water, and at the same time, the level of the pure water naturally falls. This process continues until the weight of the sugar–water solution exerts enough pressure to prevent any more water molecules from passing through the membrane. This pressure is known as *osmotic pressure.* Actually, a few water molecules (relatively speaking) diffuse back across the membrane into the pure water, but since many more of them diffuse in the opposite direction, there is said to be a *net diffusion* of water into the sugar solution.

Solutions with equal concentrations of the same solute and solvent are said to be *isotonic,* or *isosmotic.* Two such solutions, when separated by a membrane, show no net diffusion, no matter how long they are permitted to remain in their compartments, because there is no *concentration gradient—* that is, no difference in concentrations on opposite sides of the membranes. No osmotic pressure develops. With two solutions which differ in concentration, the one with the *greater concentration of solute* (or, the same thing, a lower concentration of water) is said to be *hypertonic* to the other, and the second solution is *hypotonic* to the first. The concept of *tonicity* is one of the most important in physiology. Employing this concept, it will be seen that any drug or other solution injected directly into the bloodstream must be *isotonic* to the saline (salt) solution present in the blood cells; otherwise, one of two things will happen: if the injected solution is *hypotonic* to the intracellular fluid, *endosmosis* will occur; that is, water will pass from the injected solution through the cell membrane, from a region of greater concentration of water molecules to a region of less concentration of water molecules. The blood cell will hold all the water it can but will eventually swell and burst, or *hemolyze*. If, on the other hand, the injected solution is *hypertonic* to the intracellular fluid, water will diffuse out of the cell, and the cell will shrink. *Exosmosis* will have occurred, and the wrinkled cell is said to be *crenated*. *Both hemolysis and crenation destroy the blood cell.*

THEORIES OF PERMEABILITY We have seen that some substances pass through cell membranes in accordance with the laws of diffusion. However, this law does not explain the passage of all substances through the membrane. Today, it is thought that most substances probably pass into or out of the cell in a manner prescribed by the *solvent–sieve theory* of permeability. In this theory, those substances which are *lipoid-soluble* (dissolve in fats and fatlike substances) enter or leave the cell at *lipoid areas* of the cell membrane, while *ions, lipoid-insoluble* materials, and certain other substances move through at *pores* located between lipoid areas. The pores of cell membranes are only 7 to 10 Å in diameter, and therefore act as barriers to the movement of larger particles. It is possible that the pores are covered with a thin layer of protein, and that this "lid" aids in the selective action of the membrane. In general, if the molecular weight of a substance is above 100 (as is the case with many proteins), the molecules of that substance are too large to pass through a cell pore.

Ions bearing a charge like that present on a cell membrane are rejected by the membrane, while ions having charges opposite those on the membrane are permitted to pass through.

Some substances that do not obey the laws of diffusion when moving through a cell membrane actually move *against a concentration gradient;* that is, they move from a region of lower concentration to a region of higher concentration of their molecules. This "uphill" transference of a substance is known as *active transport,* and requires the expenditure of energy. In contrast, simple diffusion might well be termed *passive transport.* The energy necessary for active transport may be furnished by such substances as *carrier ions* or *carrier molecules,* or by special *carrier enzymes.* Figure 3-7 illustrates the theory that a substance can move against a concentration gradient, by first becoming attached

Figure 3.7 Active transport. (a) Molecule A and carrier C are both outside the cell.
(b) Carrier C combines with molecule A, forming a loose complex.
(c) Carrier C transports molecule A through the cell membrane.
(d) Carrier C passes back through the cell membrane, leaving molecule A inside the cell. Carrier C is now ready to transport more A into the cell.

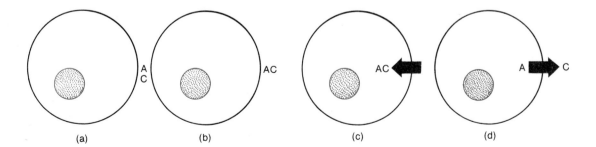

(a)   (b)   (c)   (d)

to some sort of carrier such as those just mentioned, and by then forming a *temporary complex* which moves into or out of the cell, utilizing the energy supplied by the carrier. Once through the membrane, the carrier releases the transferred substance, then moves back through the membrane in preparation for repeating the process. It is probable that carriers must be activated or "energized" by utilizing ATP supplied by the cell.

FILTRATION   Often the particles of a substance are small enough to pass through the pores of a cell membrane, and will do so if the pressure on the side where the particles are located is greater than the pressure on the other side. In other words, if the particles of the substance are small enough to enter the pores of the membrane, all that is required is a *pressure gradient* to move them across, and concentration gradients play no part in the process. This movement of particles due to pressure gradients is called *filtration;* the rate of filtration is determined solely by the amount of pressure existing on the particles to be transported. The movement of substances through capillary walls due to the force of blood pressure, and the passage of water and dissolved wastes through the membranes and blood vessels of the kidney during urine formation are examples of physiological filtration.

OSMOSIS   *Osmosis* is the *diffusion of water* or water solutions *through a membrane.* This means that *water moves from a greater concentration of its molecules to a lesser concentration of its molecules* in accordance with the law of diffusion (p. 24). In effect, the amount of solute in an aqueous solution will determine the rate of osmosis, since the amount of solute determines the concentra-tion of water molecules; that is, the more solute, the smaller the concentration of water molecules, and vice versa. The solute on one side of a membrane can be said to exert a "pull" on the water molecules that are present on that side of the membrane with relatively little or no solute; in this way an osmotic pressure is established.

The amount of osmotic pressure exerted on a membrane depends on the number of solute molecules present; and as water moves down its concentration gradient across the membrane and into the region where more solute particles are located (the hypertonic region), it will be slowed and finally stopped due to the buildup of hydrostatic pressure in the hypertonic region, and because of the resistance presented by the cell as it swells tighter and tighter (providing the water is moving into the cell, rather than out).

Phagocytosis and pinocytosis

From time to time, certain cells take in particles much too large for simple diffusion or active transport through the plasma membrane. If the material to be taken in is a solid, the cell engulfs it by simply extending protrusions of itself around the particle and closing them in pincerlike fashion (Fig. 3-8). If the cell is taking in a fluid, such as water, *long, narrow canals form* which open at the cell surface and lead into the cytoplasm. When the fluid enters a canal, small portions of the deep end of the latter are pinched off, carrying droplets of the fluid deeper into the cell, where it is *assimilated* into the cytoplasm (that is, it becomes an integral part of the cytoplasm). The engulf-

Figure 3.8   Phagocytosis. The cell gradually engulfs the solid particle, such as a bacterial cell. If a water droplet is engulfed, the process is called "pinocytosis."

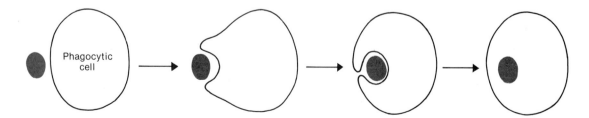

Phagocytic cell

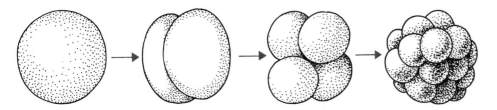

Figure 3.9 A few of the steps in the division of a fertilized egg into the ball of cells (morula) which will become the embryo.

ing of solids is known as *phagocytosis,* and the taking in of water and other fluids, *pinocytosis.* The mechanisms used by cells to accomplish these feats are not understood, but it is almost certain that *sol–gel transformations* in the cytoplasm just beneath the cell membrane are involved. *Reticuloendothelial cells,* distributed throughout the body, and certain kinds of white blood cells are continually carrying out phagocytosis and pinocytosis, engulfing and digesting bacteria and other foreign matter that might be harmful.

Cell division

Every individual begins his or her existence as *one cell,* the ovum or female sex cell, to which has been added the nuclear material of one incredibly small *sperm,* the sex cell of the male. Soon after this *fertilization* of the ovum or egg by the sperm, the former divides incompletely into two cells, each of which in turn divides into two more cells, this process continuing until a mass of cells results (Fig. 3-9).

The synthesis of new intracellular materials due to the preponderance of *anabolic* (constructive) *processes of metabolism* accompanies cell division, and *growth* results. Groups of similar cells become specialized, forming *tissues,* some of which continue to grow for over 20 years. In most tissues, cell division stops before the age of 25, and after that no new cells are formed, except for blood cells, those in the skin, and those lining body organs and other structures subject to constant wear and tear. Intracellular material breaks down even in permanent cells (such as those of the nervous system), however, and is replaced by normal metabolic processes. This takes place throughout life.

The division of cells involves two fairly distinct processes: *mitosis*—division of the nucleus into two new nuclei—and *cytokinesis,* or division of the cytoplasm. These two processes often—but not always—take place simultaneously.

MITOSIS During mitosis (Fig. 3-10), genetic material is duplicated exactly, and each *daughter cell* receives precisely the same genetic information as the other. Early in mitosis, the genetic substance becomes organized into rodlike bodies called chromosomes. Each human tissue cell contains 46 chromosomes, arranged as 23 similar pairs. For the sake of convenience, the description of the process of mitosis is usually divided into a series of stages or phases, each of which exhibits a different set of conditions in the nucleus. It should be pointed out that during actual nuclear division, one phase blends smoothly and quickly into the next, and that there is *no pause between one phase and the next.* Since mitosis involves only the nucleus of the cell, the process is often referred to as *karyokinesis,* from the Greek word *karyon,* meaning nucleus.

Unlike tissue cells, each mature reproductive cell, whether egg or sperm, contains only 23 chromosomes in its nucleus, instead of 46. This is necessary in order that the fertilized egg or ovum may contain the full complement of 46 chromosomes and no more. The nuclei of the egg and sperm arrive at this state of affairs of having only one-half the full number of chromosomes by means of a special *reduction-type cell division* called *miosis* (meiosis), which is discussed in detail in Chapter 16.

CYTOKINESIS Cytokinesis, or division of the cell cytoplasm, often accompanies mitosis, beginning in *late anaphase* and reaching com-

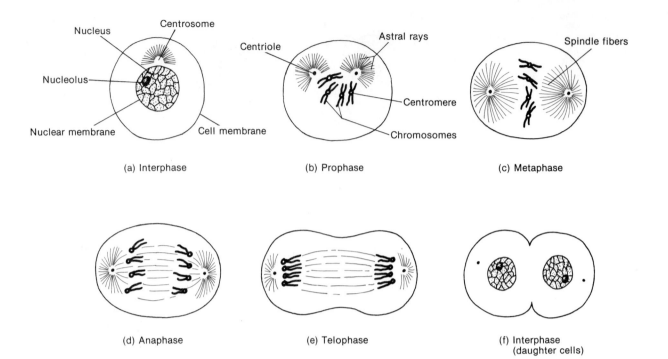

Figure 3-10 Cell division. Nuclear division is called mitosis. Division of the cytoplasm surrounding the nucleus (as seen here) is called cytokinesis.
(a) Nuclear membrane intact; chromatin appears as a network.
(b) Centrioles separate; nuclear membrane disappears, chromosomes appear.
(c) Chromosomes align on equator of a spindle.
(d) Chromosomes divide equally and move toward the poles of the cell.
(e) Cytokinesis is well under way. (f) Two nuclear membranes form;
chromatin again appears as a network. Daughter cells have formed when
cytokinesis is complete.

pletion during *telophase.* The process begins with the formation of a *cleavage furrow* encircling the cell. This furrow or groove becomes progressively deeper until it cuts completely through the dividing cell, and two new cells are produced. Little is known regarding the origin and progression of the cleavage furrow. It may possibly be due to the formation of the cell membranes of the daughter cells, or to a thin ring of cytoplasm which contracts and pinches the cell in two.

HISTOLOGY: CELLS INTO TISSUES

During early development of an infant in its mother's body, a long series of rather startling changes takes place in rapid succession. One of the very first of these changes involves the process of *differentiation,* the transformation of cells into tissues; but before the beginning of this process, the cells that comprise the future individual look very much alike, and are packed together in a tiny ball or sphere, called a *morula* (Fig. 3-9). Soon, however, cells in different portions of the sphere begin taking on various shapes and forms. Some become long and thin, some flat and rectangular, and others cube-shaped. The net result of this process—which constitutes differentiation—is the production of *groups of cells which are similar in structure and function: tissues.*

In order to study tissues better under the microscope, histologists have worked out many elaborate techniques of sectioning (slicing) and *staining* them. Depending upon the staining procedure used, various parts of the cells are colored by the stains, providing better contrast between tissues, and between the component cells of a single tissue. Many

28

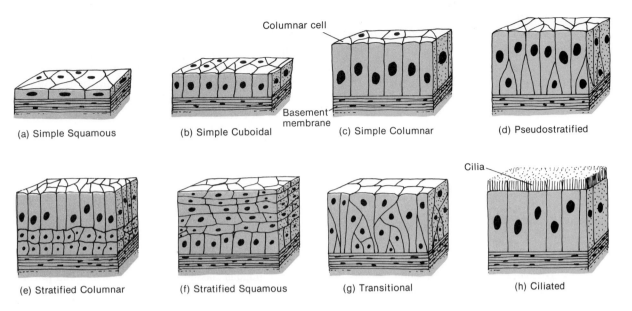

Columnar cell

Basement membrane

(a) Simple Squamous   (b) Simple Cuboidal   (c) Simple Columnar   (d) Pseudostratified

Cilia

(e) Stratified Columnar   (f) Stratified Squamous   (g) Transitional   (h) Ciliated

Figure 3-11 The chief types of epithelium.

of the features of tissues described here and in other sections of this book could never have been seen in an unstained-tissue preparation.

KINDS OF TISSUES There are several ways in which tissues may be named and grouped. In one convenient system, there are *four basic kinds* of tissues: *epithelial, connective* and *supporting, muscle,* and *nervous.*

Epithelial tissues

All substances which pass into or out of the body tissues must first go through *epithelial tissue.* The *linings* of the *digestive tract, blood vessels, trachea,* and *body cavities* consist of *sheets of epithelium,* and the *outer portion of the skin* is mostly epithelial in structure. Most materials that pass through epithelium do so by simple diffusion or filtration, through an *epithelial membrane* only *one cell thick;* but in certain parts of the body, such as the *outer portion of the skin,* the *lining of the mouth,* and the *lining of the esophagus,* epithelium serves a protective function, and is composed of layers or *strata* of cells. The cells at the surface are constantly dying and becoming *cornified* (tough and dry) and are eventually sloughed off.

They are replaced with cells which are continually produced by cell division in the deeper layers.

In certain glands, *glandular epithelial cells* produce *secretions,* such as the watery *mucus* found in the digestive tract. The free surfaces of some epithelial cells are covered with tiny cilia (which aid in the movement of substances in a manner already discussed in this chapter).

In some tissues, a great deal of *intercellular substance* is made by the cells, and this substance fills the spaces between them. This is not true of epithelial tissues; their cells are very close together, and comparatively little intercellular substance is produced. Epithelial tissues are *avascular;* that is, they have no blood vesels of their own. Connective tissue is always found beneath epithelium, and this particular connective tissue is *very vascular* (richly supplied with blood vessels) and its blood vessels serve both.

TYPES OF EPITHELIUM There are *two major groups* of epithelium, and several different *kinds* or *types* in each group. The epithelial tissues in the first group are known collectively as *simple epithelium;* they include *simple squamous, cuboidal, simple columnar,* and *pseudostratified epithelia.* In the second group are those types called stratified epithelia: stratified columnar, transitional, and stratified squamous. All of the various types of epithelium are illustrated in Fig. 3-11. Epithelium is further discussed in the considerations of the anatomy and physiology of the various organ systems.

Connecting and supporting tissues

There are two chief types of connecting and supporting tissues: *solid* and *fluid*. The solid connective tissues include bone, cartilage, and ligaments and tendons and other fibrous tissues. Blood and lymph are the fluid connective tissues, and are classed as connective because of embryological origins and because they do in fact "connect" the various parts of the body, just as a water system connects the various parts of a city.

THE SOLID CONNECTING AND SUPPORTING TISSUES   In the epithelial tissues, there are many cells and only a little intercellular substance, or *matrix*. In the solid connective and supporting tissues, just the opposite is true. In these tissues, which serve to bind the body parts together, give strength and support to body organs, and form the body framework —the *skeleton*—there are relatively few cells, and a great deal of nonliving intercellular material. In addition to cells, *three kinds of fibers* are embedded in the matrix, also called the *ground substance: elastic; collagenous,* and *reticular*. Both the matrix and the fibers are produced by the cells themselves. Depending upon the characteristics of the matrix, types of fibers predominating, and the arrangement of these fibers, solid connective and supporting tissues can be classed as *fibrous tissues, cartilage,* and *bone* (Fig. 3-12).

FIBROUS TISSUES   As the name implies, the fibrous tissues are those in which fibers are particularly numerous. Many of these fibers are *collagenous* (made of the protein collagen) and are incredibly strong. Fibrous tissues are avascular and their cells are called *fibroblasts*. Examples of fibrous tissues include *ligaments, tendons, loose and dense areolar tissues, adipose* (fatty) *tissue,* and *reticular connective tissue,* such as that of the spleen and lymph nodes.

CARTILAGE   Cartilage is a tough but resilient, flexible material found between the bones in the vertebral column, covering the contacting portions of bones in some joints, attaching ribs to the sternum or breastbone, and in other places about the body, such as the trachea, external ear, and nose. Cartilage is flexible because it does not contain the minerals found in bone. The cells of cartilage are known as *chondrocytes*. They are located in *lacunae,* small spaces scattered throughout the matrix. Cartilage, like the fibrous tissues, is avascular, and nutrients must diffuse into it from nearby tissues. Depending mostly upon the proportions of fibers to matrix, but also upon the kinds of fibers present, cartilage is classed as *hyaline, elastic,* and *fibrous*. The three kinds of cartilage are illustrated in Fig. 3-12.

BONE   Unlike cartilage, bone is extremely rigid, due to the presence of large amounts of such inorganic salts as *calcium phosphate* and *calcium carbonate*. That these minerals give bone its hardness can be demonstrated by placing a long bone in weak acid for a time and dissolving away the inorganic substances, leaving only the organics such as the protein, collagen. The bone can then be bent and twisted, and even tied in a knot. Another way in which bone differs from cartilage is in its pattern of distribution in the body. Cartilage gives support to relatively small and widely separated regions, whereas bones are all connected—with one exception, the hyoid bone—and make up an integrated body framework. Histologically, bone is known as *osseus tissue,* and its cells are called *osteocytes*. The basic unit of bone is the *Haversian system,* which consists of layers or *lamellae* of bone, tiny *spaces and canals,* and *nerves and blood and lymph vessels*. The gross (overall) and microscopic structure of bone is shown in Fig. 3-12.

THE FLUID CONNECTIVE TISSUES   Blood and lymph are the *fluid tissues*. Blood transports oxygen, nutrients, and hormones to the cells throughout the body, and carries wastes to the kidneys and other organs that serve in waste removal. Blood cells, or *corpuscles,* are suspended in a fluid matrix, the *plasma*. The uniqueness of the fluid tissues lies in the fact that their cells are constantly moving from one part of the body to another. They do this

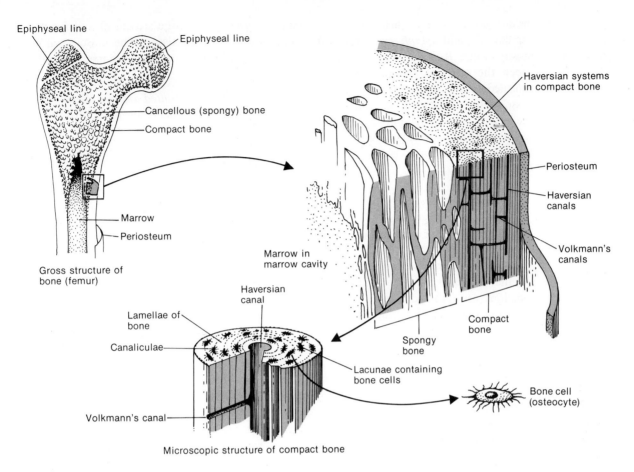

Gross structure of bone (femur)

Microscopic structure of compact bone

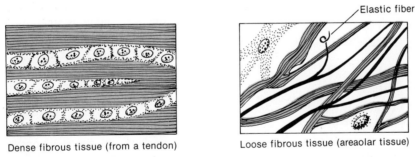

Dense fibrous tissue (from a tendon)

Loose fibrous tissue (areaolar tissue)

Three kinds of cartilage

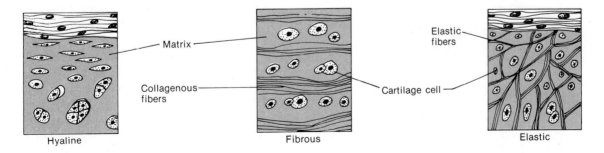

Hyaline

Fibrous

Elastic

Figure 3-12 Connective tissues.

inside *blood vessels* (arteries, veins, and capillaries) and *lymph vessels.* Lymph is mostly water. It drains from the spaces between the cells into lymph vessels, and is returned to the bloodstream by large lymph vessels which empty into veins in the base of the neck. Without lymph, cells and tissues would become dehydrated—that is, dry. Dehydration causes cells to die.

Muscle tissues

Three kinds of muscle tissues are found in the body: *skeletal, smooth,* and *cardiac.* Each of these three is modified to carry out specific functions; but even though these functions are rather different, each depends upon the one most outstanding property of all muscle—the ability to *shorten,* or *contract.* In a later chapter, the electron-microscopic structure of muscle is considered, along with a popular theory of the mechanism of muscle contraction. For the present, the discussion will be limited to a brief consideration of the three kinds of muscle tissues and of their features as viewed with an ordinary light microscope. The *muscle cell* or

Figure 3-13 The three kinds of muscle tissue.

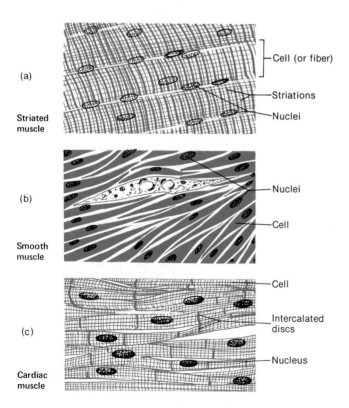

(a)

Striated muscle

Cell (or fiber)

Striations

Nuclei

(b)

Smooth muscle

Nuclei

Cell

(c)

Cardiac muscle

Cell

Intercalated discs

Nucleus

muscle fiber is the structural and functional unit of muscle tissue. The muscle cell cytoplasm is given the special name, *sarcoplasm.*

SKELETAL MUSCLE Skeletal muscle also is known as *striated muscle,* because individual cells or fibers have dark, cross-running or transverse stripes or *striations* which can be plainly seen with a light microscope. Each cell has several nuclei, and is referred to as a *syncytium,* or multinucleate mass of protoplasm. Skeletal muscle covers the skeleton and makes up most of the flesh of the body. It contracts very rapidly, and its action is classified as voluntary, because it is under the control of the will. It is responsible for body movements. Skeletal muscle is illustrated in Fig. 3-13.

SMOOTH MUSCLE Smooth muscle is so named because it lacks the cross-striations and numerous nuclei of skeletal muscle. It is also called *visceral muscle* because it is found in the walls of such visceral organs as the stomach, intestines, urinary bladder, and uterus. It is also present in the walls of blood vessels, the bile ducts (of the gall bladder and liver), and in the hair follicles (sockets) of the skin. Smooth muscle contracts very slowly; its action is not under the control of the will and it is, therefore, referred to as *involuntary muscle.* The cells of smooth muscle (Fig. 3-13) are long and slender, and somewhat cigar-shaped. One oval nucleus can be seen near the center of each cell.

CARDIAC MUSCLE Cardiac muscle or heart-muscle fibers (Fig. 3-13) each have one oval nucleus and dim striations; they can thus be said to be intermediate in type between skeletal-muscle and smooth-muscle cells. Unlike either of the two other kinds of muscle fibers however, those of cardiac muscle have *branches,* and structures known as *intercalated discs.* These latter each consist of two layers of cell membrane, one each belonging to a cardiac-muscle cell. Cardiac muscle is found only in the heart, where the fibers fuse and blend together, forming a syncytial type multinucleate mass. The action of cardiac muscle is involuntary and originates within the heart muscle itself, although the *rate* of the heartbeat (number of beats per unit of time) is under the *reflex* (involuntary or "automatic") control of the nervous system.

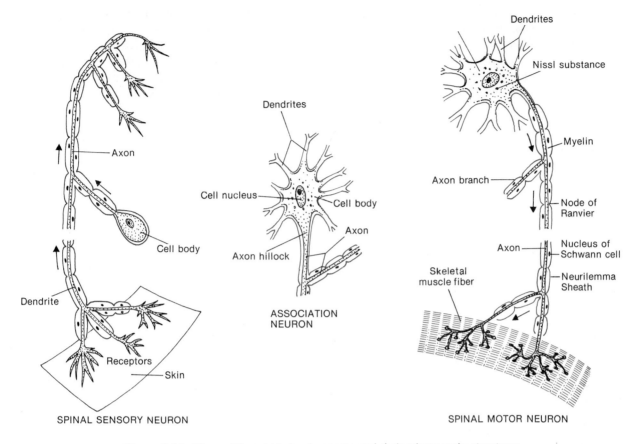

Figure 3-14 labels:

Axon

Cell body

Dendrite

Receptors

Skin

SPINAL SENSORY NEURON

Dendrites

Cell nucleus

Cell body

Axon

Axon hillock

ASSOCIATION NEURON

Dendrites

Nissl substance

Myelin

Axon branch

Node of Ranvier

Nucleus of Schwann cell

Axon

Neurilemma Sheath

Skeletal muscle fiber

SPINAL MOTOR NEURON

Figure 3-14   Three different kinds of neurons and their microscopic structures.

Nervous tissues

The two great specialties of nervous tissue are *responsiveness* or *irritability,* and *conductivity.* By means of specialized nerve endings called *receptors,* nervous tissue can respond to even very weak stimuli, such as faint sounds, tastes and odors, light touch, or the image of a moving object in dim light; then it sends impulses, via nerve cells, to the brain for interpretation and action. The nerve cell, or *neuron,* is the functional unit of the nervous system. There are several different kinds of neurons in the nervous system (Fig. 3-14); and they, along with several types of *supporting cells,* constitute the structural units of the nervous system.

Tissue transplantation

Since about 1945, we have become more and more successful in our attempts to remove tissues, even entire organs, from the bodies of persons and cause them to grow in the bodies of others. *Transplants,* as these operations are called, do not always involve more than one individual; for example, the burned skin of an arm may be replaced with grafted skin taken from the thigh of the same individual. This is known as an *autotransplant.* An *isotransplant* involves individuals of the same genetic background, such as identical twins. When a transplant is performed between individuals not genetically related, the transfer of tissue is a *homotransplant. Heterotransplants* involve members of two different animal species, such as a hamster and a cat.

Grafts or transplants attempted between individuals, unless they happen to be identical twins, are usually rejected by the recipient's body, due to the production of *antibodies* (chemical substances that attack disease organisms and foreign matter) in his bloodstream. Both drugs and X rays have been used in attempts to overcome this antibody buildup. So far, any method that suppresses the buildup of antibodies also leaves the patient overly susceptible to infection.

Bone and cartilage, teeth, blood vessels, endocrine-gland tissue, kidneys, and even hearts are being grafted or transplanted today with an encouraging degree of success. Often, tissues can be preserved chemically or by freezing until such time as they are needed. Inert (nonreactive) plastics are becoming more and more popular in the replacement of diseased or injured body parts, since they are seldom rejected by the tissues of the recipient. So far, the use of plastics has been somewhat limited to the circulatory system, in arterial grafts and artificial hearts or portions of hearts.

OUTLINE SUMMARY

1. Cells: protoplasm organized into microscopic structural and functional units of the body tissues
   A. Cell sizes and shapes
   B. Parts of a typical cell
      a. The cell nucleus and its functions
      b. The cell cytoplasm
         1. Organelles
         2. Inclusions
         3. Cilia
         4. Flagella
   C. Cell permeability: movement through the cell membrane
      a. Diffusion and osmosis
      b. Tonicity of solutions and permeability
      c. Theories of permeability
   D. Phagocytosis and pinocytosis: engulfing actions of cells
   E. Cell division
      a. Mitosis: division of the nucleus
      b. Cytokinesis: division of the cytoplasm
2. Histology: cells into tissues. Kinds of tissues
   A. Epithelial
   B. Connective and supporting
      a. Fibrous tissues
      b. Cartilage
      c. Bone
      d. Blood and lymph
   C. Muscle tissues
      a. Skeletal: the muscle of body movements
      b. Smooth: visceral muscle
      c. Cardiac: heart muscle
   D. Nervous tissue
   E. Tissue transplantation
      1. Autotransplants
      2. Isotransplants
      3. Homotransplants
      4. Heterotransplants

STUDY QUESTIONS AND PROBLEMS

1. Draw and label a diagram of a typical cell. Can all the parts you have labeled be found in every cell in the body?
2. Since some cells (nerve cells) are up to 3 ft long, why can't they be seen without a microscope? Name the only cell produced in the body that is (barely) visible to the unaided eye.
3. Describe the cell membrane. What is meant by the term *unit membrane*? How many cellular structures have membranes?
4. What is the importance of the cell nucleus? What are nucleoli?
5. List the typical organelles and inclusions of a cell. What single feature distinguishes an organelle from an inclusion?
6. Sketch the basic structure of cilia and flagella. Where would you find cilia in the body? Flagella?
7. What is meant by the statement that cells are selectively or differentially permeable? State several theories of permeability.
8. You are given a container which is divided into two compartments by a membrane permeable only to water molecules. You place a 10% solution of sodium chloride in one compartment, and a 0.85% solution of sodium chloride in the other compartment. The solvent of both solutions is water. In which direction would net diffusion occur: from the 10% solution to 0.85% solution, or from the 0.85% solution to the 10% solution? Why? What is the clinical importance of the tonicity of solutions as it is related to diffusion through cell membranes?
9. Draw a simple diagram illustrating phagocytosis. What cells of the body

are outstanding in their phagocytic action?

10. List the phases or stages of mitosis, and describe the major features of each stage. What is cytokinesis?

11. What do the abbreviations *DNA* and *RNA* represent? Briefly discuss the importance of each of these compounds, and the structure of the DNA molecule.

12. Define: *tissue, differentiation, histology,* and *section.* What is a morula?

13. List the different kinds of tissues, and the most outstanding features of each. Discuss the different kinds of epithelial tissues.

14. Define: *autotransplant, isotransplant, homotransplant,* and *heterotransplant.* What is the advantage of plastic body-replacement parts over natural organ transplants?

15. Why are blood and lymph logically called fluid tissues? Why can blood be called a connective tissue?

the body covering, or integument

The **integument**—or skin, as it is commonly called—*protects the body from invasion by bacteria and other harmful microorganisms, helps maintain a constant body temperature, prevents water loss, excretes wastes, receives four kinds of sensations, produces a vitamin,* and *absorbs certain drugs and other chemical substances.* It has a remarkable ability to *heal itself.* In order to carry out all these functions, the skin must be tough and pliable, selectively permeable, and well supplied with nerves and sensory receptors, blood vessels, and glands. The *sweat and sebaceous glands, the hair, and nails are all derivatives of the skin.*

The skin is the first body organ to be considered in detail in this book. An organ, by definition, is *any body structure made up of two or more different kinds of tissues.* Under this definition, the heart, lungs, stomach, liver, kidneys, intestines, even the bones and blood vessels are all organs. The skin and its derivatives are often referred to collectively as the *integumentary system.* (See Color Plate I.)

Microscopic anatomy of the skin

The skin is made up of two major layers, an innermost *dermis* and an outermost *epidermis,* and these are further divided into several smaller layers, as illustrated in Fig. 4-1. These smaller layers are indistinct in thin skin, such as that on the eyelid, but are easily seen in a cross-sectional microscope slide of the thick skin of the back or of the soles of the feet. The layers of the epidermis, which consist of *stratified squamous epithelium,* are (beginning with the outermost) the *stratum corneum, stratum lucidum, stratum granulosum,* and *stratum germinativum.* The cells in the first two layers are dead or dying, while those in the two deeper layers are alive and constantly dividing. The cells of the stratum corneum are scalelike, have no nuclei, and contain the hornlike protein material, *keratin.* They are constantly worn away and shed, but are replaced by cells from the stratum germinativum. The stratum lucidum, just beneath the stratum corneum, is much thinner than the layer above it, and appears translucent in stained sections. It has no sharply defined cellular structure, but contains a keratin-like substance, *eleidin.* The stratum granulosum consists of from one to three layers of flattened cells containing *keratohyalin,* present as small granules. Cell nuclei can be seen. This may be considered a transition layer, with cells "passing through" on their way to the stratum corneum.

The three upper layers of the epidermis could not exist without the stratum germinativum. Here, cells multiply and move outward, many of them eventually becoming cornified or keratinized and sloughed off when they reach the stratum corneum. The stratum germinativum has several layers of cells. Those near its upper limit are flattened and resemble those of the stratum granulo-

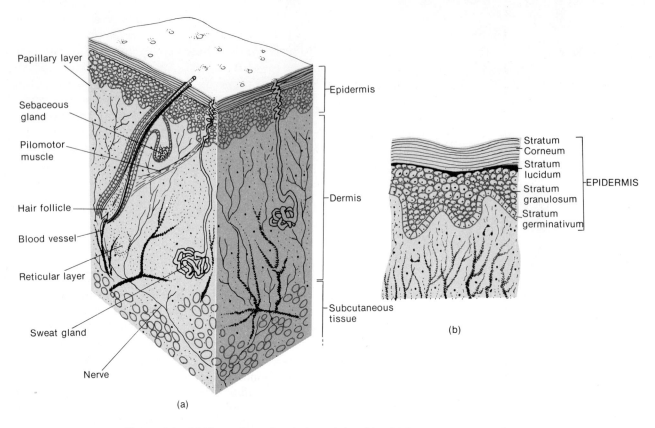

Papillary layer

Sebaceous gland

Pilomotor muscle

Hair follicle

Blood vessel

Reticular layer

Sweat gland

Nerve

Epidermis

Dermis

Subcutaneous tissue

(a)

Stratum Corneum

Stratum lucidum

Stratum granulosum

Stratum germinativum

EPIDERMIS

(b)

Figure 4-1 (a) Three-dimensional view of the skin. (b) Layers of the epidermis.

sum, while those near the dermis are cuboidal or low columnar in shape. The lower portion of the stratum germinativum is very irregular in outline, due to the many upward projections of the dermis, *dermal papillae.*

The dermis, the deeper and thicker of the two major layers of the skin, consists of *dense areolar connective tissue* (mostly bundles of collagenous fibers), with some *elastic fibers* in the more superficial (outer) portion. It is a very good example of *fibro-elastic connective tissue.* The dermis is sometimes called the *corium,* or true skin, and can be divided into a superficial *papillary layer* and a deep *reticular layer.* The papillary layer is very vascular, and supplies nourishment to both the dermis and the stratum germinativum above. The reticular layer functions mainly in giving the skin its toughness, but it also contains *sweat and oil glands, sensory receptors and nerves, blood vessels,* and *hair follicles.*

SUBCUTANEOUS CONNECTIVE TISSUE Just deep to or below the dermis of the skin is a layer of *areolar connective tissue,* called the *superficial fascia,* or *hypodermis.* It is superimposed on the tougher, denser *deep fascia* which adheres directly to the muscles covered by the skin. Fat deposits occur throughout much of this subcutaneous connective tissue, except in that of the scrotum, penis, nipple, areola (around the nipple), labia minora (around the vagina), and eyelids. The amount of fat deposited in the lower portion of the abdominal wall is often so great that the subtaneous connective tissue can be divided into *membranous and fatty layers,* especially in the female. Blood and lymph vessels, nerves and nerve endings for the sensation of pressure, portions of sweat glands and hair follicles, and smooth and striated muscle fibers are also found in or passing through subcutaneous connective tissue. Although very closely related to the skin, this layer is *not* a part of the skin itself.

38

The scalp or cranial covering is not made of skin alone. In all, it consists of *five layers,* which are as follows, named in order from superficial to deep:

1. *Skin.*
2. *Connective tissue* (subcutaneous).
3. *Aponeurosis* (tough, fibrous connective tissue, serving for the attachment of scalp muscles).
4. *Loose connective tissue* (subaponeurosis).
5. *Periosteum* (here also called *pericranium;* fibrous connective tissue that adheres tightly to all bones).

It will be noted that combining the first letters in the names of the layers produces the word SCALP.

The scalp can be very important clinically by giving the physician and nurse a clue to the general health of a patient. Also, the scalp is highly vascular, and scalp wounds can sometimes be troublesome bleeders because the dense fibrous tissue of the subcutaneous layer tends to prevent reflex constriction (narrowing) of injured blood vessels by the nervous system. Once bleeding has stopped, however, these wounds are quick to heal, due to the scalp's good blood supply. Hemorrhages and infections may spread throughout the scalp if they are located *beneath the layer of the aponeurosis.*

Hair, nails, sweat glands, and sebaceous glands

The hair, nails, sweat glands, and sebaceous (oil) glands are the derivatives of the skin. Hair in varying amounts is found on all mammals, including such diversified forms as whales, bats, and gorillas. Man is no exception. Hair can be seen on virtually any part of the human body except the palms of the hands and soles of the feet, but is most abundant on the head and in the *axillary* (armpit) and *pubic* (groin) regions. The appearance of hair in the last two loca-

tions—along with the beard in the male and development of the breasts in the female—is a sign that *puberty* (sexual maturation) has been reached. The newborn infant is covered with very fine hair, or *lanugo,* which is shed shortly after birth. A *typical hair* (Fig. 4-1) consists of a *root,* located in a *follicle* or "socket" of the skin, and a long *shaft.* Hair growth is due to the division and differentiation of cells in the *bulb region* of the root. The cells of the hair die and become *cornified* while still in the root; therefore, growth of the hair is not affected by cutting it. After death, there is no further production or differentiation of the body cells; but a portion of lately formed hair may uncoil and thus push outward from the follicle, giving the impression that hair growth has taken place.

Smooth muscle (*the arrector pili muscles*) connects the follicle region with the skin and causes the hair to "stand on end" during fright. Sebaceous glands produce oily lubricating *sebum* around the upper portion of the hair shaft. This is an example of *holocrine secretion,* in which cells of the gland itself are constantly being converted into the substance produced by the gland. Sweat glands, or *sudoriferous glands,* are found everywhere in the body covering except in the anterior portions of the penis and clitoris and in the ear drum. They are tubular, tortuous (coiled), and open as *pores* in the skin. There are two major types of sweat glands, *merocrine* (or *eocrine*) and *apocrine.* Although all sweat glands secrete sweat or *perspiration,* which has a composition similar to that of very dilute urine, some apocrine glands, such as those of the external ear openings, are modified to produce a wax called *cerumen,* and are known as *ceruminous glands.* Most apocrine glands (which are considerably larger than other sweat glands) are located in the axilla and around the nipples, vagina, and anus. These latter produce most of the odor with which sweat is associated, although bacterial action and its waste products also contribute greatly to any smell the body gives off.

The *nails* (Fig. 4-2) are hornlike derivatives of the epidermis, and consist of a *root* and a *body,* lying on an epithelial *nail bed.* They grow as cells are added on at the root. The bed is well supplied with blood vessels, which accounts for the pink color that shows through the translucent nail. The lightly colored, crescentlike portion of the nail is the *lunula.* Deep to the lunula is the *nail matrix,* where cell division resulting in growth of the nail takes place. The skin over the root of the nail is the *nail fold.* Besides being useful accessories of the fingers, the nails, by their appearance, give some indication as to the general health and personality of an individual. Very blue nails indicate a condition of *cyanosis,* due to improper oxygenation of the blood. Dirty or ragged nails hint at poor personal habits, and chewed nails at possible emotional problems.

Skin color

Melanocytes, cells found in the stratum germinativum of the epidermis, produce *melanin,* the principal coloring pigment of the skin. Melanin may be brown, black, or even yellowish, depending upon racial origin. The quantity of melanin is greater in the skin of Negroes and other dark races. A suntan depends upon the fact that exposure to sunlight causes an increase in melanin production and its deposition in the outer layers of the skin. The blood supply to the skin and the thickness of the skin itself also contribute to its color. The blood supply of the skin consists largely of rich, complex networks of coiled *arteries* and small *veins* making direct connection with each other without the usual intervening capillaries. These *arteriovenous anastomoses* play a major part in the maintenance of a remarkably constant body temperature.

The skin and body-temperature regulation

Heat is continually produced in the body by the *oxidation* or "burning" of foodstuffs in the cells. A near-constant body temperature must be maintained in spite of this heat production, so that vital cellular enzymes will not be inactivated, thereby bringing about the death of the cells. The role

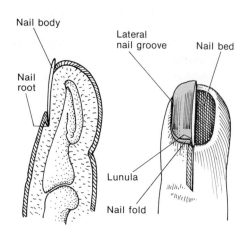

Figure 4-2 Construction of the nails.

of the skin in regulation of body temperature is a *dual one: it helps to either raise or lower the body temperature as necessary;* and *it acts as an insulator,* tending to prevent rapid changes from one temperature to another. If a person suddenly enters a very cold environment (such as a freezer locker or an icy lake) after having spent some time in a much warmer environment, reflex mechanisms of the nervous system act to constrict (narrow) the small arteries of the skin and decrease circulation there. Heat-carrying blood is immediately shunted (rerouted) to the muscles and vital organs, and even though the skin itself may become quite cool, the internal body temperature remains near 98.6°F. Conversely, entering an extremely warm environment brings about dilation (expansion) of the vessels of the skin and an increase in sweating. The net result is a loss of body heat by *radiation* into the atmosphere, facilitated by *evaporation* of the perspiration. The physiological mechanisms involved in body-temperature regulation are discussed more fully in the chapters concerned with the functions of the nervous system and the metabolism of foods.

How the skin protects

A very important way in which the skin serves as an organ of protection depends upon its *secretions.* Perspiration and sebum form an antiseptic film over the body, one which *helps prevent dehydration, neutralizes acids and bases,* and *retards the absorption of poisonous substances.* So long as the skin remains intact, the keratin of the epidermis is tough enough to bar the passage of parasites, bacteria, fungi, and most chemicals. Relatively few types of bacteria, all considered harmless, normally reside on the skin; but if personal cleanliness habits are poor, *pathogenic* (disease-causing) bacteria and fungi may become prevalent, especially in the genital and anal regions and between the toes.

The skin as an excretory organ

By means of its apocrine and merocrine sweat glands, the skin excretes a thin fluid called *perspiration.* Perspiration is about 99% water; the remaining 1% is solid matter, about 50% of which consists chiefly of the inorganic salt sodium chloride and 50% organic substances, such as urea, uric acid, ammonia, creatinine, glucose, lactic acid, amino acids, and even traces of vitamins B and C. Apocrine perspiration is particularly odorous; the presence of volatile fatty acids and ammonia combine with the waste products of bacterial action to produce this odor, especially where sweat is trapped among hairs, as it often is in the axillary region.

Absorption by the skin

In good health, the skin is permeable to few substances with which it would normally come in contact. In general, it can be stated that the skin *permits the passage of certain gases and some lipoid-soluble agents and blocks the transfer of water and electrolytes.* A few lipoid-soluble substances to which the skin is permeable include vitamins A, D, and K, the sex hormones testosterone and progesterone, salts of arsenic, antimony, mercury, copper, and lead (after being rendered lipoid-soluble by the fatty acids in sebum), methyl salicylate, and several phenolic compounds. Methyl salicylate, a synthetic oil of wintergreen, is often used in liniments designed to help relieve stiffness of muscles.

Virtually all gases pass through the skin with relative ease, with the notable exception of *carbon monoxide.* Gas molecules of oxygen, carbon dioxide, hydrogen sulfide, nitrogen, ammonia, and hydrogen cyanide readily penetrate the epidermis and travel through the sweat and sebaceous glands. It should be pointed out that the amounts of oxygen and carbon dioxide that can be transmitted through the skin are far below those required for even a brief period of respiration (breathing).

The skin as a sensory organ

In addition to containing autonomic nerve fibers* that control by reflex action the dilation and constriction of blood vessels and secretions of sudoriferous and sebaceous glands, the skin is richly supplied with nerves bearing endings specialized for the reception of the sensations of *touch* (*tactile sense*), *pressure, temperature,* and *pain.* In general, the cutaneous branches of spinal nerves (those connecting with the skin) each supply certain regions of the skin called *dermatomes* (Fig. 4-3). There is, however, a good deal of overlap between the area supplied by the branches of one spinal nerve and the one adjacent to it, and the loss of one cutaneous branch of a spinal nerve does not always result in extensive loss of sensation.

The skin and vitamin D

Vitamin D, necessary for the normal growth and development of bones, is manufactured in the skin when the *ultraviolet portion of sunlight* reacts with *sterol compounds* present in the skin.

Regeneration or healing of the skin

Within a few hours following a cut or other wound of the skin, *fibroblasts* begin

---

* Autonomic nerve fibers are those found in that portion of the nervous tissues that functions in a completely involuntary (reflex) manner—the autonomic nervous system (see Chapter 7).

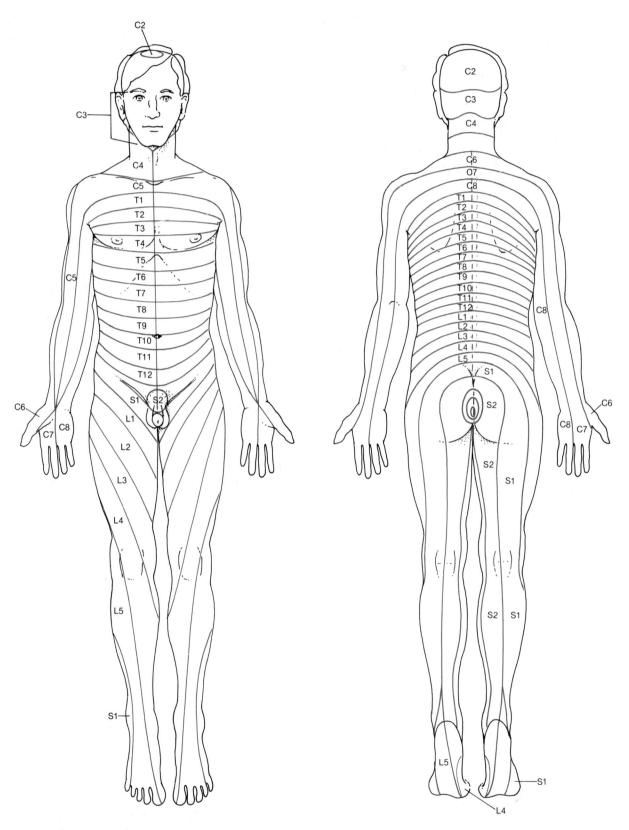

Figure 4-3 Dermatomes. Areas of the skin supplied by cutaneous branches of spinal nerves. "C" numbers indicate cervical nerves; "T," thoracic nerves; "L," lumbar nerves, and "S," sacral nerves.

proliferating (multiplying) and moving from the edges of the wound toward the central portion. Together with *fibrin* from the wound clot and newly formed capillaries, they constitute *granulation tissue. Collagen fibers* soon form from a substance secreted by the fibroblasts, and healing and the formation of scar tissue result. If the general health is good, keeping a wound in the skin clean and making sure that it has a good blood supply will do much to promote rapid healing.

Clinical considerations

Careful examination of the skin often yields information useful to the physician in making a diagnosis, more so if the patient is a Caucasian, or "white" person. Extremely pale skin sometimes indicates *anemia* (reduced amount of red-blood pigment, hemoglobin); a yellowish skin color is associated with certain liver diseases and the presence of liver-bile pigments in the blood; in cyanosis, not only are the nails blue, but portions of the skin have a bluish cast, especially the skin of the lips. An individual suffering from Addison's disease (due to insufficient hormone secretion by the adrenal glands) exhibits a *"bronzed"* skin. Such childhood diseases as chickenpox, scarlet fever, and measles have their characteristic *skin rashes.* Skin *lesions* (sores) known as *pustules* are associated with syphilis and other diseases.

The skin of the nipple of the female breast is pink until pregnancy, when the color changes permanently to dark brown.

COMMON SKIN DISORDERS Disorders and abnormalities affecting principally the skin range from sunburn to skin cancer. *Dermatitis* is a general medical term meaning an inflamed skin, and may sometimes be associated with vitamin deficiencies. A *cyst* is a fluid-filled sac in the skin; the fluid is watery, but is not pus—a *pustule* is a pus-filled, raised area. A flattened, fluid-filled area is a *wheal,* while an open, nonhealing sore is an *ulcer* or *ulceration.* A crack in the skin is usually called a *fissure. Corns* and *callouses* are thickened areas of epidermis brought about in response to long periods of pressure and friction on the feet or hands. *Boils* and *carbuncles* are rather extensive localized bacterial infections. *Urticaria* is typified by raised, itching, white patches on the skin, and is commonly called "nettlerash" or "hives." *Diaphoresis* means excessive sweating or perspiration. If the hair or nails are brittle and dry, and the scalp dry and flaky, poor general health may well be suspected.

**OUTLINE
SUMMARY**

1. The integument or skin
   A. Functions
      a. Protection
      b. Body-temperature regulation
      c. Conservation of body water
      d. Excretion of wastes
      e. Reception of outside stimuli
      f. Vitamin production
      g. Absorption of drugs and other agents
   B. Microscopic structure
      a. Major layers
         1. Epidermis (outer layer)
         2. Dermis (deeper layer)
      b. Sublayers
         1. Of the epidermis: stratum corneum, stratum lucidum, stratum granulosum, stratum germinativum
         2. Of the dermis: papillary layer and reticular layer
      c. Subcutaneous connective tissue: tela subcutanea, or superficial fascia
   C. The scalp: the cranial covering—five layers, which are (from superficial to deep)
      a. Skin
      b. Connective tissues (subcutaneous)
      c. Aponeurotic layer (tough connective tissue)
      d. Loose connective tissue
      e. Pericranium (the periosteum of the skull)
   D. Derivatives of the skin
      a. Hair
      b. Nails
      c. Sweat glands
      d. Sebaceous (oil-secreting glands)
   E. Skin color: due mainly to melanin, the chief pigment of the skin, and to the rich blood supply of the skin. Melanin

is produced by specialized cells of the stratum germinativum, melanocytes

F. The skin and body-temperature regulation
   a. Regulates the amount of blood available to muscles and vital organs by reflex vasoconstriction and vasodilation
   b. Acts as an insulator of the body, by virtue of its fat deposits
   c. Cools the body when necessary by secreting perspiration, and permits it to retain heat by slowing secretion of perspiration
G. How the skin protects
   a. Antiseptic action of perspiration and sebum
   b. Helps prevent dehydration
   c. Serves as a barrier against parasites, bacteria, fungi, and many chemical substances
H. The excretory functions of the skin
   a. Perspiration: about 99% water, 1% solids, including sodium chloride, urea, uric acid, ammonia, creatinine, glucose, lactic acid, amino acids
I. Substances absorbed by the skin
   a. Lipoid soluble substances: vitamins A, D, and K; the hormones testosterone and progesterone; methyl salicylate; phenols; and salts, such as those of arsenic, antimony, mercury, copper, and lead.
   b. Gases: oxygen, carbon dioxide, hydrogen sulfide, nitrogen, ammonia, and hydrogen cyanide (a deadly poison)
J. Sensation by the skin: sensory nerve endings are present which detect the following
   a. Touch (tactile sense)
   b. Pressure
   c. Temperature changes
   d. Painful stimuli
K. Vitamin production by the skin: the skin produces vitamin D when ultraviolet rays of the sun convert sterols in the skin to this vitamin
L. Regeneration (healing) of the skin
   a. Shortly after a wound occurs, fibroblasts begin multiplying rapidly and move from the edges of the wound to the central portion
   b. Fibroblasts, fibrin in the blood clot, and new capillaries form granulation tissue
   c. Fibroblasts produce a substance which becomes collagen fibers, which in turn make up a good portion of scar tissue

STUDY QUESTIONS AND PROBLEMS

1. List seven important functions of the skin. What are the derivatives of the skin?

2. Name the two major layers of the skin. In what layer of the epidermis are cells produced?

3. Give two other terms for superficial fascia. Is it a part of the skin itself?

4. List the five major layers of the scalp, in order from superficial to deep. Hemorrhages and infections spread most easily if they are located beneath what layer of the scalp?

5. A physician examines the nails of his patient and concludes that the blood of the patient is not being properly oxygenated. What condition of the nails would lead the physician to draw such a conclusion?

6. What is an arteriovenous anastomosis? How can it help to maintain a constant body temperature?

7. About what percentage of perspiration is water? List six organic substances found in perspiration. What is the chief inorganic salt of perspiration?

8. In general, the skin permits the absorption of certain substances or materials and blocks the passage of others. Give examples of those which can pass through the skin and of those which cannot normally do so.

9. The sensory nerve endings of the skin are specialized to receive four kinds of sensations. What are they? What is a dermatome?

10. Mrs. B., a patient, asked her nurse how sitting in the sun would help her to obtain more vitamin D. What would be a good way for a nurse to explain this to Mrs. B?

11. Mr. J. is admitted to a hospital, and the examining physician immediately concludes that Mr. J. could possibly be

the body covering, or integument

suffering from Addison's disease. What is the appearance of Mr. J.'s skin?

12. What is dermatitis? A cyst? A wheal? A pustule? A fissure?

13. Bobby G. is a patient who has brittle, dry hair and nails and a dry, flaky scalp. What is the general condition of his health?

14. What is granulation tissue? Describe healing and scarring.

15. In general, would you consider the bacteria that live on the skin harmful or harmless?

16. Name the body areas that can breed harmful bacteria if they are not kept clean.

the body framework

Bone, cartilage, and the white fibrous connective-tissue ligaments that hold bones together at joints help the body to retain its shape and form. Together they make up the body framework or *skeleton* (Fig. 5-1 and Color Plates II, III, IV, and VIII).

Functions of the skeletal system

The skeleton and its component bones perform several functions, all of which are necessary to the maintenance of good health. These functions are as follows:

1. *Support.*
2. *Permission of movement,* by virtue of the joints or *articulations* between bones.
3. *Formation of blood cells* in the *bone marrow,* a process called *hemopoiesis.*
4. *Protection;* as examples, protection of the brain by the skull, and of the heart and lungs by the bones of the thorax.
5. *Detoxification,* or removal of certain poisonous substances from other parts of the body, brought to the bones by the circulation of the blood.
6. *Provision of areas for attachment of skeletal muscles.*
7. *Storage of minerals,* such as *calcium* and *phosphorus.*

The major features of a bone

No single bone bears all the features of all the bones in the skeleton. A long bone, such as the tibia or shin bone, however, bears many of these features, and will serve as a "typical" bone (Fig. 5-2).

Long bones have enlarged ends or *epiphyses* (sing., *epiphysis*) and an elongated portion, the *diaphysis* or *shaft.* Hard, dense, *compact bone* is thickest in the region of the shaft, where strength is needed. The epiphyses are mostly *cancellous* or *spongy bone,* containing numerous small spaces, and covered with a thin layer of compact bone. Throughout the length of the shaft is a narrow space, the *medullary canal* lined with a tough connective tissue membrane, the *endosteum,* and containing the material of the *bone marrow,* or *inner substance.* Another tough membrane, the *periosteum,* adheres tightly to the outer surface of the bone. The epiphyses of long bones are enlarged, and therefore give stability to the joints they enter into. Muscles attach to epiphyses, and articular surfaces of the epiphyses are covered with a layer of *hyaline cartilage* (here called *articular cartilage*). The proximal epiphyses of the adult humerus and femur contain red marrow, while the other epiphyses contain yellow marrow. The periosteum contains bone-forming cells called *osteoblasts,* and is therefore important in bone growth and repair. The endosteum supplies cells that become osteoblasts as the need arises. The periosteum sends penetrating fibers (*Sharpey's fibers*) into bone, thereby forming a strong bond between the two structures. Ligaments and muscle tendons intermesh with periosteal fibers, anchoring muscle to bone.

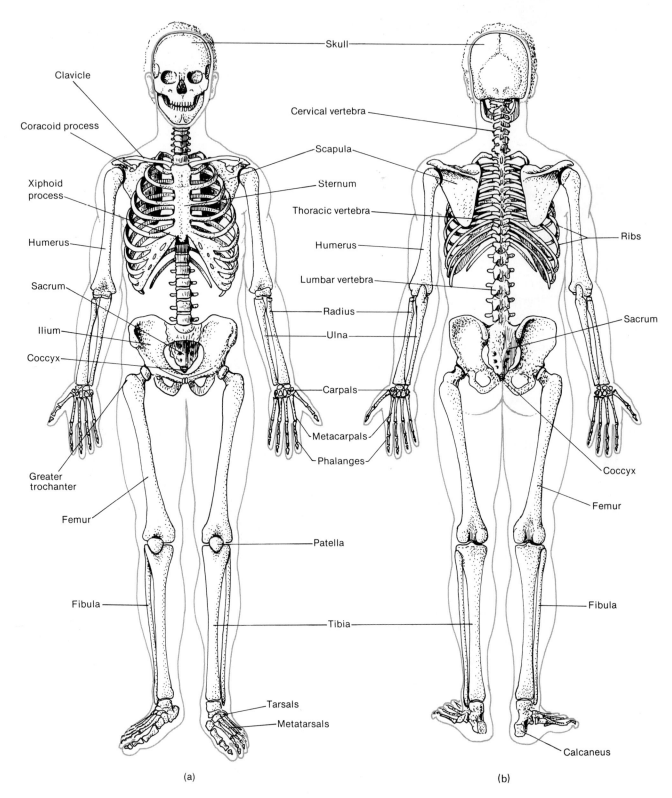

Figure 5-1   The skeleton: (a) Anterior view. (b) Posterior view.

Bone marrow consists of a meshwork (*reticulum*) of special *reticular cells,* developing blood cells, and/or fat. Red marrow is called "red" because the red blood cells it is producing give it a red color. Since it produces blood cells, red marrow is also called *hemopoietic tissue.* Yellow marrow is called "yellow" because the fat cells it contains impart a yellow color. It is not actively engaged in the production of blood cells, but can produce them if the need arises.

The histology and development of bone

The basic unit of structure of bone or *osseus tissue* is the microscopic *Haversian system* or *osteon* (Fig. 5-3). Each bone consists chiefly of innumerable Haversian systems. An osteon is made up largely of minerals and other inorganic substances, arranged in concentric layers or *lamellae.* In the center of each osteon is a canal, the *central or Haversian canal,* through which course blood and lymph vessels and nerves. Mature bone cells or *osteocytes* are located in small boatlike cavities between the lamellae of the osteon, *lacunae.* Tiny channels running at right angles to the long axis of the bone, *canaliculi,* connect adjacent lacunae with each other and the most central lacunae with the Haversian canal. Canaliculi are formed by cytoplasmic extensions of maturing bone cells called *osteoblasts.* Nutrients from the blood vessels reach the inner parts of bone by diffusing through the complex network of canals and canaliculi. Compact bone consists chiefly of Haversian systems or units fitted closely together, while cancellous bone contains many spaces enclosed by thin processes of bone material, *trabeculae* (Fig. 5-2). Trabeculae are arranged in such a manner that they strengthen bones against stress and strain. Bone material consists of *cells, fibers,* and a *solid matrix,* or *ground substance,* rich in minerals. The fibers of bone, which cannot usually be seen because of the dense, homogeneous matrix, are of the collagenous type. Matrix, not cells, predominates in bone. The bones

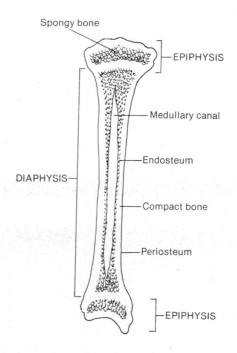

Figure 5-2 The gross structure of a long bone (tibia).

of the body are derived from the middle primary germ layer of cells of the embryo, the *mesoderm* (see Chapter 16). Bone development begins with the formation of a *cartilaginous-membrane skeleton* during the first three months of pregnancy. During the *last six months of pregnancy,* much of this cartilage and membrane is replaced by bone, during the processes of *endochondral* and *intramembranous ossification.* The maturation processes of bone are complete at about age 21 in both sexes, but growth of the long bones continues for a few more years, to approximately age 25. Some of the bones formed by replacement of membrane (*membrane bones*) are the bones of the cranium and face and the scapulae. Most of the other bones of the skeleton are formed by the replacement of cartilage by bone, and are known as *endochondral bones.* Bone matrix contains collagen, a leathery organic *cementing substance,* and deposits of hard *inorganic salts.* Much of the salt content of bone is *hydroxyapatite,* $[Ca_3(PO_4)_2]_3 \cdot Ca(OH)_2$. The second most abundant salt is *calcium hydroxide* or *lime. Calcium carbonate*

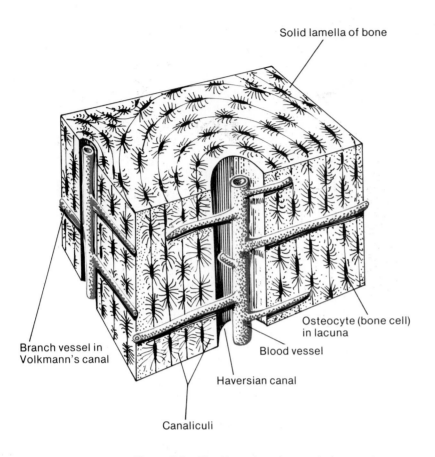

Solid lamella of bone

Osteocyte (bone cell)
in lacuna

Branch vessel in
Volkmann's canal

Blood vessel

Haversian canal

Canaliculi

Figure 5-3 The Haversian system of compact bone.

($CaCO_3$) is also present in small amounts. The organic portion of bone provides some degree of flexibility (more so in youth), while the inorganic salts provide reinforcement and rigidity so necessary in the support of body structure and weight. A discussion of the processes of endochondral and intramembranous ossification follows.

ENDOCHONDRAL OSSIFICATION During this type of bone formation, hyaline cartilage is *replaced* by bone (*not* changed into bone, as is commonly supposed). Most of the bones in the skeleton are formed in this manner. First, cartilage cells become enlarged in areas of cartilaginous "bone models" called *ossification centers*. In the formation of long bones, three such centers occur: one in the midpoint of the diaphysis (shaft) and one in each of the epiphyses (ends). The enlarged cartilage cells soon break down and disappear, leaving spaces in the ossification centers. Bone-forming cells called *osteoblasts* appear in the spaces, and bring about the formation of the organic

components of the bone that are being laid down, *collagenous fibers* and *cementing substances.* The cementing substances, which belong to a group of compounds called *mucopolysaccharides,* aid the collagenous fibers in forming the bone matrix. While the organic components of bone are being formed, minerals—especially calcium salts—are being deposited and blood vessels ramify throughout the newly forming bone. Collagen is formed by the endoplasmic reticulum of osteoblasts, and cementing substances by their Golgi bodies.

Eventually, osteoblasts become osteocytes. The central portion of bones becomes cancellous or "spongy" and the peripheral portions more dense or compact. A medullary or marrow cavity, endosteum, and periosteum develop.

INTRAMEMBRANOUS OSSIFICATION Here, the ossification centers develop within the membranes that will be replaced by the bones of the cranium, face, and scapulae. Osteoblasts in these centers deposit matrix material in the form of calcium salts. Many of these osteoblasts eventually become osteocytes. A thin region of cancellous bone is formed, sandwiched between two layers of compact bone. In the skull, cancellous or spongy bone is given the special name *diploe.*

THE ROLE OF NUTRITION IN BONE FORMA-TION It has been found that adequate amounts of *protein* and *vitamin C* are necessary in the formation of collagenous fibers and cement substance by osteoblasts, and that *calcium salts* and *vitamin D* are essential to the deposition of calcium salts in the matrix of bone.

At the point of junction between the epiphyses and diaphysis of long bones is a section of cartilage, the *epiphyseal plate,* which persists until the bone has reached its maximum length. By examining a long bone with X rays, it is possible to determine whether or not further growth is possible. If an epiphyseal plate is present, growth can occur; if not, then growth is complete.

Homeostatic equilibrium between bone deposition and reabsorption

It comes as a surprise to many students that bone is not simply laid down or deposited on a "once-and-for-all" basis. In a living person, the bones are just as alive as any other tissue; some osteoblasts are always present, and constantly deposit new bone, throughout life. They are opposed in this process by large, multinucleate cells, *osteoclasts,* located in the bone cavities. Osteoclasts *reabsorb* bone, and calcium and phosphate salts are carried away in the extracellular fluid to be used in other parts of the body during the process. The *homeostatic balance* between the osteoblastic deposition and osteoclastic reabsorption of bone is an important segment of the metabolism of calcium in the body. Excessive stress placed on bones, such as that seen in athletes and young children, causes osteoblastic activity to become somewhat greater than osteoclastic activity, with the result that the bones affected become stronger and straighter than they ordinarily would. Even poorly set broken bones may straighten, provided the

patient has not reached old age. The role of calcium in the overall homeostasis of the body is discussed in Chapter 13.

Changes in the skeleton with age

With time, the deposit of organic substances in bone slows and the bones become more brittle and susceptible to fracture. With the loss of teeth, the mandible often shows marked *atrophy* (decrease in size), and somewhat resembles its appearance in the infant—that is, small in proportion to the remainder of the skull. *Kyphosis* or stooped-shoulder appearance often develops, and *sesamoid bones* may form within the tendons of such muscles as the gastrocnemius and under the great toe. The xiphoid process of the sternum usually ossifies.

Hemopoiesis

Hemopoiesis is the physiological word for blood-cell formation. The red blood cells (*erythrocytes*), platelets (*thrombocytes*), and most of the white blood cells (*leucocytes*) are formed in the red bone marrow. A detailed discussion of hemopoiesis is presented in Chapter 10.

Cartilage

Cartilage is commonly known as *gristle.* It supports the nose and ears, connects the ribs to the breast bone, and acts as a cushion between two adjacent vertebrae. Cartilage also covers the articular surfaces of bones, helping to keep them friction-free as they move over one another. The shoulder, elbow, hip, and knee joints are particularly dependent on cartilage for ease of movement and shock absorption.

Although cartilage resembles bone because it is composed largely of intercellular substance and relatively few cells, it differs from bone in being much more flexible. The flexibility of cartilage is due to its gel-type matrix, which lacks the calcium and other mineral salts of bone. The matrix of cartilage gets its strength from the numerous collagenous fibers embedded throughout its substance.

Cartilage has no blood vessels, and nutrients and oxygen reach the cells of cartilage —*chondrocytes*—by diffusing from the capillaries of the *perichondrium* (the fibrous covering of cartilage) through the gelatinous matrix.

Depending upon the proportions of fibers to matrix and also upon the kinds of fibers present, cartilage is classed as *hyaline, elastic,* and *fibrous.* Hyaline, the most common type of cartilage, has a somewhat glassy appearance. It is found in many of the joints of the body, in the nasal septum, and in the trachea (windpipe) and bronchi (branches of the trachea). Elastic cartilage gives support to the external portion of the ear and to the *pharyngotympanic* (Eustachian) tube connecting the pharynx with the middle ear. Fibrocartilage (fibrous cartilage) is present in the intervertebral discs and in the joint between the two pubic bones (*symphysis pubis*). Figure 5-4 illustrates the three kinds of cartilage.

GROSS ANATOMY OF THE SKELETAL SYSTEM

Both anterior and posterior views of the skeleton (without ligaments or other articular structures) are shown in Fig. 5-1. Although many of the *213 ** bones of the skeleton are labeled in the figure, a substantial number of them—such as the extremely tiny bones of middle ear—cannot be pictured in a drawing of this size and are, therefore, illustrated separately.

Bone shapes and sizes

Anatomists often group bones according to their general shape, classifying them as *long, short, flat, irregular,* and *sesamoid* or rounded.

LONG BONES   It was stated previously that long bones have enlarged ends or epiphyses

* The number 213 is not a constant one, as the reader will discover later in this chapter.

and an elongated portion, the diaphysis or shaft (Fig. 5-2). Hard, dense, compact bone is thickest in the region of the shaft, where strength is needed. The epiphyses are mostly cancellous or spongy bone, containing numerous small spaces, and covered with a thin layer of compact bone. Throughout the length of the shaft is the medullary canal, lined with a tough connective tissue membrane, the endosteum, and containing the material of the bone marrow, or inner substance. The periosteum adheres tightly to the outer surface of the bone. The *radius and ulna* of the forearm, *humerus* of the upper arm, and *femur, tibia, and fibula* of the lower extremity are examples of long bones.

SHORT BONES   These consist mostly of cancellous bone covered with a thin layer of compact bone. There is no shaft. The wrist bones or *carpals* and the *tarsals* or ankle bones are examples of short bones.

FLAT BONES   Included in this classification are such osseus structures as the shoulderblade or *scapula,* the *ribs,* and certain bones of the skull and pelvis. Flat bones consist of a fairly thin layer of cancellous bone sandwiched between two thin layers of compact bone.

IRREGULAR BONES   These bones cannot be classed as being long, short, or flat. The bones of the *middle ear* (*ossicles*) and the *vertebrae* are irregularly shaped bones. Like other bones, they are made up of cancellous tissue covered by compact material.

SESAMOID BONES   Sesamoid bones are named for their fancied resemblance to sesame seeds. They are for the most part *supernumerary*—that is, they are "extra" bones. They often develop in tendons beneath the big toe and above the heel. The kneecap or *patella* is one sesamoid bone that is always present, and is by far the largest.

Bone markings

The points at which blood vessels pass through bones, muscles attach to bone, or bones articulate with each other are often seen as holes, ridges, and bumps called *bone*

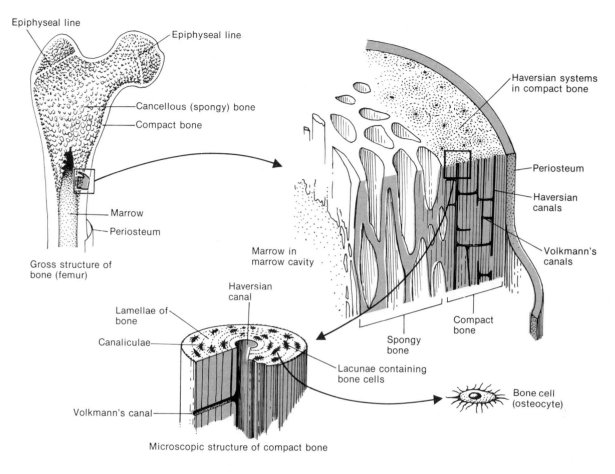

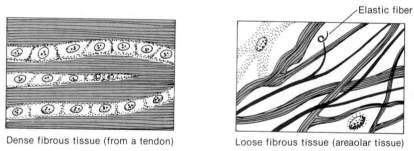

Dense fibrous tissue (from a tendon)

Loose fibrous tissue (areaolar tissue)

Three kinds of cartilage

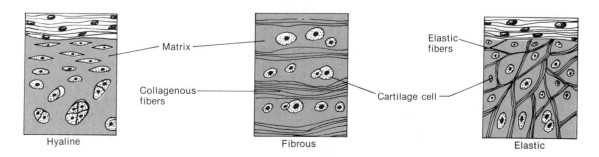

Hyaline

Fibrous

Elastic

Figure 5-4 Connective tissues.

markings. The anatomical words used for these markings are not always consistent; but in general, a bump or projecting portion of a bone is called a *process,* a depression (hole that does not go all the way through) is a *fossa* (pl., fossae), and a hole that penetrates the outer, compact layer or passes completely through the bone is a *foramen* (pl., foramina). The following descriptions include most of the terms in common use.

CONDYLE This is usually a rather large rounded process or projection, located where the bone articulates with another bone. Two examples are the *occipital condyles* at the base of the skull (they articulate with the first cervical (neck) vertebra or *atlas*) and condyles on the distal end of the femur, which articulate with the *tibia.*

EPICONDYLE An epicondyle is a raised area or projection on a condyle. As examples: the *lateral epicondyle* and *medial epicondyle* of the femur.

CREST A crest is a ridge on a bone, usually rather narrow. A clasic example is the *iliac crest,* or crest of the ilium. A *line* is a bone ridge that is not as outstanding as a crest.

SPINE This is a rather sharp, slender process, such as the spines of the ilium (*anterior superior and inferior,* and *posterior superior and inferior*). Probably the best example is the *spinous process* located on the posterior or dorsal portion of each vertebra. Sometimes the word spine is loosely used when referring to the entire spinal column or vertebral column.

TROCHLEA This process is so named because it somewhat resembles a pulley (*trochlea,* in Latin). One trochlea is found at the distal end of the humerus.

TUBERCLE A tubercle is usually relatively small and rounded, such as the *pubic tubercle.* A *tuberosity* might be described as a large tubercle, and the *ischial tuberosity* is an easy one to locate. When we sit down, we literally sit on our ischial tuberosities.

TROCHANTER The *greater and lesser trochanters* of the femur are the only examples of this bony process. Trochanters are rather rough in appearance, and give attachment to muscles.

FORAMEN A foramen is a hole in a bone, as previously described. A tiny hole in the surface of a bone, permitting the passage of blood vessels, is a *nutrient foramen;* a tendon and part of a muscle traverse the *obturator foramen* of the pelvis; while the mental nerve emerges through the *mental foramen* of the mandible (jaw bone). The spinal cord passes through the *foramen magnum* at the base of the skull. A *meatus* is a foramen of relatively great depth, a *canal.* The canal of the outer portion of the ear is the *external acoustic (auditory) meatus.*

SINUS A sinus (where the skeletal system is concerned) is a hollow or cavity inside a bone, exemplified by the *air sinuses* of the skull.

SULCUS This term is applied to various grooves in the surfaces of bones, such as the *intertubercular sulcus* or *bicipital groove* located at the proximal end of the humerus. One of the tendons of the biceps brachii muscle, located in the arm, glides back and forth in this patricular sulcus.

HEAD AND NECK These are terms used to describe the ball portion of a ball-and-socket joint and that part of the bone supporting the ball, respectively. The head and neck of the humerus and femur are outstanding examples.

DIVISIONS OF THE SKELETON

It is convenient to separate the skeleton mentally into two major divisions, the *axial skeleton,* consisting of the skull, vertebral column, bones of the thorax, and the hyoid bone; and the *appendicular skeleton,* which includes the bones of the upper extremity and shoulder, and those of the lower extremity and pelvis.

Axial skeleton: the skull

There are 28 bones in the skull, but only one of them is freely movable, the bone of the lower jaw, or *mandible.* (The ear ossicles barely move in response to sound vibrations transmitted from the eardrum.) The bones of the skull can be divided into two groups: those which comprise the bony structure of the face, the *facial bones;* and those making up that portion of the skull that houses the brain and special sense organs, the *cranium.*

BONES OF THE FACE There are 14 bones of the face: 2 *nasal,* 2 *maxillary,* 2 *zygomatic,* 1 *mandible,* 2 *palatine,* 1 *vomer,* 2 *lacrimal,* and 2 *inferior nasal conchae or turbinates.* By examining the various drawings of the skull (Figs. 5-5 and 5-6), the relative size and shape of each of these bones can be seen, as well as their positions in relation to each other and to the other bones of the skull. If possible, the student should study both intact and sectioned skulls, or accurate models of these. The following are a few points to be noted when examining the bones of the facial portion of the skull:

1. *Nasal Bones.* Oblong and thin, the nasal bones join each other, forming the upper portion of the bridge of the nose; in life, the lower portion of this bridge is cartilage. In Fig. 5-5, note the bones with which the nasal bones join or articulate. Note that, inside the skull, they join the *perpendicular plate of the ethmoid bone.*

2. *Maxillary Bones, or Maxillae.* These are large bones, and together they comprise a good deal of the facial bone structure. It will be noted that every bone of the face *except* the mandible joins the maxillae; and these latter bones contribute to the formation of the eye sockets, or *orbits,* the *hard palate* (roof of the mouth), and walls of the *nasal cavities.* The sockets for the upper teeth are in the maxillae. The maxillary sinuses are located within these bones.

3. *Zygomatic Bones.* These are the *cheekbones.* Each helps form an orbit and is joined by the *zygomatic process of a temporal bone* and a similar process of the *maxillary bone,* forming a *zygomatic arch.*

4. *Mandible.* Commonly referred to as the *jawbone,* the mandible has a ∪-shaped portion, the *body,* and two upright *rami* at the posterior ends. Each ramus forms an angle, the *angle of the mandible,* with the body. By means of a *condyle,* each ramus articulates with the *mandibular fossa of the temporal bone.* Nerves and blood vessels for the teeth enter the *mandibular foramen* located on the inner surface of the ramus. Nerves and vessels supplying the tissues covering the chin

pass through the *mental foramen* located on the anterior lateral aspect of the mandible.

5. *Palatine Bones.* These bones form only a small portion of the *palate,* most of this structure being comprised of the palatine processes of the *maxillary bones.* In addition to helping make up the hard palate, the palatine bones help form the floor of the orbits and the walls and floor of the nasal cavities.

6. *Vomer.* This small bone helps form the posterior portion of the partition or *septum* between the two nasal cavities. It gets its name from its resemblance to a plow (*vomer,* in Latin).

7. *Lacrimal Bones.* The lacrimals are thin, small bones which contribute to the formation of the lateral wall of each nasal cavity and the medial wall of the orbit.

8. *Inferior Nasal Conchae.* Long and somewhat curved, these bones lie along the lateral walls of the nasal cavities. Above them are the *superior and middle conchae,* both processes of the *ethmoid bone,* a bone of the cranium.

BONES OF THE CRANIUM If the 6 ear ossicles are included, there are 14 bones of the cranium: 1 *occipital,* 2 *parietal,* 1 *frontal,* 2 *temporal,* 1 *ethmoid,* 1 *sphenoid,* 2 *malleus,* 2 *incus,* and 2 *stapes,* the last 6 being the *ear ossicles.* Some important points to remember concerning the bones of the cranium follow:

1. *Occipital Bone.* Located at the back and underside of the skull, the large occipital bone bears the weight of the head on two processes, the *occipital condyles.* The spinal cord begins at the *foramen magnum* of the occipital bone. The *external occipital protuberance* and *external occipital crest* are important areas of muscle attachment. Inside the skull (Fig. 5-6 on pp. 58-59), the occipital bone supports a good portion of the brain, and a portion of the *transverse sinus,* a large blood channel, makes a groove in the bone.

2. *Parietal Bones.* Each parietal bone joins its fellow of the opposite side and the frontal bone to form a region called the *calvaria* or "skullcap." The inner surface is grooved by blood vessels and very slightly by the ridges (gyri) of the largest part of the brain, the *cerebrum.*

3. *Frontal Bone.* The frontal bone is the bone of the *forehead.* It helps form the superior portion of each orbit, and separates the interior of the skull from the nasal cavi-

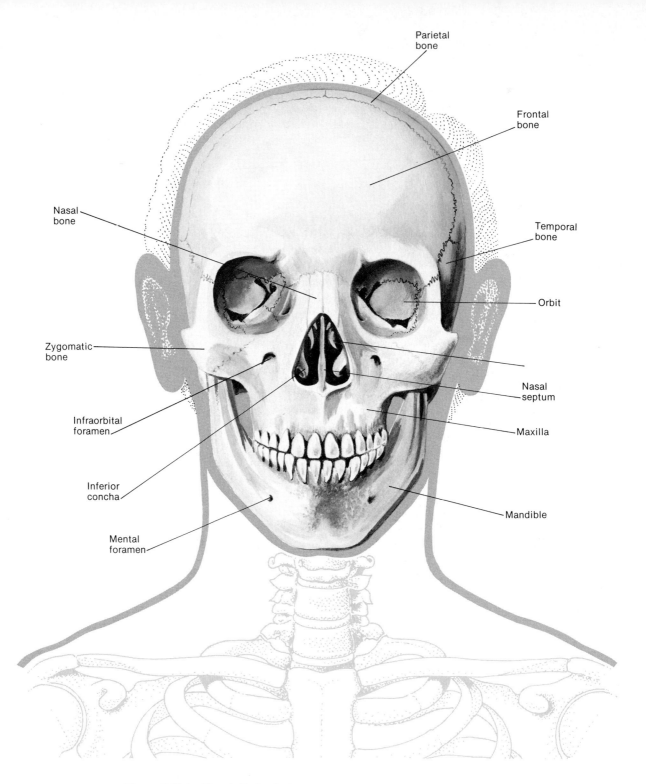

Figure 5-5(a) The skull, front view.

ties. The *lacrimal gland* (tear gland) rests in a shallow depression of the frontal bone, in the lateral portion of the orbit. The *frontal sinuses* lie within the bone, deep to the medial portions of two ridges, the *super-ciliary arches*. The *glabella* is a clinical reference landmark on the frontal bone. It is the smooth area just superior to the nose.

4. *Temporal Bones.* Each temporal bone gives housing to the middle and internal portion of an ear. Only the extreme anterior portion of the temporal bone is in the temple region, which is formed mostly by the sphenoid and frontal bones. The temporal bone has a *zygomatic process* that joins the zygomatic bone and maxillary bone, creating

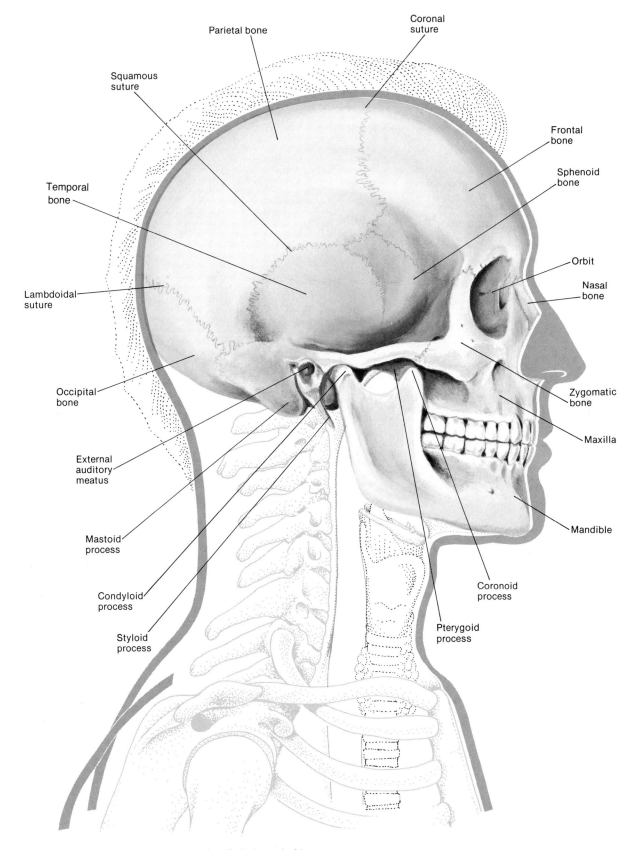

Parietal bone

Coronal suture

Squamous suture

Frontal bone

Sphenoid bone

Temporal bone

Orbit

Nasal bone

Lambdoidal suture

Occipital bone

Zygomatic bone

External auditory meatus

Maxilla

Mastoid process

Mandible

Condyloid process

Styloid process

Coronoid process

Pterygoid process

Figure 5-5(b) The skull, lateral view.

the *zygomatic arch*. The *mandibular fossae* of the temporal bones receive the condyles of the mandible at the *only* joints between

the lower jaw and the remainder of the skull. Below and posterior to the *external acoustic meatus* is the *mastoid process,* containing

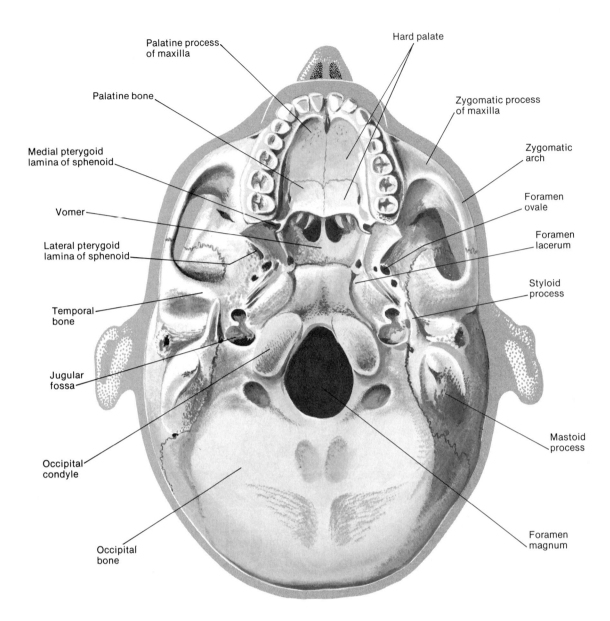

Figure 5-6(a) The entire skull from beneath.

Labels on figure:
Palatine process of maxilla
Palatine bone
Medial pterygoid lamina of sphenoid
Vomer
Lateral pterygoid lamina of sphenoid
Temporal bone
Jugular fossa
Occipital condyle
Occipital bone
Hard palate
Zygomatic process of maxilla
Zygomatic arch
Foramen ovale
Foramen lacerum
Styloid process
Mastoid process
Foramen magnum

the relatively large *mastoid spaces or air cells.* Only a thin layer of bone separates these spaces from the brain, and an ear infection that spreads to them can cause an inflammation of the brain coverings or meninges, called *meningitis.* The *styloid processes,* long and narrow, are seen projecting downward from the temporal bone. They serve as points of muscle attachment.

5. *Ethmoid Bone.* The ethmoid is highly irregular in shape. It gives support to the nasal cavity and its perforated process, the *cribriform plate,* forms the roof of this cavity. Branches of the *olfactory nerve*—the nerve of smell—pass through the cribriform plate of the ethmoid and into the upper nasal region. The *superior and middle nasal con-* chae are processes of the ethmoid bone, and the superior portion of the *nasal septum* is formed by it. Situated deep within the skull, the shape of the ethmoid is difficult to discern unless the bone is isolated.

6. *Sphenoid Bone.* The shape of the sphenoid bone is even more complex than that of the ethmoid. The sphenoid has several projections or processes, including two which are called the *greater wings* and two known as *lesser wings.* It has often been remarked that an isolated sphenoid bone resembles a large moth or butterfly. The sphenoid helps support the brain, and contains the *sphenoid air sinuses.* The *pituitary gland or hypophysis* rests in a saddle-shaped portion of the sphenoid, the *sella turcica.* The

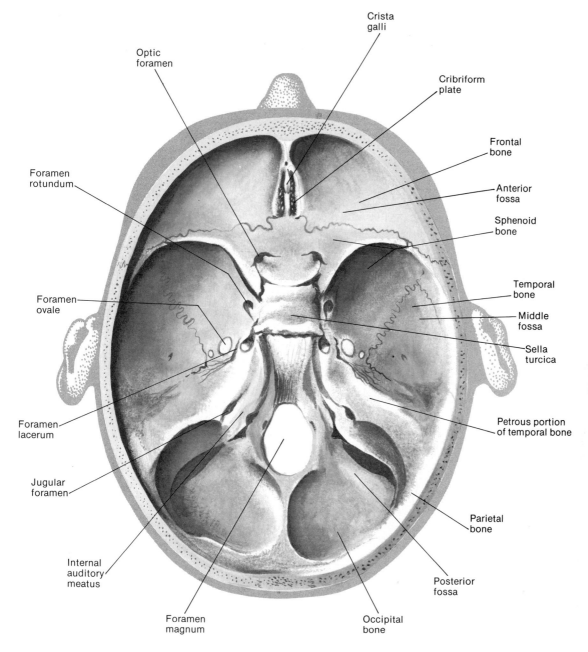

Optic
foramen

Crista
galli

Cribriform
plate

Frontal
bone

Anterior
fossa

Sphenoid
bone

Temporal
bone

Middle
fossa

Sella
turcica

Petrous portion
of temporal bone

Parietal
bone

Posterior
fossa

Occipital
bone

Foramen
magnum

Internal
auditory
meatus

Jugular
foramen

Foramen
lacerum

Foramen
ovale

Foramen
rotundum

Figure 5-6(b) The floor of the cranium.

optic nerve—the nerve of sight—passes through the *optic foramen* of the sphenoid bone. Other nerves, to be described later, pass through a slit lying lateral to the optic foramen, the *superior orbital fissure,* while still others emerge through the *foramen rotundum* and *foramen ovale.*

7. *The Ear Ossicles.* The earbone or ossicle commonly called the "hammer" is the *malleus.* It is attached to the eardrum or *tympanic membrane,* and vibrates in response to sound waves picked up by this membrane. The malleus transfers these vibrations to the ossicle with which it is directly linked, the *incus* or "anvil," which in

turn causes the last ossicle, the *stapes* ("stirrup") to move, causing impulses to be carried via sound receptors and the acoustic nerve to the brain, where they are interpreted as sound. The bones of the middle ear are so small they are best studied from drawings and large-scale models. They are illustrated in Fig. 5-7 and will again be considered in the discussion of the physiology of hearing.

THE HYOID BONE   The hyoid bone, located in the throat region, is unique in that it serves as a point of attachment for some of the muscles of the tongue and floor of the mouth but *does not articulate with any other bone.* Although it is not a bone of the skull proper, it is customarily considered with that portion of the skeleton. The hyoid is shaped somewhat like a horseshoe, with a body, two *greater cornua* or "horns," and two *lesser cornua* (Fig. 5-8). It is situated in the wall of the upper part of the throat, just above the larynx or voicebox, and may be palpated by placing a thumb and finger high and posteriorly under the lateral portions of the mandible and firmly squeezing medially.

Features of the skull as a whole

SUTURES   Upon carefully examining a skull, it is noted that the bones of the cranium fit together at jagged lines or joints. These are the *sutures* of the skull, and they all have anatomical names. Running across the skull between the frontal bone and the two parietal bones is the *coronal suture.* The line of separation between the parietal bones is the *sagittal suture.* Each parietal bone is separated from a portion of a temporal bone by a *squamous suture,* and the *lambdoidal suture* lies between the occipital bone and the two parietal bones. For several weeks after birth, the frontal bone consists of right and left halves. Normally, these halves become completely fused, and no line of separation remains, even during early childhood. Now and then, however, the fusion is incomplete, resulting in a line running down the middle of the frontal bone which is given the name *metopic suture.* The metopic suture is sometimes mistaken for skull fracture during X-ray examination of an accident victim.

FONTANELS   At birth, *ossification* or bone formation is incomplete, and the cranial bones do not join each other at all points. At *six locations,* the skull consists *only of a membrane and the scalp.* These so-called openings in the brain case, which serve to permit the bones to move during childbirth and allow the brain to quickly grow larger after birth, are known as *fontanels* (Fig. 5-9). The largest of these membranous areas is the *anterior* fontanel, located at the anterior superior part of the skull, and bound by the frontal bone and the two parietal bones. At the other ends of the parietal

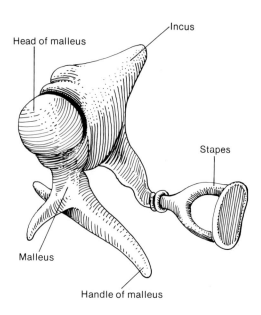

Figure 5-7   The ossicles, or bones of the middle ear.

bones, just anterior to the occipital bone, is the *posterior* fontanel. *Anterolateral* and *posterolateral* fontanels are positioned on either side of the skull. The former are bound by the frontal, temporal, and parietal bones, while the latter are surrounded by the parietal, temporal, and occipital bones. After

Figure 5-8   The hyoid.

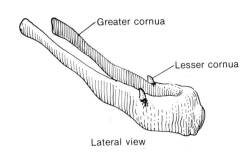

Lateral view

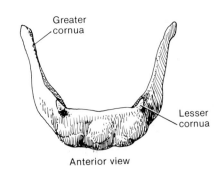

Anterior view

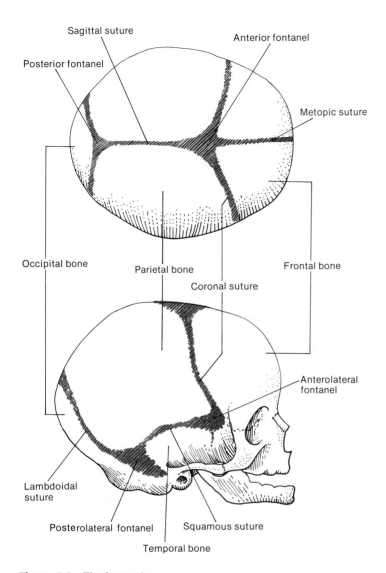

Sagittal suture

Anterior fontanel

Posterior fontanel

Metopic suture

Occipital bone

Parietal bone

Frontal bone

Coronal suture

Anterolateral fontanel

Lambdoidal suture

Posterolateral fontanel

Squamous suture

Temporal bone

Figure 5-9 The fontanels.

birth, the posterior fontanel is the first to close, being completely obliterated by about the second month. It is followed in the third month by the anterolateral fontanels, then by the anterior and posterolateral openings by about the eighteenth month or even the second year.

SUPERNUMERARY BONES Frequently, extra cranial bones will develop during ossification, *especially along the lambdoidal or coronal sutures,* near the anterior and posterior fontanels. These bones are small, have no regular shape, and are known as *sutural or Wormian bones.*

SINUSES The air sinuses of the skull have been mentioned in connection with the bones in which they are found. *All sinuses communicate directly with the nasal cavity* (Fig. 5-10).

CRANIAL FOSSAE The skull has several large depressions known as *fossae,* but when one speaks of skull fossae without being specific, he is usually referrering to the three large depressed areas on the inner surface of the floor of the skull: the *anterior fossa, middle fossa,* and *posterior fossa,* known collectively as the *cranial fossae* (Fig. 5-6). The anterior fossa overlies the orbits, and consists of portions of the frontal, sphenoid, and ethmoid bones. The temporal, sphenoid, and parietal bones make up the middle cranial fossa, while the largest fossa, the posterior one, consists of the occipital, sphenoid, and temporal bones. All three fossae serve to *support the brain* and, by means of many small openings, permit the passage of nerves and blood vessels into and out of the skull. The largest of these holes is the *foramen magnum,* through which passes the spinal cord.

DIFFERENCES IN THE SKULL ACCORDING TO SEX The skulls of men and women are very much alike. When filled with a liquid, the skull of a man will hold an average of 150 cubic centimeters (cc) more than that of a woman; and in general, the bones of a man's skull are somewhat heavier than those of a woman.

EFFECTS OF AGING ON THE SKULL After birth, the fontanels begin their closing process, and simultaneously the skull bones and brain grow larger, resulting in a child with a head that is relatively large in proportion to the rest of the body. At about the age of seven, growth in the head region slows, then accelerates again for a time during sexual maturation. The skull of an adult is relatively small, and with old age the mandible atrophies, tending to return to its smaller infantile state.

The vertebral column

THE VERTEBRAL COLUMN AS A WHOLE The skull rests atop a series of bones stacked one upon the other, the *vertebral column* (spinal column or "spine") (Fig. 5-11). This extremely important portion of the skeleton

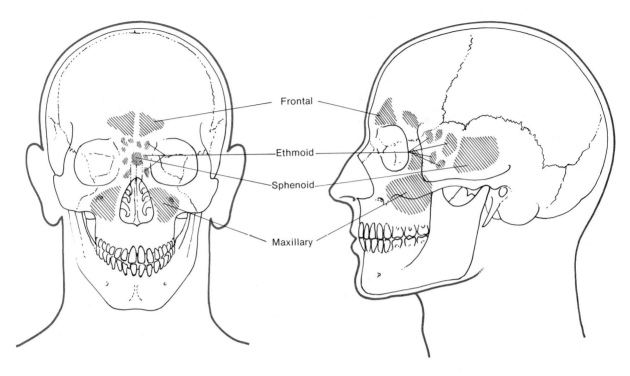

Figure 5-10 The air sinuses of the skull. All drain into the nasal cavity.

gives support to the trunk, provides places for the attachment of the ribs and bones of the pelvis, permits a good deal of movement, and houses and protects the spinal cord. Muscles and ligaments, the latter made of strong fibrous connective tissue, bind the *vertebrae* (sing., *vertebra*) together. Movement is possible because of the presence of cartilaginous *intervertebral discs,* located between adjacent vertebrae. Rather than being simply a straight stack of bones, the vertebral column shows several bends or *curvatures.* In the neck region is the *cervical curvature,* which is convex anteriorly; next, proceeding inferiorly, is the *thoracic curvature,* concave anteriorly; then the *lumbar curvature,* convex anteriorly; and finally the *sacral curvature* or pelvic curvature, which is concave anteriorly. Clinically (that is, in hospitals and in doctors offices), three major types of *abnormal curvatures* of the vertebral column are seen.

1. *Kyphosis.* An exaggerated thoracic curvature, or "hunchback."

2. *Scoliosis.* A lateral curvature.

3. *Lordosis.* A lumbar curvature that is exaggerated.

The first of these is the most common, and is seen mostly in old age and among persons who work in a stooped position. The latter two are usually caused by disease or are present at birth.

The vertebral column is about 71 centimeters (cm) long and consists of 33 vertebrae. There are 7 *cervical,* 12 *thoracic,* 5 *lumbar,* 5 *sacral,* and 4 *coccygeal* bones in the adult vertebral column, with the sacral vertebrae being fused into one unit, the *sacrum,* and the coccygeal vertebrae fused into a tiny structure, the *coccyx.* The vertebrae in each portion of the column have characteristics found only in that portion; that is, there is *no such thing as a truly typical vertebra.* There are, however, rather typical cervical vertebrae, typical thoracic vertebrae, and so on.

FEATURES COMMON TO MOST VERTEBRAE (Fig. 5-12) Each vertebra has a large, disclike anterior portion, flattened at the superior and inferior aspects, the *centrum or body,* and a posterior portion, the *neural arch,* the latter enclosing the spinal cord. The actual hole formed by the neural arch is the *vertebral foramen;* and when stacked together as

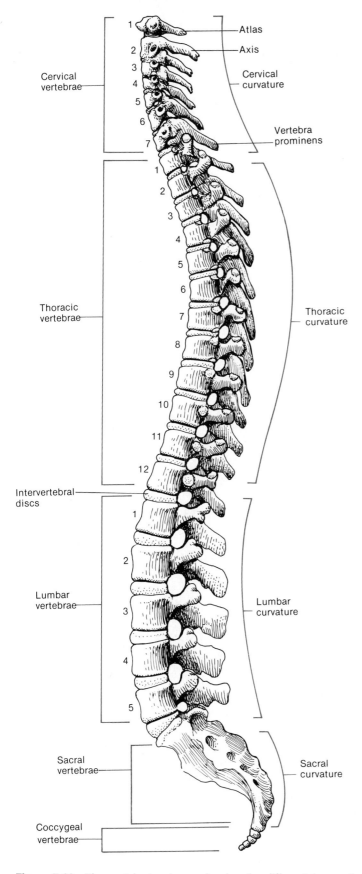

Figure 5-11 The vertebral column, showing the different types of vertebrae and curvatures.

Labels on figure:
- Cervical vertebrae
  - 1 Atlas
  - 2 Axis
  - 3
  - 4
  - 5
  - 6
  - 7
- Cervical curvature
- Vertebra prominens
- Thoracic vertebrae (1–12)
- Thoracic curvature
- Intervertebral discs
- Lumbar vertebrae (1–5)
- Lumbar curvature
- Sacral vertebrae
- Sacral curvature
- Coccygeal vertebrae

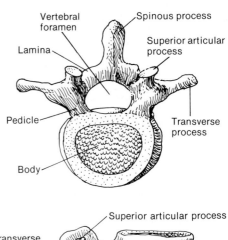

Labels: Vertebral foramen, Spinous process, Lamina, Superior articular process, Pedicle, Transverse process, Body

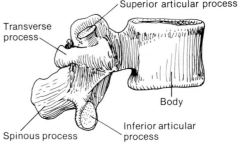

Labels: Superior articular process, Transverse process, Body, Spinous process, Inferior articular process

Figure 5-12 Main features of a vertebra.

they are in the intact vertebral column, the vertebral foramina comprise the *vertebral canal* or *neural canal*. Each neural arch is formed by two processes of the centrum, the *pedicles,* and two *lamina* which are fused with the pedicles and with each other. A *spinous process* is found projecting dorsally at this latter point of fusion. Six other processes originate on the neural arch: *two superior articular processes, two inferior articular processes,* and *two transverse processes.* Careful examination of Fig. 5-11 or of an articulated vertebral column reveals that the superior articular processes of a vertebra fit into the inferior articular processes of the vertebra above it.

COMPARISON OF VERTEBRAE IN DIFFERENT PORTIONS OF THE VERTEBRAL COLUMN
One of the best ways to become familiar with the intricacies of the vertebral column is to examine in detail the main features of the vertebrae in each of its portions.

1. *Cervical Portion.* The most outstanding feature of cervical vertebrae is the presence of a hole, the *transverse foramen,* in each transverse process. The *vertebral artery* (see

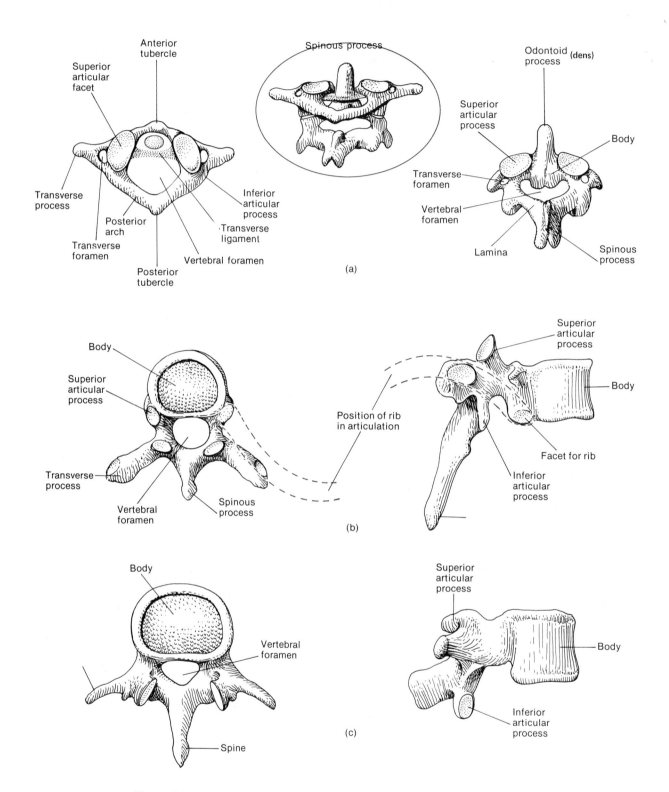

Figure 5-13 Different types of vertebrae. (a) The upper two cervical vertebrae (the atlas and the axis). (b) A typical thoracic vertebra. (c) Lumbar vertebra.

Fig. 5-13) passes through the upper six of these foramina on each side of the neck, on its way to help supply the brain with blood. Occasionally, the artery will be found tra-versing the foramen of the seventh cervical vertebra on one side, but both foramina of this vertebra are usually occupied *only by veins*. The *atlas* or first cervical vertebra

(Fig. 5-13) has no centrum, and the *occipital condyles* of the skull rest on its superior articular processes. A band of connective tissue, the *transverse ligament* divides the large hole in the atlas into *anterior and posterior arches*. A process of the axis (second cervical vertebra), the *dens* (Fig. 5-13), projects upward through the anterior arch of the atlas, and when the head is rotated in a horizontal plane—as when signifying "no"—the axis pivots about the dens. When the head is nodded in assent, the occipital condyles glide on the superior articular processes

of the atlas. The spinous process of the seventh cervical vertebra is rather long, and is sometimes used as a landmark because it is often palpable at the back of the neck. It is referred to as the *vertebra prominens*. The spinous processes of the third, fourth, and fifth cervical vertebrae are often split or *bifid*.

2. *Thoracic Portion.* Just as the cervical vertebrae are distinguished by their transverse foramina, thoracic vertebrae can be identified by *articular facets on the centrum* (Fig. 5-13). These facets represent one point of contact between thoracic vertebrae and ribs. Some of the spinous processes of thoracic vertebrae are bent almost directly downward, and overlap one another like shingles on a roof.

3. *Lumbar Portion.* Spinous processes of lumbar vertebrae are short and massive in appearance, as are the transverse processes. The superior articular processes face medially, and the inferior processes are directed laterally. The spinal cord proper *ends* at the level of the upper border of the *second lumbar vertebra;* therefore, a lumbar puncture for the purpose of examining the cerebrospinal fluid or administration of anesthetic during childbirth (saddle block anesthesia) is made between *lumbar vertebrae 3 and 4 or 4 and 5.* This is true because the outer coverings of the cord, filled with cerebrospinal fluid, extend an appreciable distance below the cord proper. The fourth lumbar vertebra is located at the level of an imaginary line drawn between the two iliac crests.

4. *Sacral Portion.* The five sacral vertebrae are fused in the adult, forming a unified structure, the *sacrum* (Fig. 5-14), which lies between the innominate bones or os coxae. Four ridges cross the sacrum, and anterior and posterior *sacral foramina* are positioned at either end of these ridges. In life, these foramina serve for the passage of vessels and nerves. The *vertebral canal* continues inside the sacrum, and a group of spinal nerves, the *cauda equina* ("horse's tail"), lies in this portion of the canal. The anterior surface of the uppermost sacral vertebra is called the *sacral promontory,* and is often used as a reference point. Posteriorly, the bony structure of the vertebral canal is *incomplete* at the level of the *last two sacral vertebrae.* This opening is the *sacral hiatus.* Covered only by ligaments applied to the sacrum and coccyx, it is often utilized as an injection site for caudal anesthesia, used during childbirth

Figure 5-14 The sacrum and coccyx.

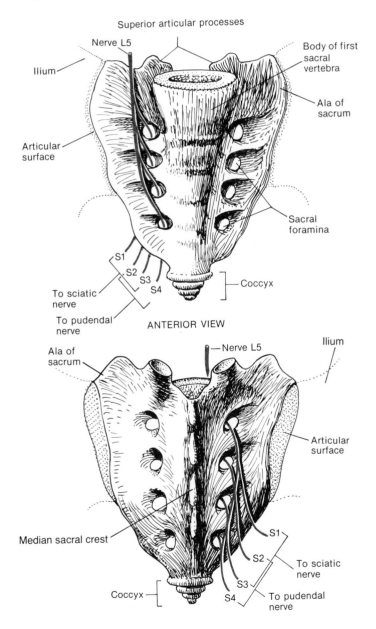

Superior articular processes

Nerve L5

Ilium

Body of first sacral vertebra

Ala of sacrum

Articular surface

Sacral foramina

S1
S2
S3
S4

Coccyx

To sciatic nerve

To pudendal nerve

ANTERIOR VIEW

Nerve L5

Ilium

Ala of sacrum

Articular surface

Median sacral crest

S1
S2
S3
S4

To sciatic nerve

To pudendal nerve

Coccyx

POSTERIOR VIEW

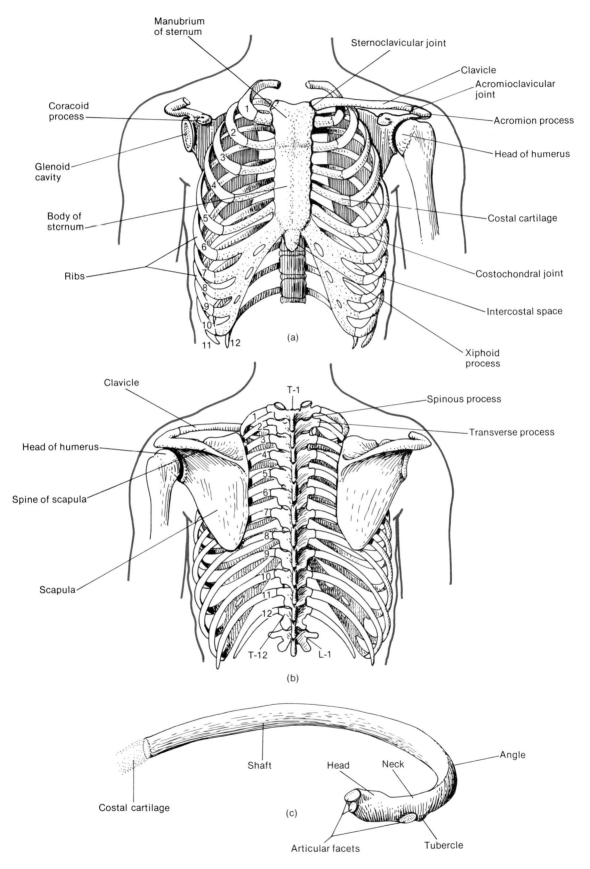

Figure 5-15 Bones of the thorax. (a) Anterior view. (b) Posterior view. (c) A typical rib.

or surgery in the pelvic region. In this procedure, the anesthetic solution acts on the roots of spinal nerves emerging from the sacral and coccygeal portions of the vertebral column. Inasmuch as the spinal cord proper does not continue below the level of the second lumbar vertebra, the anesthetist's needle does not penetrate the outer cord coverings as it does during lumbar puncture.

5. *Coccygeal Portion.* The four fused bones of the coccyx are attached below the last sacral vertebra. The long, thin, *filum terminale,* an extension of the spinal cord coverings, attaches the spinal cord to the coccyx.

Bones of the thorax

The bones of the thorax include the *ribs* and *sternum* or breastbone (Fig. 5-15 and Color Plates II, III, and VIII).

THE RIBS   Usually, there are 12 pairs of ribs, but occasionally there may be 11, 13, or even 14 pairs. There is no truth to the myth that man has one less rib than woman. All of the ribs articulate posteriorly with vertebrae, then curve downward and anteriorly, where *ten pairs join the sternum.* Two pairs fall far short of the sternum, and are known as "floating" ribs. Ribs attach to the sternum by means of *costal cartilages;* the costal cartilages of ribs 1 through 7 are the only ones to reach the sternum *directly.* The cartilages of ribs 8, 9, and 10 are attached indirectly by means of the cartilages above them. The first seven pairs of ribs are known as "true" ribs, and the lower five pairs as "false" ribs. The lower two ribs, even though they do not reach the sternum, still have cartilages on their tips, and these are easily palpable. Fairly frequenly, the transverse processes of one or two of the lower cervical vertebrae will grow to extra length, creating what is known as a *cervical rib.* By bringing about pressure on sensory nerves, these so-called ribs can cause enough pain and discomfort to necessitate their surgical removal.

A *"typical" rib* (Fig. 5-15) has a *head* which joins the centrum of one or more vertebrae; a *neck;* a *tubercle* which articulates with the transverse process of a vertebra; and a long curved *body.* The neck joins the body at a point called the *angle* of the rib. The tubercle is located at this point. The first rib is broad and flattened, and more sharply curved than the others. The *subclavian artery* and several nerves, all supplying the upper extremity, cross the superior surface of the upper rib and make grooves in it. The lower edge of each rib is grooved for the passage of *intercostal nerves and blood vessels.*

THE STERNUM   The sternum consists of three portions: the *manubrium, body,* and *xiphoid process.* The body is made up of *four fused sections.* The junction of the manubrium with the body forms the *sternal angle* (Fig. 5-15), one of the most important clinical landmarks on the front of the chest. The *second rib joins the sternum at this point,* and ribs may be conveniently counted in the living subject by beginning at the sternal angle. Deep to this angle lie the large blood vessels continuous with the upper portion of the heart and the bifurcation or branching of the trachea into right and left bronchi.

The medial ends of the *clavicles* or collarbones articulate with the manubrium of the sternum. The xiphoid process is at first cartilaginous, but *ossifies* with age. The sternum is a favored site for obtaining samples of *hemopoietic (blood-forming) tissue* during diagnosis of suspected blood diseases. A needle is inserted into the marrow of the sternum and a sample withdrawn in an operation known as a *sternal puncture.*

Appendicular skeleton: bones of the shoulder girdle and upper extremity

The *shoulder girdle consists* of two pairs of bones which attach the arms to the trunk, the *clavicles* and *scapulae.* These two pairs of bones serve as points of attachment for many muscles (21 on each scapula alone), a number of which help to bind the upper extremities to the trunk. It is fortunate that such an extensive muscular connection exists, because *each upper extremity joins the trunk at only one articulation,* that between the medial end of the clavicle and the manubrium of the sternum—that is, the *sternoclavicular articulation.*

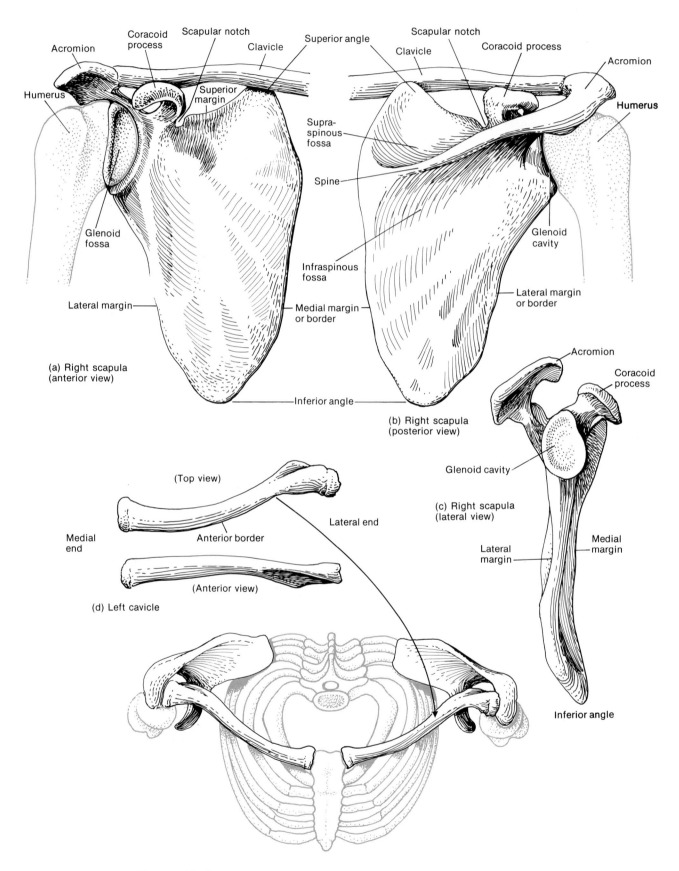

Acromion
Coracoid process
Scapular notch
Clavicle
Superior angle
Humerus
Superior margin
Glenoid fossa
Lateral margin
Inferior angle

(a) Right scapula
(anterior view)

Scapular notch
Clavicle
Coracoid process
Acromion
Humerus
Supra-spinous fossa
Spine
Glenoid cavity
Infraspinous fossa
Lateral margin or border
Medial margin or border

(b) Right scapula
(posterior view)

Acromion
Coracoid process
Glenoid cavity

(c) Right scapula
(lateral view)

Lateral margin
Medial margin
Inferior angle

(Top view)
Lateral end
Medial end
Anterior border
(Anterior view)

(d) Left cavicle

Figure 5-16 Bones of the shoulder girdle.

68

THE CLAVICLE   The clavicle or collarbone (Fig. 5-16 and Color Plate II) is doubly curved, rounded on the medial end, and flattened on the lateral end. The lateral end articulates with the acromion process of the scapula. The clavicle serves as an anterior *brace or strut,* helping to prevent dislocation of the shoulder. On occasion, an individual is born without clavicles. It is then possible for a second person to grasp the arms of the first and hold them together above the elbows.

THE SCAPULA   (See Fig. 5-16 and Color Plate VIII.) The scapula or shoulder blade is triangular in general outline and has a flattened *body* and *two processes,* the *coracoid* and *acromion.* The latter process is the enlarged end of a reinforcing ridge, the *spine of the scapula.* That portion of the dorsal surface of the scapula superior to the spine is the *supraspinous fossa,* while that inferior to the spine is the *infraspinous fossa.* The *subscapular fossa* is the entire ventral or costal surface of the scapula. The scapula has *three angles:* the *superior angle, inferior angle,* and *lateral angle.* The *glenoid fossa,* which is the socket for the ball-and-socket joint of the shoulder, is located at the lateral angle. The head of the humerus fits into this shallow socket, and is relatively easily displaced from it during a dislocation of the shoulder. The scapula also has *three borders: superior, medial* or *vertebral,* and *lateral* or *axillary.* The acromion articulates with the lateral end of the clavicle, but the coracoid serves only as a structure for muscle attachment.

THE HUMERUS   The humerus (Fig. 5-17 and Color Plate VI) is the only bone in the arm proper. At the elbow, it is joined by the radius and ulna, which are bones of the forearm. That portion of the humerus that articulates with the glenoid fossa of the scapula, the *head,* is rounded and partially encircled at its base by a groove, the *anatomical neck.* At the head end of the humerus but opposite to it are two prominences, the *greater and lesser tubercles.* A groove between these tubercles is called the *intertubercular sulcus or bicipital groove.* The tendon for the head of the biceps brachii muscle lies in this groove and attaches to the rim of the glenoid fossa of the scapula. All these

are found at the *proximal end* of the humerus; at the *distal end* are the *medial and lateral epicondyles, capitulum, trochlea, coronoid fossa, olecranon fossa,* and *groove for the ulnar nerve.*

That portion of the humerus located between the proximal and distal ends is the *shaft.* At the proximal end of the shaft is the *surgical neck,* a common site of fracture. On the shaft about midway between the ends is the *deltoid tuberosity,* the point of insertion of a large muscle of the shoulder, the *deltoid muscle.* A tiny *nutrient foramen* is often seen near the tuberosity. In life, a small artery enters the bone through this foramen. The *groove for the radial nerve* winds around a portion of the humerus just distal to the deltoid tuberosity. The *capitulum* of the humerus articulates with the proximal end of the radius, while the *trochlea* joins the proximal end of the ulna. The coronoid process of the ulna fits into the *coronoid fossa* of the humerus when the elbow is flexed (bent); when the elbow is extended (straightened) the olecranon process of the ulna fits into the *olecranon fossa* of the humerus.

THE RADIUS   When the body is in the anatomical position, palms facing forward, the radius is positioned on the *lateral* side of the forearm (Fig. 5-18 and Color Plate VI). When the hand is pronated, only the upper portion of the radius remains parallel to the other bone of the forearm, the ulna, and the two bones form an elongated $\times$ (Fig. 5-18), *the radius following the thumb during pronation.* The radius is the shorter of the two bones. Its proximal end consists of a disclike *head* which fits on a short *neck.* The distal end, which is the larger of the ends, shows a drawn-out tip, the *styloid process.* The radius has a *tuberosity* on the medial aspect of the shaft, near the proximal end. This process is the point of insertion (attachment) of the tendon of the *biceps brachii muscle.* The head of the radius articulates with the capitulum of the humerus, and with the radial notch of the ulna. Distally, the radius articulates with two of the wrist bones, the *scaphoid and lunate.*

THE ULNA   (See Fig. 5-18 and Color Plate VI.) When the forearm is *supinated,* the ulna lies along its medial side, *parallel* to the radius. The longer of the two bones of the

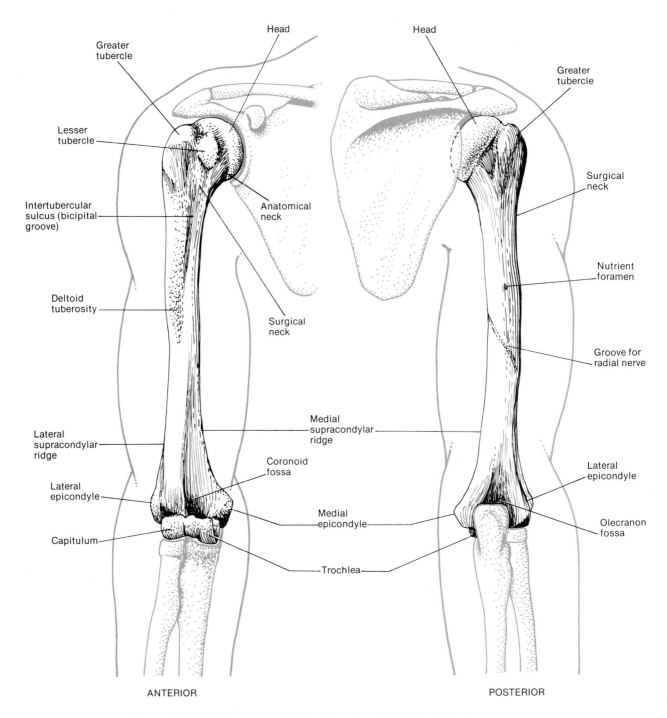

Head

Greater
tubercle

Lesser
tubercle

Intertubercular
sulcus (bicipital
groove)

Deltoid
tuberosity

Lateral
supracondylar
ridge

Lateral
epicondyle

Capitulum

Anatomical
neck

Surgical
neck

Medial
supracondylar
ridge

Coronoid
fossa

Medial
epicondyle

Trochlea

ANTERIOR

Head

Greater
tubercle

Surgical
neck

Nutrient
foramen

Groove for
radial nerve

Lateral
epicondyle

Olecranon
fossa

POSTERIOR

Figure 5-17 Right humerus. Left: Anterior view. Right: Posterior view.

forearm, the ulna articulates with the humerus and radius at its proximal end, and with the radius at its distal end. The distal end of the ulna, the *head,* presents a *styloid process* near its medial border. The trochlea of the humerus fits neatly between the olecranon and coronoid processes at the proximal end of the ulna. The *semilunar notch* of

the ulna fits into the trochlea of the humerus.

THE CARPALS The wrist is known anatomically as the *carpus,* and the eight bones which support it as *carpals* (Fig. 5-19 and Color Plate VI). The carpals are arranged in two irregular rows, *proximal and distal,* with four bones in each row. The proximal row con-

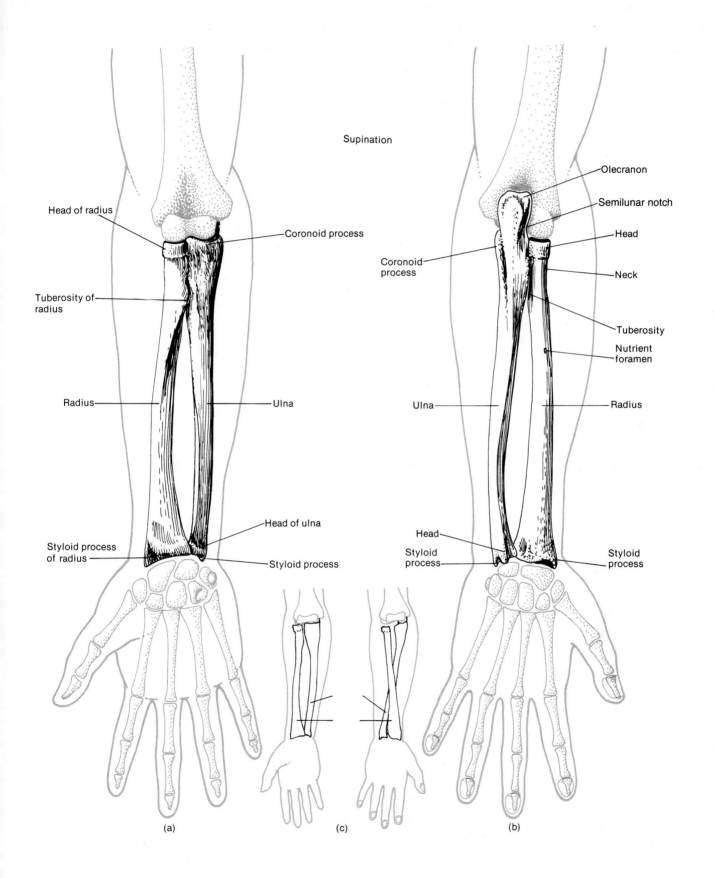

Supination

Head of radius

Coronoid process

Tuberosity of radius

Radius

Ulna

Styloid process of radius

Head of ulna

Styloid process

Olecranon

Semilunar notch

Coronoid process

Head

Neck

Tuberosity

Nutrient foramen

Ulna

Radius

Head

Styloid process

Styloid process

(a)

(c)

(b)

Figure 5-18 Right radius and ulna. (a) Anterior view. (b) Posterior view. (c) Position of the two bones in supination and pronation.

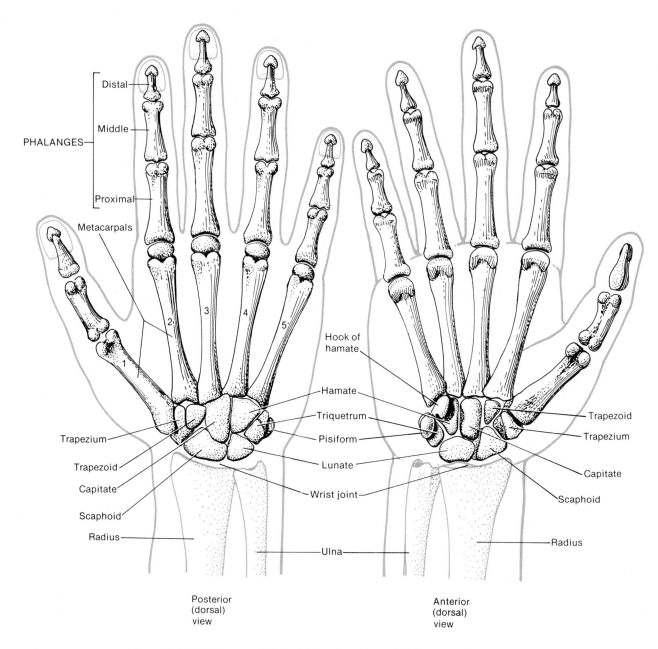

PHALANGES
- Distal
- Middle
- Proximal

Metacarpals

Trapezium
Trapezoid
Capitate
Scaphoid
Radius

Hook of hamate
Hamate
Triquetrum
Pisiform
Lunate
Wrist joint
Ulna

Trapezoid
Trapezium
Capitate
Scaphoid
Radius

Posterior (dorsal) view

Anterior (dorsal) view

Figure 5-19 The bones of the right hand, wrist, and digits.

tains (from lateral to medial) the *scaphoid, lunate, triquetrum,* and *pisiform bones.* The *trapezium, trapezoid, capitate,* and *hamate* comprise the distal row. Two carpal bones serve to orient one who is learning to identify them: the pisiform, or smallest carpal, located on the medial side of the wrist; and the hamate, which has a large hook, a point of muscle attachment. The carpal bones are bound quite closely together by ligaments; therefore, the range of movements permitted between them is quite restricted. The sca-

phoid and lunate articulate with the distal end of the radius.

BONES OF THE HAND   The anatomical term for hand is *manus,* and the bones of the hand are customarily divided into two groups: the *metacarpals,* which are the bones of the palm; and the *phalanges,* or bones of the digits (fingers). Metacarpals, rather than having individual names, are *numbered* from 1 to 5, beginning with the metacarpal of the *pollex* or thumb and counting medially to the metacarpal of the little finger, digit 5 (Fig. 5-19 and Color Plate VI). Each metacarpal has a *base* which articulates with one or more carpals, and a *head* that joins the proximal phalanx of the corresponding digit. The *shaft* of a metacarpal is relatively long and slightly curved. The *knuckles* consist of the heads of the metacarpals, which become prominent when the fist is clenched.

There are 14 *phalanges* in each hand. *Each digit has three: a proximal, middle or intermediate,* and *distal phalanx*—except the thumb, *which has only two, proximal and distal.*

Bones of the pelvic girdle and lower extremity

The pelvis or *pelvic girdle* (Fig. 5-20 and Color Plate VIII) is formed by two *os coxae* (innominate bones, hip bones), together with the *sacrum* and *coccyx.* The combined weight of the trunk, head, and upper extremities rests on the pelvis at its point of contact with the fifth lumbar vertebra. In life, the female organs of reproduction and a

Figure 5-20 The pelvis.

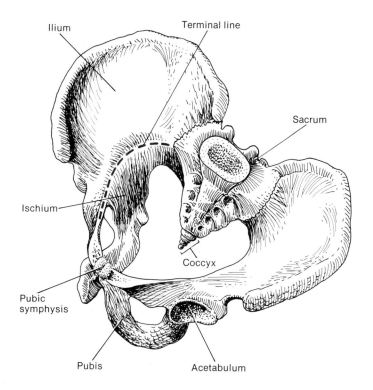

Ilium

Terminal line

Sacrum

Ischium

Coccyx

Pubic symphysis

Pubis

Acetabulum

portion of the male reproductive organs, the nerves and blood vessels of the lower limb, the urinary bladder, and the terminal portion of the large intestine all are contained in the pelvic cavity. The bony structure of the pelvic girdle, held firm by ligaments, offers a great deal of protection for these important structures.

OS COXAE   Early in life, three separate bones fuse to form each hip bone or os coxae: the *ilium, ischium,* and *pubis* (Fig. 5-21). One point of fusion is in the *acetabulum,* the socket that receives the head of the femur to form the hip joint. The pubis and ischium also unite below the largest foramen in the skeleton—the *obturator foramen*—through which pass the obturator nerve, artery, and vein, as well as a portion of a muscle. In life, this foramen is almost completely closed by a sheet of connective tissue, the *obturator membrane.*

ILIUM   This large, irregularly shaped bone provides the greatest single contribution to the os coxae. A bowl-shaped region of its body, the *iliac fossa,* supports a great deal of the pelvic floor. A tough band of connective tissue, the *inguinal ligament,* extends from the anterior superior iliac spine to the pubic bone (near the symphysis pubis, the joint between the two pubic bones), delimiting a portion of the *inguinal canal,* a site of hernia (rupture). Through the inguinal canal pass the *femoral nerve, artery,* and *vein* on their way to the lower extremity. The *iliac crest* and various spines of the ilium (previously described) serve as important reference points. To many portions of the ilium are attached the various ligaments which serve to bind the bones of the pelvis together into a sturdy unit. Many of the muscles of the buttocks and pelvis attach to the ilium. The *greater sciatic notch* transmits the *sciatic nerve,* the largest nerve in the body, as it descends into the thigh.

ISCHIUM   The most inferior-posterior portion of the os coxae is formed by the *ischium.* The most outstanding feature of this bone is its *large tuberosity,* which receives the body weight when the individual is in the sitting position.

PUBIS   The two pubic bones join anteriorly, forming the *symphysis pubis* or *pubic sym-*

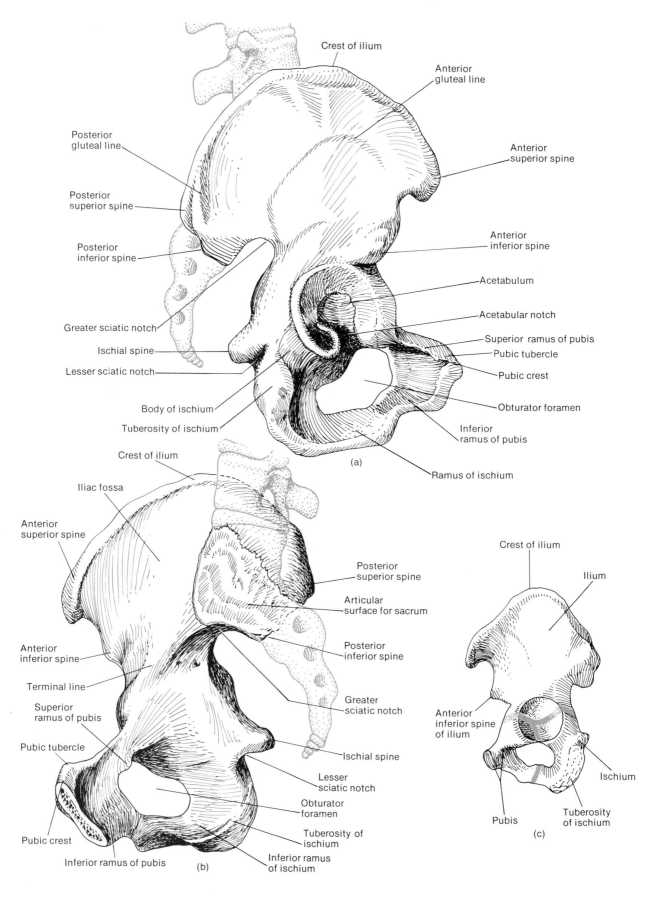

Crest of ilium

Anterior
gluteal line

Posterior
gluteal line

Anterior
superior spine

Posterior
superior spine

Anterior
inferior spine

Posterior
inferior spine

Acetabulum

Acetabular notch

Greater sciatic notch

Superior ramus of pubis

Ischial spine

Pubic tubercle

Lesser sciatic notch

Pubic crest

Body of ischium

Obturator foramen

Tuberosity of ischium

Inferior
ramus of pubis

Ramus of ischium

(a)

Crest of ilium

Iliac fossa

Anterior
superior spine

Posterior
superior spine

Articular
surface for sacrum

Posterior
inferior spine

Anterior
inferior spine

Terminal line

Greater
sciatic notch

Superior
ramus of pubis

Pubic tubercle

Ischial spine

Lesser
sciatic notch

Obturator
foramen

Tuberosity of
ischium

Pubic crest

Inferior ramus
of ischium

Inferior ramus of pubis

(b)

Crest of ilium

Ilium

Anterior
inferior spine
of ilium

Ischium

Pubis

Tuberosity
of ischium

(c)

Figure 5-21   Right os coxae, or innominate bone. (a) Lateral view. (b) Medial view.
(c) Formation of os coxae by union of ilium, ischium, and pubis.

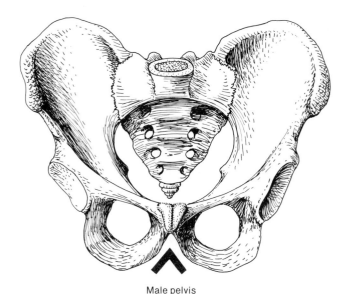

Male pelvis

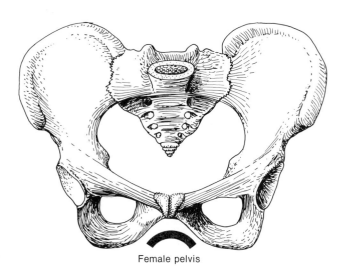

Female pelvis

Figure 5-22 Comparison of male and female pelvis.

sists of the *arcuate line of the sacrum and ilium* and the *eminence and iliopectineal line of the pubis. The brim of the pelvis is made up of two terminal lines plus the symphysis pubis and sacral promontory.* The false pelvis lies above the brim. Included in the true pelvis are the lower portions of the *ilium, ischium,* and *pubis,* and the *sacrum* and *coccyx.* The false pelvis includes the *upper portions of the ilia.* As might be expected, the true pelvis of the female is of the greatest clinical importance. It must be large enough to allow the passage of an infant's head during childbirth. The dimensions of the cavity, as well as those of the *outlet* (inferior opening) and *inlet* (superior opening) of the true pelvis, are critical.

SEX DIFFERENCES IN THE PELVIS   The overall features of the pelvis often vary somewhat from one individual to the next, but there are certain general differences between the male and female pelvis which are fairly constant and warrant examination. Stating these differences *from the standpoint of the female pelvis,* they are as follows (Fig. 5-22):

1.   The inlet and outlet are larger, and more circular.

2.   The entire pelvis is not as deep.

3.   The sacrum is broader and not so curved.

4.   The arch formed by the rami of the pubic bones (pubic arch) is more rounded.

5.   The greater sciatic notch is larger.

6.   The obturator foramen is more triangular in outline.

7.   The acetabula face more anteriorly, and are smaller.

8.   The pelvic bones are thinner and lighter.

9.   The anterior superior iliac spines, ischial spines, and ischial tuberosities are more widely spaced.

THE FEMUR   (See Fig. 5-23 and Color Plate VIII.) The femur is the thighbone, and the longest, heaviest, strongest bone in the skeleton. It is enveloped by the large muscles of the thigh. Often compared to the humerus of the upper extremity, the femur has as its main features a *head, neck, shaft, lateral and medial condyles, greater and lesser trochanters,* and a *linea aspera.* The head of the

physis. The rami of the pubic and ischium bones form most of the obturator foramen.

THE ARTICULATED PELVIS   (See Fig. 5-20.) Each os coxae articulates with the sacrum and, at the pubic symphysis, with its fellow of the opposite side. There are several important *landmarks and measurements of the pelvis,* and the structure is commonly divided clinically into *two portions:* the *true pelvis or pelvis minor;* and the *false pelvis, or pelvis major.* The true pelvis is that portion of the pelvic cavity situated *below the right and left terminal lines* which form the *brim of the pelvis* (Fig. 5-20). Each terminal line con-

femur is the ball portion of the ball-and-socket hip joint, and is held in the acetabulum of the os coxae by a round ligament, the *ligamentum teres,* and a tough *fibrous capsule* surrounding the joint. The neck of the femur is a *common fracture site,* especially in the aged. Until fairly recently, these fractures were often debilitating and extremely slow to heal. Today they can be reduced by attaching the parts of the broken bones together with various types of pins, plates, and screws made of an inert metal. The patient may soon be able to walk, long before the bone itself has healed.

In addition to the os coxae, the femur articulates distally with the *tibia* and *patella* (kneecap). The *trochanters, trochanteric crest, gluteal tuberosity,* and *linea aspera* all serve for the attachment of muscles. The femurs do not extend downward in a perfectly vertical plane, but are *inclined medially,* so that the knees are in line with the *body's center of gravity,* or maximum weight. This fact, coupled with the wider pelvis of the female, causes many women to be somewhat "knock-kneed."

THE PATELLA (See Fig. 5-23.) The patella is a sesamoid bone, lying *within the tendon of the quadriceps femoris muscle group* on the anterior aspect of the thigh. This tendon bridges the front of the knee and inserts on the tibia. The patella is a triangular, flattened bone, somewhat teardrop-shaped in outline. The point of the teardrop is the *apex* and, in an articulated skeleton, points downward. The patella is a "floating" bone and serves to permit the quadriceps tendon to cross the knee joint.

THE TIBIA (See Fig. 5-23.) The tibia is the *shinbone,* and the larger and more medial of the two bones of the leg. Its anterior border is a sharp ridge, subcutaneous and easily palpated; the medial aspect of its distal end forms the *medial malleolus* of the ankle. On its *lateral aspect,* the tibia articulates with the *fibula* at both its proximal and distal portions. The *upper portion* of the tibia supports the *condyles of the femur,* and the *lower end* rests on the *talus* bone of the foot. The anterior and medial aspects of the tibia

serve as important areas of muscle attachment, but a portion of both these areas are subcutaneous and fairly easy to injure.

THE FIBULA The more lateral of the two bones of the leg, the fibula (Fig. 5-23) is extremely slender and twisted. It *does not articulate with either the patella or femur* and, therefore, is not one of the bones of the knee joint. The enlarged proximal end of the fibula is the *head,* while the corresponding portion of the distal end forms the *lateral malleolus* of the ankle. The lateral malleolus extends farther distally than the medial malleolus. The fibula articulates with the *tibia* at its proximal end, and with the *tibia and talus* at its distal end. It is considered to be *one of the bones of the ankle joint.*

BONES OF THE ANKLE AND FOOT (See Fig. 5-24 on p. 80.) The *tarsal bones* of the ankle and foot correspond to the carpals of the wrist. There are seven tarsals: *calcaneus, talus, navicular, cuboid,* and *lateral, medial,* and *intermediate cuneiforms.* The *body weight* is concentrated upon the *two largest tarsals,* the *calcaneus* and *talus.*

1. *Talus.* The talus, which has a *head, neck,* and *body,* articulates with the distal end of the tibia above and the calcaneus below, thus receiving the weight of the body and transferring it to the calcaneus. It also articulates with the distal end of the fibula and with the navicular.

2. *Calcaneus.* After receiving the body weight from the talus, the calcaneus passes this weight on to the ground or other substrate. The calcaneus is the *largest of all the tarsals,* and its posterior end is the bone of the *heel.* The calcaneus articulates with the talus by means of two articular areas on the superior aspect of the calcaneus, and by means of a shelflike process on its medial surface, the *sustentaculum tali.*

3. *Navicular.* The tarsal bone located just anterior to the talus, on the medial aspect of the foot, is the irregularly shaped navicular. It articulates posteriorly with the talus and anteriorly with all the cuneiform bones.

4. *Cuboid.* The roughly cube-shaped cuboid is positioned laterally in the foot, and articulates medially with the navicular and lateral cuneiform, posteriorly with the cal-

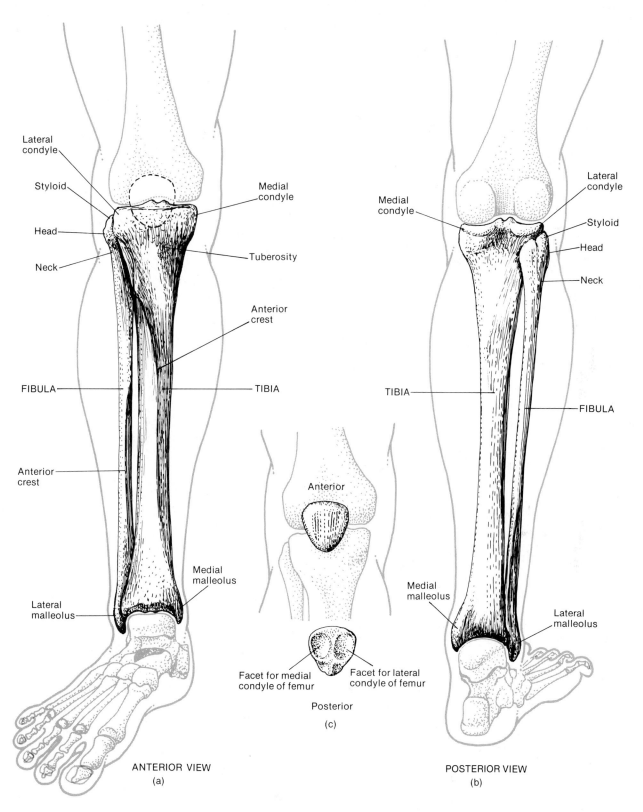

Figure 5-23 Bones of the thigh and leg. (a) and (b) Anterior and posterior view of the fibula and tibia. (c) Patella, or kneecap.

77

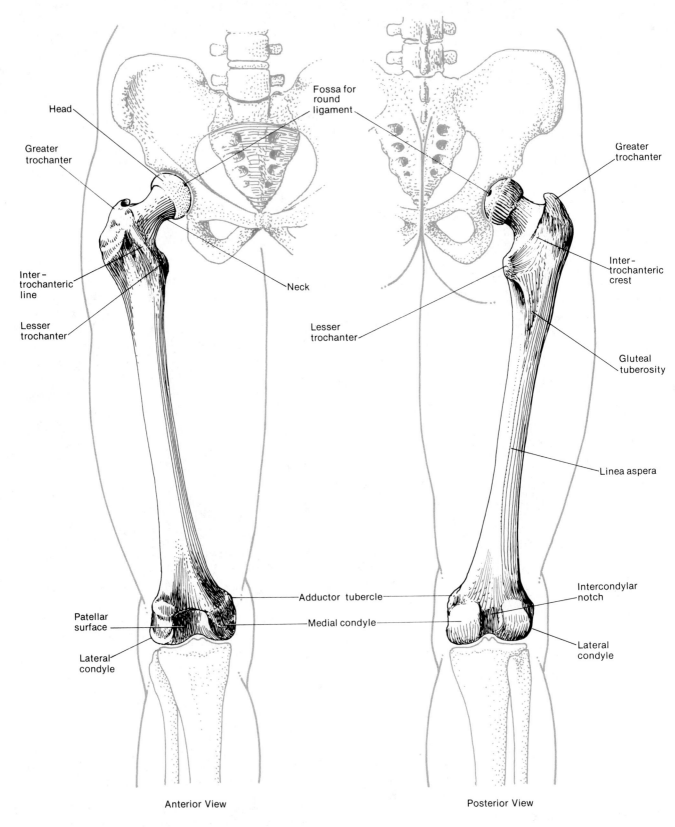

Head

Greater trochanter

Fossa for round ligament

Inter-trochanteric line

Lesser trochanter

Neck

Greater trochanter

Inter-trochanteric crest

Lesser trochanter

Gluteal tuberosity

Linea aspera

Adductor tubercle

Patellar surface

Medial condyle

Intercondylar notch

Lateral condyle

Lateral condyle

Anterior View

Posterior View

Figure 5-23(d) Right femur.

78

caneus, and anteriorly with the fourth and fifth metatarsals.

5. *Cuneiforms.* These rather wedge-shaped bones are arranged in a transverse row posterior to the first four metatarsals, and articulate with these bones. The medial cuneiform also articulates with the navicular and intermediate cuneiform; the intermediate with the navicular and medial and lateral cuneiforms; and the lateral cuneiform with the navicular, cuboid, and intermediate cuneiforms (Fig. 5-24).

6. *Metatarsals* (See Fig. 5-24.) Like the metacarpals of the hand, the metatarsals are not named, but *numbered* from 1 to 5. The *most medial* is designated number 1. The metatarsals are long and slender, and their anterior ends are known as *heads*. Range of movement of the large (great) toe is not as great as that of the thumb, due to parallel arrangement of all the metatarsals. During locomotion, *body weight is transmitted largely to the first metatarsal.* The metatarsals articulate anteriorly with the proximal phalanx of the corresponding digit.

7. *Phalanges* (See Fig. 5-24.) As in the hand, there is a total of 14 phalanges. Each digit has three *except* the large toe, which has only two.

ARCHES OF THE FOOT   The arrangement of the bones of the foot normally is such that *three strong arches* are produced: *two longitudinal arches—medial* and *lateral—and one transverse arch* (Color Plate VIII). Architects have known for many centuries that arches are among the strongest structures known. Tendons of leg muscles plus tough ligaments hold the bones of the foot arches together just firmly enough so that the arches have a certain degree of "give" or spring. If these supporting structures weaken—as they sometimes do—a condition known as *fallen arch* or "flatfoot" results, and must often be corrected by means of special exercises or artificial supports. Bones taking part in each arch are as follows:

1. *Medial Longitudinal Arch.* First three metatarsals, talus, calcaneus, navicular, and three cuneiforms.

2. *Lateral Longitudinal Arch.* Fourth and fifth metatarsals, cuboid, and calcaneus.

3. *Transverse Arch.* The cuneiforms, metatarsals, and cuboid.

ARTICULATIONS OR JOINTS

There are many articulations present in the skeleton (Fig. 5-25 and Color Plate VIII). The movements which these articulations permit range from *extreme mobility at the shoulder joint* to the *complete immobility at the joints of the skull.* The bones taking part in any articulation must be held securely together. Immobile joints such as the sutures of the skull depend upon the *interdigitations* of the edges of the bones to keep them intact, while the bones of joints permitting wide ranges of movement are often bound together by *ligaments, fibrous joint capsules,* and *muscles which bridge them.* Those joints with capsules naturally have joint cavities. Often these cavities are lined with a special membrane, the *synovial membrane,* which secretes and fills the *joint cavity* with lubricating *synovial fluid.* Many joints contain small sacs called *bursae* which facilitate movement of tendons or muscles over bone or other unyielding surfaces. Synovial membranes *line all bursae.* Some joints have discs of cartilage called *articular discs,* and the articular surfaces of bones are often overlaid with cartilage. Most of the movable joints of the body are of the synovial type.

In the following section, the various movements permitted by joints are described, and following that, a classification of joints (based upon their structure and the kinds and amounts of movement which they permit) is presented (Table 5-1).

Terms used in describing body movements

(See Fig. 5-26.) Terms concerned with body movements are most often used to describe changes in position of the extremities; however, other applications will be indicated from time to time in the following discussion.

FLEXION   This is a term indicating that *the two end portions of an extremity are being*

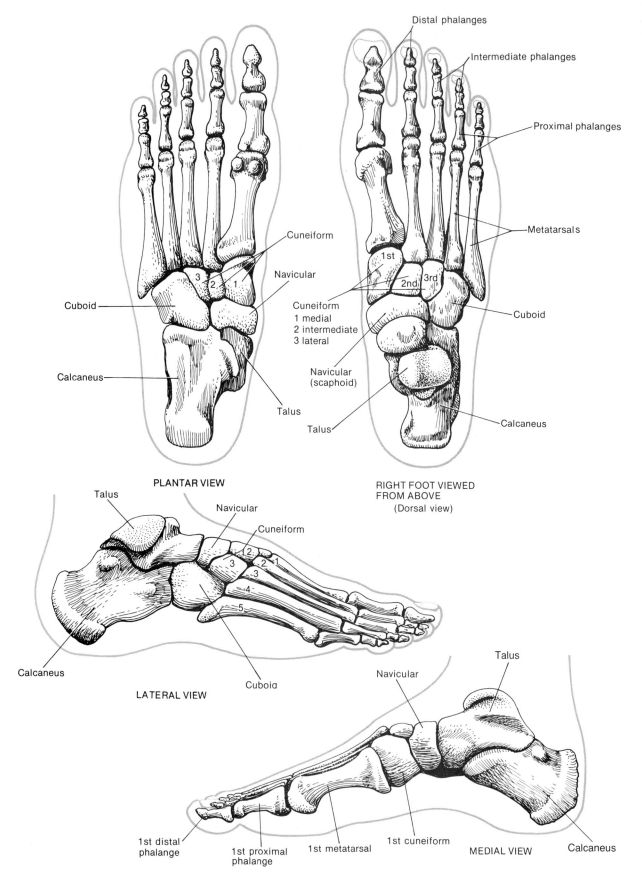

Figure 5-24 Bones of the right ankle and foot.

Distal phalanges

Intermediate phalanges

Proximal phalanges

Metatarsals

Cuboid

Calcaneus

Talus

Cuneiform
1 medial
2 intermediate
3 lateral

Navicular (scaphoid)

Cuneiform

Navicular

Cuboid

Calcaneus

Talus

PLANTAR VIEW

RIGHT FOOT VIEWED FROM ABOVE
(Dorsal view)

Talus

Navicular

Cuneiform

Calcaneus

Cuboid

LATERAL VIEW

Talus

Navicular

1st distal phalange

1st proximal phalange

1st metatarsal

1st cuneiform

MEDIAL VIEW

Calcaneus

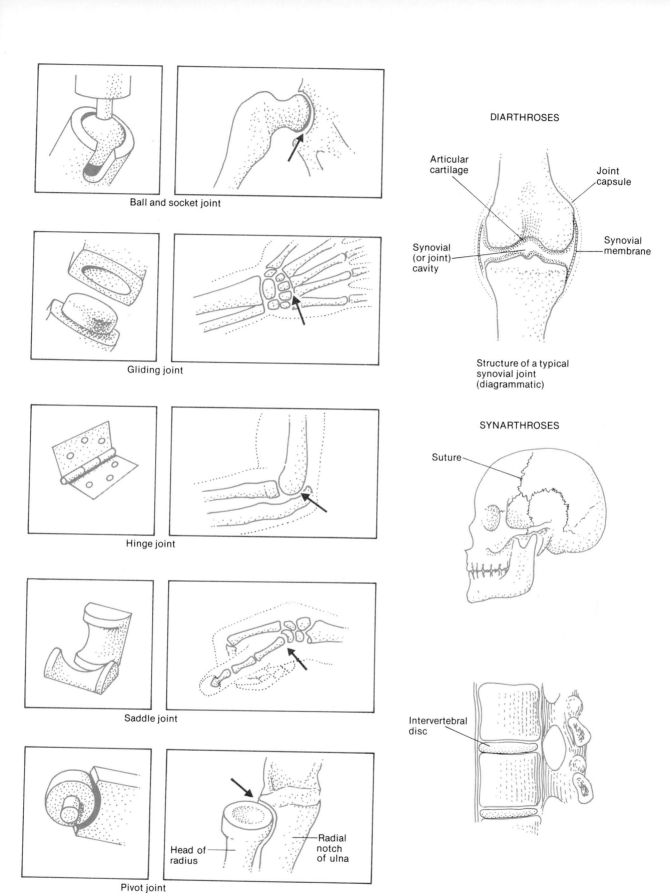

DIARTHROSES

Articular cartilage

Joint capsule

Synovial (or joint) cavity

Synovial membrane

Structure of a typical synovial joint (diagrammatic)

SYNARTHROSES

Suture

Intervertebral disc

Ball and socket joint

Gliding joint

Hinge joint

Saddle joint

Head of radius

Radial notch of ulna

Pivot joint

Figure 5-25 Different types of arthroidal joints.

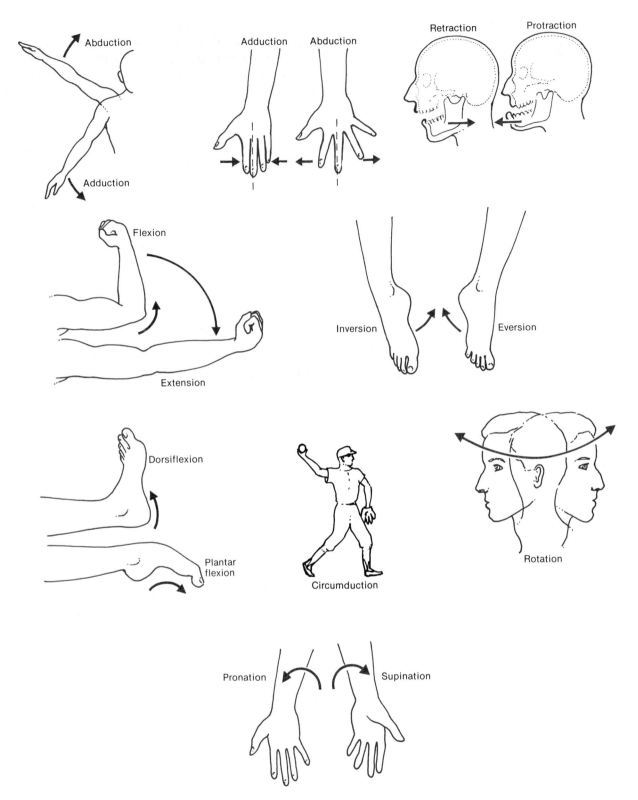

Figure 5-26 Body movements.

brought closer together, as when the hand is brought toward the shoulder; this term is also used to describe bending of the neck or other portion of the vertebral column in a forward direction, and raising the top of the foot superiorly.

EXTENSION   The opposite of flexion, extension involves *moving the two ends of an extremity apart,* as when straightening the upper limb from a bent (flexed) position. Bending the neck or other section of the vertebral column backward is another example of extension. Usage of the terms flexion and extension can sometimes become quite complicated; for example, moving the thigh backward while bending the knee puts the thigh in the extended position, while the leg proper is being flexed at the knee.

ROTATION   Rotation is a term that indicates the *partial revolving of a body part on that part's long axis.* Standing in the anatomical position and turning the upper portion of the trunk in either direction (that is, twisting right or left) rotates the vertebral column. Moving the hand so that the palm faces in a direction other than the original one involves rotation of the forearm; the same applies to the foot and leg, respectively. It should be mentioned that rotation which brings the palm of the hand forward is given the special name *supination.* In the anatomical position, the hand has already been supinated, and rotation that brings the palm to face backward is called *pronation.*

INVERSION   This term is confined to the feet. It means that the feet have been turned inward so that the *soles face one another.*

EVERSION   Eversion is the opposite of inversion. In this movement, the *soles of the feet face laterally,* or outward.

ABDUCTION   Abduction is usually used to indicate movement of an extremity laterally, *away from the median plane* of the body.

ADDUCTION   This is the *opposite of abduction* (note the difference in spelling). In this movement, an extremity is moved toward the median plane. By drawing an imaginary line down the center of the middle finger, it is possible to abduct and adduct the other fingers, and even perform these movements with the middle finger itself, using the imaginary line as a reference point.

CIRCUMDUCTION   Circumduction is a *composite movement* that involves successive flexion, extension, and medial and lateral rotation. It is perhaps best seen in a motion such as that employed by a pitcher swinging a baseball in a vertical circle. In circumduction, a *cone* is described. In this particular instance, the path followed by the pitcher's hand outlines the *base* of the cone, while the *apex* is at the shoulder.

PROTRACTION   This movement is performed by the lower jaw or mandible, the tongue, and the head, when either is protruded or pushed forward.

RETRACTION   Retraction is the opposite of protraction; that is, the jaw, tongue, or head is drawn backward.

ELEVATION   This movement can be performed by the mandible and scapulae. Closing the mouth involves elevating the jaw, while raising the shoulders in a shrugging movement elevates the scapulae.

DEPRESSION   Depression is the opposite movement of elevation. The lowering of the mandible during the opening of the mouth and the lowering of the shoulders from a shrugged position are examples of depression.

TABLE 5-1

A classification of joints

    I. SYNARTHRODIAL. A synarthrosis has no joint cavity, and no movement is permitted. The participating bones are in close contact with each other.

       A. *Suture.* Only the bones of the skull have sutures. The bones are first united by fibrous tissue, but this disappears with age.

       B. *Synchondrosis.* Found between the epiphyses and shaft of maturing bones, this type joint disappears when growth has stopped. Hyaline cartilage is present until this takes place.

       C. *Syndesmosis.* Dense connective tissue binds the bones together in this type joint. The distal articulation between the tibia and fibula is a syndesmosis.

II. AMPHIARTHRODIAL. An amphiarthrosis permits a small amount of movement. Fibrocartilage is placed between the bones, and there are ligaments and some capsules present. Some have joint cavities. The union between the manubrium and body of the sternum, and those between the bodies of the vertebrae, as well as between the bones of the symphysis pubis, are all examples of amphiarthrodial joints.

III. DIARTHRODIAL. When considered as a group, a wide variety of movements is possible in joints of this classification, including gliding, pivoting or rotating about a long axis, flexion, extension, abduction, adduction, and circumduction. A diarthrosis has a true joint cavity, ligaments, and a covering of hyaline cartilage on the articular surfaces of the bones involved. The subdivisions of diarthroses are as follows:

A. *Gliding or arthrodial* joints, such as those between carpals and between tarsals.

B. *Pivot or trochoid* joints, which permit rotation around the long axis of a bone. Examples are found at the joint between the head of the radius and capitulum of the humerus, and between the first two cervical vertebrae, the atlas and axis.

C. *Hinge or ginglymus* joints, such as those found at the knee and elbow; permit movement back and forth in one plane.

D. *Biaxial or saddle* joints, such as the joint between the carpals and radius. These permit movements in two planes at right angles to each other.

E. *Ball-and-socket* joints, such as the joints of the shoulder and hip. The former is the only joint permitting complete or true circumduction, in which the upper extremity is straightened and swung in a circle so that the complete movement described is a cone. The hip joint permits modified circumduction.

Bones as levers

Many body movements make use of the principles of *leverage.* A *lever* consists of a fixed point or *fulcrum,* a point of *resistance,* and a source of power or *force* (Fig. 5-27). There are *three classes of levers: first-class levers,* in which *the fulcrum is placed between the resistance and the power; second-class levers,* with the *resistance between the fulcrum and the power,* and *third-class levers,* with the *power or force placed between the resistance and the fulcrum.* Examples of these classes of levers in the body are illustrated in Fig. 5-27. In this drawing, the muscles represent the force or power; when the muscles contract, they move the resistance around the joint, which represents the fulcrum. It should be pointed out that resistance often consists simply of the weight of the body or its parts; for example, in moving the hand to the head, the resistance is represented by the weight of the upper extremity. In many cases, leverage provides the body with a *mechanical advantage,* so that the amount of force required to carry out a body movement is not nearly so great as it would be if there were no levers in the body. This is the case in the second-class lever seen in Fig. 5-27; here, the calf muscles lift the weight of the entire body up onto the toes.

THE TEETH

The teeth or *organs of mastication* (Fig. 5-28 and Color Plate III) cut, tear, and grind food. The *incisors* do the *cutting, canines tear,* and *molars grind.* Each kind of tooth is shaped and modified to do its particular pob. In the *adult half-jaw,* either upper or lower, there are *two incisors, one canine or cuspid, two premolars or bicuspids,* and *three molars,* for a total of eight teeth. Since there are four such half-jaws, there is a grand total of 32 teeth in the mouth of the adult. The last or third molars are the so-called *wisdom teeth;* no correlation has been established between these teeth and wisdom, however.

If numerals are used to represent the numbers of each kind of tooth in each half-jaw, a relationship known as the *dental formula* can be written, as follows:

Dental formula $= \dfrac{\left(\begin{array}{c}\text{Number of teeth in}\\ \text{half of upper jaw}\end{array}\right)}{\left(\begin{array}{c}\text{Number of teeth in}\\ \text{half of lower jaw}\end{array}\right)}$

$= \dfrac{2\text{–}1\text{–}2\text{–}3}{2\text{–}1\text{–}2\text{–}3}$

Although there are 32 adult or "permanent" teeth, there are only 20 teeth in the jaw of a child. These are the *deciduous* or *"baby"* teeth, and the dental formula is:

$$\dfrac{2\text{–}1\text{–}2\text{–}0}{2\text{–}1\text{–}2\text{–}0}$$

Figure 5-27 The different classes of levers and examples of how they are represented in the body.

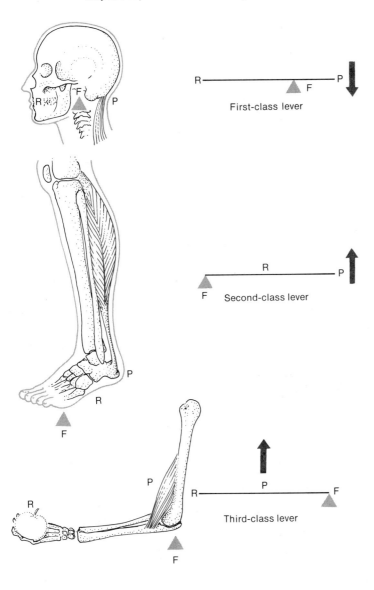

First-class lever

Second-class lever

Third-class lever

Deciduous teeth begin erupting through the gums or *gingiva* when the baby is about six months old. They are usually all gone by the thirteenth year, having begun to loosen at about six years.

A typical tooth

A typical tooth (Fig. 5-28) consists of a *crown, neck,* and *root.* Above the gum, the tooth is covered with a very hard substance, *enamel,* which consists of fibers of the protein *keratin,* and *crystalline calcium carbonate* and *calcium phosphate.* Enamel is formed by *ameloblasts*—specialized epithelial cells—before the teeth erupt. Below the gum line, the tooth is covered by a thin layer of bony *cementum.* It is the cementum, along with collagen fibers that extend between it and the bone of the jaw, that holds a tooth firmly in place. The nerves, vessels, lymphatics and connective tissue found in the central portion of a tooth make up the *pulp,* which is enclosed within the *pulp cavity. Odontoblast cells* line the pulp cavity and produce the thickest layer of the tooth, *dentin.*

It has been found that thyroid and growth hormones can bring about faster tooth development and eruption. The normal hardening of teeth depends to a very large extent upon adequate amounts of *vitamin D, phosphate,* and *calcium* in the diet, as well as certain levels of *parathyroid hormone* in the blood.

Disorders involving the teeth and gums

Dental *caries* (cavities) and *malocclusion* are the two most common disorders of the teeth. Tooth decay may be due to acid-producing bacteria in the mouth, bacteria that produce proteolytic enzymes, or other factors. Drinking water containing only about one part per million of the element *fluorine* helps teeth to resist decay about twice as much as otherwise. Fluoridated toothpastes and the application of a fluoride by a dentist may also be useful in preventing caries. Women should drink fluoridated

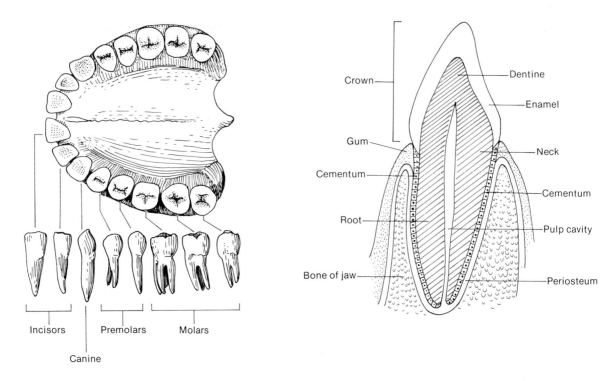

Figure 5-28 The teeth. Left: Permanent teeth of upper jaw. Right: Longitudinal section of a tooth.

water during at least the first three months of pregnancy.

Malocclusion is a condition, often hereditary, in which the teeth of the upper jaw do not meet properly with the teeth of the lower jaw during the "bite" or *occlusion.* Also, individual teeth may be out of line in their sockets or *alveoli.* Normally, the front teeth of the lower jaw fit slightly behind those of the upper jaw during occlusion, resulting in a slight *overbite.* Occasionally, the front teeth of the mandible lie anterior to those of the maxilla, producing a *prognathism.* Most cases of malocclusion of any sort can be greatly helped by the *orthodontist*—a dentist specializing in such disorders—provided he sees the patient at least by the time of adolescence. Tension-applying wires and elastic braces are used over a period of time, and a process of redistribution of the bone material of the alveoli takes place. Bone is absorbed in one portion of the alveolar proc-

ess and laid down in another portion as the tooth is slowly forced about.

Transplantation of teeth is now meeting with some degree of success. A tooth accidentally dislodged may often be successfully reinserted in its socket, and teeth have been removed from the jaw of one person and inserted successfully into the jaw of another. Teeth of inert metals and plastics have been screwed into the jawbone, but these are often rejected by the gum tissue, which sloughs away.

The gums or gingiva are susceptible to a number of disorders, ranging from a simple inflammation or *gingivitis* to *periodontal disease* or *pyorrhea,* a serious inflammation which loosens the teeth to the point of falling out, and even to *ulceration* and *cancer.* The condition of the gums is sometimes a useful diagnostic aid, especially in those cases where the gum condition indicates possible vitamin deficiencies.

OUTLINE SUMMARY

1. The body framework, or skeleton, consists of bone, cartilage, and ligaments, plus joints between the bones

2. Functions of the skeletal system
   A. Support
   B. Permission of movement

C. Blood-cell formation (hemopoiesis)
D. Protection
E. Detoxification (removal of poisons)
F. Provision for muscle attachment
G. Mineral storage
3. The major features of a bone
   A. Bone parts
      a. Epiphyses or ends
      b. Diaphysis or shaft
      c. Marrow or inner substance
      d. Periosteum, the outer covering
      e. Endosteum, the inner lining
4. The histology and development of bone
   A. Haversian system: basic unit of bone structure
   B. Bone material
      a. Bone cells
      b. Fibers
      c. Matrix or ground substance
         1. Cementing substances
         2. Collagenous fibers
   C. Ossification
      a. Intramembranous
      b. Endochondral
5. Cartilage
   A. Hyaline
   B. Elastic
   C. Fibrous
6. Gross anatomy of the skeletal system
   A. Bone shapes and sizes
      a. Long bones
      b. Short bones
      c. Flat bones
      d. Irregular bones
      e. Sesamoid bones
   B. Bone markings
      a. Condyle
      b. Epicondyle
      c. Crest
      d. Spine
      e. Trochlea
      f. Tubercle
      g. Trochanter
      h. Foramen
      i. Sinus
      j. Sulcus
      k. Head and neck
7. Divisions of the skeleton
   A. Axial skeleton
      a. Bones of the skull (28)
         1. Bones of the face (14)
            2 nasal
            2 maxillary
            2 zygomatic
            1 mandible
            2 palatine
            1 vomer
            2 lacrimal
            2 inferior nasal conchae
         2. Bones of the cranium (14)
            1 occipital
            2 parietal
            1 frontal
            2 temporal

1 ethmoid
1 sphenoid
2 malleus bones ⎫
2 incus bones   ⎬ ear ossicles
2 stapes bones ⎭
The hyoid bone may also be included with the bones of the skull
   b. Features of the skull as a whole
      1. Sutures: where skull bones fit together
      2. Fontanels: temporary holes in the cranium
      3. Supernumerary bones: formed by extra sutures
      4. Sinuses: air spaces within skull bones
      5. Cranial fossae: large depressions in the floor of the skull
      6. Sexual differences in the skull: bones of the male skull are somewhat heavier, and the cranial capacity slightly greater
      7. Effects of aging on the skull: fontanels close in early life, skull bones grow until after puberty, and the mandible tends to atrophy with age
   c. The vertebral column. Main features:
      1. Four curvatures: cervical, thoracic, lumbar, and sacral
      2. About 71 cm long, and consists of 33 vertebrae: 7 cervical, 12 thoracic, 5 lumbar, 5 sacral, and 4 coccygeal. Those in the sacrum and in the coccyx are fused together
   d. Features of a typical vertebra
      1. Centrum or body
      2. Neural arch, enclosing the vertebral foramen
      3. Two pedicles and two lamina forming the neural arch
      4. A spinous process at the point of fusion of the lamina
      5. Two superior and two inferior articular processes
      6. A pair of transverse processes
   e. Features of vertebrae in different portions of the vertebral column
      1. Cervical: have foramina in transverse processes
      2. Thoracic: have articular facets on centrum, for articulation with ribs
      3. Lumbar: have massive transverse and spinous processes, no transverse foramina, no articular facets on centrum
      4. Sacral: fused into one sacrum
      5. Coccygeal: fused into one coccyx
   f. Bones of the thorax

1. Ribs: "true," "false," and "floating"
2. Typical rib: note features
3. Sternum. Parts: manubrium, body, xiphoid

B. Appendicular skeleton
   a. Bones of the shoulder girdle and upper extremity
      1. The shoulder girdle: clavicle and scapula
      2. The upper extremity: humerus, or bone of the brachium; radius and ulna, bones of the forearm; carpals, or bones of the wrist; metacarpals, the bones of the hand; and phalanges, the bones of the digits
   b. Bones of the pelvic girdle and lower extremity
      1. The pelvic girdle: os coxae (2), sacrum, and coccyx. Each of the os coxae consists of a fused ilium, ischium, and pubis
      2. The articulated pelvis: has clinically important bony landmarks and diameters
   c. Sex differences in the pelvis: the following features distinguish the female pelvis from the male pelvis
      1. Larger inlet and outlet
      2. Shallower overall structure
      3. Broader, straighter sacrum
      4. More rounded pubic arch
      5. Larger greater sciatic notch
      6. Triangular obturator foramen
      7. Smaller acetabula, directed more forward
      8. Lighter bones
      9. More widely spaced anterior superior iliac spines, ischial tuberosities, and ischial spines
   d. Bones of the lower extremity
      1. Femur: bone of the thigh
      2. Tibia and fibula: bones of the leg
      3. Tarsals: bones of the ankle
      4. Metatarsals: bones of the foot
      5. Phalanges: bones of the digits
      6. Patella: the kneecap, a sesamoid bone
   e. Arches of the foot
      1. Medial longitudinal arch: formed by the first 3 metatarsals, talus, calcaneus, navicular, and 3 cuneiforms
      2. Lateral longitudinal arch: fourth and fifth metatarsals, cuboid, and calcaneus
      3. Transverse arch: cuneiforms, metatarsals, and cuboid

8. Articulations: joints between bones, some movable, others are not. Partial classification of joints:
   A. Synarthrodial: no joint cavity, no movement possible (example: sutures of the skull)
   B. Amphiarthrodial: limited movement permitted. Some have joint cavities. Example: intervertebral joints
   C. Diarthrodial: wide variety of movements possible. True joint cavity, with lubricating (synovial) fluid. Examples: ball-and-socket joints of the shoulder and hip

9. Changes in the skeleton with age
   A. Bones become more brittle and subject to fracture, due to the slowing of the deposition of organics in their matrix
   B. Mandible tends to atrophy, especially if teeth are lost
   C. Kyphosis may develop (stoop shoulder)
   D. Sesamoid bones may form within muscle tendons

10. Hemopoiesis: formation of blood cells in the bone marrow. Red cells, platelets, and most white cells are formed there

11. The teeth: organs of mastication
    A. Incisors: cutting teeth; two in each adult half-jaw
    B. Canines: tearing teeth; one in each adult half-jaw
    C. Premolars: grinding teeth; two in each adult half-jaw
    D. Molars: grinding teeth; three in each adult half-jaw
    E. A typical tooth consists of
       a. Crown
       b. Neck
       c. Root (surrounded by the gingiva or gums)
    F. Disorders of the teeth and gums
       a. Caries: cavities caused by decay
       b. Malocclusion: improper "bite"
       c. Gingivitis: inflammation of the gums
       d. Pyorrhea: an inflammatory disease, which can destroy gum tissue and loosen the teeth

1. Briefly describe the Haversian system. What is the scientific term for mature bone cells?

2. List seven functions of the skeletal system. Could any one of these functions be lost and health maintained?

3. List the five groups of bones according to their shape. Where would you find each of these in the skeleton?

4. What is cancellous bone? Compact bone?

5. Define *condyle, epicondyle, crest, spine, trochlea, tubercle, trochanter, foramen, sinus, sulcus, head, neck.*

6. What are the two major divisions of the skeleton? In general, what are the bones that belong to each division?

7. Make a list of the bones of the skull. Can you separate these into bones of the face and bones of the cranium?

8. Doctor Q. notes that his patient appears to have a slight skull fracture in the frontal bone. But upon closer examination of the X-ray photograph, the physician decides that one of the skull sutures has failed to close properly during growth and development. Which suture would this be?

9. How many fontanels are present in the skull at birth? Make a list of these, and the bones which form them.

10. What are the sesamoid bones? Name a sesamoid bone of the body that is present in everyone and, therefore, not considered to be supernumerary. What is another name for supernumerary bones of the skull?

11. Define these terms: *kyphosis, scoliosis,* and *lordosis.*

12. Sketch and label a typical vertebra from the side and from above. List the major features of cervical, thoracic, and lumbar vertebrae.

13. List the bones of the shoulder girdle and those of the pelvic girdle.

14. List nine sex differences in the pelvis.

15. What is a diarthrodial joint? Amphiarthrodial? What is a synchondrosis? Syndesmosis? Where are all these found in the body?

16. Describe endochondral and intramembranous ossification.

17. Write the dental formula for an adult, and explain what it means.

18. What is malocclusion? What are the two major types?

19. List the three kinds of cartilage and state one location in the body where you would expect to find each.

20. What are Sharpey's fibers?

21. Name the two kinds of bone marrow and state the chief characteristics of each.

22. Why is bone marrow called hemopoietic tissue?

23. Contrast the matrix of bone with that of cartilage.

24. What is hydroxyapatite?

25. What is the name of the group of compounds to which the cementing substances of bone belong?

26. Where do the cementing substances originate?

27. How does cartilage get its nutrients and oxygen?

the skeletal muscles and body movements

The scientific study of body movements is *kinesiology;* and the ultimate aim of this chapter is to understand the underlying mechanisms of certain body movements—such as those seen in walking, running, swimming, breathing, chewing, and the movements of facial expression—by analyzing these movements much as a *kinesiologist* would.

All the body movements depend upon the most outstanding property or specialty of skeletal muscle (or any type muscle): **contractility,** or the ability to shorten. Muscle tissue can shorten in length to a much greater degree than any other type tissue. True, muscle does have some power of *conductivity,* and can transport a sort of electrical type impulse, similar to a nerve impulse; but this job is much better performed by nerve tissue. In this chapter, the *anatomy and physiology* of the major skeletal muscles, their *attachments to the skeleton and to each other,* and their *nerve supplies* will receive primary consideration. For purposes of illustration and comparison, however, some of the characteristics of *smooth and cardiac muscle* will be mentioned from time to time. A more detailed discussion of cardiac muscle will be found in the chapter concerned with the circulatory system, and smooth muscle is considered mainly in the chapters describing the blood vessels and digestive system. The major skeletal muscles are illustrated in Color Plates II through VIII.

Gross and microscopic anatomy of a typical skeletal muscle

A longitudinal section of a skeletal muscle such as the *biceps brachii* reveals that it consists chiefly of a very large number of elongated, *striated* (striped), *multinucleate cells or fibers,* arranged parallel to the long axis of the muscle. The fibers are only 0.01 to 0.15 mm in diameter, but range from 1 to 12 cm in length. On cross-section (Fig. 6-1), it is seen that a muscle actually consists of bundles of the aforementioned fibers, *fasciculi.* Each fasciculus is enclosed in a connective-tissue coat, the *perimysium.* A sheath around each muscle fiber (outside the *sarcolemma,* or cell membrane) is the *endomysium;* while still another layer of connective tissue covers the entire muscle, and is called the *epimysium.* The epimysium is continuous with the strong connective-tissue *tendons* which often attach muscle to bone. With an ordinary light microscope, it can be seen that the striated muscle cell has from several to many nuclei and, therefore, fits the qualifications of a *syncytium,* a multinucleate mass of protoplasm. With an electron microscope, it can be seen that each muscle fiber consists of a number of *fibrils* (or *myofibrils*), illustrated in Fig. 6-1. Mitochondria and the muscle-cell nuclei lie near the fibrils. Figure 6-2 shows diagrammatically the fine structure of a single fibril. Each consists of alternating *light* (*isotropic*) and *dark* (*anisotropic*)

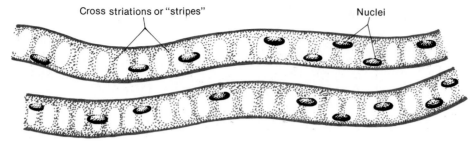

Cross striations or "stripes"

Nuclei

PORTIONS OF TWO STRIATED MUSCLE FIBERS

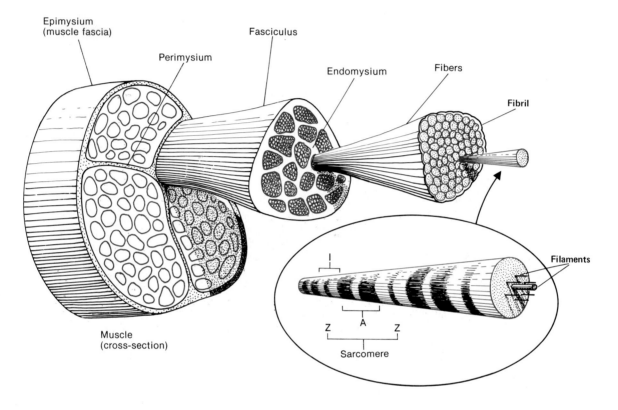

Epimysium (muscle fascia)

Perimysium

Fasciculus

Endomysium

Fibers

Fibril

Muscle (cross-section)

Filaments

Sarcomere

Figure 6-1 Construction of a skeletal muscle.

areas or *bands,* often called *I-bands* and *A-bands.* The dark bands are produced by overlapping or interdigitating *filaments* (fine strands) of two *muscle proteins, actin* and *myosin.* Although both types of filaments are extremely thin, those containing myosin are much thicker than the actin filaments. It is these light and dark bands that give skeletal muscle fibers their cross-striped appearance and the name striated muscle.

Light bands on the muscle fibril are made up of *actin filaments alone.* Where the two types of filaments overlap, they are connected by tiny *protoplasmic "bridges"* of

myosin which run transversely in the fibril. Running across each *I-band* (isotropic band) halfway between its two ends, is a dark line, the *Z membrane* or *membrane of Krause.* That portion of a myofibril between one Z membrane and the next is the *sarcomere,* and is considered to be the *unit of muscle contraction;* in other words, the contraction of a muscle fiber—and ultimately, that of an entire muscle—is the *sum total of the contraction of its sarcomeres.* The exact mechanism which brings about the contraction of the sarcomere is not clear; however, it is known that when contraction takes place,

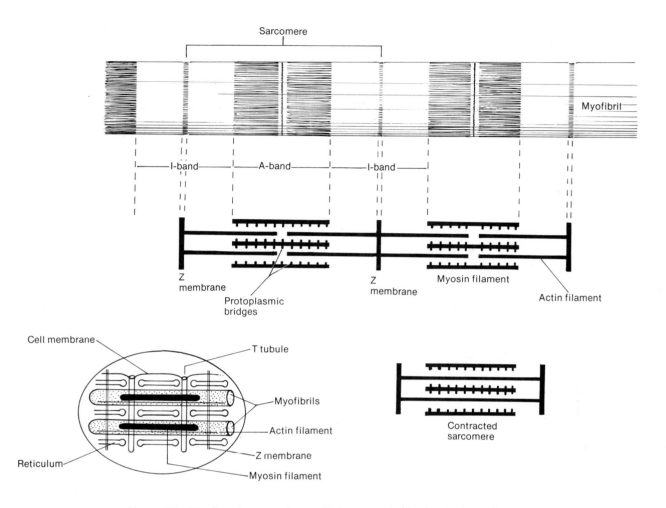

Sarcomere

Myofibril

I-band

A-band

I-band

Z membrane

Protoplasmic bridges

Z membrane

Myosin filament

Actin filament

Cell membrane

T tubule

Myofibrils

Actin filament

Z membrane

Myosin filament

Reticulum

Contracted sarcomere

Figure 6-2 The fine structure of a myofibril, as revealed by the electron microscope.

the myofilaments seem to slide over each other, thereby decreasing the length of the sarcomere. It is probable that the myosin bridges bring about contraction by pulling on the actin filaments.

The nerve supply
of skeletal muscle

Muscle contraction is *initiated* by the triggering action of *nerve impulses* which reach the muscle fibers by traveling over *motor neurons* (nerve cells) contained in the *nerves* that can be seen entering the muscles. Nerves supplying (connecting with) most of the skeletal muscles originate (have their beginning) at the *spinal cord* and are, therefore, called *spinal nerves* (Fig. 7-21). Those

supplying the muscles of the head begin in the *brainstem region* (at the top of the spinal cord, and connected with it) mostly in or around the *medulla oblongata* of the brain, and are called *cranial nerves*. Upon penetrating a muscle, a nerve immediately breaks up into a number of branch neurons—or more exactly, *axons*—which in turn contact muscle fibers by means of tiny buttonlike endings called *motor end plates*. An axon may branch enough to supply as many as *100 muscle fibers* (Fig. 6-3). The point at which a motor end plate contacts a muscle fiber is known as the *neuromuscular* (or *myoneural*) *junction;* and any given neuron and the muscle fibers it supplies constitutes a *motor unit*. An impulse traveling over a motor neuron causes all the muscle fibers supplied by that neuron and its branches to *contract as a unit*. Impulses are transmitted from motor end plate to sarcolemma by means of acetylcholine, released at the motor end plate.

The blood supply of skeletal muscle

Because of the great amount of work they are required to do in moving the body or its parts, muscles need large quantities of *energy;* and a plentiful supply of *oxygen* is necessary in order that this energy may be utilized. This oxygen can reach the muscles *only in the blood,* which is pumped to the muscles in *arteries.*

Muscle tone

Even during fairly strenuous work, all of the muscle fibers in a muscle do not ordinarily contract at the same time; instead, some cells are contracting while others are relaxed, and a *system of constant rotation* is in effect; that is, the cells "take turns." Even when an individual is sleeping, a small percentage of the cells are in a state of contraction, bringing about a certain degree of firmness to the muscles, a condition called *tone or tonus.* With aging or poor health, muscles often tend to lose some or all of their tone. In good health, tone is maintained by a constant flow of impulses sent to the muscles by the brain and spinal cord.

At rest, relatively few muscle fibers are active at any one time. When stress is placed on a muscle, as in lifting a series of increasingly heavier weights, more and more fibers are brought into play. This increase in the number of contracting cells is called *recruitment.*

Laboratory experiments with isolated muscles and muscle fibers

Physiologists have learned much about the way in which muscles and muscle fibers act by removing them from animals in the laboratory, then artificially stimulating these muscles and observing their actions. Muscle

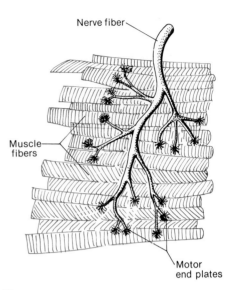

Figure 6-3 A motor unit.

cells respond to a number of *stimuli,* such as *electric shock; changes in temperature, pH,* and *ionic concentrations;* and *certain chemicals.* In the laboratory, electricity is customarily used as a source of stimulation. There are several advantages to this: the *strength of the current can be varied accurately and at will* and *stimulation can be stopped instantly;* and *a current just strong enough to bring about maximum contraction of a fiber or entire muscle does not injure the muscle tissue.*

Electrical stimuli can be classified according to their *strength.* A stimulus that is too weak to bring about a response is known as a *subthreshold or subminimal stimulus;* one that is just strong enough to cause one or more muscle fibers to contract is a *threshold or minimal stimulus;* while a stimulus that brings about a maximum response in a whole muscle is a *maximal stimulus*—an increase in the strength of the stimulus above this point *does not* bring about a greater force of contraction. In the case of an isolated muscle cell, a threshold stimulus is all that is necessary in order to bring about a *maximum response.* In other words, *if the muscle fiber contracts in response to a stimulus, it contracts maximally or not at all.* This is known as the *all-or-none principle or law.* This principle holds only for *individual muscle fibers and motor units,* and not entire muscles, because a weak stimulus may activate only a few muscle fibers in an intact muscle, and a much stronger stimulus may be required in order to get all the fibers in the muscle to contract. Also, the all-or-none principle holds only when conditions are kept *constant.* For example, if a muscle fiber is stimulated several times in rapid succession, it may build up a certain amount of heat and contract with successively greater force; or it may become fatigued and refuse to contract at all.

APPARATUS USED IN RECORDING MUSCLE CONTRACTIONS All records of muscle contractions should include *time markings,* indications of the exact *instance of stimulation,* and marks by which one can judge the *magnitude of the response.* A very old but still useful device for recording muscle activity is the *kymograph.* Special slick paper is attached to the cylinder or drum of the kymograph, then smoked by revolving it over a kerosene flame. The drum is then placed on the shaft of a spring-wound or electrically driven motor, and set to turning. As the drum revolves, the kymograph is moved close to a stand on which a muscle is suspended, until the writing stylus just scratches the surface of the soot, exposing a line of white paper. When the muscle is stimulated and contracts, a record such as that in Fig. 6-4 is produced. Soot is used on the drum because it creates little friction as the muscle stylus moves through it. After the record is complete and any pertinent data have been scratched into the soot, the paper is removed from the drum, dipped in shellac, and hung up to dry. Improved kymographs employ an ink writing mechanism rather than a smoked drum.

A more modern and much more efficient apparatus for studying muscle phenomena and other physiological events is the *polygraph.* It is an instrument that consists of several *channels,* each of which is capable of recording a separate physiological event, such as *muscle contraction, blood pressure, heartbeat, electrical activity of the heart* (*electrocardiogram*), and many others. Each channel of the polygraph is made up of *three basic components:* a *transducer,* an *amplifier,* and a *recording pen.* The transducer converts motion, electrical activity in tissues, and other manifestations of energy into electrical *signals* which are then fed into the amplifier.

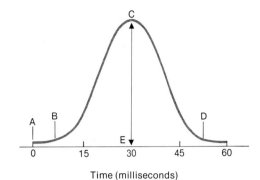

Figure 6-4 A single twitch (simple twitch). A = point of stimulation. B = beginning of contraction. C = end of contraction and beginning of relaxation. D = completion of relaxation. A — B = latent period. B — C = contraction phase. C — D = relaxation phase. C — E = height or magnitude of contraction.

In the amplifier, the signals are greatly increased in strength (*amplified*) and sent to the recording-pen motor. The motor drives the pen or *stylus* so that it makes an *inked record* of the physiological activity on graph paper, which in turn moves along under the recording pen. The polygraph has the great advantage of being able to detect and amplify extremely tiny *electrical potentials or charges at the body surfaces;* therefore, such tracings as the *electrocardiogram, electroencephalogram* (a recording of brain-wave activity), and *pneumogram* (tracings of thoracic capacity) are possible and even commonplace. By means of the proper attachments, blood-pressure readings can be recorded, heart sounds made audible, and monitoring devices such as audible "beepers" and cathode-ray oscillographs utilized. In the U. S., one of the most widely used physiological polygraphs is the *Physiograph.*

SINGLE TWITCH OR SIMPLE CONTRACTION Skeletal muscle contracts much more rapidly than either cardiac muscle or smooth muscle; skeletal muscles are, therefore, commonly used to demonstrate "typical" muscle contractions. The muscles of *poikilothermic* or "cold-blooded" animals such as reptiles and amphibians are more tenacious than those of mammals and other warm-blooded animals when removed from the body. The cells live longer and do not fatigue as rapidly. If the *gastrocnemius* or calf muscle of a frog is

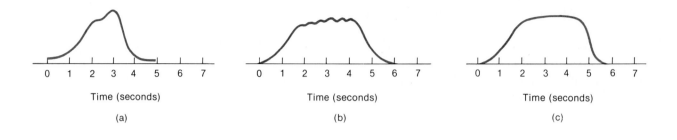

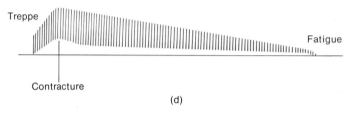

Figure 6-5 Different types of muscle phenomena. (a) Summation of stimuli. (b) Incomplete tetanus. (c) Complete tetanus. (d) Treppe, contracture, and fatigue.

removed and attached to a recording apparatus such as those previously described, and a brief threshold stimulus is applied, a tracing or *myogram* similar to that shown in Fig. 6-4 is obtained. This recording of a *single twitch* or simple contraction can be divided into the following parts:

1. *Latent Period.* The length of time between application of the stimulus and the beginning of actual shortening or contraction of the muscle. Precise measurements have shown this to be on the order of 0.004 second (sec) for frog muscles, and much less than this for mammalian muscle; ordinary laboratory equipment usually shows the latent period as lasting about 0.01 sec, and the true latent period must be determined by using precise research equipment.

2. *Contraction Phase.* This is the period of time during which actual shortening of the muscle is taking place. The contraction phase or period lasts about 0.04 sec in frogs and is shorter in human muscles.

3. *Relaxation Phase.* After a muscle has contracted and the stimulus is removed, it relaxes until the stimulus is again applied. About 0.05 sec is required for relaxation of a frog muscle, and less for that of a human.

4. *Magnitude of Contraction.* The upper limit to which the recording pen or stylus rises during the contraction phase of a muscle

is the magnitude of contraction, and is an indication of the relative degree of force with which the muscle is contracting.

OTHER TYPES OF MUSCLE CONTRACTIONS
The single twitch is a very simple type of muscle contraction, and is very useful in analyzing muscle contraction; but it is one which does not often occur in the living body. Impulses are constantly being sent over the motor nerves to muscles involved in a particular movement, rather than in spaced intervals as when single twitches are produced in the laboratory.

If a *second threshold stimulus* is applied to a frog gastrocnemius muscle just after it has begun to contract in response to the first stimulus, a curious thing happens: the effect of the second stimulus is *"added"* to that of the first, and the magnitude of contraction is greater than it would have been had the muscle been permitted to respond only to the first stimulus. This "addition of stimuli" is more properly known as *summation,* and is illustrated in Fig. 6-5. If the second stimulus is applied too soon after the first, no summation occurs. There is a very short interval, perhaps a few thousandths of a second in duration, during which a second stimulus will not affect the magnitude of contraction, no matter how strong the second stimulus may be. This short time interval is called the *absolute refractory period*. That period during which a second stimulus brings about summation is known as the *relative refractory period*. It might be asked, what would happen if, instead of only two stimuli, a long series of stimuli is applied to the muscle? There are two possible answers to this question. First, if the individual stimuli of the series are given so that each falls within the relative refractory period of the preceding one, the graphic record of muscle action or myogram will show a long series of summations in "stairstep" fashion, called *treppe* or "warmup" phenomenon. This is possibly due to the fact that since heat is produced during contraction, the chemical reactions of contraction are carried to completion more efficiently; however, experiments with athletes and warming-up exercises have often been more or less inconclusive. In some research efforts along this line, test subjects have even been hypnotized, so that when they awoke they did not know whether or not they had carried out warming-up exercises. In these cases, there was no significant difference in the performances of those who had warmed up and those who had not. There does seem to be a definite *psychological benefit* in warmup exercises, however, and most athletes still perform them to some degree before entering competition. If, instead of using the technique that produces treppe, stimuli are applied so that each is given a short time after the relaxation phase of the preceding contraction has begun, a condition called *tetanus results*. There are *two stages of tetanus: incomplete,* during which portions of the individual contractions are discernible; and *complete tetanus,* which is a smooth, sustained contraction during which no individual contractions can be detected. Most of the movements we perform daily are of the *tetanic type.* Myograms of treppe, incomplete tetanus, and complete tetanus are shown in Fig. 6-5. It can be seen that complete tetanus might also be called *"plateau phenomenon."*

The preceding should not be confused with the tetanus of "lockjaw" fame, which is a pathological condition brought about by a microorganism, *Clostridium tetani*. In this case, the muscle fibers contract convulsively, but do not relax. Although the muscles used in chewing are strongly contracted so that the jaws are, in effect, locked, many of the other skeletal muscles—particularly those of the lower back and extremities—are involved as well.

CONTRACTURE AND FATIGUE   It is possible, under carefully controlled conditions, to stimulate a muscle rapidly enough and long enough to bring about an extra-long contraction, with relaxation taking place very slowly. This type of muscle action lasts much longer than ordinary tetanic contractions, and is called *contracture* (Fig. 6-5). Contracture may be due to the accumulation of waste products within the muscle.

It is also possible to stimulate a laboratory muscle over and over again until it fails to respond to any stimulus, no matter how strong. This is *complete fatigue,* and is not seen in healthy human muscles, no matter how strenuous the exercise in which an individual may be taking part.

It should be pointed out that in many muscle contractions that take place in the body, *no actual shortening of the muscle is involved.* One may strain to lift an automobile, for example, and many muscles contract but do not shorten, because the lifting is not accomplished and no movement takes place; tension of the involved muscles increases, however. Muscle actions involving *changes in tension but no change in length* of the muscle are known as *isometric contractions.* These are employed in the popular isometric exercising. The converse of an isometric contraction is an *isotonic one.* Here, *the muscle tone or tension remains constant, but the length undergoes change.* All of our *body movements* are of course of the isotonic variety, while isometric contractions are important in maintaining *posture.*

RESPONSE TO STRETCH   It has been found that, up to a point, a muscle will contract with more force when its fibers are stretched than when they are perfectly relaxed. For example, in the laboratory, a muscle will contract with more and more force as weights are added to it, within limits. This principle is important in heart action, as the ventricle contracts with greater force and sends more blood surging through the body when this chamber is filled with enough blood to slightly distend the muscle of its walls. This peculiarity of muscle is known as *Starling's law,* and, when applied to cardiac muscle, *Starling's law of the heart.*

The chemistry of muscle contraction

COMPOSITION OF MUSCLE Muscle tissue, even though firm and strong when palpated, is about *three-fourths water.* The remaining 25% consists of actin, myosin, troponin, other proteins (20% of the total weight of muscle) and nonprotein organics and minerals (5%). Several of the nonprotein organic substances—such as *adenosine triphosphate, phosphocreatine, creatine,* and *urea*—contain nitrogen. An extremely important organic compound stored in muscle is *glycogen. Potassium* is the most abundant mineral element in muscle, although it makes up only about 4 milligrams per gram (mg/g) of analyzed muscle tissue. Other minerals—such as sodium, calcium, phosphorus, and magnesium—are present only in trace amounts. Muscle has its own oxygen-carrying iron-protein pigment, *myoglobin,* or "muscle hemoglobin." As might be expected, this compound is chemically very similar to *hemoglobin,* the oxygen-carrying pigment of the blood; and like hemoglobin, myoglobin holds oxygen in loose combination.

THE REACTIONS OF CONTRACTION The complete story of the *conversion of chemical energy stored in muscle cells* to the *mechanical energy of muscle contraction* is yet to be told. That the reactions are many and complex is certain; therefore, a summary of only the most widely accepted concepts is included here.

Ramifying throughout the sarcoplasm of a muscle cell is a network of tubules and sacs called the *sarcoplasmic reticulum.* This structure represents the endoplasmic reticulum found in other cells. At many points along the external surface of the sarcolemma of a muscle fiber, tiny openings exist. These are the openings of a system of tubules that course transversely into the sarcoplasm. Collectively, they are called the *T system* (Fig. 6-2). When a nerve impulse reaches a muscle fiber, an impulse is set up in that fiber and passes inward from the sarcolemma over the T tubules. When this happens, calcium ions are released from the sacs of the sarcoplasmic reticulum. In the sarcoplasm, the calcium ions combine with the muscle protein, troponin. When a muscle fiber is not contracting, troponin prevents the interaction of myosin and actin. But once troponin is bound by calcium, it loses its inhibiting qualities, and myosin interacts with actin. Myosin cross bridges attach to actin filaments and pull them toward the central portion of the sarcomere. Actin filaments slide over myosin filaments and the sarcomere shortens.

ENERGY FOR CONTRACTION The *ultimate source of energy for muscle contraction* is the same as that required for metabolism to go on in any cell: *the oxidation of a carbohydrate such as glycogen to carbon dioxide and water.* (See the discussion of intermediate metabolism and cellular respiration, Chapter 13.) This process is much too slow, however, to be utilized as a source of *immediate energy* for the rapid contractions of which muscles are capable. Here, reactions must be literally lightning fast. The most popular concept regarding the source of immediate energy for muscle contraction is that this source is the high-energy phosphate compound ATP (*adenosine triphosphate*), a chemical that causes contraction when added to laboratory muscle preparations. The interaction of actin and myosin requires energy, and there is ample evidence to indicate that this energy is supplied by the breakdown of ATP.

It is known that following the transmission of a nerve impulse over a motor neuron, *acetylcholine* is released at the neuromuscular junction or motor end plate. This chemical carries the impulse across the *synaptic gap* between the nerve endings and the muscle fibers they supply, and probably *increases the permeability of the muscle-cell membrane to calcium ions,* which then (in some manner not yet understood, and possibly with the aid of an enzyme, *adenosine triphosphatase*) *catalyze the hydrolytic breakdown of ATP to adenosine diphosphate* (ADP). In this reaction, the *terminal phosphate group* is separated from the remainder of the molecule, and energy is released as the high-energy phosphate bond that held it is broken:

$$A - P \sim P \not{/} P \xrightarrow[\text{and ATP-ase}]{\substack{\text{Catalysis} \\ \text{by Ca}^{++}}} A - P \sim P + P + \text{ENERGY}$$

ATP ADP Phosphate

The dotted line in the equation indicates the bond that is broken during the reaction. The energy released by the breakdown of ATP may activate the tiny protoplasmic bridges between the actin and myosin filaments, *and contraction takes place.*

Actually, very little ATP is stored in muscle, and since it is constantly being used up during muscle contraction, it must be constantly replaced. The replacement of ATP depends upon two sources:

1. *Phosphocreatine,* a compound found only in muscle tissue, and consisting of creatine attached to a phosphate group by a high-energy bond, gives up its phosphate to ADP, and by so doing forms ATP in mitochondria:

$$\text{Phosphocreatine} + A - P \sim P \rightarrow A - P \sim P \sim P + \text{Creatine}$$

ADP ATP

This reaction is *anaerobic;* that is, it does not require oxygen. The energy released when phosphate splits off phosphocreatine is used to drive the synthesis of new ATP to completion. In another series of reactions, ATP from the large mitochondria of muscle cells supplies the energy for reformation of phosphocreatine. ATP is synthesized in the mitochondria from adenosine and phosphate which come from the digestion and assimilation (taking into the cell protoplasm) of foods. Hydrogen ions, oxygen, and an energy source are required for this synthesis to take place. The hydrogen ions, like the adenosine and phosphate, come from digested foods. Oxygen is provided by the blood, which brings it from the lungs.

The energy required for the synthesis of ATP in mitochondria comes from the breakdown of such simple carbohydrates or monosaccharides as glucose, which in turn are eaten or produced by the breakdown of the complex carbohydrate or polysaccharide, glycogen, which is stored in large quantities in muscle tissue and in the liver.

2. *By means of the normal process of metabolism,* in which glucose is hydrolyzed in a process known as *glycolysis,* and eventually, during a repeating series of events called the *citric acid cycle,* ATP, carbon dioxide, and water are produced (see Chapter 13).

RELAXATION OF MUSCLE FIBERS For a muscle fiber to relax, the series of events that led to its contraction must be reversed. Calcium ions separate from troponin and reenter the sacs of the sarcoplasmic reticulum, and myosin-actin interaction is once again inhibited by the freed troponin.

OXYGEN DEBT During exercise, lactic acid is produced, and there is not time enough for oxygen to diffuse from the lungs into the bloodstream and be carried to the muscle cells in order to oxidize this lactic acid back to pyruvic acid; nevertheless, *this oxidation must take place in every living cell if that cell is to remain alive.* In muscle cells, this oxidation is "postponed until a more convenient time," so to speak, and an *"oxygen debt"* occurs. ATP is hydrolyzed anaerobically—that is, without oxygen; glycolysis is also anaerobic. The oxygen that is combined with myoglobin is quickly used up. During vigorous exercise, the production of lactic acid becomes greater and greater, and more oxygen is required in order to (indirectly) oxidize it to pyruvic acid. Deep, rapid breathing, panting, or even gasping occurs, carrying more oxygen into the lungs and eventually to the tissues. As the oxygen debt is "paid off," breathing returns to normal.

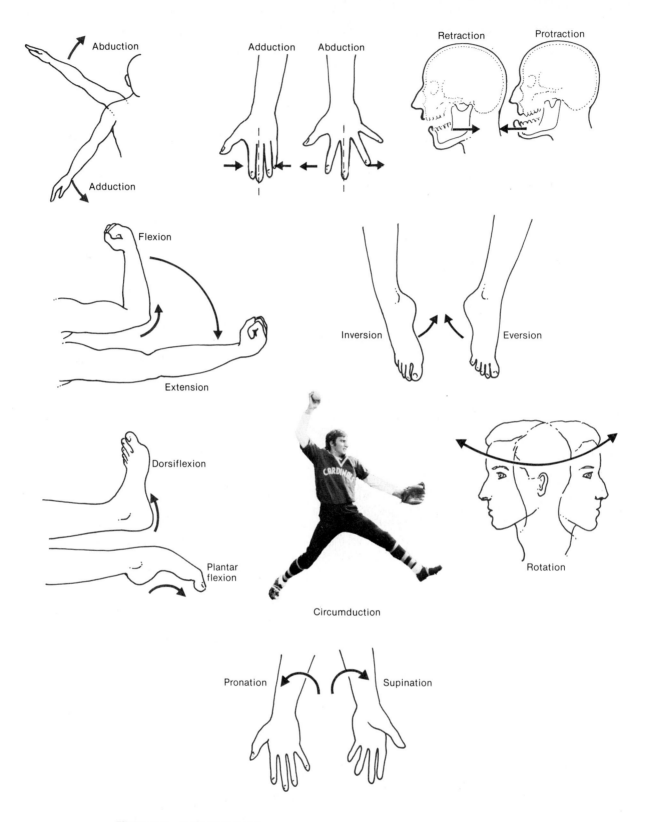

Figure 6-6 Body movements.

It can readily be seen that without the ability to incur oxygen debt, physical exertion would be impossible. Oxygen debt often amounts to *several liters,* and is incurred only during strenuous activity. Normally, a *homeostatic state* exists between the oxygen used by the muscles and that supplied by the lungs, and it is not necessary to resort to heavy breathing during moderate physical activity.

BODY MOVEMENTS AND POSTURE

There are several ways in which the study of muscle action in relation to movements of the body can be approached. Perhaps one of the best ways is to consider some of the more common movements and *analyze them*—that is, determine which muscles are responsible for certain movements, and examine some of the mechanisms they use in order to effect these movements. Before we can begin such analyses, however, we shall need certain tools in the form of definitions of terms and other information regarding certain aspects of muscle behavior. We should know, for example, what muscles can and cannot do; and we should know something about *muscle work, levers,* and *muscle efficiency*. The features of the various *muscle attachments* are also of some concern. The terms used in describing body movements are of particular importance.

Terms used in describing body movements

(See Figure 6.6.) At this point, the student should review the discussion of body movements in Chapter 5.

Muscle levers and mechanical advantage

It should be clearly understood that *muscles are capable of only one forceful action that involves movement, pulling,* which they do by contracting or shortening. When muscles lengthen they are relaxing. This is a passive process, and does not require energy; so actively, muscles can only pull, and *never push*. Any pushing that we do (such as sticking out our tongue, jutting the jaw forward, or moving a lawnmower) is the result of muscles pulling on bones or on each other, often using leverage provided by the bones. Levers often offer a *mechanical*

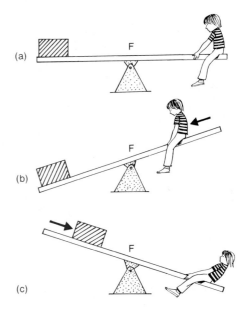

Figure 6-7 Using a seesaw to illustrate the principle of leverage and adjustment.

advantage, enabling a muscle to do much more work (in effect) than it would otherwise be able to do. The concept of mechanical advantage might best be illustrated by considering the example of a seesaw (Fig. 6-7). If a child of a certain weight is sitting on one end of the board, and a box of bricks weighing exactly the same as the child is placed on the other, and the two are equal distances from the fulcrum, they are balanced; but if the child moves toward the fulcrum, he is lifted easily by the weight of the bricks, *which now have a mechanical advantage*. Conversely, if the child remains at his end of the board and the bricks are placed nearer the fulcrum, the *child* has the mechanical advantage. One example of mechanical advantage in humans is the biceps-muscle tendon which in some people is inserted into the forearm farther away from the elbow joint than normally (Fig. 6-8). If a weight is placed in the hand of an individual with a "long insertion" such as this, he can lift the weight, by raising the forearm only, with greater ease than a person with similar muscular build but having a normal "short insertion" of the biceps. Another example of mechanical advantage in movement—and one which everyone has—is seen by raising the entire body weight onto the toes. This is accomplished by means of a second-class lever as described in Chapter 5.

101

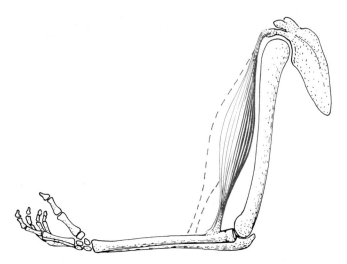

Figure 6-8 A long insertion of the biceps brachii muscle provides more mechanical advantage.

Muscle work

Muscle work can be defined as the *movement of some resisting force or object through a distance.* Work always requires energy. The resistance need not be great; even moving the little finger or blinking an eye requires some muscular work, though far less, of course, than walking or many other body movements. Work can be expressed in various units, such as *kilogram-meters* (kg-m), *gram-centimeters* (g-cm), or *foot-pounds* (ft-lb). Whatever the units employed, work can be calculated by simply *multiplying the weight* (or amount of other resisting force expressed as weight) *by the height to which the weight is lifted* (or by the distance through which some other resisting force is moved):

$$\text{Work} = \text{Height} \times \text{Weight}$$

For example, if a bag of sand weighing 100 lb is lifted a distance of 4 ft, then the work done is $4 \times 100 = 400$ ft-lb.

Muscle attachments

In general, it can be said that skeletal muscles are relatively long and narrow, and that both ends of muscles are attached to bones. There are many exceptions to this rule of thumb, however, because some muscles are broad and flat, and some attach to *other muscles* rather than to bone. The "typical" skeletal muscle has a fixed end, or *origin,* and a movable end, or *insertion* (Fig. 6-9). Some muscles have multiple origins and insertions; for example, the *biceps brachii muscle* of the upper extremity has two origins (hence the name *biceps*), one on the glenoid tuberosity of the scapula, and one on the coracoid process of the same bone. This muscle also has two insertions, one by *tendon* (a tough, cordlike structure made of connective tissue) to a tubercle at the proximal end of the radius and one by a flat band of connective tissue, the *bicipital aponeurosis,* which fuses with the deep fascia of certain muscles of the forearm. The origins and insertions of several muscles are shown in Fig. 6-9. Tendons vary in length from less than an inch to more than a foot. Aponeuroses are wide, flat, and thin. The most extensive aponeurotic attachments of muscles are found in the muscles overlying the trunk, such as the *latissimus dorsi.*

Classification of muscles according to function

Few body movements are brought about by the action of a single muscle acting alone; rather, *a movement is usually the result of two or more muscles acting together,* as *synergists.* A case in point is the synergistic action of the biceps brachii, brachialis, and brachioradialis muscles during *flexion of the forearm* (bending the elbow and bringing the hand closer to the shoulder). Those muscles acting most directly and most powerfully during a given movement are known as *prime movers* or *agonists.* The prime movers during forearm flexion are the brachialis and biceps brachii, which are assisted by the brachioradialis.

When a movement (such as flexion) takes place, *muscles capable of carrying out an opposing movement must relax.* The movement opposite to flexion of the forearm is *extension* of the forearm; thus the *triceps*

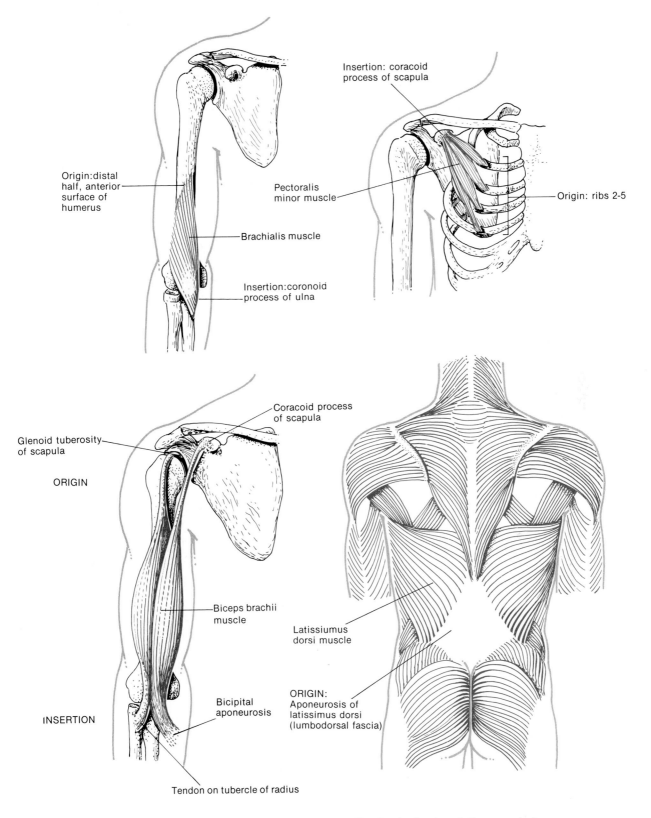

Origin:distal
half, anterior
surface of
humerus

Brachialis muscle

Insertion:coronoid
process of ulna

Insertion: coracoid
process of scapula

Pectoralis
minor muscle

Origin: ribs 2-5

Coracoid process
of scapula

Glenoid tuberosity
of scapula

ORIGIN

Biceps brachii
muscle

Bicipital
aponeurosis

INSERTION

Tendon on tubercle of radius

Latissiumus
dorsi muscle

ORIGIN:
Aponeurosis of
latissimus dorsi
(lumbodorsal fascia)

Figure 6-9 Some typical muscle attachments. Usually, the fixed or stationary end of
a muscle is designated its origin, and the movable end its insertion.

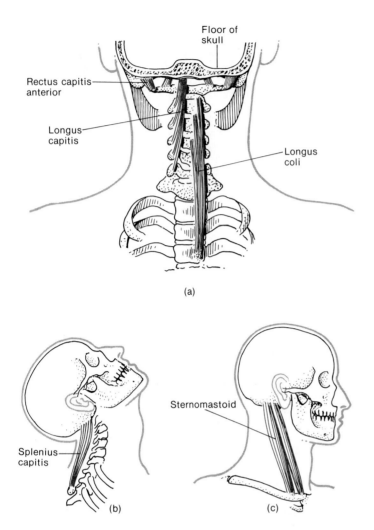

Figure 6-10 Some of the muscles that move the head. (a) Flexors. (b) An extensor. (c) A rotator.

In this discussion, the chief functions of the major muscles will be emphasized, and little mention will be made of minor functions. One of the best ways to learn the chief actions of the major muscles is to analyze the most outstanding movements and determine the muscles which are most responsible for bringing these movements about. The origin and insertion of each muscle and the nerve supply to it are presented in tabular form following consideration of each muscle group.

Movements of the head

The major movements of the head are *flexion* (tilting the head forward and downward), *extension* (bending the head backward), and *rotation* (as when signifying "no"). The *longus coli, longus capitis,* and *rectus capitis anterior* are the chief flexors of the head (Fig. 6-10). The main extensors of the head are the *splenius capitis muscles.* The latter are assisted by the *semispinalis capitis* and *longissimus,* which are also important in this action. The *sternomastoid* muscles are the chief rotators of the head, when they are acting *singly.* Acting together —that is, *synergistically*—the sternomastoids pull the head forward, and tend to elevate the chin. By various combinations of contractions and relaxations of all the foregoing muscles, most of the various movements of the head are carried out. It should be made clear that these muscles are assisted in their actions by numerous small muscles which will not be considered in this discussion. With the exception of the sternomastoid muscles, the movers of the head cannot easily be *palpated* (identified by touch).

Movements of the lower jaw

The lower jaw or mandible moves during two of the most important activities of man, *eating* and *talking.* The three most outstanding movements during these two actions are raising or *elevation,* lowering or *depression,* and side-to-side or *grinding* movements. The muscles responsible for these actions are the *muscles of mastication* or chewing muscles (Fig. 6-11). Muscles elevating the mandible

brachii muscle, an extensor of the forearm, must relax before the flexors can act, and vice versa. Muscles which act in opposition to other muscles are called *antagonists.* If the forearm is held rigid and stiff in a fixed position, the flexors and extensors are both contracting at the same time, and are working antagonistically toward each other.

In addition to flexor and extensor muscles, there are also *abductors, adductors, levators, depressors, retractors, protractors, sphincters,* and *rotators.* Most movements of the body or its parts are far from simple, and are often the result of complex actions of groups of flexors, extensors, rotators, and so on. For example, some rotators can serve as flexors in certain instances, and vice versa; and some abductors can act as flexors, or extensors, depending upon the initial position of the body part and the action carried out.

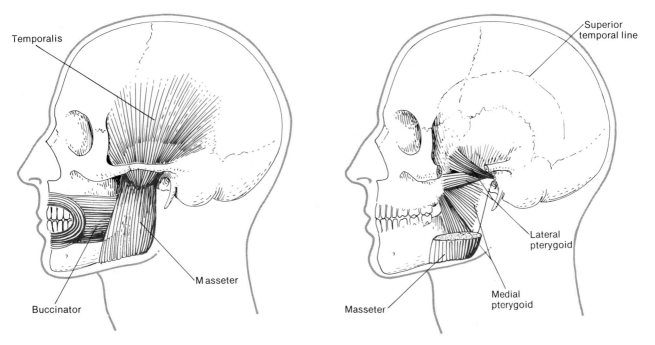

Figure 6-11 The muscles of mastication, or chewing, and the buccinator.

TABLE 6-1

Muscles that move the head

Muscle	Origin	Insertion	Action	Nerve
Longus coli	Midcervical to upper thoracic vertebrae	Mid- and upper cervical vertebrae	Flexion of head	Cervical spinal nerves
Longus capitis	Cervical vertebrae 3–6	Base of occipital bone	Flexion of head	Cervical spinal nerves 1, 2, and 3
Rectus capitis anterior	Atlas	Base of occipital bone	Flexion of head	Cervical spinal nerves 1 and 2
Splenius capitis	Seventh cervical and upper three thoracic vertebrae, and *ligamentum nuchae* on back of neck	Occipital bone	Extension of head	Cervical spinal nerve 2
Semispinalis capitis	Lower four cervical and upper five thoracic vertebrae	Occipital bone	Extension of head	Occipital and cervical spinal nerves
Longissimus capitis	Lower four cervical and upper five thoracic vertebrae	Mastoid process of temporal bone	Extension of head	Cervical spinal nerves
Sternomastoid	Upper end of sternum and medial end of clavicle	Mastoid process of temporal bone	Acting singly, rotate head, synergistically, pull head forward, elevate chin	Accessory (cranial nerve XI)

include the *temporalis, masseter,* and *medial pterygoid.* The *lateral pterygoids* depress the mandible. Most of the side-to-side grinding movements of chewing result from the alternate contraction and relaxation of the pterygoid muscles on either side. The pterygoids act synergistically to cause the jaw to jut forward (*protract*). *Retraction* is accomplished by the temporalis muscle. Of this group, only the masseter is easily palpated. This is best done by having the subject tightly clench the teeth, and watching for a "lump" on the side of the jaw. All of the muscles that move the mandible are paired.

It might be well noted that when contracting at their maximum force, the elevators of the mandible are extremely powerful. The jaw muscles of a healthy young adult can exert a pressure of over 200 pounds. The synovial joint between the condyle of the mandible and the mandibular fossa of the skull is so constructed as to easily permit all of the previously described movements and the force of abnormally hard usage, such as cracking nuts with the teeth; however, it is not extremely difficult to dislocate the mandible from the fossa by opening the mouth to an extra wide angle while the subject is under anesthesia, or during an extra vigorous yawn.

The movements of facial expression

The movements of the face vary widely from one racial group to another, and between individuals of the same race. The faces of Caucasians and Negroids tend to be very mobile, while Mongoloids are usually not so expressive. A person whose facial expression changes very little from one mood to another is said to be "poker-faced." The eight muscles which have the most to do with facial expressions are the unpaired *corrugator, orbicularis oris,* and *platysma;* the paired *orbicularis oculi, zygomaticus major, risorius,* and *buccinator;* and the *epicranius,* some portions of which are paired (*auricularis* portions), some unpaired (*frontalis* and *occipitalis*) (Fig. 6-12). With the exception of the platysma, these muscles are for the most part unpalpable. They are very thin, and are called *cutaneous muscles* because of their attachments to the skin and their position in relation to it. Mostly, they take origin from the skull surface and fascia and insert into the skin and neighboring muscles. The epicranius has three portions—*frontalis, occipitalis,* and *auricularis*—the last consisting of auricular muscles which can be divided

TABLE 6-2

Muscles that move the lower jaw

Muscle	Origin	Insertion	Action	Nerve
Temporalis	Temporal fossa of skull	Ramus and coronoid process of mandible	Elevation of mandible	Mandibular division of trigeminal (cranial nerve V)
Masseter	Zygomatic arch	Ramus of mandible	Elevation of mandible	Mandibular division of trigeminal
Medial pterygoid	Palatine bone, lateral pterygoid plate, and a tuberosity on the maxilla	Ramus of the mandible, near the angle	Elevation of mandible*	Mandibular division of trigeminal
Lateral pterygoid	Great wing of sphenoid and lateral pterygoid plate	Neck of condyle of mandible	Depression of mandible*	Mandibular division of trigeminal

*The pterygoids acting synergistically protract the mandible; also, grinding movements depend largely upon alternate contraction and relaxation of the pterygoid muscles on either side.

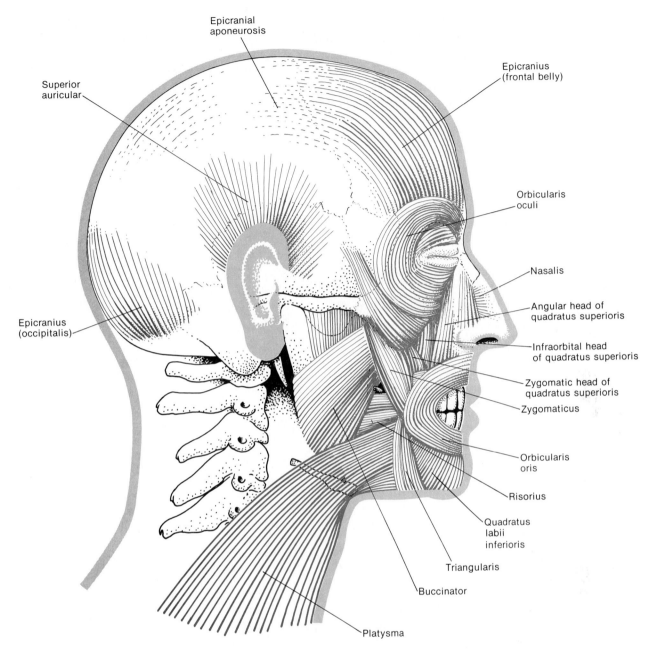

Epicranial
aponeurosis

Superior
auricular

Epicranius
(frontal belly)

Epicranius
(occipitalis)

Orbicularis
oculi

Nasalis

Angular head of
quadratus superioris

Infraorbital head
of quadratus superioris

Zygomatic head of
quadratus superioris

Zygomaticus

Orbicularis
oris

Risorius

Quadratus
labii
inferioris

Triangularis

Buccinator

Platysma

Figure 6-12 The major muscles of facial expression.

into three slips—*anterior, superior,* and *posterior.* The frontalis elevates the eyebrows and wrinkles the forehead by pulling the scalp forward. The occipitalis muscles pull the scalp backward. The auricularis muscles are no longer of importance to man, but in many animals they are still well developed and can move the ears quite freely. The corrugator causes the forehead to wrinkle. The orbicularis oculi muscles close the eyelids, help wrinkle the forehead, and squeeze the

lacrimal (tear) sac. They are antagonists of the levator palpebrae superioris muscles, which elevate the upper eyelid. The orbicularis oris muscle forms a circle around the mouth in the same manner as the orbicularis oculi encircle the eyes; this muscle purses the lips. A kiss has been described as *the anatomical juxtaposition of two orbicularis oris muscles in a state of contraction.* The zygomaticus major muscles pull the corners of the mouth backward and upward during

107

smiling and laughing; and the risorius muscles serve essentially the same function. Spreading over the front of the neck from chin to chest is the thin, broad, platysma muscle. During strong contraction, it causes vertical folds to appear in the neck, and can pull down the corners of the mouth and lower lip. In many grazing animals, such as cattle, the platysma can be contracted rapidly in order to flick away insects. The chief muscle of the wall of the cheek is the buccinator. It can tighten the cheeks, and aids in keeping food in position between the teeth for chewing. Both buccinators acting together make it possible for man to exert enough pressure in his mouth to play a wind instrument. The fibers of the buccinator run at right angles to those of the masseter muscle. The *facial nerve* supplies all the muscles of facial expression.

TABLE 6-3

The muscles of facial expression

Muscle	Origin	Insertion	Action	Nerve
Epicranius				
a. Frontalis	Galea aponeurotica (fibrous connective tissue covering of the skull)	Into corrugator and orbicularis oculi muscles	Elevates eyebrows, wrinkles forehead	Facial (cranial nerve VII)
b. Occipitalis	Mastoid process and superior nuchal line of skull	Galea aponeurotica	Pulls scalp backward	Facial
c. Auricularis	Fascia on lateral aspect of skull	Into external ear, anteriorly, superiorly, and posteriorly	Moves ears slightly	Facial
Corrugator	Medial end of superciliary arch	Into deep surface of skin of forehead	Wrinkles forehead	Facial
Orbicularis oculi	Frontal, maxillary, and lacrimal bones	Skin and fascia around eye and lids	Closes eyelids, wrinkles forehead, squeezes lacrimal sac	Facial
Orbicularis oris	In several layers, embedded in the wall of the mouth	Skin and fascia around lips and mouth	Purses the lips	Facial
Zygomaticus major	Zygomatic bone	Among fibers of orbicularis oris	Pulls corners of mouth backward and upward	Facial
Risorius	In connective tissue and fascia covering the masseter	Skin at angle of the mouth	Same as zygomaticus	Facial
Platysma	In fascia covering pectoralis major and deltoid muscles	Skin of the mandible and the orbicularis oris muscle	Tightens skin of neck, pulls down corners of mouth and lower lip	Facial
Buccinator	Maxilla and mandible (lateral portions)	Among fibers of orbicularis oris	Tightens cheeks, keeps food between teeth	Facial

Movements of the eyeball

Strictly speaking, the muscles that move the eyeball are not muscles of facial expression. They are so closely related, however, that they will be considered at this time. All movements of the eyeball are described in relation to a *primary position,* in which the eye is looking straight ahead. The eyeball can be considered to move around *three axes: anteroposterior, vertical,* and *transverse.* Upward movement around the transverse axis is *elevation;* downward movement about the same axis is *depression.* Lateral movement about the vertical axis is *abduction,* and its opposite (with the eye looking at the nose) is *adduction.* When one eye is adducted, the other is normally abducted, insuring *stereoscopic* (three-dimensional) *vision* in any direction. Revolving the eyeball about the anteroposterior axis is *rotation.* If the top of the eyeball is rotated medially, the rotation is called *intorsion,* while rotating the top of the eyeball laterally is *extorsion.*

The muscles that move the eyeball are known as the *extrinsic muscles* of the eye (Fig. 6-13). The *ciliary muscle* (which helps to change the shape of the lens during focusing) and the *dilator* and *constrictor muscles* of the iris (the structure that regulates the amount of light entering the eye) are known as the *intrinsic muscles* of the eye. These are discussed in Chapter 8. Movements of the eye usually involve more than one muscle; however, the chief actions of the extrinsic eye muscles are summarized in Table 6-4.

TABLE 6-4

The extrinsic muscles of the eye

Muscle	Origin	Insertion	Action	Nerve
Superior rectus	Tendinous ring around optic foramen	Superiorly onto eyeball	Elevation, adduction, medial rotation	Cranial nerve III, the oculomotor
Inferior rectus	Similar to superior rectus	Inferiorly onto eyeball	Depression, adduction, lateral rotation	Oculomotor
Lateral rectus	*Similar to previous two muscles*	On lateral side of eyeball	Abduction	Cranial nerve VI, the abducens
Medial rectus	*Similar to previous three muscles*	On medial side of eyeball	Adduction	Oculomotor
Superior oblique	Above optic foramen	Tendon passes through a fibrous "pulley" in anterior orbit, then inserts on eyeball	Turns eyeball downward and laterally, with medial rotation	Trochlear (cranial nerve IV)
Inferior oblique	Medially in floor of orbit	Passes under eyeball and inserts laterally	Turns eye up and laterally, with lateral rotation	Oculomotor

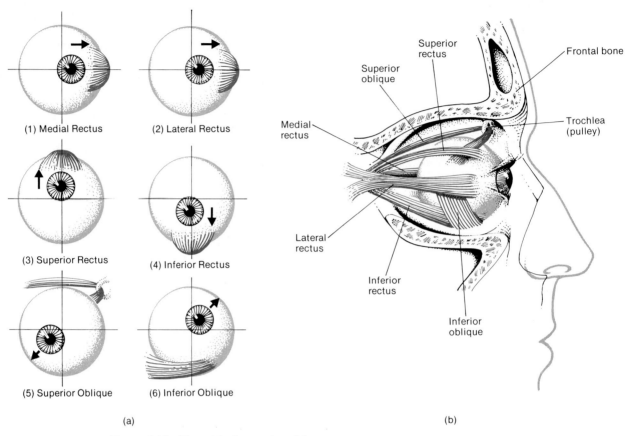

(1) Medial Rectus   (2) Lateral Rectus

(3) Superior Rectus   (4) Inferior Rectus

(5) Superior Oblique   (6) Inferior Oblique

(a)

Superior rectus

Superior oblique

Medial rectus

Lateral rectus

Inferior rectus

Inferior oblique

Frontal bone

Trochlea (pulley)

(b)

Figure 6-13 The extrinsic muscles of the eye.

Movements of the vertebral column

Some movements of the upper end of the vertebral column have already been described in the discussion of movements of the head. Although some bending and rotation is permitted in all portions of the vertebral column, it is *most freely movable in the lumbar region.* The chief movements possible in this region are *flexion* (bending farward), *extension* (bending backward), *lateral flexion or abduction* (bending sideways), and *rotation* (about the long axis) (Fig. 6-14). The *chief flexors* of the vertebral column in the lumbar region are the *psoas major* and *rectus abdominis* muscles (Fig. 6-15). The psoas major cannot be palpated, but the rectus abdominis can be felt by having the subject do sit-ups, thereby greatly increasing the tension on it. The rectus abdominis becomes outstanding in physical culturists such as weight-lifters. Both recti muscles are en-

closed in a tough connective-tissue covering, the *rectus sheath,* which has three transverse partitions, thereby dividing each muscle into four segments. The muscles are separated longitudinally by another partition of the sheath, the *linea alba,* or "white line."

Extension of the vertebral column is carried out chiefly by the *erector spinae* and *quadratus lumborum* muscles (Fig. 6-16). The erector spinae (or *sacrospinalis,* its old name) divides into three small portions or slips at its insertion; from medial to lateral, they are called *spinalis, longissimus,* and *iliocostalis.* When acting synergistically, the two quadratus lumborum muscles function as *extensors* of the vertebral column in the lumbar region; but contraction of only one of either quadratus or erector spinae can *flex* the vertebral column laterally. *Rotation* is brought about by contraction of several muscles on one side. Flexors and extensors of the vertebral column are important in the *maintenance of posture.*

110

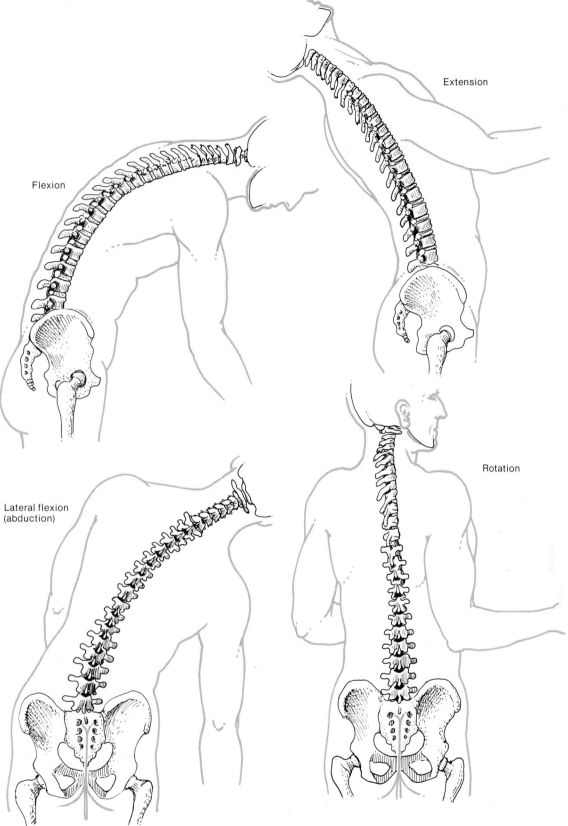

Extension

Flexion

Lateral flexion
(abduction)

Rotation

Figure 6-14 Movements of the vertebral column.

TABLE 6-5

Muscles that move the vertebral column *

Muscle	Origin	Insertion	Action	Nerve
Psoas major	Transverse processes of all lumbar vertebrae	Lesser trochanter of femur	Flexion of vertebral column in lumbar region	Lumbar spinal nerves 2 and 3
Rectus abdominis	Pubic crest	Lower end of sternum and cartilages of ribs 5–7	Flexion of vertebral column in lumbar region	Thoracic spinal nerves 1–12
Erector spinae	All lumbar vertebrae, thoracic vertebrae 11 and 12, crest of ilium, back of sacrum	Spinalis: posterior portion of thoracic vertebrae Longissimus: thoracic vertebrae and ribs Iliocostalis: ribs 6–12, near their angles	Extension of vertebral column (synergistically); lateral flexion (abduction) when acting singly	Branches of spinal nerves of the region
Quadratus lumborum	Posterior portion of iliac crest, lumbar vertebrae 2–5	Lumbar vertebrae 1–4 and twelfth ribs	Extension of vertebral column (synergistically); lateral flexion (abduction) when acting singly	Spinal nerves: thoracic 12 and lumbar 1

*Rotation of the vertebral column is accomplished by contraction of several muscles on one side.

Figure 6-15   Chief flexor muscles of the lumbar portion of the vertebral column.

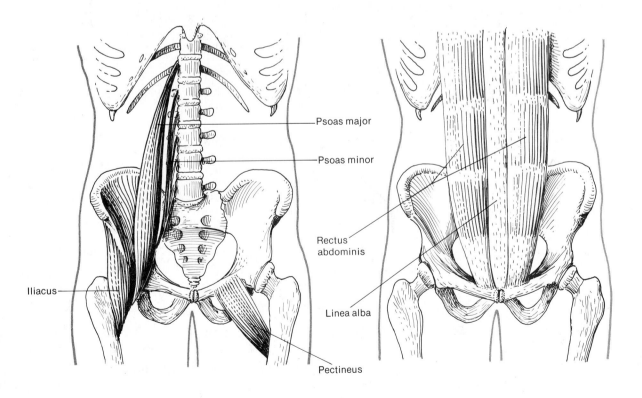

TABLE 6-6

Muscles involved in breathing and in moving the abdominal wall

Muscle	Origin	Insertion	Action	Nerve
Diaphragm a. Sternal portion	Inner surface of xiphoid	Central tendon of strong connective tissue	Moves air into and out of thorax during process of breathing	Phrenic (paired)
b. Costal portion	Inner surfaces, costal cartilages 6–12	*Same as above*		*Same as above*
c. Lumbar portion	By two crura from upper two or three lumbar vertebrae	Central tendon		Phrenic
External intercostals	Lower borders, ribs 1–11	Upper borders, ribs 2–12	Expands chest during quiet inspiration	Intercostal branches of spinal nerves
Internal intercostals	Lower borders, ribs 1–11	Upper borders, ribs 2–12	Helps compress chest during quiet expiration	*Same as above*

Note: The fibers of the external intercostals run downward and forward, while those of the internal intercostals course downward and backward, criss-crossing those of the former muscles.

Muscle	Origin	Insertion	Action	Nerve
External oblique	Ribs 5–12; slips interdigitate like fingers with slips of the serratus anterior muscle	Linea alba and crest of the ilium	Aids in forcing air out during expiration	Thoracic spinal nerves 7–12, lumbar spinal nerves 1 and 2
Internal oblique	Crest of ilium, inguinal ligament, and fascia of the lumbar region	Costal cartilages of ribs 10, 11, and 12, pubic crest, linea alba	Aids in forcing air out during expiration	*Same as above*
Transversus abdominis	Inner surfaces, ribs 7–12, crest of ilium, and inguinal ligament	Linea alba	Aids in forcing air out during expiration	Thoracic spinal nerves 7–12
Levatores costarum (12 pairs)	Transverse processes of seventh cervical and thoracic vertebrae 1–11	Near the angle on outer surface of each rib below	Elevates ribs during vigorous inspiration	Thoracic spinal nerves

*Movements of
the abdominal wall*

Ordinarily, we do not think of the abdominal wall as being mobile; and in fact, with the exception of bending forward or backward at the waist, movements of the abdomen are rather slight. In some instances, the abdominal muscles are antagonistic to the diaphragm, and when they contract and compress the abdomen, the diaphragm tends to relax and move upward. When the diaphragm contracts and moves downward, the abdominal muscles normally relax. When an increase in pressure is needed within the abdomen, as during *defecation, urination, vomiting,* or *childbirth,* the abdominal muscles contract and supply this pressure. They work as antagonists to the back muscles and *help maintain posture.* Further information regarding the abdominal muscles is included in Table 6-6 and the discussion to follow.

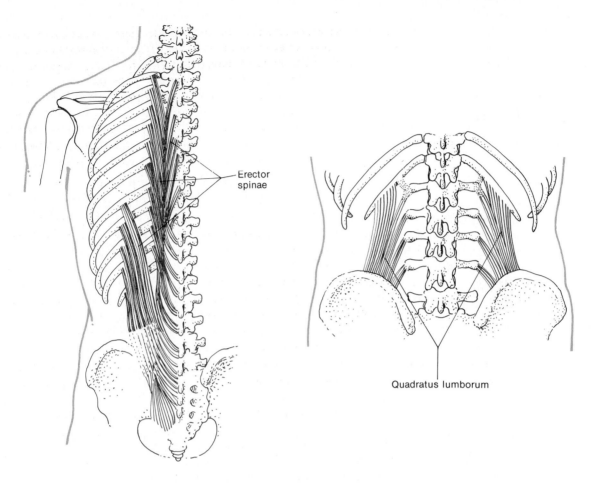

Erector
spinae

Quadratus lumborum

Figure 6-16   Chief extensor muscles of the lumbar portion of the vertebral column.

The movements of breathing

During normal quiet breathing, movement of the chest and abdomen is so slight as to be almost undetectable; but following vigorous exercise, the chest wall expands and relaxes deeply and rapidly, as does the abdominal wall, while inside, the diaphragm is moving vigorously up and down. The act of breathing has two phases—*inspiration,* during which the chest expands and air moves into the lungs, and *expiration,* when the chest relaxes and air moves out. Various muscles are involved in carrying out each phase. Muscles taking part in quiet inspiration include the *diaphragm* and *external intercostals* (Fig. 6-17). In more vigorous inspiration, the *pectoralis major, serratus anterior, trapezius,* and *levatores costarum* muscles also elevate the ribs and expand the chest. The *internal intercostals* and four pairs of abdominal muscles—the *internal oblique, external oblique, transversus abdominis* and *rectus abdominis* (Fig. 6-18)—contract rather weakly during *expiration.* On the whole, expiration is a passive process, following *relaxation of the inspiratory muscles;* however, during forceful expiration, the expiratory muscles contract with much more vigor.

The diaphragm is the *main organ of breathing,* and could carry out the process alone if required to do so. It consists of muscle fibers and tough connective tissue, in the form of a dome separating the thorax from the abdomen. The origin of the diaphragm is very extensive, and can be divided into three portions—*sternal, costal,* and *lumbar.* This latter portion is in the form of two long arms or *crura,* which attach to the upper two or three lumbar vertebrae. Table 6-6 includes the most important muscles that move the abdominal wall and those concerned with breathing.

The pectoralis major, serratus anterior, and trapezius muscles are concerned pri-

114

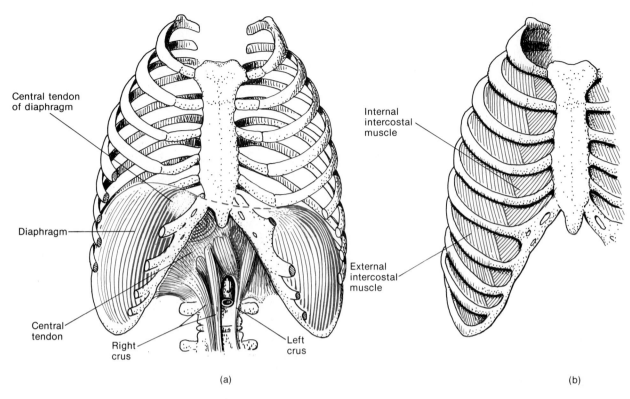

Central tendon
of diaphragm

Diaphragm

Central
tendon

Right
crus

Left
crus

(a)

Internal
intercostal
muscle

External
intercostal
muscle

(b)

Figure 6-17 The chief muscles of breathing or respiration. (a) The diaphragm.
(b) Intercostal muscles.

Figure 6-18 Muscles of the abdominal wall, and the levatores costarum muscles.
Both groups sometimes assist in respiratory movements.

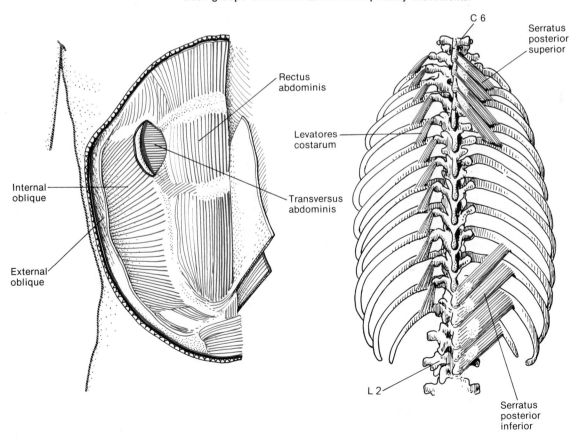

Rectus
abdominis

Internal
oblique

External
oblique

Transversus
abdominis

C 6

Serratus
posterior
superior

Levatores
costarum

L 2

Serratus
posterior
inferior

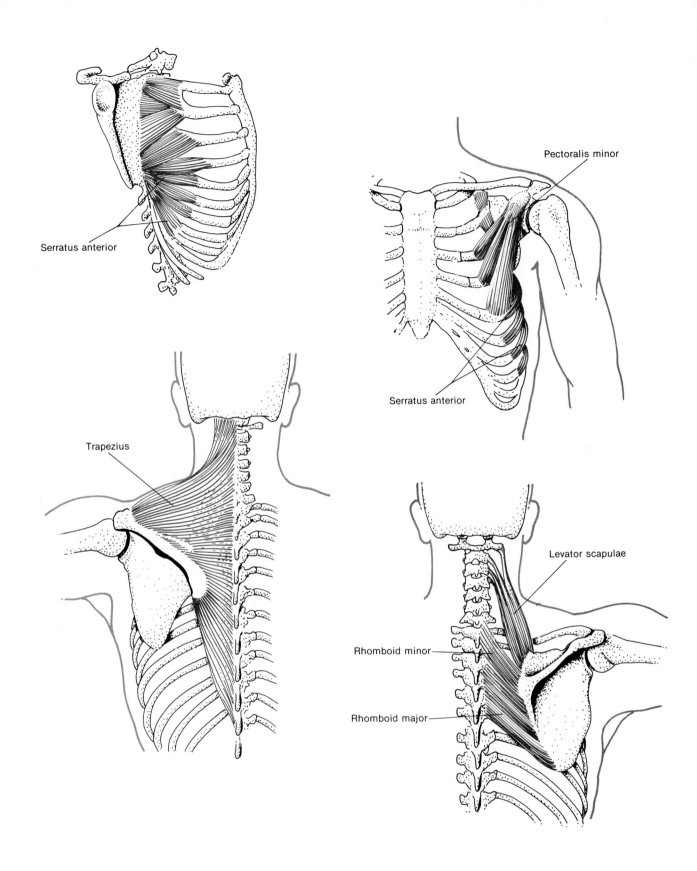

Figure 6-19 Muscles that move the shoulder.

marily with movements of the upper extremity; therefore, they are considered in the section to follow.

Movements of the upper extremity

THE SHOULDER Movements of the shoulder always involve the scapula or "shoulder-blade." Twenty-one muscles attach to the scapula and affect its action, but only a few of these will be considered here. Table 6-8 on p. 118 lists the principal movements of the scapula, and the major muscles that bring them about.

The serratus anterior (Fig. 6-19) gets the first part of its name from its sawtoothed or *serrated* edge, and is designated *anterior* because there are also *posterior* serratus muscles—the *serratus posterior superior* and *inferior* (Fig. 6-18). The pectoralis minor (Fig. 6-19) is one of the muscles of the important pectoral region, the front of the chest. The trapezius, along with the muscle of the opposite side, forms a kite-shaped sheet of muscle that covers much of the upper back. The rhomboid major is the larger of two muscles of rhomboidal shape that attach to the scapula, while its "little sister," the rhomboid minor, is located somewhat higher up than the bigger muscle. The levator scapulae is the most important "shoulder-shrugging" muscle. See further Table 6-9 on p. 118.

THE UPPER ARM Movements of the upper arm or brachium are closely associated with movements of the shoulder and forearm. However, there are certain basic actions that can be studied in relation to the brachium alone. These are:

1. flexion
2. extension
3. abduction
4. adduction
5. rotation
6. circumduction

Tables 6-7 and 6-10 list the major muscles involved in each of these movements (see also Figs. 6-20 and 6-21).

TABLE 6-7

Movements of the upper arm

Movement	Muscles	Movement	Muscles
Flexion	Coracobrachialis Biceps brachii *	Rotation	
		a. Medial rotators	Subscapularis Pectoralis major Latissimus dorsi Teres major Anterior portion of the deltoid
Extension	Teres major Latissimus dorsi		
Abduction	Deltoid Supraspinatus		
		b. Lateral rotators	Infraspinatus Posterior portion of the deltoid
Adduction	Rhomboid major Rhomboid minor Latissimus dorsi Pectoralis major Teres major	Circumduction	*Most or all of the above muscles,* alternately contracting and relaxing as individuals and groups

* The biceps brachii is primarily a flexor of the forearm, and acts as a flexor of the upper arm only when the elbow is held rigid, in a fixed position.

117

TABLE 6-8

Movements of the scapula

Movement	Description	Muscle(s)
Abduction	(Movement away from vertebral column)	Serratus anterior and pectoralis minor
Adduction	(Movement toward vertebral column)	Trapezius, rhomboid major, rhomboid minor
Elevation	(Raising scapula as in shrugging)	Levator scapulae
Depression	(Lowering scapula)	Pectoralis minor
Upward rotation	(Lateral border of scapula moves upward)	Trapezius
Downward rotation	(Lateral border of scapula moves downward)	Pectoralis minor and rhomboid major

TABLE 6-9

Muscles that move the shoulder

Muscle	Origin	Insertion	Action	Nerve
Serratus anterior	Outer surface of ribs 1–9	Costal surface of scapula, along vertebral margin	Abducts scapula	Long thoracic
Pectoralis minor	Ribs 3, 4, and 5 near their cartilages	Coracoid process of scapula	Abducts scapula	Medial anterior thoracic
Trapezius	External occipital protuberance, ligamentum nuchae, spinous processes of C–7 and all thoracic vertebrae	Acromion and spine of scapula and lateral $\frac{1}{3}$ of clavicle	Adducts scapula	Accessory nerve (cranial nerve XI) and cervical spinal nerves 3 and 4
Rhomboid major	Spinous processes of second through fifth thoracic vertebrae	Vertebral margin of scapula, below spine of scapula	Adducts scapula	Dorsal scapular
Rhomboid minor	Spinous processes of last cervical and first thoracic vertebrae	Vertebral margin of scapula, above level of spine	Adducts scapula	Dorsal scapular
Levator scapulae	Transverse processes of first four cervical vertebrae	Vertebral margin of scapula, above level of spine	Raises scapula	Dorsal scapular and cervical spinal nerves 3 and 4

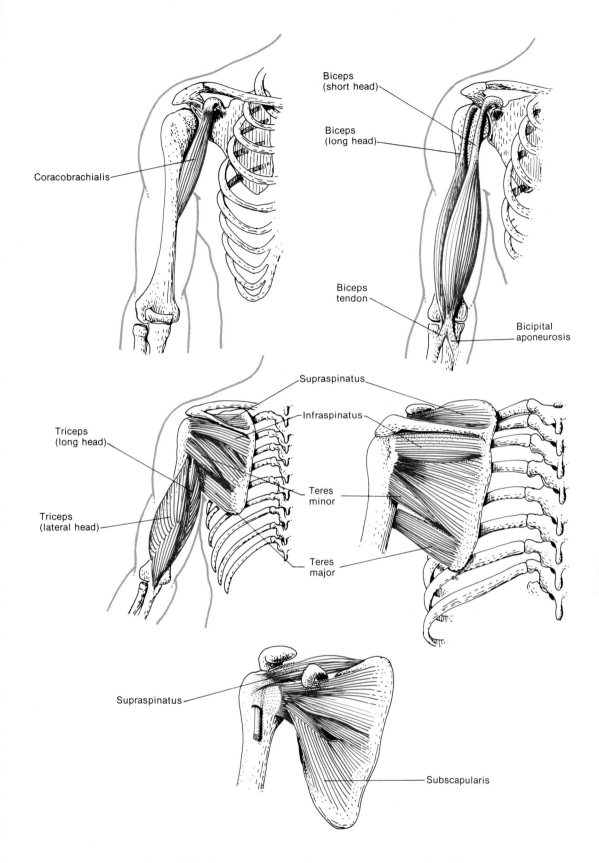

Figure 6-20 Muscles that move the upper arm. See also Fig. 6-21.

TABLE 6-10

Muscles that move the upper arm

Muscle	Origin	Insertion	Action	Nerve
Coracobrachialis	Coracoid process of scapula	Just proximal to midpoint of humerus, on its medial aspect	Flexion	Musculocutaneous
Biceps brachii				
a. Long head	Just above glenoid fossa of scapula	By tendon into tuberosity of radius; and by the flat bicipital aponeurosis into fascia at proximal end of forearm	Flexion when elbow is held fixed	Musculocutaneous
b. Short head	Coracoid process near coracobrachialis	Common insertion with long head	Same as long head	Musculocutaneous
Teres major	Inferior angle of scapula, on dorsal surface	Into humerus, by flat tendon to medial side of bicipital groove	Extension, medial rotation, and adduction	Lower subscapular
Subscapularis	Subscapular fossa	Lesser tuberosity of humerus	Medial rotation	Upper and lower subscapular
Latissimus dorsi	Spines of thoracic vertebrae 7–12; aponeurosis (lumbodorsal fascia) with muscle of opposite side; iliac crest	By a narrow, flat tendon into the bicipital groove of the humerus	Adduction and medial rotation	Thoracodorsal
Deltoid	Spine of scapula, acromion process, lateral 1/3 of clavicle	Deltoid tuberosity of humerus	Abduction, lateral rotation, and medial rotation	Axillary
Supraspinatus	Supraspinous fossa of scapula	Greater tuberosity of humerus	Abduction	Suprascapular
Infraspinatus	Infraspinous fossa of scapula	Center of greater tuberosity of humerus	Lateral rotation	Suprascapular
Pectoralis major	Medial 1/2 of clavicle, most of sternum, cartilages of ribs 1–7, and aponeurosis with external oblique	On humerus, just lateral to the bicipital groove	Adduction and medial rotation	Medial and lateral pectoral nerves

THE FOREARM The forearm or *antebrachium* is capable of flexion, extension, supination (lateral rotation), and pronation (medial rotation). Only two movements are possible at the elbow joint proper (between the distal end of the humerus and proximal end of the ulna)—flexion and extension. Medial and lateral rotation are the chief movements permitted at the joint between the head of the radius and the capitulum at the distal end of the humerus. The *brachialis, brachioradialis,* and *biceps brachii* are the *flexors* of the forearm. The latter two muscles also act to flex the upper arm, but only when the elbow is *fixed*—that is, held rigid. The biceps is the most prominent when the forearm is flexed against resistance, such as when small boys "make a muscle," and is, therefore, the most palpable of the forearm flexors. Most *extension* of the forearm is brought about by contractions of the *triceps brachii muscle* (Fig. 6-22). The triceps has three heads of origin: *long head, lateral head,* and *medial head.* Much of the triceps is palpable on the back of the upper arm when the upper limb is held rigidly extended and rotated medially. *Supination* consists of rotating the forearm so that the palm faces

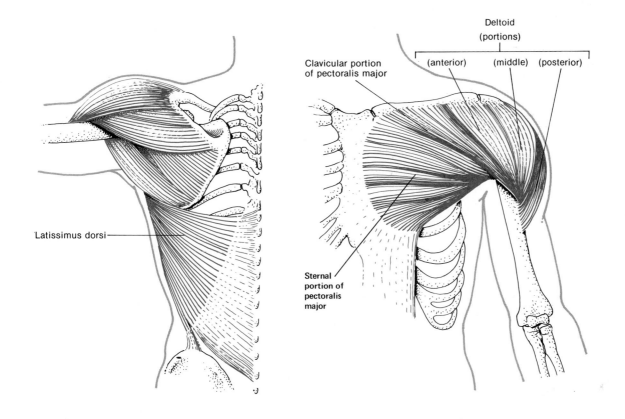

Figure 6-21 Muscles that move the upper arm. See also Fig. 6-20.

anteriorly and the thumb is positioned laterally. This action is brought about chiefly by the *supinator* and *biceps brachii* muscles.

Pronation, the opposite movement of supination, is accomplished primarily by the *pronator teres* and *pronator quadratus.*

Figure 6-22 Muscles that move the forearm. See also the biceps brachii, Fig. 6-20.

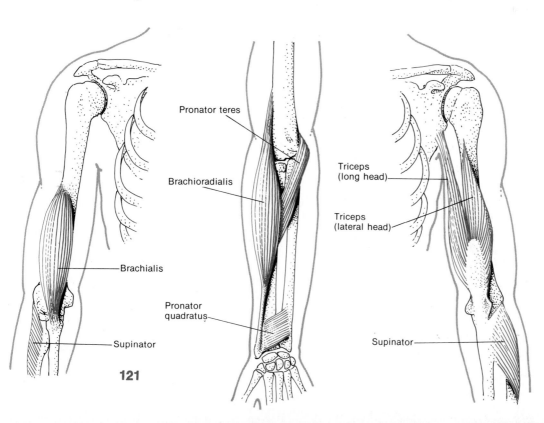

121

TABLE 6-11

Muscles that move the forearm

Muscle	Origin	Insertion	Action	Nerve
Brachialis	Distal ⅔ of anterior aspect of humerus	Coronoid process of ulna	Flexion	Musculocutaneous
Brachioradialis	Distal third of lateral aspect of humerus	Lateral side of styloid process of radius	Flexion	Radial
Triceps				
a. Long head	Just below glenoid fossa of scapula	Olecranon process of ulna	Extension	Radial
b. Lateral head	Lateral and posterior aspect of humerus	*Same as above*	*Same as above*	Radial
c. Media head	Posterior distal portion of humerus	*Same as above*	*Same as above*	Radial
Supinator	Lateral epicondyle of humerus and supinator crest of ulna	Anterior and lateral surfaces of upper ⅓ of radius	Supination	Radial
Pronator teres	Medial epicondyle of humerus and medial side of coronoid process of ulna	Midway on lateral surface of radius	Pronation	Median
Pronator quadratus	Distal quarter of anterior surface of ulna	Distal quarter of anterior surface of radius	Pronation	Median

Biceps brachii (see Table 6-10)

THE WRIST Flexion, extension, abduction, and adduction, respectively, take place when the hand is bent forward, backward, laterally, and medially at the wrist. *Flexion* is accomplished by the *flexor carpi radialis* and *flexor carpi ulnaris* muscles, assisted by the *palmaris longus, flexor digitorum superficialis,* and *flexor digitorum profundus.* The flexor carpi radialis tendon (Fig. 6-23) can be palpated at the anterior and lateral surface of the wrist, and the flexor carpi ulnaris muscle can be felt a few centimeters below the medial epicondyle of the humerus, on the anterior aspect of the forearm. The flexor carpi radialis arises, along with the flexor carpi ulnaris and most of the other abovementioned muscles, from a *common flexor tendon* attached to the medial epicondyle of the humerus. The *radial artery is lateral to* *its tendon at the wrist,* and is a common site for obtaining the heart rate or *pulse.* The palmaris longus can best be identified as a tendon in the center of the anterior forearm that becomes prominent upon making a fist. This muscle is supposed to be an asset to a violinist, but is absent in some people. The *median nerve* is lateral to its tendon at the wrist. The flexors digitorum superficialis and profundus cannot be easily palpated, although the superficialis muscle, along with the flexors carpi radialis and ulnaris and palmaris longus are among the most superficial muscles on the anterior aspect of the forearm.

Extension of the hand at the wrist is performed by the *extensor carpi radialis longus, extensor carpi radialis brevis,* and *extensor carpi ulnaris,* assisted by the *ex-*

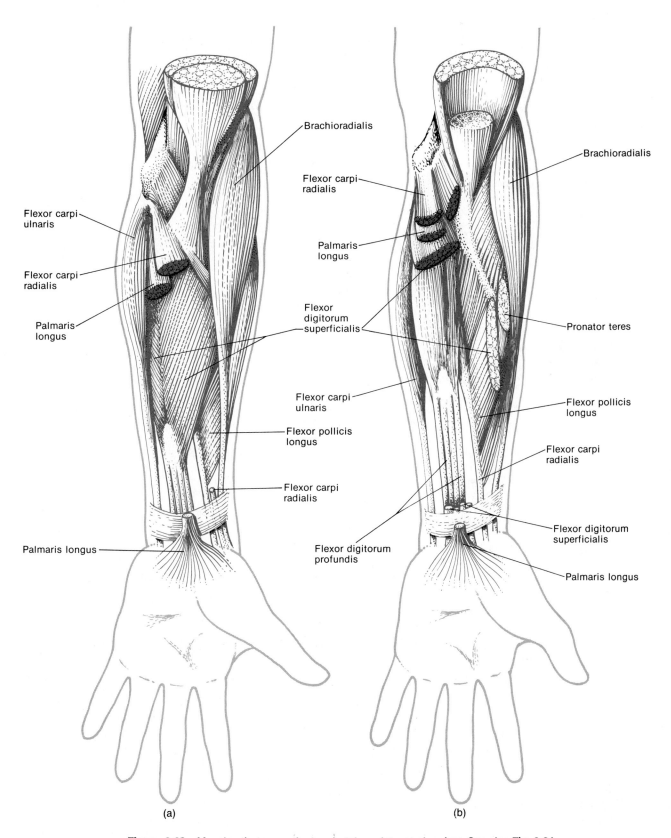

Flexor carpi
ulnaris

Flexor carpi
radialis

Palmaris
longus

Brachioradialis

Flexor carpi
radialis

Palmaris
longus

Flexor
digitorum
superficialis

Flexor carpi
ulnaris

Flexor pollicis
longus

Flexor carpi
radialis

Palmaris longus

Flexor digitorum
profundis

Brachioradialis

Pronator teres

Flexor pollicis
longus

Flexor carpi
radialis

Flexor digitorum
superficialis

Palmaris longus

(a)

(b)

Figure 6-23 Muscles that move the hand at the wrist, anterior view. See also Fig. 6-24.

tensor digitorum (Fig. 6-24). This last muscle acts more in *extension of the medial four digits* than in extension of the wrist. *Abduction* of the hand at the wrist is carried out by the *extensors carpi radialis longus* and *brevis,* assisted by the *flexor carpi radialis;* while *adduction* is due to the action of the *extensor carpi ulnaris,* assisted somewhat by the *flexor carpi ulnaris.*

The *flexor digitorum superficialis* acts mainly to flex the *proximal* and *intermediate phalanges* of digits 2, 3, 4, and 5, while the

TABLE 6-12

Muscles that move the hand at the wrist

Muscle	Origin	Insertion	Action	Nerve
Flexor carpi radialis	From a common tendon attached to the medial epicondyle of the humerus	Proximal ends of metacarpals 2 and 3	Flexion, abduction	Median
Flexor carpi ulnaris	a. Humeral head: from common tendon b. Ulnar head: from olecranon and dorsally on proximal portion of ulna	Metacarpal 5 and two carpals, the pisiform and hammate	Flexion, adduction	Ulnar
Palmaris longus	Common flexor tendon	Transverse carpal ligament at the wrist, palmar aponeurosis of volar aspect of hand	Flexion	Median
Flexor digitorum superficialis	a. Humeral head: by common tendon b. Ulnar head: coronoid process of ulna c. Radial head: oblique line of radius	By four tendons to phalanges of digits 2–5	Flexion of wrist and proximal and intermediate phalanges of digits 2, 3, 4, and 5	Median
Flexor digitorum profundus	Anterior surface of much of ulna and from an interosseus membrane between radius and ulna	Passes through split tendons of flexor digitorum superficialis to distal phalanx of digits 2–5	Flexion of wrist and distal phalanges of digits 2, 3, 4, and 5	Ulnar and median
Extensor carpi radialis longus	On humerus (lateral supracondylar ridge)	Proximal end of second metacarpal	Extension, abduction	Radial
Extensor carpi radialis brevis	Common extensor tendon, attached to lateral epicondyle of humerus	Dorsally at proximal end of third metacarpal	Extension, abduction	Radial
Extensor carpi ulnaris	Extensor tendon and upper dorsal portion of ulna	Proximal end of fifth metacarpal	Extension	Radial
Extensor digitorum	Common extensor tendon	Digits 2–5 as far distally as outer tip of intermediate phalanx	Extension of wrist and medial four digits	Radial

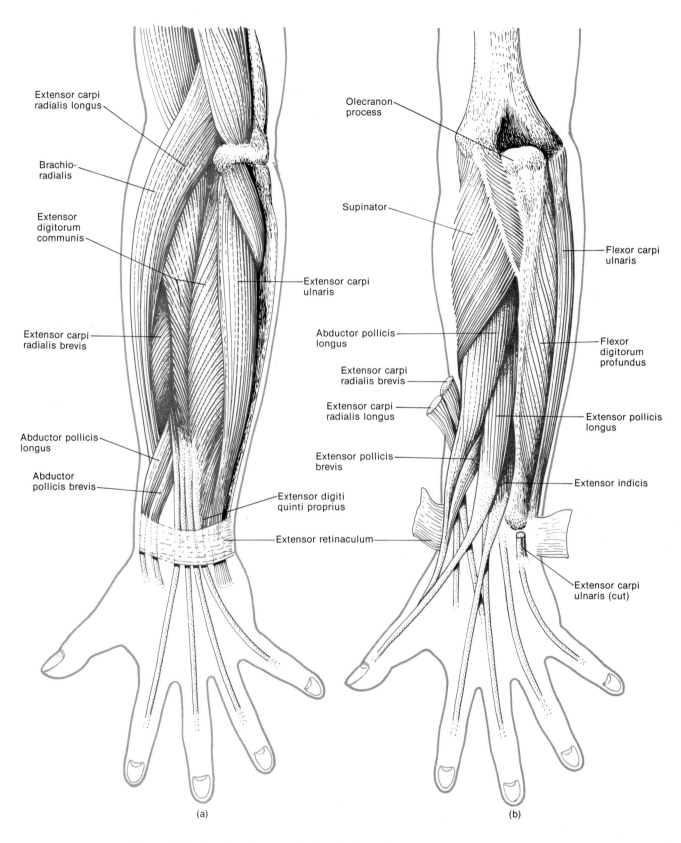

Extensor carpi
radialis longus

Brachio-
radialis

Extensor
digitorum
communis

Extensor carpi
radialis brevis

Abductor pollicis
longus

Abductor
pollicis brevis

Extensor carpi
ulnaris

Extensor digiti
quinti proprius

Extensor retinaculum

Olecranon
process

Supinator

Abductor pollicis
longus

Extensor carpi
radialis brevis

Extensor carpi
radialis longus

Extensor pollicis
brevis

Flexor carpi
ulnaris

Flexor
digitorum
profundus

Extensor pollicis
longus

Extensor indicis

Extensor carpi
ulnaris (cut)

(a)

(b)

Figure 6-24 Muscles that move the hand at the wrist, posterior view. See also Fig. 6-23.

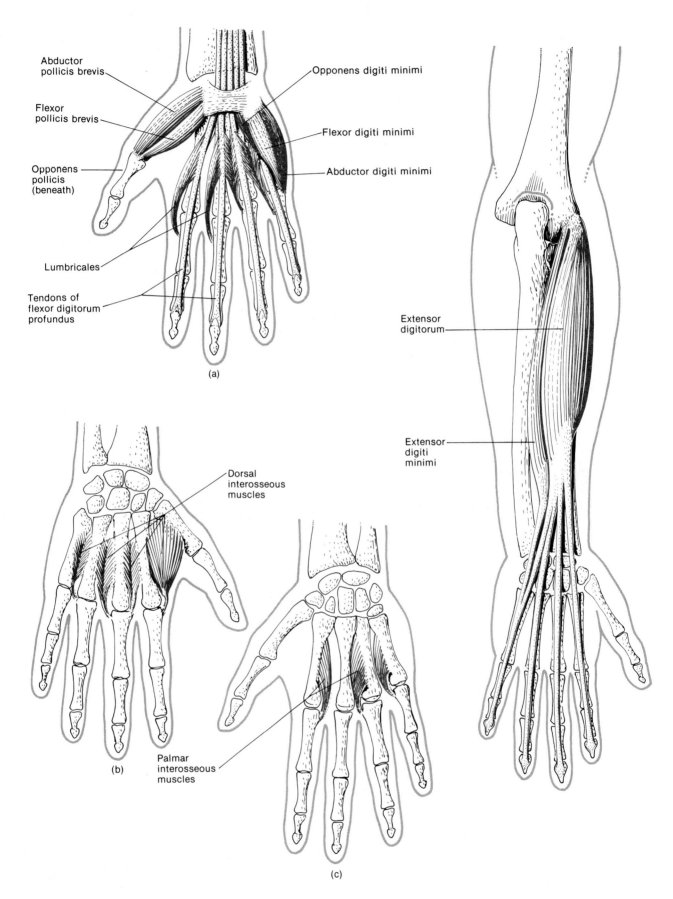

Abductor pollicis brevis

Flexor pollicis brevis

Opponens pollicis (beneath)

Lumbricales

Tendons of flexor digitorum profundus

Opponens digiti minimi

Flexor digiti minimi

Abductor digiti minimi

(a)

Dorsal interosseous muscles

Palmar interosseous muscles

(b)

(c)

Extensor digitorum

Extensor digiti minimi

Figure 6-25 Muscles that move the digits. See also Fig. 6-26.

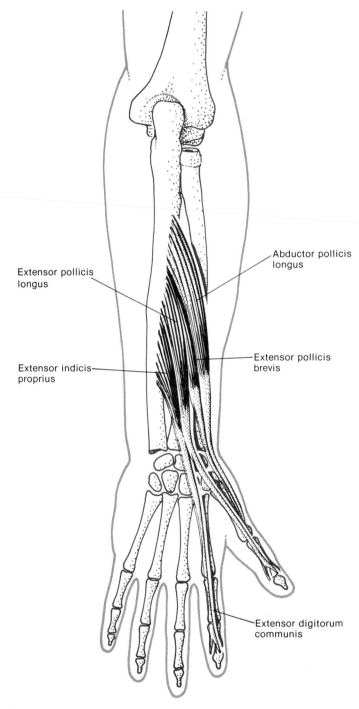

Extensor pollicis longus

Abductor pollicis longus

Extensor pollicis brevis

Extensor indicis proprius

Extensor digitorum communis

Figure 6-26 Muscles that move the digits—in this case, the thumb and forefinger. See also Fig. 6-25.

profundus muscle works chiefly to flex the *distal phalanges* of these same digits.

THE DIGITS The digits or fingers can all be flexed, extended, adducted, and abducted. Abduction and adduction of the middle finger (digit 3) consists of moving it away

from and toward its central axis. Digit 1, the thumb, is capable of carrying out—in addition to these four movements—a very special action involving its touching the tips of each of the other digits: *opposition.* Man is the only primate with a truly *opposable thumb.* In the following discussion, the actions of muscles of the medial four digits will be considered first, followed by those of the thumb.

Flexion of digits 2, 3, 4, and 5 is accomplished by the *flexor digitorum superficialis, flexor digitorum profundus,* and the *lumbricale muscles.* The first two muscles have been previously discussed. The small lumbricales (Fig. 6-25) have the unique ability to *flex the fingers* (at the joints between the metacarpals and the first phalanges) *and extend them* (at the joints between the phalanges). *Extension of the medial four digits* is brought about by the actions of the *extensor digitorum, extensor indicis,* and *extensor digiti minimi. The extensor indicis extends the proximal phalanx of digit 2,* the index finger. *Abduction of digits 2 and 4 away from the central axis of digit 3,* and *abduction of digit 3 in either direction away from that axis* depends upon the *dorsal interosseus muscles* (Fig. 6-25). *Abduction of digit 5* is accomplished by the *abductor digiti minimi muscle. The palmar (volar) interosseus muscles* carry out *adduction of digits 2, 4, and 5 toward digit 3.* The two *dorsal interosseus muscles* inserting on the third digit are *antagonists* of each other, and *adduction of the third digit* back to the straight position requires the *relaxation of one interosseus and contraction of the other.* (See Table 6-13.)

THE THUMB It was previously pointed out that the thumb (or pollex) is capable of all four basic movements of the other digits, plus a very special movement, *opposition.* The actions of the thumb and the muscles involved in each action can be outlined as follows: *flexion* of the thumb follows action of the *flexor pollicis longus* and *flexor pollicis brevis. Extension* depends upon contraction of the *extensor pollicis longus* and *extensor pollicis brevis* (Fig. 6-26). Shortening of the *abductor pollicis longus* and *abductor pollicis brevis* muscle carries out *abduction* of the thumb, while *adduction* is the responsibility of the *adductor pollicis.* This last muscle also assists the *opponens pollicis* in the act of *opposition.* During opposition, the opponens

TABLE 6-13

Muscles that move the digits

Muscle(s)	Origin	Insertion	Action	Nerve
Lumbricales	Each from a tendon of the flexor digitorum profundus	Each with a tendon of the extensor digitorum into the base of a distal phalanx	Flexion of digits 2–5 at metacarpophalangeal joints; extension of same digits at interphalangeal joints	Medial two muscles by ulnar nerve; lateral two by the median nerve
Extensor indicis	Dorsal surface of ulna	Proximal phalanx of digit 2	Extension of forefinger (digit 2)	Radial
Extensor digiti minimi	Common extensor tendon	Proximal phalanx of digit 5	Extension of little finger (digit 5)	Radial
Dorsal interosseus muscles	From metacarpals 2–5	Proximal phalanges of digits 2, 3, and 4	Abduction of digits 2, 3, and 4; adduction of digit 3	Ulnar
Palmar or volar interosseus muscles	Each from a metacarpal	Proximal phalanges of digits 2, 4, and 5	Adduction of digits 2, 4, and 5	Ulnar
Abductor digiti minimi	Pisiform bone and tendon of flexor carpi ulnaris	Proximal phalanx of digit 5	Abduction of digit 5	Ulnar

TABLE 6-14

Muscles that move the thumb

Muscle	Origin	Insertion	Action	Nerve
Flexor pollicis longus	High on ulna and most of anterior surface of radius	Distal phalanx of thumb	Flexion	Median
Flexor pollicis brevis	Transverse carpal ligament and trapezium	Proximal phalanx of thumb	Flexion	Radial
Extensor pollicis longus	Posterior aspect of ulna about its middle third	Distal phalanx of thumb	Extension	Radial
Extensor pollicis brevis	Fairly high on posterior surface of radius and on interosseus membrane	Proximal end of proximal phalanx of thumb	Extension	Radial
Abductor pollicis longus	Fairly high on posterior surfaces of ulna and radius	Laterally into proximal end of first metacarpal	Abduction	Radial
Abductor pollicis	On scaphoid, trapezium, and transverse carpal ligament	Proximal end of proximal phalanx of thumb	Abduction	Median
Adductor pollicis				Ulnar
	a. Oblique head: trapezium, trapezoid, capitate, and metacarpals 2 and 3	Medial side of proximal portion of proximal phalanx of thumb	Adduction; assists in opposition	
	b. Transverse head: palmar surface of metacarpal 3		*Same as above*	
Opponens pollicis	Trapezium and transverse carpal ligament	Anterior surface and lateral side of first metacarpal	Opposition	Median

pollicis pulls the first metacarpal anteriorly and medially so that the thumb touches end-to-end with any of the other digits desired. When the thumb is forcibly abducted—bent laterally and upward, toward the radial side of the forearm—a shallow depression appears at its base; this is the *"anatomical snuff-box,"* so called because of its reputed former use as a snuff-sniffing device. The "box" is *formed by the tendons of the extensor pollicis longus and extensor pollicis brevis muscles.* Deep in the floor of the area lies a *branch of the radial artery.* The *main trunk* of the artery pulsates on the volar aspect of the wrist, *just lateral to the tendon of the flexor carpi radialis muscle.* (See Table 6-14.)

*Movements of
the lower extremity*

THE THIGH   The muscles of both the upper and lower limbs are covered by tough deep fascia beneath the loose areolar tissue that makes up the superficial fascia. Folds of this deep fascial covering extend inward between certain muscles and groups of muscles, delimiting the fleshy portions of the limbs into *compartments.* The deep fascia of the lower extremity is especially tough, and in the thigh is given the name *fascia lata.* Two *intermuscular septa* of the thigh, one lateral and one medial, extend from the fascia lata inward to the linea aspera of the femur, and one ex-

TABLE 6-15

Muscles that move the thigh

Muscle	Origin	Insertion	Action	Nerve
Iliacus	Most of inner surface of ilium, iliac crest, and several nearby ligaments	Shaft and lesser trochanter of femur and tendon of psoas major	Flexion	Femoral
Psoas major	Transverse processes of all lumbar vertebrae	Lesser trochanter, along with the iliacus	Flexion	Lumbar spinal nerves 2 and 3
Gluteus maximus	Posterior lateral portion of ilium, sacrum, coccyx, and nearby ligaments	Gluteal tuberosity and iliotibial tract	Extension	Inferior gluteal
Tensor fascia lata	Anterior border of ilium and iliac crest	Iliotibial band at about the middle third of the thigh	Abduction	Superior gluteal
Gluteus medius	Upper lateral surface of the ilium	Greater trochanter	Abduction	Superior gluteal
Adductor magnus	Rami of ischium and pubis, and ischial tuberosity	Linea aspera and adductor tubercle of medial epicondyle	Adduction	Obturator and sciatic
Adductor longus	Front of superior ramus of pubis	Linea aspera near midpoint of femur	Adduction	Obturator
Adductor brevis	Inferior ramus of pubis	Upper portion of linea aspera	Adduction	Obturator
Piriformis	Lateral portion of internal surface of sacrum	Top of greater trochanter	Lateral rotation	Sacral spinal nerves 1 and 2
Gluteus minimus	Outer surface of lower 1/2 of ilium	Front of greater trochanter	Medial rotation	Superior gluteal

tends from the fascia covering the posterior surface of the thigh to the femur. These septa divide the thigh into three compartments—*anteromedial* (which contains the extensors), *medial* (adductors), and *posterior* (flexors). Extra thick portions of the fascia lata form the *gluteal aponeuroses* over a large part of the buttocks and the *iliotibial tract* or band that extends inferiorly over the thigh to the lateral condyle of the tibia.

Movements of the thigh include *flexion* (forward and upward), *extension* (backward and upward), *abduction* (away from the midline), *adduction* (toward the midline), and *medial and lateral rotation* (about the long axis of the femur). All these movements depend upon the freedom permitted by the ball-and-socket—type hip joint. It should be pointed out that the trunk can be flexed (moved forward and downward) at the hip joint when the thigh is held fixed, as when bending over a table or stooping to pick up an object; it can also be extended or *dorsiflexed,* as when leaning backward. The chief muscles involved in the first movement are the *psoas major* and *minor, iliacus,* and *sartorius.* The pelvis and hence the trunk are tilted backward by the *hamstring muscles*

(see the next section) when the lower extremity is held rigid.

Flexion of the thigh follows contraction of the *iliopsoas muscle,* which is actually two muscles combined, the *iliacus* and *psoas major. Extension* of the thigh is due mainly to action of the *heaviest muscle in the body,* the *gluteus maximus* or butock muscle. The thigh is *abducted* by the *tensor fascia lata* and *gluteus medius muscles,* and *adduction* is done chiefly by the *adductor magnus, adductor longus,* and *adductor brevis.*

The main *lateral rotator* of the thigh is the *piriformis muscle,* and the chief *medial rotator* is the *gluteus minimus,* which lies deep to the gluteus medius and piriformis. The iliopsoas muscle is almost impossible to palpate, but the gluteus maximus is readily palpable as the fleshy prominence of the buttock. The tensor fascia lata can be felt just in front of the greater trochanter, the gluteus medius a few inches above and in front of the trochanter. The adductor magnus can be felt on the medial and posterior aspect of the femur, and the adductor longus just below the pubis. The deeper-lying adductor brevis cannot be palpated. Figures 6-27 and 6-28 illustrate the major muscles of the thigh.

Figure 6-27   Muscles that move the thigh. See also Fig. 6-28.

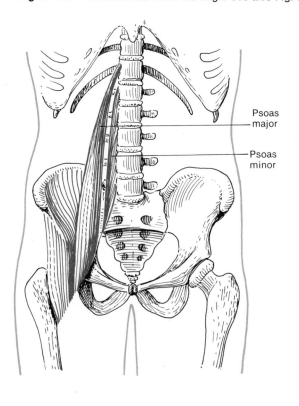

Psoas major

Psoas minor

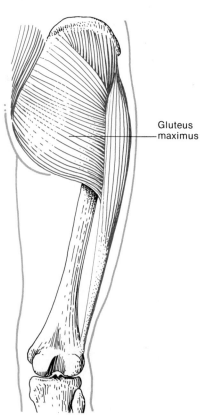

Gluteus maximus

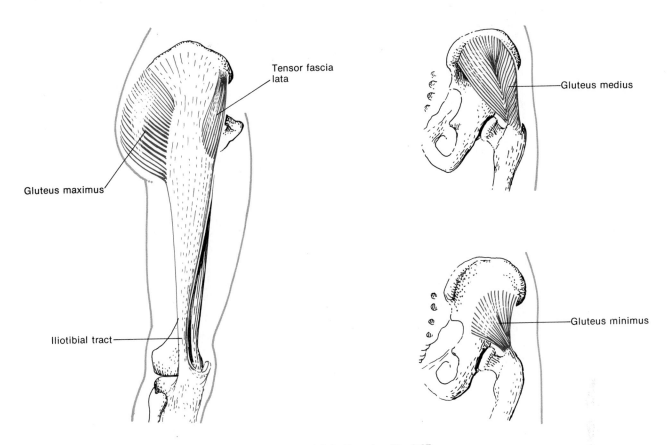

Figure 6-28 Muscles that move the thigh. See also Fig. 6-27.

THE LEG (See Figs. 6-29 and 6-30.) Some of the muscles of the leg have attachments as high as the pelvis, and may help to rotate, adduct, and abduct the entire lower extremity; but their principal function is to bring about the two movements possible at the

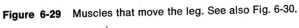

Figure 6-29 Muscles that move the leg. See also Fig. 6-30.

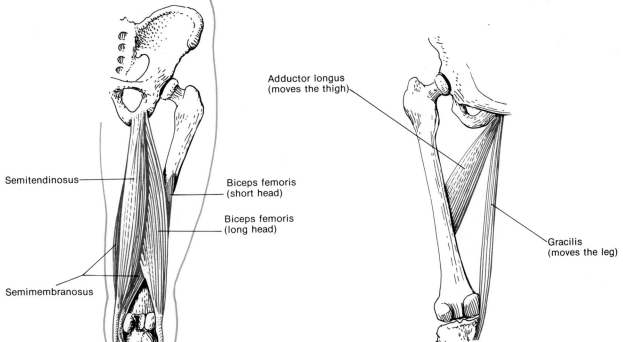

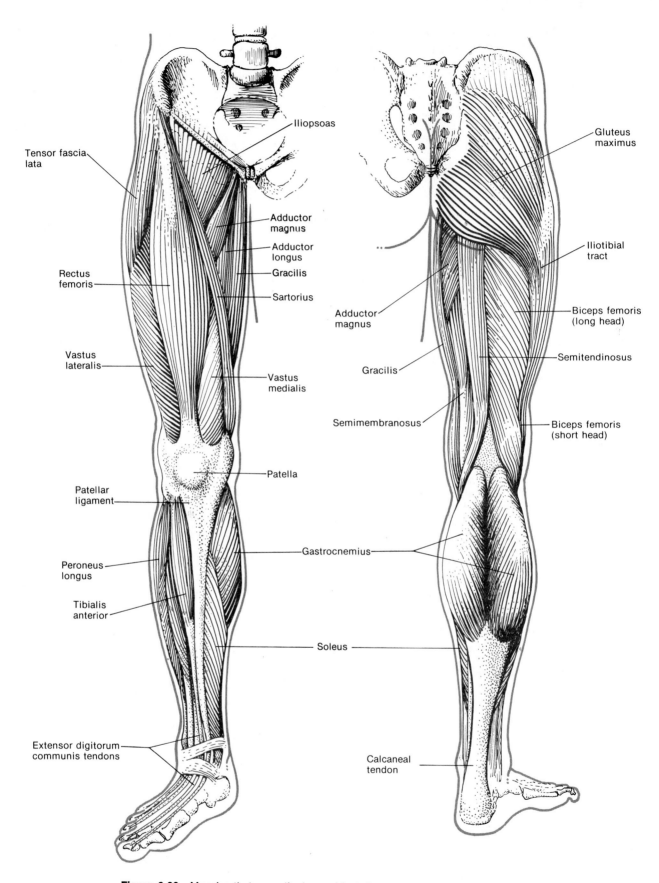

Figure 6-30 Muscles that move the leg and foot. See also Fig. 6-29.

Iliopsoas

Tensor fascia lata

Adductor magnus

Adductor longus

Gracilis

Sartorius

Rectus femoris

Vastus lateralis

Vastus medialis

Patella

Patellar ligament

Peroneus longus

Tibialis anterior

Gastrocnemius

Soleus

Extensor digitorum communis tendons

Gluteus maximus

Iliotibial tract

Biceps femoris (long head)

Adductor magnus

Semitendinosus

Gracilis

Semimembranosus

Biceps femoris (short head)

Calcaneal tendon

knee joint—*flexion* (bending the lower extremity at the knee) and *extension* (straightening the lower extremity at the knee). The main *flexors* of the leg include the *biceps femoris* on the posterior lateral portion of the thigh; *semitendinosus,* rather medial in position to the biceps; *semimembranosus,* deep to the previous two muscles; *gracilis,* on the medial side of the thigh; and *sartorius,* the so-called "tailor's muscle," running across the anterior and medial aspects of the thigh. The first three of these—biceps femoris, semitendinosus, and semimembranosus—are known as the *"hamstring" muscles,* and are antagonists of the *quadriceps femoris muscles* that extend the leg. The biceps femoris is best palpated on the lateral posterior aspect of the thigh, near the knee, while the semitendinosus is felt on the posterior medial side. The semimembranosus lies deeper than these two muscles and is not easily palpated. The gracilis can be felt high on the medial side of the thigh, just below the pubis, while the sartorius can be palpated only in thin or highly muscular persons, and then only near the anterior superior iliac spine.

The chief *extensors* of the leg are those included in the large, powerful *quadriceps*

TABLE 6-16

Muscles that move the leg

Muscle	Origin	Insertion	Action	Nerve
Biceps femoris				
a. Long head:	Ischial tuberosity	Head of fibula and lateral condyle of tibia	Flexion	Sciatic
b. Short head:	Linea aspera, lateral intermusclar septum		*Same as above*	
Semitendinosus	Ischial tuberosity, with biceps femoris	Medial side, proximal end of tibia	Flexion	Sciatic
Semimembranosus	Upper part of ischial tuberosity	Posteriorly on medial condyle of tibia	Flexion	Sciatic
Gracilis	Inferior ramus of pubis and part of pubic symphysis	Medially, near proximal end of tibia	Flexion	Obturator
Sartorius	Anterior superior iliac spine	Medially, near proximal end of tibia	Flexion	Femoral
Rectus femoris	By two heads, one from the anterior inferior iliac spine, one from the upper edge of the acetabulum	By quadriceps tendon to tibial tuberosity	Extension; flexes the thigh when knee is held fixed	Femoral
Vastus lateralis	Linea aspera and greater trochanter	Quadriceps tendon	Extension	Femoral
Vastus medialis	Linea aspera	Quadriceps tendon	Extension	Femoral
Vastus intermedius	Anterior and lateral surfaces of femur, and lower 1/2 of linea aspera	Quadriceps tendon	Extension	Femoral

femoris group. These four muscles are the *rectus femoris* (the most anterior of the four), *vastus lateralis* (lateral to and behind the rectus femoris), *vastus medialis* (medial to and behind the rectus femoris), and *vastus intermedius* (deep to the rectus femoris and vastus medialis). The rectus femoris can also flex the thigh when the lower leg is held in a fixed position at the knee. All four muscles in this group unite in a common tendon, the *quadriceps tendon or patellar tendon,* which inserts on the tuberosity near the proximal end of the tibia. The patella is enclosed in this tendon. The rectus femoris muscle is palpable over most of the anterior aspect of the thigh, the vastus lateralis over the anterolateral side of the thigh, and the vastus medialis on the anteromedial side. The vastus intermedius lies deep to the rectus femoris and, therefore, cannot be palpated.

THE FOOT   The ankle joint, like the knee joint, is a hinge-type joint, and permits two movements: *flexion* and *extension.* For movements of the foot, the special term *dorsiflexion* is used when raising the foot upward, and *plantar flexion* is used when moving it downward; these two terms correspond to flexion and extension, respectively. It will be recalled that *inversion* and *eversion* are also carried out by the foot. These movements take place chiefly between the tarsal bones, rather than at the ankle joint. Muscles concerned with *dorsiflexion* of the foot include the *tibialis anterior* and *peroneus tertius.* The former muscle also

TABLE 6-17

Muscles that move the foot *

Muscle	Origin	Insertion	Action	Nerve
Tibialis anterior	Lateral tibial condyle and lateral surface of tibia	First cuneiform and base of first metatarsal	Dorsiflexion and inversion	Anterior tibial
Peroneus tertius	Distal third of fibula and intermuscular septum	Base of fifth metatarsal	Dorsiflexion and eversion	Anterior tibial
Gastrocnemius	Media head: medial condyle of femur; lateral head: lateral condyle of femur	With soleus, into calcaneus by means of the calcaneal tendon (tendon of Achilles)	Plantar flexion	Tibial
Soleus	Head and upper shaft of fibula and upper tibia	With gastrocnemius by means of calcaneal tendon into calcaneus	Plantar flexion	Tibial
Tibialis posterior	Upper half of posterior surface of tibia and fibula	Mainly into navicular bone, but with some insertion into the cuneiforms, metatarsals 2, 3, and 4, and the talus	Plantar flexion and inversion	Posterior tibial

* See Table 6-18 for information concerning the flexor hallucis longus, extensor hallucis longus, flexor digitorum longus, and extensor digitorum longus muscles.

helps to *invert* the foot, and the latter helps *evert* it. The *plantar flexors* of the foot include the powerful *gastrocnemius* or "calf muscle," the *soleus,* and *tibialis posterior. Inversion* of the foot is accomplished by the *tibialis anterior, tibialis posterior, flexor hallucis longus,* and *flexor digitorum longus* muscles; the major *evertors* are the *extensor digitorum longus, extensor hallucis longus,* and *peroneus tertius.*

The tibialis anterior can be palpated as it crosses the tibia from lateral to medial; the peroneus tertius can be felt along the lateral aspect of the fibula. The gastrocnemius is easily seen and felt on the calf of a person standing on his toes, and covers a great deal of the soleus, a portion of which is palpable laterally on the lower leg. The tibialis posterior is a deep-lying muscle and cannot be palpated.

THE TOES (See Fig. 6-31.) Although the toes are capable of some abduction and adduction, the chief movements carried out by them are *flexion* (curling downward) and *extension* (bending upward and backward). The muscles of flexion are the *flexor hallucis longus* and *flexor digitorum longus;* those of extension include the *extensor hallucis longus* and *extensor digitorum longus.* The hallucis muscles supply the great (big) toe, while the other muscles supply the remaining digits. There are many more muscles bringing about movements of the toes and helping to support the arches of the foot, but most of them are of minor importance in carrying out the major movements. The distal portion of the flexor hallucis longus can be palpated on the medial side of the calcaneal tendon at the heel, but the flexor digitorum longus cannot be felt. The extensor hallucis longus can be palpated at its distal portion on top of the foot near the great toe, and the extensor digitorum longus can be felt just lateral and somewhat posterior to the tibialis anterior, lateral to the tibia.

In Figures 6-32 and 6-33, the major muscles are illustrated as they appear in the intact body.

TABLE 6-18

Muscles that move the toes

Muscle	Origin	Insertion	Action	Nerve
Flexor hallucis longus	Distal ⅔ of posterior surface of fibula and interosseus membrane of leg	Base of distal phalanx of great toe	Flexion of great toe	Posterior tibial
Flexor digitorum longus	Most of posterior surface of tibia, on its shaft	Undersurface of base of distal phalanx of the four lateral toes	Flexion of lateral four toes	Posterior tibial
Extensor hallucis longus	Central ½ of anterior surface of fibula and interosseus membrane of leg	Base of distal phalanx of great toe	Extension of great toe	Anterior tibial
Extensor digitorum longus	Upper ¾ of anterior surface of fibula, lateral condyle of tibia	Dorsal surface of middle and distal phalanges of four lateral toes	Extension of lateral four toes	Anterior tibial

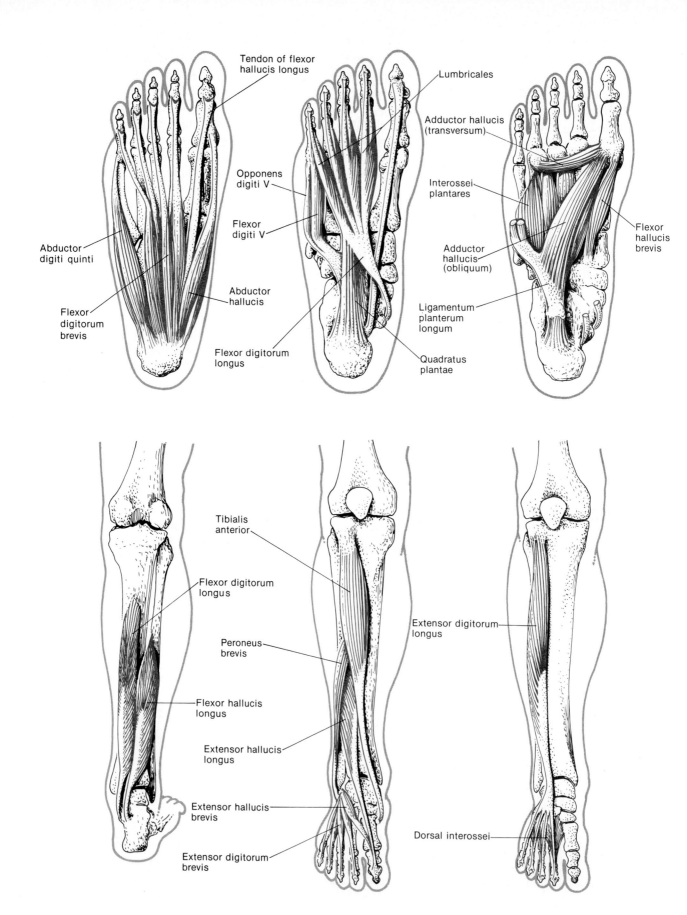

Figure 6-31 Muscles that move the digits of the foot.

136

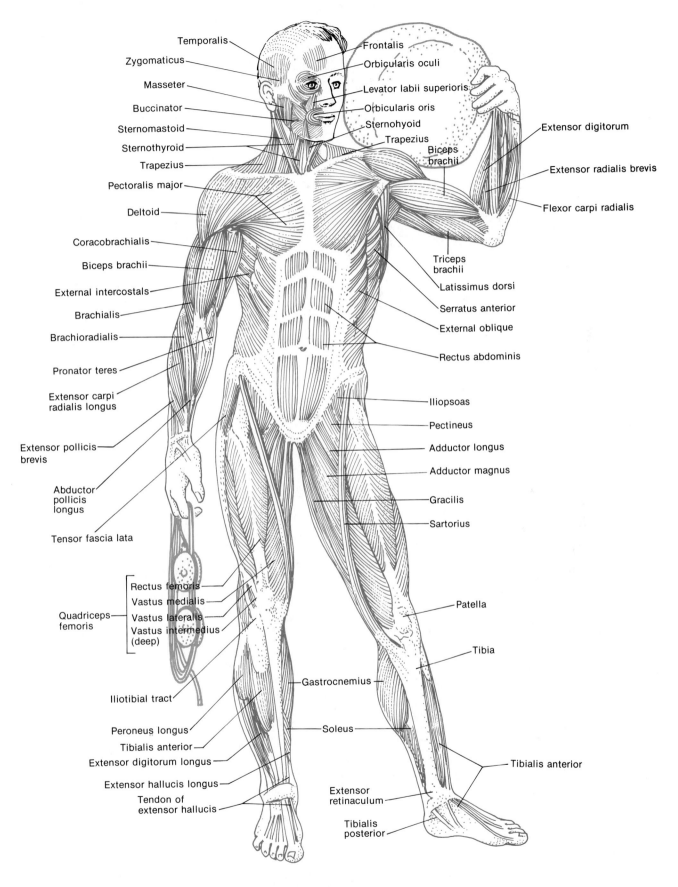

Figure 6-32 Major muscles of the body, anterior view.

137

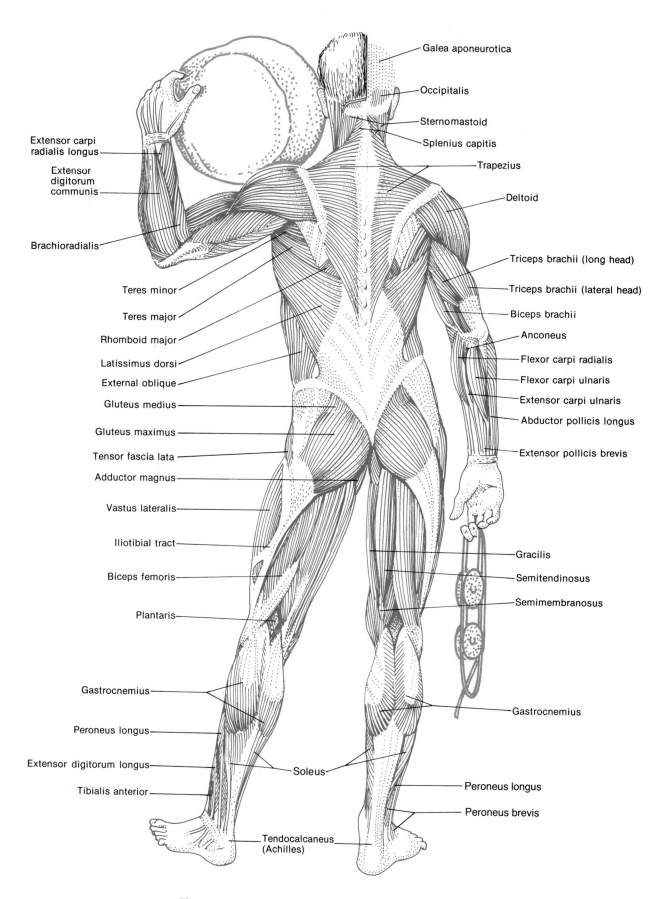

Extensor carpi
radialis longus

Extensor
digitorum
communis

Brachioradialis

Teres minor

Teres major

Rhomboid major

Latissimus dorsi

External oblique

Gluteus medius

Gluteus maximus

Tensor fascia lata

Adductor magnus

Vastus lateralis

Iliotibial tract

Biceps femoris

Plantaris

Gastrocnemius

Peroneus longus

Extensor digitorum longus

Tibialis anterior

Tendocalcaneus
(Achilles)

Galea aponeurotica

Occipitalis

Sternomastoid

Splenius capitis

Trapezius

Deltoid

Triceps brachii (long head)

Triceps brachii (lateral head)

Biceps brachii

Anconeus

Flexor carpi radialis

Flexor carpi ulnaris

Extensor carpi ulnaris

Abductor pollicis longus

Extensor pollicis brevis

Gracilis

Semitendinosus

Semimembranosus

Gastrocnemius

Peroneus longus

Peroneus brevis

Soleus

Figure 6-33 Major muscles of the body, posterior view.

SOME ANALYSES OF
SKELETAL MUSCLE ACTIVITY

Posture

Posture can be defined as the *position of the body at any given time when not recumbent* (lying down). The muscular action necessary in order to maintain a given position is often involuntary, depending entirely upon intact *nervous system reflex arcs* (Chapter 7).

STANDING   Good posture while standing demands that much of the vertebral column and long axes of the bones of the lower extremity be fairly straight *with reference to a line passing from the mastoid process to the floor* (Fig. 6-34). In a person of average weight, this represents the *line of gravity* of the body. Such a line passes through most of the *cervical* and *lumbar vertebrae,* just *posterior to the center of the hip joints,* and slightly *anterior to the center of the knee and ankle joints.* In this position, each of the weight-bearing bones and joints can more effectively contribute to the efficient support of the body. In good standing posture, there is equal pressure on the weight-bearing joint cartilages, including the intervertebral discs. Equally important conditions are that tension in ligaments of the joints be equalized, that there be equal tonus in antagonistic muscle groups, and that the body weight be evenly distributed on the weight-bearing portions of the feet. In the erect posture, the *flexors* and *extensors* of the *neck, trunk,* and *lower extremities* all maintain a moderate amount of contraction, working in opposition so as to maintain the upright stance.

SITTING   In the sitting position, the role of the muscles of the lower extremity is minimized, with those located below the knee contributing little or nothing to maintenance of posture; otherwise, the requirements for good posture while sitting are the same as while standing.

Locomotion

Locomotion involves the *movement of the entire body from one place to another, under its own power.* The most common

Figure 6-34   Correct posture while standing. (Contemporary Studio.)

method of locomotion is *walking* and variations of walking, such as running, jogging or trotting, hopping, and skipping. Another form of locomotion, important as a form of recreation and physical exercise, is swimming.

WALKING   Walking has often been described as an activity during which one starts to fall prone, then prevents himself from doing so by quickly thrusting a leg forward, the process being repeated over and over again, for as long as necessary in order to get the

139

person where he is going. Smooth, graceful walking requires the use of many muscles, levers, and reflex arcs all operating in highly complex cycles. The following description of the walking process, although greatly simplified, will serve to illustrate some of the principal mechanisms involved.

During walking, each lower extremity swings somewhat like the pendulum of a clock, but in this case the pendulum is jointed near the *midpoint* of its "arm" (*knee joint*), and actually bears the weight of its "clock" (*the body*) during alternate strokes. The act of walking can, therefore, be said to consist of two *phases*—the *supporting phase* and the *swinging phase*. The supporting phase of one lower extremity overlaps slightly the supporting phase of the other, during the time when both feet are on the ground. Once a step is taken, gravity and momentum serve to carry out most of the swinging phase, assisted by flexor action of the *rectus femoris, tensor fascia latae,* and *pectineus muscles.* (These and other muscles contract strongly in order to produce the first step.) During flexion of the thigh, the *extensor muscles of the lower leg* maintain just enough tension to keep the foot prepared for contact with the ground; but during propulsion, the *gastrocnemius and soleus* are very important in raising the body on the toes and giving it a shove. The supporting phase of walking depends at first upon the momentum provided by the forward motion of the body, then the shortening of *extensors of the thigh,* such as the *gluteus maximus,* assisted by the *hamstrings* and *adductor magnus.*

RUNNING   Running is much like a fast walk, but during the run there is *no point at which both feet touch the ground at the same time,* as there is in walking. Instead, the body is carried through the air in leaps, due to the propelling action of the *plantar flexors of the foot, flexors of the leg,* and *momentum of the trunk.* In vigorous running, momentum can be augmented by driving the weight of the upper extremities forward one at a time, in synchronization with the running step. Those muscles of the lower extremity utilized for running are identical to those used for

walking, but they are used with much more vigor and force.

SWIMMING   OR   AQUATIC   LOCOMOTION
Swimming differs from walking and running in several important ways. For example, the *effect of gravity is minimized* when a person enters water; but this benefit is offset by the *great resistance the body meets with as it moves through the water.* This resistance is much greater than that encountered by a body moving through air; the greater density of water as compared to air accounts for this. In locomotion over ground, propulsion is brought about mainly by pushing against the ground with the lower extremities. In propulsion through water by ordinary techniques of swimming (such as the crawl stroke), *the upper extremities play the major roles* by pulling and pushing in the water, while movements of the thighs, legs, and feet are of *secondary importance.* A very brief outline of the muscle action is as follows: upon beginning the crawl (Fig. 6-35), the upper extremity is *flexed and abducted at the shoulder* by the *biceps brachii, brachialis, deltoid,* and *other muscles,* and *flexed at the elbow* by the *flexors* of the *forearm* such as the *biceps brachii, brachialis,* and *brachioradialis.* Next, the upper extremity is *straightened* by the *extensors,* such as the *triceps brachii* and *anconeus,* in preparation for the downstroke. During the downstroke, the upper limb is held rigid at the elbow by the *antagonistic action* of the *flexors* and *extensors,* and the entire limb is pulled downward, backward, and medial-ward by the *pectoral muscles, teres major, latissimus dorsi,* and others. Until the extremity reaches the vertical position, it is pulling the body through the water, using the hand like the blade of a paddle. Once the hand passes the vertical position and starts upward, it is *pushing* instead of *pulling.* The *teres major, latissimus dorsi,* and *posterior part of the deltoid* carry out this action. After the upper extremity has been *hyperextended* until the elbow reaches the surface of the water and the hand gets to the upper thigh, the hand is raised from the water and the cycle is begun all over again. The actions of the crawl are such that there

Figure 6-35 The major movements of the crawl stroke in swimming.

is some overlap between the pulling action of one arm and pushing action of the other. The feet are usually held plantar flexed, and the lower extremities are alternately flexed and extended, somewhat at the knee but mainly at the hip joint.

The muscles and homeostasis

The production of heat in muscles, helping to maintain a suitably high body temperature, the movement of muscles during ingestion and digestion of food, the milking action of muscles on veins (thereby aiding venous circulation), even the utilization of oxygen and glycogen and production of lactic acid during their normal metabolism, all are involved with that state of dynamic equilibrium that constitutes *homeostasis*. Heart muscle and smooth muscle keep the cells and tissues supplied with oxygen and nutrients, constrict and dilate blood vessels as required in maintaining a constant blood pressure, control the secretions of glands, and otherwise contribute to the economy of body organs and their functions.

OUTLINE SUMMARY

1. Body movements depend upon: the ability of muscles to shorten or contract

   A. Anatomy of a typical skeletal muscle
      a. Each muscle consists of fasciculi (bundles) of elongated, cross-striated, multinucleate cells
      b. Each muscle cell or fiber consists of myofibrils, which in turn are made up of still smaller units, sarcomeres
      c. The sarcomere consists of actin, myosin, and other muscle proteins
      d. The endomysium covers the muscle-cell membrane or sarcolemma; the perimysium surrounds each fasciculus; and the epimysium covers the entire muscle. All these membranes except the sarcolemma are made of connective tissue

   B. The nerve supply of skeletal muscle
      a. Triggers the process of muscle contraction
      b. The nerves involved originate at the spinal cord and brain stem
      c. The point at which a nerve cell or its axon branch contacts a muscle fiber is the neuromuscular junction
      d. A motor unit is made up of a motor neuron and all the muscle fibers it supplies

   C. The blood supply of skeletal muscle: carries oxygen and nutrients to the muscle cells, and carries wastes away from them

141

D. Muscle tone: in health, every muscle is in a partial state of contraction, even during sleep. The greater the stress, the larger the number of muscle fibers that contract

E. Laboratory experiments with muscles and muscle fibers

a. Muscles respond to a variety of stimuli, including electric shock, temperature changes, change in pH and ion concentration, and certain chemicals. Electrical stimuli are commonly used in the laboratory

b. Classification of electrical stimuli
1. Subthreshold: too weak to bring about a detectable response
2. Threshold: barely strong enough to cause a response
3. Maximal: results in a maximum response

c. All-or-none principle: if a muscle fiber contracts in response to a stimulus, it contracts maximally or not at all

d. Apparatus used in recording muscle contractions
1. Kymograph
2. Polygraph

e. Single twitch: a single muscle contraction, resulting from a single stimulus
1. Latent period
2. Contraction phase
3. Relaxation phase

f. Summation: the "addition" of effects of two or more threshold stimuli, producing a greater magnitude of contraction or response than that normally resulting from a single threshold stimulus

g. Treppe phenomenon: results when a series of stimuli is given so that each falls within the relative refractory period of the preceding contraction

h. Tetanus: contractions resulting when stimuli are applied shortly after the relaxation phase of preceding contractions have begun
1. Incomplete tetanus: a discernible series of partially "blended" contractions
2. Complete tetanus: a smooth, sustained contraction, during which the individual contractions of incomplete tetanus cannot be detected; results from a series of rapid contractions blended together

i. Contracture and fatigue: contracture is the extremely slow relaxation of a muscle due to overstimulation; fatigue, the inability of a muscle to contract, due to depletion of its chemicals by repeated contraction

j. Isotonic and isometric contractions: contractions during which there is no change in muscle tone are isotonic; those in which the length of the muscle remains constant are isometric

k. Warmup phenomenon: laboratory preparations of muscles seem to contract more efficiently after contracting a few times, thereby producing heat

l. Response to stretch: Starling's principle states that, up to a point, a muscle contracts with greater force when its fibers are being stretched

F. The chemistry of muscle contraction

a. Composition of muscle: muscle tissue is about 75% water, 20% protein, and 5% nonprotein organics and minerals. Important nonprotein organics include ATP, phosphocreatine, creatine, and urea (all of which contain nitrogen), and glycogen (which does not). Potassium is the most abundant mineral element. The oxygen-carrying iron–protein pigment of muscle is called myoglobin

b. The reactions of contraction: The ultimate source of energy for muscle contraction is the oxidation of carbohydrate such as glycogen; however, this process is too slow for immediate use. The immediate-energy source of contraction is thought to be ATP, which may be split when nerve impulses reach the muscle, causing the energy of one of the phosphate bonds in each ATP molecule to start the chain of events on its way. As soon as energy is available, actin filaments slide between myosin filaments, and the sarcomere—and subsequently, the myofibril, fiber, and entire muscle—contracts

c. Oxygen debt: during exercise, the oxidation of lactic acid to pyruvic acid is temporarily postponed, and oxygen must be eventually used to convert lactic to pyruvic. This postponement is called oxygen debt

2. Some aspects of body movements and posture

A. Certain muscles and muscle groups carry out certain movements

B. Since muscles can only pull and never push, they often act as the force of levers, and utilize mechanical advantage

C. Muscle work: the movement of some resisting force or object through a distance. One way to express work is as follows

$$\text{Work} = \left(\begin{array}{c}\text{Resistance,} \\ \text{in pounds}\end{array}\right) \times \left(\begin{array}{c}\text{Distance, in feet,} \\ \text{through which the} \\ \text{resistance is moved}\end{array}\right)$$

(The product is expressed in terms of foot-pounds)

D. Muscle attachments: muscles are attached to bones, to each other, and sometimes to both. They may be attached directly or by means of tendons and aponeuroses. In general, the fixed end of a muscle is its origin, the movable end its insertion

E. Classification of muscles according to function
   a. Muscles that act together to produce a movement are called synergists
   b. Muscles that act in opposition to each other are antagonists
   c. Muscles that act most powerfully during any given movement are called prime movers
   d. Muscles can usually be classed as flexors, extensors, abductors, adductors, levators, depressors, retractors, protractors, sphincters, or rotators

F. The major movements of the body include those of
   a. The head
   b. The lower jaw
   c. Facial expression
   d. The eyeball
   e. The vertebral column
   f. The abdominal wall

g. Breathing
h. The upper extremity
   1. Shoulder
   2. Upper arm
   3. Forearm
   4. Wrist
   5. Digits
i. The lower extremity
   1. Thigh
   2. Leg
   3. Foot
   4. Toes

G. Posture: the position of the body when not recumbent. Muscle action involved is often entirely reflex in character
   a. Standing: flexors and extensors of the neck, trunk, and lower extremities maintain at least moderate contraction, tensing and relaxing as necessary
   b. Sitting: muscles of the lower extremity are much more relaxed than when standing

H. Locomotion: movement of the body from one place to another, under its own (muscular) power
   a. Walking: involves the alternate swinging of each lower extremity forward, pendulum fashion, then riding the weight of the body in a forward direction on this pendulum
   b. Running: similar to a fast walk, but both feet are never on the ground simultaneously (as in walking)
   c. Swimming: here the effect of gravity is minimized, due to the buoyancy of water; but greater resistance to forward motion is encountered, because of the much greater density of water as compared to that of air. In the most popular swimming stroke, the "crawl," the upper extremities are used to a very great extent, in contrast to locomotion on land.

STUDY QUESTIONS AND PROBLEMS

1. What is the most outstanding physiological property of muscle?

2. Outline a description of the gross and microscopic structure of a typical skeletal muscle. What is the ultimate unit of muscle contraction?

3. Briefly discuss the nerve supply of skeletal muscle. What is another name for neuromuscular junction?

4. What is muscle tone? Recruitment?

5. Classify laboratory stimuli according to their strength. Will an entire muscle contract maximally or not at all?

6. Draw a sketch of the recording resulting from a simple or single muscle twitch, and label all its parts. As a rule, do our body movements depend upon the simple twitches of muscles?

7. Define: *summation, treppe, complete and incomplete tetanus, contracture,*

and *fatigue.* Do our muscles ever reach complete fatigue in normal activity, or in rather strenuous physical exercise?

8. Very briefly, outline the chemistry of muscle contraction. What compound is thought to be the source of immediate energy of contraction? What is oxygen debt?

9. Describe the three classes of levers, and give examples in the body.

10. A basket of apples weighing 60 lb is lifted 3 ft into a truck. How much work has been done, in foot-pounds? Write the formula for calculating work.

11. Discuss the meaning of the terms *origin* and *insertion* (of muscles).

12. Discuss what is meant by flexors, rotators, extensors, supinators, pronators, elevators, and depressors.

13. Doctor C. finds that his patient cannot turn his head to the left. What long muscle, attaching to the sternum and mastoid bone, could be involved?

14. Mrs. Y. complains that she cannot grind her food properly, and that her "jaw muscles" seem to be weak. What group of muscles might be suspected of not functioning properly?

15. Patient D. enters the hospital for neurological tests. He has a masklike face, and cannot smile, frown, etc. Tests confirm that a pair of nerves is involved. Which pair?

16. What muscles are involved in normal breathing?

17. What muscles are involved in vigorous breathing?

18. Make a list of the major muscles involved in walking, swimming, and standing upright (as when watching a parade).

integration and control by the nervous system

O ur every thought and action, as well as every physical and mental sensation we experience, is intimately associated with the nervous system. No matter whether we are solving one of the many problems of everyday living, watching a favorite television program, playing tennis, or even sleeping, we are completely dependent upon this complex arrangement of nerve cells in the brain, spinal cord, and nerves to do its job. The two specialties of nervous tissue are **responsiveness** or *irritability;* and **conductivity,** the ability to convey or transmit electrical-type *nerve impulses* from one part of the body to another. Thousands of these high-speed impulses dart constantly throughout and among the structures comprising the nervous system, keeping us informed of any changes in either external or internal environment, helping us to make appropriate adjustments to these changes when necessary. Many of these adjustments are carried out *reflexly,* completely below the level of consciousness; for example, regulation of *body temperature, heart rate,* and *urine formation* is to a very great extent under control of the nervous system. The body processes are not always regulated by this system alone—the endocrine or ductless-gland system produces hormones which aid in this regulation—but the nervous system plays the chief role. The *functional unit* of the nervous system, which also serves as its most important structural unit, is the *nerve cell* or **neuron.** A drawing showing the main features of a so-called typical neuron, and illustrating the major kinds of neurons, is presented in Fig. 7-1. Neurons have a cell body and two types of protoplasmic extensions or processes—*axons* and *dendrites.* Impulses flow toward the cell body over the dendrites, which are called *afferent processes;* and impulses flow away from the neuron cell body over axons, known also as *efferent processes.*

The cell body of a neuron is necessary to the survival of the entire neuron. It is within the cell body that the vital processes of neuron metabolism take place; and separation of the cell body from axon or dendrites causes the death of those processes, even though the cell body itself survives. The cell bodies of certain neurons in the brain are capable of sending out impulses without prior stimulation.

SUPPORTING CELLS Neurons are the functional units of the nervous system, but they constitute only one kind of structural unit found in nervous tissue. Special cells, *neuroglia,* help to give nervous tissue support and structural integrity. There are three major types of neuroglia: *astrocytes, oligodendroglia,* and *microglia.* In addition to helping support nervous tissue, microglia may also act as phagocytes, engulfing cellular debris and potentially harmful bacteria and other microorganisms.

THE NERVE IMPULSE

Characteristics of the impulse

Nerve impulses travel over neurons in *nerves* and *nerve roots,* and over *tracts* and

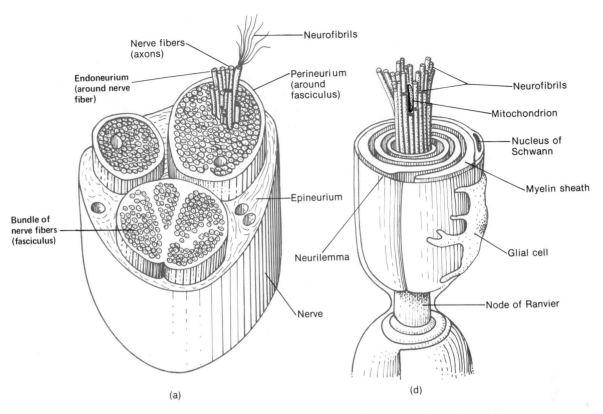

Figure 7-1 The structure of nerve cells and nerves. (a) Construction of a typical nerve. (b) The fine structure of an axon and its neurilemma sheath.

pathways (groups of neurons) in the brain and spinal cord. The nerve impulse itself must be considered: its *nature, speed, origin, method of propagation,* and certain other characteristics. A nerve impulse may be defined as *a self-propagating wave of negativity, traveling along a neuron or across a synapse (junction) between one neuron and another, or between a neuron and an effector, such as a muscle or gland.* The impulse is *not* a simple electrical current.* Neurons are poor conductors of electricity, and when they are forced to conduct it, the strength of the current decreases with distance traveled. A nerve impulse retains its strength no matter how long the neuron or how many synapses it must travel over; this is so because the impulse is continually being regenerated as it moves along; the fastest nerve impulses reach a speed of only about *390 feet per second* (fps)—much slower than the speed of electricity, which is 186,000 miles per second (mi/sec).

* An electrical current may be defined as the movement of electrons along a conductor.

What initiates a nerve impulse? Any change in the external or internal environment that can be detected by the various kinds of specialized *receptors* found at *peripheral nerve endings* (those located at the distal ends of nerves) or the reception by a *motor neuron* of an impulse transmitted from a *sensory neuron,* or from centers in the *brain* or *brainstem.* In the laboratory, isolated nerves can be stimulated by striking and pinching them and by placing them in contact with acid, salt, or other chemicals (thereby changing the pH or ionic qualities of the environment), and by many other methods. The most common laboratory stimulus is an *electrical current.* Properly controlled, electricity does not injure nerve tissue; and it provides a stimulus that can be stopped and started at will. Its strength is easily and precisely regulated. Not all electrical stimuli are of sufficient strength to produce a response in a nerve, however. A stimulus that is too weak to cause an impulse to move along a nerve cell in a nerve or other nervous system structure is called a *subthreshold* or subminimal (subliminal) stimulus;

and one that is just strong enough to do so is a *threshold* or minimal (liminal) stimulus. No matter how much the strength of a stimulus is increased above the threshold level, there is no corresponding increase in the speed or intensity of the impulse. It is apparent that nerve cells obey the *all-or-none law or principle,* in much the same manner of a muscle cell; and as with muscle cells, the all-or-none principle applies only during *constant conditions.* For example, if the frequency of the stimulus is increased, the intensity of the response is apparently greater; at least, the *cerebral cortex* (outer layer of the cerebrum, the largest part of the brain) interprets painful stimuli as being more intense when they are applied at greater frequency. Also, different neurons in the same nerve or pathway have different thresholds; so even though neurons exhibit an all-or-none response, *nerves themselves do not.*

It has been known since about 1900 that ions are present both inside and outside nerve cells and that, in the resting neuron, the concentration of *sodium ions* within the selectively permeable membrane of the nerve cell is *low,* while outside the membrane (in the intercellular fluid), the concentration of these ions is *high.* It was also known that,

within the cell, there is a *high* concentration of *potassium ions,* chloride (cl⁻) ions, and *negative organic ions.* The result is an *electrical-potential difference in charge* across the cell membrane, with the *inside* of the neuron *more negatively charged* than the *outside,* and the neuron was said to be *polarized.* Today, we call this condition the *resting potential* (Fig. 7-2). It has been found that, during the transmission of an impulse, the selectivity of the membrane is somehow temporarily altered, permitting *sodium ions* to rush *into* the cell and a few *potassium and organic ions* to move *out.* The result is that the *inside* of the cell becomes *positively charged* with respect to the outside. Almost immediately, the membrane alters its permeability to potassium ions, and they quickly move inside the cell, with the result that the inside is again negative relative to the outside. When the first movement of ions takes place, the resting potential is destroyed—that is, the neuron is *depolarized*—and an *action potential* takes its place. Within a fraction of a second, this action potential causes the adjacent point on the neuron membrane to alter its permeability and acquire an action potential of its own. In effect, the action potential "moves" along the nerve cell much in the manner of a spark moving along a

Figure 7-2 Nerve impulse transmission. (a) Resting axon. (b–d) Depolarization and repolarization in response to a stimulus.

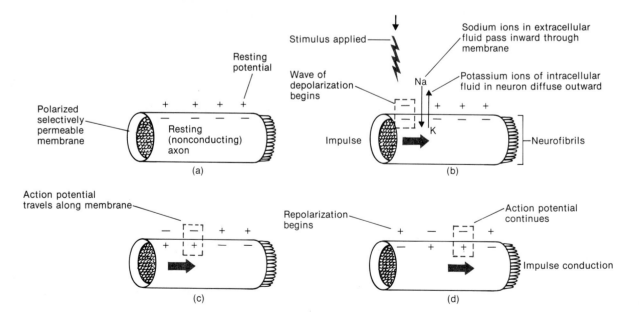

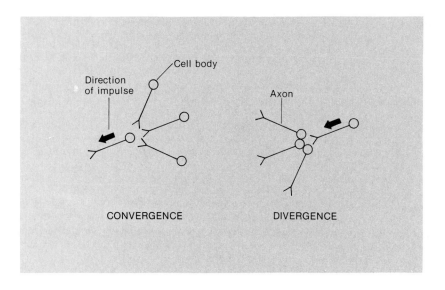

Direction of impulse

Cell body

Axon

CONVERGENCE

DIVERGENCE

Figure 7-3 Convergence and divergence of impulses.

fuse. This "moving" action potential constitutes the *nerve impulse.* Within 0.001 to 0.002 sec, the sodium ions rush outside the nerve-cell membrane and the potassium ions rush in, and the neuron is again in its original state of ionic balance. This last movement of ions is thought to take place by an *active-transport mechanism* (see Chapter 3) called a *sodium–potassium pump,* involving one or more *carrier substances* for its operation. The reason that the *intensity* (strength) and *velocity* (speed) of nerve impulses do not decrease with distance along the neuron is due to the fact that the impulse traveling along a neuron is *constantly regenerated* from one point to the next, instead of merely originating at one source and never being renewed, as is the case with an electrical current. A wave of *depolarization* of the cell membrane is closely followed by a wave of *repolarization,* so quickly that the neuron will again transmit an impulse within about 0.0005 to 0.002 sec, the *refractory period* of the neuron. By using very precise physiological instruments, it is possible to show that this extremely short time interval can be divided into two even shorter periods—the *absolute refractory period,* during which no new impulse will be conducted, and the *relative refractory period,* during which the neuron is regaining its normal transmitting characteristics—and will conduct an impulse if an especially strong stimulus is applied.

Facilitation and summation

Nerve cells can and do send out impulses after being *facilitated* by the simultaneous arrival of several impulses from different neurons. It is not necessary that any one of these impinging impulses be of threshold strength; in fact, some of them can even arrive at the neuron before the others and build up a *local excitatory state,* thus facilitating the firing of the recipient neuron by impulses which would otherwise be considered too weak in intensity to initiate an impulse in another neuron. The effect is that the subthreshold impulses "add together" or *summate.* The sending of several impulses from different nerve fibers to one other is called *convergence* (Fig. 7-3). Its opposite is *divergence,* an arrangement by which a single neuron sends impulses to several others simultaneously. Actually, there are two types of summation—*spatial* and *temporal.* Spatial summation—summation in space or position—has just been described; it depends upon the principle of convergence. Temporal summation, on the other hand, is summation in *time.* If subthreshold stimuli are applied to a neuron rapidly enough, a local excitatory state is soon built up just as it is when several subthreshold impulses are arriving from different neurons (as in spatial summation), the cell soon fires and the impulse is conducted.

149

SIGNIFICANCE OF NEURON DIAMETER   The *larger the diameter of a nerve fiber, the faster the impulse,* and conversely. The largest sensory neurons mediate the general sensations of temperature, tactile sense (touch), pressure, proprioception (position of body parts in space), and pain; the largest motor neurons are concerned with contraction of voluntary muscle. Both these types are classed physiologically as *A-fibers,* and conduct impulses at a speed of about 100 meters per second (m/sec). Preganglionic fibers of the *autonomic nervous system* (ANS)—the completely reflex portion of the nervous system—and many afferent neurons of the *peripheral nervous system* (PNS) are somewhat smaller in diameter than the largest neurons, and conduct impulses at somewhat slower speeds than the latter. The PNS afferent fibers are concerned with pain impulses, and are known as *B-fibers* or *B–neurons;* *C-fibers* are the smallest in diameter, and conduct the slowest (about 0.5 m/sec). *Postganglionic autonomic neurons* are placed in this class, along with certain fibers of the PNS that mediate impulses concerned with the sensations of pressure, temperature, and pain. *Myelinated* neurons conduct impulses at a more rapid rate of speed than *nonmyelinated* neurons, indicating that the fatty myelin surrounding them may serve as a sort of *insulator* for the former neurons. Discussions of the central, peripheral, and autonomic nervous systems are presented in later sections of this chapter.

Inhibitory neurons

So far in this discussion, neuron action has been generally pictured as bringing about some positive sensation or action; that is, when an impulse passes over a neuron, we are supposed to experience a sensation, a muscle or visceral organ is expected to contract, or a gland to secrete. The fact is, some neurons actually *prevent* other neurons from firing or sending out impulses. When such an *inhibitory neuron* is stimulated, it probably increases the permeability of a second neuron (with which it synapses) to potassium ions rather than to sodium ions, and the inside of the neuron acted upon becomes more negative with respect to the outside than

normally. The second neuron now fails to discharge. Why should one neuron inhibit another? There are many instances in which this action is necessary to normal body functions. The *reciprocal action* of flexor and extensor muscles is an outstanding example. When an extensor muscle of the arm contracts, a flexor must relax, and vice versa. Certain reflexes must often be inhibited and their actions temporarily postponed until a more suitable time. For example, we inhibit the breathing reflex when diving and swimming under water; and as we grow up, the (publicly) socially unacceptable (but biologically necessary) processes of urination and defecation are normally postponed until they can be performed in private.

Synaptic transmission

The terminal buttons of each axon make near-physical connections with the dendrites and cell bodies of one or more

Figure 7-4   Two neurons in synapse with a third neuron.

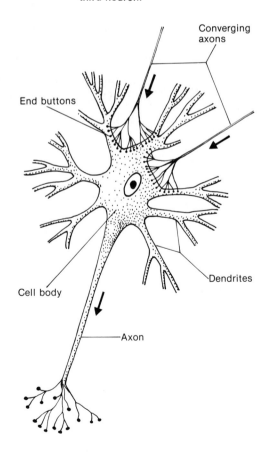

neurons (Fig. 7-4). There are many buttons at the end of an axon, and several (rather than just one) always lie very close to the cell bodies of the neuron or neurons entering into this arrangement, called a *synapse.* In most synapses, the membrane of each terminal button is separated from that of the dendrite or cell body with which it synapses by a gap of only some 20 millimicrons (mμ), some by even less. Most synaptic conduction or transmission in the PNS and ANS is thought to be carried out by the *transmitting agent acetylcholine,* which is released by terminal buttons into the synaptic gap and then quickly inactivated by the enzyme *cholinesterase.* Acetylcholine may also be employed in certain synapses within the CNS (central nervous system); however, it appears that there are several chemicals serving as transmitting agents in the brain and spinal cord. In function, all such chemicals apparently lower the polarization of the membrane on the cell body or dendrite of the *postsynaptic neuron* (the neuron on the distal side of the synapse) causing a *new* nerve impulse to be generated. This process is repeated as often as is necessary in order for the impulse to reach its final destination. The fact that transmitter agents are released only by axons (and not by cell bodies or dendrites) accounts for the fact that *transmission across a synapse is in one direction only: always from axons to the cell body and dendrites of the next neuron, and never in the reverse direction.* Thus *the synapse determines the direction an impulse will take within the nervous system.* True, an axon stimulated at its midpoint will send impulses in both directions simultaneously; but in the body, nerve cells are stimulated at their ends, rather than in the middle. When such an experiment is performed, one impulse will travel along the axon to the terminal buttons, cross the synapse, and cause the next neuron to discharge, or an effector to react; but the other impulse will move to the cell body of the stimulated neuron and stop.

Transmission at
neuromuscular junctions

The main features of the point at which motor fibers enter a skeletal muscle—the *neuromuscular junction*—include a *terminal branch of an axon,* a *specialized area* on a muscle just beneath this terminal branch, and a *gap* (similar to that of a synapse) between them (Fig. 7-5). The entire structure is only about 0.05 mm in diameter, and acetylcholine is the agent that conveys the impulse across the gap. *Visceral motor endings*—those supplying cardiac muscle, smooth muscle, and glands, via the autonomic nervous system—are roughly similar to those of striated muscle. Neuromuscular junctions are also known as *myoneural junctions.*

Organization of
the nervous system

When beginning a study of the nervous system, it is convenient and customary to divide the overall system into smaller "systems." It should be borne in mind, however, that these divisions are purely arbitrary; in reality, these subsystems are intimately connected, both physically and functionally. These smaller divisions are the **central nervous system** (CNS), **peripheral nervous system** (PNS), and **autonomic nervous system** (ANS). The central nervous system (Fig. 7-7) consists of the *brain* and *spinal cord.* The brain itself is made up of the *cerebrum, cerebellum,* and *brainstem;* the last structure consists of the *pons, medulla oblongata,* and associated nervous tissues. The peripheral nervous system is made up of the *nerves* that

Figure 7-5 A motor unit.

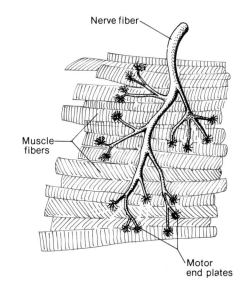

Nerve fiber

Muscle
fibers

Motor
end plates

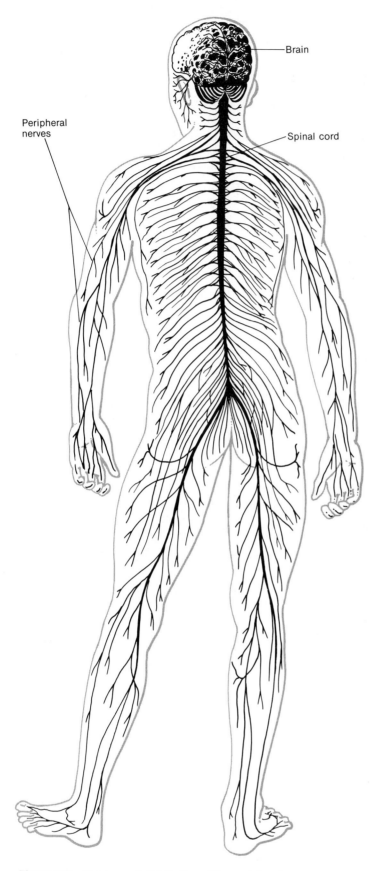

Figure 7-6 The general distribution of the peripheral nerves.

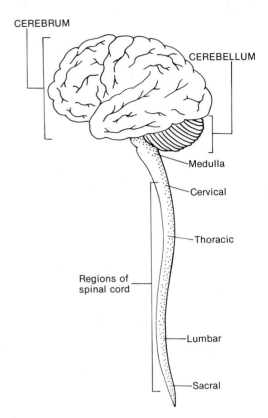

CEREBRUM

CEREBELLUM

Medulla

Cervical

Thoracic

Regions of
spinal cord

Lumbar

Sacral

Figure 7-7 The chief organs of the central nervous system.

branch off the brain itself (*cranial nerves*) and those extending outward from the spinal cord (*spinal nerves,* Fig. 7-6). The autonomic nervous system sends neuron processes along with those of the peripheral nervous system, and has some neurons which are entirely its own.

THE CENTRAL NERVOUS SYSTEM

The cerebrum and its functions

The *cerebrum* (Figs. 7-8 and 7-9 and Color Plates IV, V, and VIII) is the largest and most complex portion of the brain. It consists of two identical halves or *hemispheres,* completely separated by a deep cleft, the *longitudinal fissure,* except deep inside, where they are connected by a broad band of fibers or neurons called the *corpus callosum* and three lesser connections or *commissures,* the *fornix* and *anterior* and *posterior commissures.* The crossing of fibers in the corpus callosum and other commissures causes

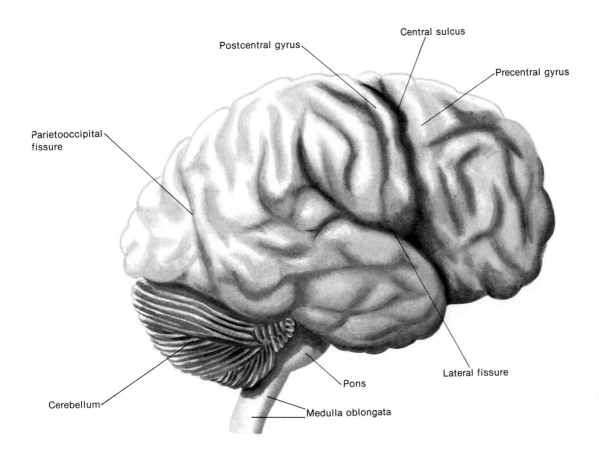

Postcentral gyrus

Central sulcus

Precentral gyrus

Parietooccipital fissure

Lateral fissure

Pons

Cerebellum

Medulla oblongata

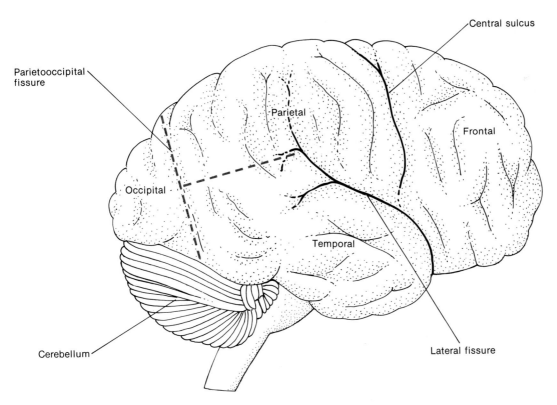

Central sulcus

Parietooccipital fissure

Parietal

Frontal

Occipital

Temporal

Cerebellum

Lateral fissure

Figure 7-8 External features of the cerebrum.

153

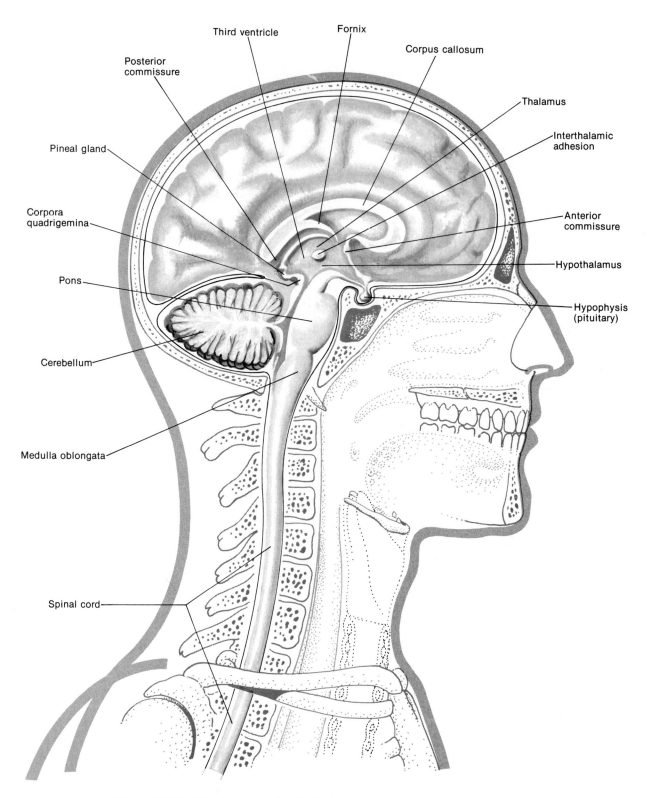

Figure 7-9(a) Structures associated with the cerebrum.

much of the right half of the brain to be connected with the left side of the body, and vice versa.

Upon carefully examining the cerebrum externally, it will be seen that, from the side, it somewhat resembles a large mitten. A long

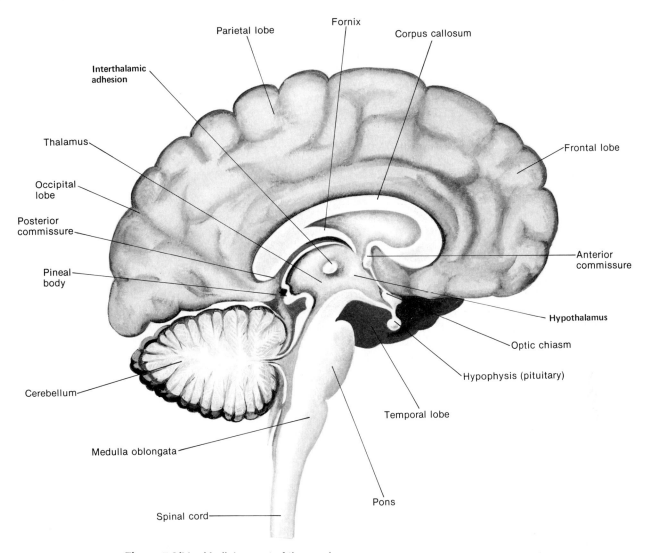

Figure 7-9(b) Medial aspect of the cerebrum.

cleft, the *lateral fissure* (fissure of Sylvius), separates the "thumb" from the upper part of the mitten; while the upper part is partially separated into anterior and posterior portions by a groove, which does not quite reach the lateral fissure on each side, the *central sulcus* or sulcus of Rolando.

On the rear portion of the cerebral hemisphere, the *parietooccipital fissure* can be seen. By using these fissures and sulci as landmarks, each cerebral hemisphere can be divided into four large *lobes: frontal, parietal, occipital,* and *temporal.* It will be noted that these lobes are not sharply demarked, and in fact blend into one another at several points. The boundaries of cerebral lobes are somewhat arbitrary, and must be imagined when examining a brain specimen in the

laboratory. Each of these lobes rests in its respective *cranial fossa* of the skull. A fifth lobe, the *insular lobe* (also called simply insula, and island of Reil) lies deep to the frontal and temporal lobes. The surface of the human cerebrum is highly folded or convoluted, providing a greater surface area than could otherwise be accommodated within the cranial vault. In general, the term meaning a ridge portion of a convolution is *gyrus;* the groove on either side of a gyrus is a *sulcus;* while an especially deep groove or cleft is a *fissure.* This system of terminology is not, unfortunately, strictly adhered to by many authors and instructors.

It must be clearly understood that man is only beginning to unravel some of the mysteries involved in the functioning of the

155

SENSORY

MOTOR

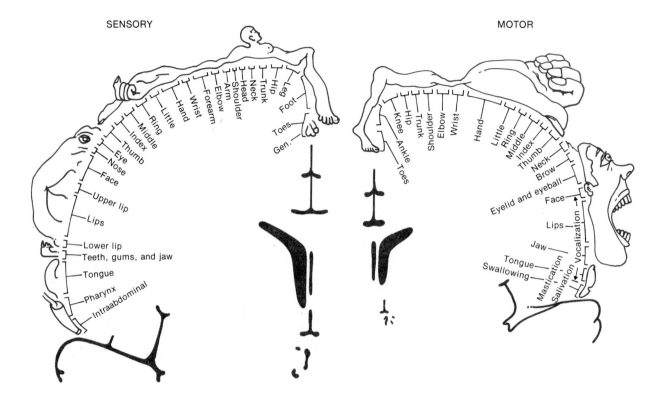

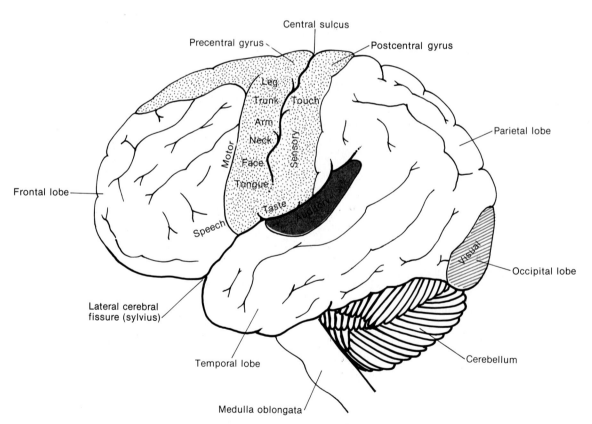

Figure 7-10 How certain motor activities and sensations are represented in the cerebral cortex.

brain. There is much that we do not know; for example, no one knows where the seats of memory and will power are located. Experimenters do not simply open the skull of a living human and run a series of tests; data must be accumulated from patients with brain *lesions* (diseased areas) and *trauma* (wounds), and these data must be evaluated over periods of years. When an individual must have a portion of his brain exposed during surgery, he is often conscious (the brain itself is *insensitive to pain*), so portions of the brain may be lightly stimulated and the patient asked to describe any sensations he may experience. Also, motor reactions (movements) are noted. These data, together with that accumulated from animal experimentation and detailed microscopic examination, constitute man's knowledge of his brain. It should also be pointed out that the brain and the *"mind"* are not synonymous. The brain is a dissectible organ; but the mind is an abstraction, referring to mental activity that takes place in the physical organ, the brain.

Functions of the different lobes of the cerebrum

Although there is considerable overlap in the functions of adjacent cerebral lobes, each lobe does often seem to have its specialty. A description of the known functions of the lobes of the cerebrum follows.

FRONTAL LOBE   Located in this portion of the cerebrum are the seats of voluntary movements and personality and at least some of the neurons concerned with memory and speech (Fig. 7-9). It has been found that stimuli applied to the *precentral gyrus* (the fold immediately anterior to the central sulcus) elicits motor responses in the order illustrated in Fig. 7-10. It will be noted that the area serving the muscles of the lowermost portion of the body is uppermost on the gyrus, and that this "upside-down" order is adhered to, with the top portion of the body being represented on the lowest portion of the gyrus. The role played by the frontal lobe (or any other portion of the brain) in the personality of the individual is poorly understood.

PARIETAL LOBE   This lobe of the cerebrum is involved in a wide variety of general sensory functions. The sensations of *heat, cold, pain, touch, pressure,* and *position of body parts in space (proprioception or stereognosis)* all reach consciousness here, after having been brought to the cerebrum as impulses traveling over specialized receptors and nerves of the peripheral nervous system. Like general motor functions, general sensations are represented in inverted order in the cerebrum, many of them in the *postcentral gyrus* of the parietal lobe. There is evidence that at least some portion of the sense of taste reaches consciousness in this lobe.

OCCIPITAL LOBE   In this lobe, which forms the extreme posterior end of each cerebral hemisphere, a very special sense, *vision,* is centered. When we see something, specialized endings have been stimulated in the *retina* of the eye. The impulse which results from the stimulation of these cells by light travels over the *optic nerve, optic tract,* and *optic radiation,* all of which lead in this respective order to cells in the *occipital lobe.* We do all our "seeing" with these cells, the eye itself acting only as an elaborate *receptor organ.*

TEMPORAL LOBE   Another special sense, hearing or *audition,* is interpreted in this lobe of the cerebrum. The sense of smell (*olfaction*) may be seated in a gyrus located in the most inferior and medial portion of this lobe, as well as the closely related sense of taste (*gustatory sense*). At least a portion of the speech and language center is located in the temporal lobe. Figures 7-8 and 7-10 summarize current knowledge of some cerebral functions.

CEREBRAL WHITE AND GRAY MATTER   Upon examination of either a frontal or horizontal section made through the cerebrum, it is easily seen that the appearance of brain tissue is not uniform throughout. Instead, there is an irregularly shaped mass of pale *white matter,* covered by an extremely thin layer of *gray matter,* the *cerebral cortex* (Fig. 7-11). The cortex is only 1.5–4.5 mm thick. Other gray substance, called *deep gray matter,* forms what are known as the *basal nuclei,* which are situated deep within the cerebral hemispheres (Fig. 7-11). Gray

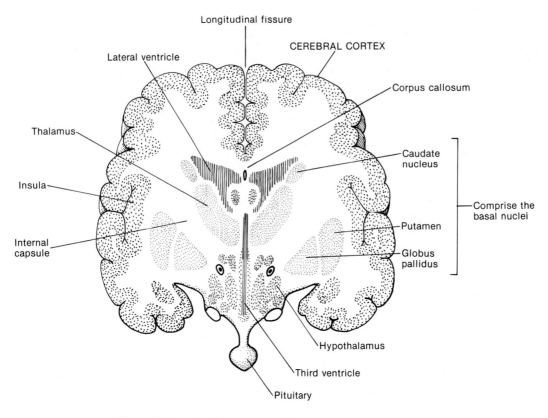

Figure 7-11 The white matter and gray matter of the cerebrum (frontal section).

Figure 7-12 The cerebellum and related structures.

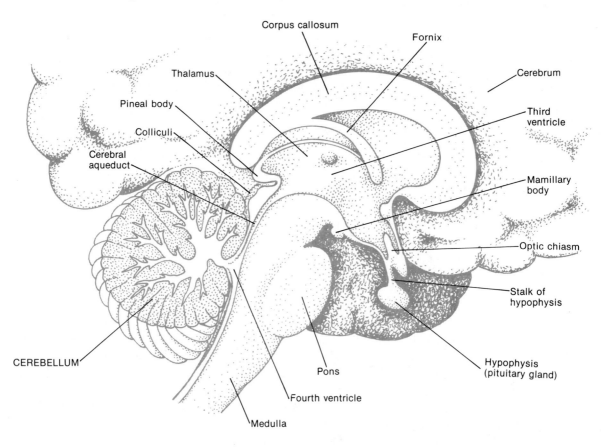

matter consists chiefly of *neuron cell bodies,* while white matter is made up mostly of *myelinated axons* or "fibers." Three kinds of fibers comprise the white matter of the cerebrum: *association fibers* connecting one lobe of a cerebral hemisphere with adjacent lobes, and individual gyri of these lobes with each other; *commissural fibers* joining the cortex of one hemisphere with that of the other; and *projection fibers* that connect the cerebrum with the brainstem and spinal cord. The cortical gray matter of the brain, with its 12 to 14 billion neurons, initiates our *every thought* and *voluntary action.* It also has great influence over all reflexes. Reasoning, memory, emotion, foresight, intelligence, personality, interpretation of the special sensations, speech mechanisms, and other mental activities are all begun or stored in the cerebral cortex.

The cerebellum

The *cerebellum* (Fig. 7-12 and Color Plates V, VI, and VIII) lies beneath the occipital lobes of the cerebrum. It consists of two *hemispheres* connected by a narrow, wormlike lobe, the *vermis.* Gray matter in the cerebellum, like that of the cerebrum, is found both externally (in the cerebellar cortex) and internally as aggregations of cell bodies, here called *cerebellar nuclei.* In the nervous system, a *nucleus* may be defined as *a collection or aggregation of nerve cell bodies within the central nervous system,* and does not refer to the cell nuclei themselves. A *ganglion,* as distinguished from a nucleus, is *a collection of cell bodies lying outside the brain or spinal cord*—that is, outside the central nervous system.

The gyri and sulci of the cerebellum are narrow and numerous, and somewhat straighter than those of the cerebrum. Two types of neuron-fiber tracts are found in the cerebellum: *association* and *projection.* Association fibers connect the cells of the cerebellar cortex with the cells of the nuclei lying in the white matter, while projection fibers connect it with the medulla oblongata, pons, and thalamus—all of which are parts of the *brainstem*—and spinal cord. Those fibers joining the cerebellum with the midbrain—an extremely deep portion of the brain—are

grouped together into two *superior cerebellar peduncles;* those leading to the *pons* located just above the medulla comprise the *middle cerebellar peduncles;* and the cerebellum is connected to the medulla and spinal cord by the *inferior cerebellar peduncles.* Functionally, the cerebellum is concerned with coordination of the actions of muscles and muscle groups. *Smooth, precise body movements* depend upon "computer action" on the part of the cerebellum as it receives impulses from the cerebrum and skeletal muscles, evaluates them and sorts them out, and relays the "information" to those muscles that are required to bring about a given action. The maintenance of posture and equilibrium depends to a large extent on the influence of the cerebellum on the postural muscles. The cerebellum is not concerned with conscious activity in any way.

The brainstem

If the cortex of both the cerebrum and cerebellum is removed, a stalklike mass of central-nervous-system tissue remains—the *brainstem* (Fig. 7-13 and Color Plate VIII). It includes the *medulla, pons, mesencephalon* or midbrain, *diencephalon* or tweenbrain, and the previously mentioned *basal nuclei.*

THE MEDULLA Anatomically, the medulla oblongata can be considered to be simply the enlarged upper end of the spinal cord. There is no line of demarcation between medulla and cord—the latter ends at the *foramen magnum*—and *no portion of the brain lies outside the skull.* In the adult, the medulla is only about an inch long, and above is continuous with the pons. Although the medulla resembles the spinal cord externally, and some fiber tracts of the cord travel through the medulla, important differences in the arrangement of gray and white matter are seen in cross-sections of the two. Some of the main external features of the medulla are illustrated in Fig. 7-13. Ventrally, an *anterior median fissure* is bordered by two ridges, the *pyramids*—two fiber tracts of white matter that cross or *decussate* at the lower end of the medulla. Dorsally, a *posterior median sulcus* and two *dorsolateral sulci* are easily seen. On either side of the posterior median sulcus is a ridge, the *fasciculus gracilis,* and just lateral

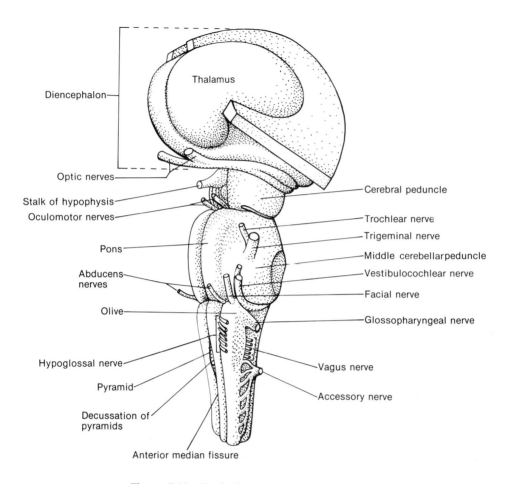

Diencephalon

Thalamus

Optic nerves

Stalk of hypophysis

Oculomotor nerves

Pons

Abducens nerves

Olive

Hypoglossal nerve

Pyramid

Decussation of pyramids

Anterior median fissure

Cerebral peduncle

Trochlear nerve

Trigeminal nerve

Middle cerebellarpeduncle

Vestibulocochlear nerve

Facial nerve

Glossopharyngeal nerve

Vagus nerve

Accessory nerve

Figure 7-13 The brainstem.

to either fasciculus gracilis is another ridge, the *fasciculus cuneatus.* A depression in the dorsum of the most superior portion of the medulla forms the lower half of one of the spaces where cerebrospinal fluid is made, the *fourth ventricle* (Fig. 7-12). The upper portion of this ventricle is formed by the pons. In life, the fourth ventricle is covered with a thin, non-nervous-tissue membrane, the roof or *tectum* of the fourth ventricle. An *inferior cerebellar peduncle* is seen lying on either side of the ventricle. A *ventro-lateral sulcus* is easily identified on either lateral aspect of the medulla, and between this and the dorso-lateral sulcus is an oval, raised area, the *olive.* The roots of the *hypoglossal nerve* (cranial nerve XII) emerge from the medulla in the ventrolateral sulcus, and those of the *accessory nerve* (XI), *vagus nerve* (X), and *glossopharyngeal nerve* (IX) emerge from the dorsolateral sulcus. Cranial nerves IX, X, XI, and XII have their nuclei of origin in the medulla.

The importance of the medulla cannot be overemphasized. Not only does it contain the nuclei of several cranial nerves, but *vital reflex centers* concerned with the control of breathing, the rate of heartbeat, and diameter of blood vessels are also located within it, as are control centers for swallowing, coughing, vomiting, sneezing, and hiccupping. It is easy to see how damage to the medulla by disease or accident could result in death. The medulla is made up mostly of *white-matter fiber tracts* that carry motor and sensory impulses between the brain and spinal cord, and intermingled white and gray matter called *reticular formation.* This portion of the brain makes important connections with the pons, cerebellum, and thalamus; and all neuron pathways between the brain and spinal cord pass through the medulla.

THE PONS   The pons (Fig. 7-13) lies just superior to the medulla. It connects the medulla and cerebellum with the mesencephalon or midbrain, and joins the two cerebellar hemispheres. A portion of its dorsal surface forms part of the *floor of the fourth ventricle.* The *superior cerebellar peduncles* are seen bordering this portion of the fourth ventricle. Ventrally and laterally, the *trigeminal nerves* (cranial nerves V) are rooted in the pons, while the *abducens nerves* (VI), *facial nerves* (VII), and *acoustic* or *auditory nerves* (VIII) are seen emerging at the junction between pons and medulla. Internally, the pons contains the *nuclei* of all the cranial nerves just mentioned. Like that of the medulla, most of the substance of the pons is white matter and reticular formation. A respiratory nucleus, the *pneumotaxic center,* and reflex pathways involving breathing, pupillary action, and eye movements pass through the pons.

THE MESENCEPHALON   The midbrain or mesencephalon is quite small, and lies between the pons and the diencephalon, joining the pons and cerebellum to the diencephalon and cerebrum (Fig. 7-13). Ventrally, the midbrain presents two large ropelike bundles of fibers, the *cerebral peduncles,* and dorsally, four raised areas, *quadrigeminal bodies,* consisting of two *superior* and two *inferior colliculi.* Each colliculus has an armlike band of fibers or *brachium* which extends to the thalamus—a structure located in another portion of the brain, the *diencephalon.* A pair of *oculomotor nerves* (III) and *trochlear nerves* (IV) can be seen as they reach the surface between the cerebral peduncles and the pons, on the ventral side of the brain stem. The trochlear nerves are placed far laterally, and actually emerge from the dorsal aspect of the brain stem (Fig. 7-13). A narrow channel-like cavity, the *cerebral aqueduct,* passes through the midbrain, joining the fourth ventricle of the medulla and pons with the third ventricle of the diencephalon. The mesencephalon is an important reflex center. The superior colliculi are concerned with visual reflexes, the inferior colliculi with auditory reflexes. The impulses of these reflexes travel over the appropriate cranial nerves—such as impulses for the *pupillary light reflex,* which are carried over the oculomotor nerve, cranial nerve III. The midbrain has both gray matter and white matter, and like the pons and medulla,

an area where gray and white are intermingled called a *reticular formation. Part of the nucleus of the trigeminal nerve lies within the midbrain, and the entire nuclei of the oculomotor and trochlear nerves are found there.* The most outstanding aggregation of cell bodies in the mesencephalon is the *red nucleus,* so called because of the reddish pigment deposited within its substance. The red nucleus relays impulses back and fourth between the cerebrum, cerebellum, pons, and medulla, and its importance can scarcely be overestimated.

THE DIENCEPHALON   Between the mesencephalon and the cerebral hemispheres lies the diencephalon or "tweenbrain" (Fig. 7-13). It consists of the *thalamus, epithalamus, subthalamus,* and *hypothalamus,* and has its own cavity, the *third ventricle,* the walls of which are formed by the two thalami. The third ventricle connects with the *fourth ventricle* by means of a narrow canal, the *cerebral aqueduct.* At the base of each thalamus lies the subthalamus and hypothalamus, forming the lower portion of the walls and floor of the third ventricle. Those structures lying posterosuperior to the thalamus comprise the epithalamus. The small subthalamus contains the *nucleus of Forel* and a fiber tract, the *field of Forel,* which may receive impulses arriving from the midbrain and project them on their way to the cerebral cortex. The hypothalamus includes the *pituitary gland* or *hypophysis;* the *pituitary stalk (infundibulum); tuber cinerum* (area at the base of the infundibulum); small, breastlike *mammillary bodies;* and the *optic chiasm,* a crossing point at which the optic nerves become known as optic tracts. The pituitary gland has hormonal functions that are important in growth regulation, maintenance of blood pressure, lactation (milk secretion), the metabolism of carboyhdrates and fats, and many other physiological processes. The mammillary bodies, by means of their own nuclei, receive and send along impulses which are destined to arrive at appropriate portions of the cerebral cortex where they are interpreted as *odors.*

Considered as a group, the functions of the hypothalamus are many and varied. In addition to its ability to relay impulses between the cerebral cortex and the autonomic nervous system, the hypothalamus is important in sexual activities, in the maintenance of normal body temperature, in keeping us awake when necessary, in control of the appetite, water balance of the body, secretion of hormones by the posterior portion of the pituitary gland, and in the coordination of various functions of the autonomic nervous system. It has been found that the hypothalamus plays an important role in sending along impulses from higher centers to the visceral organs, sometimes to such an extent that pain or other distressful symptoms may appear, producing a *psychogenic* or *psychosomatic illness* rather than an actual organic illness.

The epithalamus is made up of the *pineal body, habenular trigone,* and a band of cross-running white fibers lying just anterior to the superior colliculi and joining together the halves of the diencephalon, the *posterior commissure.* The pineal body is usually less than 1 cm long. It may somehow be concerned with normal sexual maturity or growth, or both. Corresponding roughly to the tuber cinerum is the habenular trigone, from which springs the stalk of the pineal body. Nuclei located in the trigone are important in the transmission of olfactory impulses.

The last portion of the diencephalon to

be discussed is the thalamus proper. The thalami are masses of gray matter inside a thin covering of white matter. Each thalamic mass is usually—but not always—connected to the thalamus of the opposite side by an *intermediate mass* or band of gray matter. Each thalamus contains many nuclei, arranged in five groups. Among the most important areas of the thalamus are the *medial and lateral geniculate bodies* and the *pulvinar* (Fig. 7-14). Due to its many nuclei and their interconnections and connections with both higher and lower centers in the nervous system, the thalamus is a great relaying and integrating center for both motor and sensory impulses. The majority of the impulses arriving at the cerebral cortex have traveled through one or more nuclei of the thalamus, and in fact, the thalamus itself has been found to be capable of conscious interpretation of some sensations, though with a poor degree of preciseness or *discrimination.* Our ability to concentrate upon a given task may depend upon the activation of the appropriate area of the cerebral cortex by the thalamus. Our degree of wakefulness seems to be dependent at least to some extent upon the thalamus, and neurologists have often associated this part of the brain with abstract mental states such as "pleasantness" and "unpleasantness." Many reflexes, especially

Figure 7-14 The two thalami and their connecting structure—
the massa intermedia or intermediate mass.

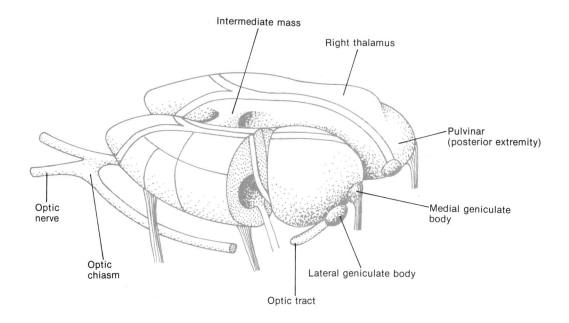

visual and auditory reflexes, are mediated by the *geniculate bodies* and the thalamus proper.

THE BASAL NUCLEI   Embedded within the substance of each cerebral hemisphere, inferior and lateral to either thalamus, lies a cluster of nuclei, the previously mentioned *basal nuclei* (Figs. 7-11 and 7-15). Included within this group are gray masses known as the *putamen, globus pallidus,* and *caudate nucleus.* Layers of white-matter fibers, the *internal* and *external capsules,* enclose and penetrate the nuclei, giving them a striated or striped appearance. The nuclei together with the surrounding and interspersed white matter comprise a *corpus striatum* on either side of the brain. The *coordination of body movements* may depend to a large extent upon integration of impulses within the basal nuclei of the corpus striatum.

The spinal cord

Many of the impulses traveling back and forth between the brain and that portion of the body below the head do so along the tracts and pathways located in the *white matter of the spinal cord,* and by way of the *31 pairs of spinal nerves* that branch off the cord (Fig. 7-21 and Color Plate VIII). Other impulses travel over the autonomic fibers in cranial nerve X, the *vagus,* and cranial nerve XI, the *accessory nerve.*

Although the spinal cord is some 43 cm long in adults, *it extends only about two-thirds the length of the vertebral canal or spinal canal* in which it courses. Composed of both gray matter and white matter, with the former (in cross-section) in the shape of an **H** (or at some cord levels, a butterfly) (Fig. 7-16), the spinal cord is said to *begin* at the level of the *foramen magnum* or upper border of the first cervical vertebra, and to *extend* to the level of the *second lumbar vertebra,* where the tapered caudal end is given the name *conus medullaris.* At its origin, the cord is continuous with the medulla. It will be noted that the relative positions of the gray and white matter of the cord are just the *reverse* of those in the cerebellum and outer portions of the cerebrum.

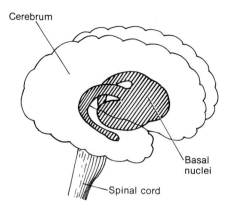

Figure 7-15   The position of the basal nuclei within the cerebrum.

Spinal-cord gray matter lies deep rather than superficial as does the cortex of the cerebrum and that of the cerebellum. This gray matter consists mainly of neuron cell bodies, and the white matter consists of fiber tracts or pathways which carry impulses up and down the cord. As we shall see, some of these impulses reach the brain or originate there, while others do not. The spinal cord is invested with the same three coverings or *meninges* that surround the brain, which are discussed in a later section of this chapter; suffice it to say here that even though the spinal cord proper falls far short of reaching the lower end of the spinal canal, the tough outermost covering or *dura mater* reaches as far caudally as the second sacral vertebra, and a fine filament of fibrous tissue continuous with the innermost cord covering, called the *pia mater,* attaches to the upper segment of the coccyx. This filament is called the *filum terminale.* The middle cord covering, or *arachnoid mater,* ends at the same vertebral level as the dura.

Upon divesting a spinal cord of its meninges, it is seen that the external surface presents an *anterior median fissure, posterior median sulcus,* and *dorsolateral* and *ventrolateral sulci* along each half of the cord (Fig. 7-16). *Dorsal intermediate sulci* are present in the cervical and thoracic portions. By use of the dorsolateral and ventrolateral sulci, each half of the spinal cord is conveniently divided into *anterior, lateral,* and *posterior funiculi.* The dorsal intermediate sulcus further divides the dorsal funiculus of the cervical and thoracic portions of the cord into two smaller regions or fasciculi—the *fasciculus gracilis* and *fasciculus cuneatus.*

Spinal nerves can be seen beginning as *dorsal and ventral roots* emerging at regular intervals along the spinal cord. The dorsal or posterior roots spring from the *dorsolateral sulcus,* the ventral or anterior roots from the region of the *ventrolateral sulcus.* An enlargement, the *dorsal-root ganglion,* is present on each dorsal nerve root, and consists of a collection of cell bodies of neurons that carry impulses into the cord from outside the central nervous system (*afferent neurons*). The roots of most spinal nerves are short; but those in the *lumbar and sacral regions* are extra long, descending from the lower thoracic and upper lumbar portions of the cord and existing in the lower lumbar and sacral regions. An isolated spinal cord, with its long nerve roots hanging from the lower end, reminded early neuroanatomists of a horse's tail; so they named this portion of the cord the *cauda equina.*

Two slight swellings can be noted on the spinal cord: the *cervical and lumbar enlargements.* The cervical enlargement is located between *cervical vertebra 3 and thoracic vertebra 2,* the lumbar enlargement between *thoracic vertebrae 9 and 12.* Located in the cervical enlargement are the origins of the nerves supplying the upper limb, while the lumbar enlargement contains the elements of origin of the nerves supplying the lower limb.

During growth, the vertebral column increases in length much faster, and reaches a far greater total length, than does the spinal cord, with the result that the segments of the cord (points of branching of the spinal nerves) are not located on the same level as the same number segment of the vertebral column. The spinal-cord segments are almost on the same level with the spinal-column level in the cervical region, but vertebrae of corresponding segment numbers are lower and lower as one proceeds down the cord, until finally the nerve roots of the cauda equina must be especially long in order to exit far below the point of termination of the spinal cord proper.

INTERNAL STRUCTURE OF THE SPINAL CORD

On cross-section, as was previously mentioned, it is seen that the gray matter of the

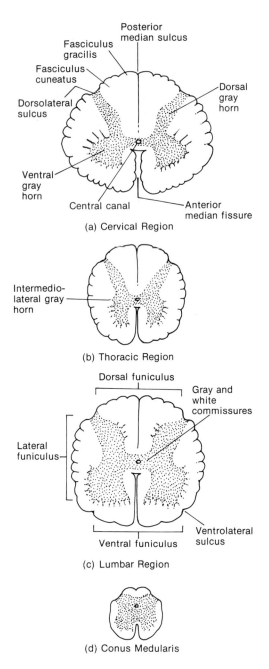

Figure 7-16 Features of the spinal cord, as seen on cross-section.

spinal cord is shaped like an **H** in some portions and somewhat like a butterfly in others, is centrally located, and is surrounded by white matter (Fig. 7-16). The dorsal limbs of the gray substance are called *dorsal or posterior gray horns* (or columns), the ventral limbs *ventral* or *anterior gray horns* (or columns). The cell bodies of neurons forming the *anterior rootlets* of a typical spinal nerve lie within the anterior or ventral gray horn substance. Those giving rise to *dorsal rootlets* of the spinal nerve lie within a *dorsal-root or posterior-root ganglion* just outside the spinal cord proper. In the thoracic and upper cervical portions of the cord, *intermediolateral gray horns or columns* are seen. The gray masses running the length of either lateral half of the spinal cord are connected in the midline by a continuous band, the *gray-and-white commissure.* Inside the commissure is a tiny channel filled with cerebrospinal fluid, the *central canal.* The gray substance varies considerably both in *amount and shape* in different portions of the spinal cord. As would be expected, the large numbers of cell bodies of neurons supplying the upper and lower extremities are reflected in the *amount of gray substance* in the *cervical and lumbar portions* of the cord. The spinal cord also has its own *reticular formation,* found mostly within the gray columns, but also spreading into the lateral funiculus on either side of the cord. In the white matter of the spinal cord lie the neuron tracts or pathways that carry impulses up the cord from the spinal nerves to the brain, and down the cord from the brain to the spinal nerves. The major neuron tracts of the spinal cord as well as those of higher portions of the nervous system are discussed in detail in a later section of this chapter.

The lateral corticospinal and ventral corticospinal tracts are parts of a complex known as the *pyramidal system,* which begins in the motor areas of the cerebrum and conveys voluntary motor impulses to the skeletal muscles. Many *reflex centers* are located in the gray matter of the spinal cord, and these are discussed further in a later section of this chapter, after consideration of the peripheral nervous system.

THE PERIPHERAL NERVOUS SYSTEM

The peripheral nervous system is made up of *cranial, spinal,* and *autonomic nerves,* and links the central nervous system with all parts of the body. These nerves are each of one of *three functional classes: motor or efferent, sensory or afferent,* and *mixed.* Afferent nerves convey impulses from the various receptors of the body *to* the central nervous system; efferent nerves transmit impulses *from* the central nervous system to the body organs; and mixed nerves carry impulses in *both directions* because they are made up of both motor and sensory neurons. Although it is common practice to describe the cranial nerves as being either purely motor, purely sensory, or mixed, it has been found that five of these nerves (numbers III, IV, VI, XI, and XII), formerly thought to be purely motor, carry afferent impulses necessary to the sense of *proprioception.* Proprioception involves the knowledge of position of body parts in space, and is sometimes called muscle sense.

Cranial nerves

There are 12 pairs of cranial nerves, and they appear on the undersurface of the brain, near the pons, medulla, and diencephalon (Fig. 7-17). The *olfactory* and *optic* nerves emerge in the vicinity of the *diencephalon;* the *oculomotor, trochlear,* and *trigeminal* nerves emerge near the *anterior and lateral borders of the pons;* and the *abducens, facial, acoustic, glossopharyngeal, vagus, hypoglossal,* and *accessory* nerves emerge at the *anterior and lateral borders of the medulla.* These are only the *superficial* origins of the cranial nerves, as seen on gross dissection. The *deep origins*—that is the location of the cell bodies of the neurons of each nerve—are included in the discussions to follow (Fig. 7-18). Salient features of each of the cranial nerves will presently be considered, and are summarized in Table 7-1. Traditionally, these nerves are *numbered* as well as named, beginning with the *most anterior,* the olfactory, as the first nerve, and proceeding backward in numerical order. By custom, roman numerals are used in the numbering. This has proven to be a great convenience, because the nerves can be written or spoken of without resorting to their names, which are often long and complex. For example, the *glossopharyngeal nerve* can be written N IX, or simply IX, when used in the proper context, and is referred to verbally as *"nerve nine."*

OLFACTORY NERVE (I) *Purely sensory* in function, the first cranial nerve has its *cells*

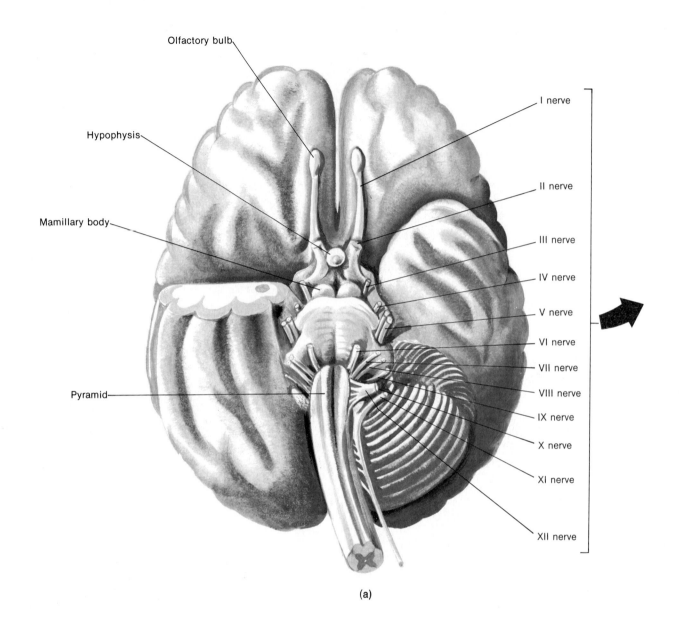

Olfactory bulb

Hypophysis

Mamillary body

Pyramid

I nerve

II nerve

III nerve

IV nerve

V nerve

VI nerve

VII nerve

VIII nerve

IX nerve

X nerve

XI nerve

XII nerve

(a)

of origin in the mucous membrane lining the nasal cavities. Axons of these cells assemble into some 40 tiny nerve *filaments* that pass through the *cribriform plate of the ethmoid bone* and join the *olfactory bulbs* lying beneath the frontal lobes of the brain. Here, synapse is made with the cell bodies that comprise most of the substance of the bulbs, and axons pass posteriorly in the *olfactory nerves* and *tracts* to the cerebral cortex. In reality the olfactory nerves are tracts of the central nervous system, and not true nerves. They might more aply be called extensions of the brain. Dendrites of the cell bodies in the nasal mucosa are specialized to respond

to the presence of molecules of odorous substances in the atmosphere; but impulses must travel all the way into the cerebral cortex— *the temporal lobe*—in order to be interpreted as an odor.

OPTIC NERVE (II) This is the nerve of *vision;* and like the olfactory nerve, it is not a true nerve, but a tract of the brain. *Cells of origin* are located in the extreme posterior portion (retina) of the eye, and axon fibers group together as the *optic nerves.* After entering the cranial vault by way of the *optic foramen,* the optic nerves pass posteriorly a short distance, then meet at the floor of the

166

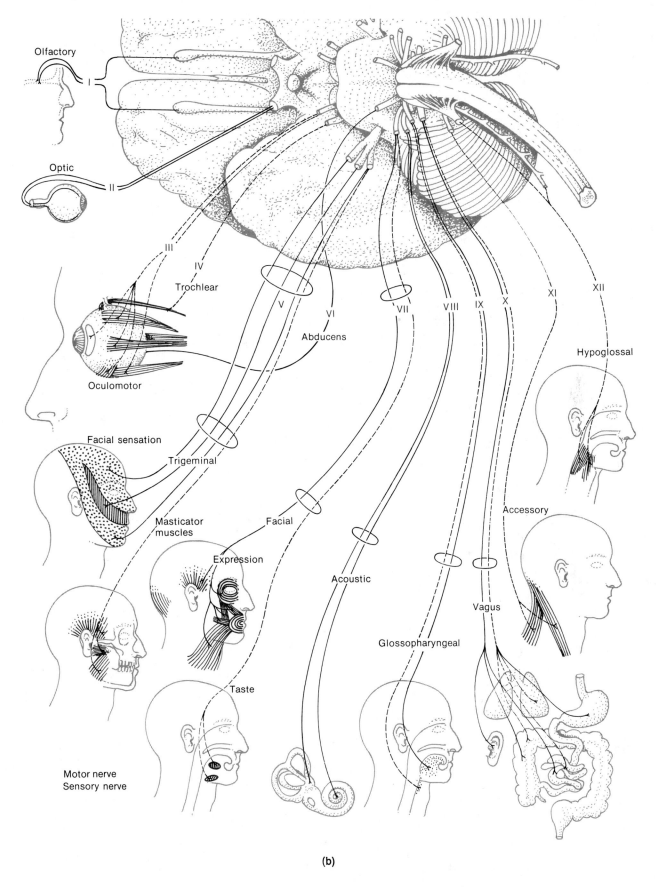

Olfactory

I

Optic

II

III

IV

Trochlear

V

VI

Abducens

Oculomotor

VII

VIII

IX

X

XI

XII

Hypoglossal

Facial sensation

Trigeminal

Masticator muscles

Facial

Accessory

Expression

Acoustic

Vagus

Glossopharyngeal

Taste

Motor nerve
Sensory nerve

(b)

Figure 7-17 The cranial nerves. (a) Superficial origins (facing page). (b) General distribution.

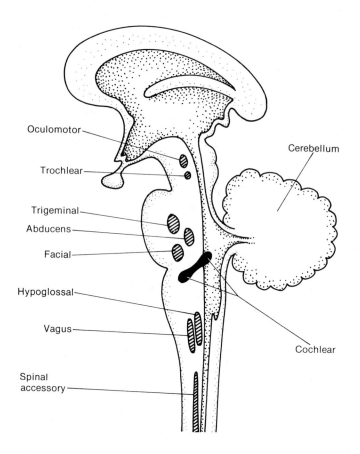

Oculomotor
Trochlear
Trigeminal
Abducens
Facial
Hypoglossal
Vagus
Spinal
accessory

Cerebellum

Cochlear

Figure 7-18   Deep origins of some of the cranial nerves.
See text description of these and the origins of those
that do not appear in the drawing.

diencephalon, where they appear to *decussate* or cross to the opposite side. Posterior to this junction, they are called *optic tracts,* and the $\times$-shaped structure thus formed is called the *optic chiasm.* Only a relatively small portion of the fibers of the optic nerves actually cross at the chiasm (Fig. 8-5), many of them simply bending and remaining on the same side of the brain (see Chapter 8). The neurons of the optic tracts *synapse in the thalamus* with neurons leading to the *visual cortex* in the *occipital lobe,* with neurons in the *superior colliculus* of the midbrain *concerned with visual reflexes,* and with cells located in the *nucleus of the oculomotor nerve,* which is involved in *pupillary light reflexes.* The optic nerve has only *afferent* (sensory) fibers.

OCULOMOTOR NERVE (III) An *efferent* nerve, that is, one having mainly motor fibers, cranial nerve III sends efferent impulses to *four of the six skeletal muscles of the eye* (superior, medial, and inferior rectus,

and *inferior oblique) and *mediates afferent proprioceptive impulses from these same muscles. Autonomic efferent fibers* are also found in this nerve. Cell bodies of those *motor axons* to the four eye muscles supplied lie in the *oculomotor nucleus of the mesencephalon,* while those of the *autonomic motor fibers* are located in the *nucleus of Edinger–Westphal,* also in the midbrain. These fibers synapse in the *ciliary ganglion* (Fig. 7-32) with *cells that supply the ciliary muscles and iris of the eye.* The oculomotor nerve passes through the *superior orbital fissure* on its way to the eye.

TROCHLEAR NERVE (IV) Another nerve that reaches the orbit by way of the superior orbital fissure, the trochlear nerve is *mainly motor* in function, but also conveys *proprioceptive impulses* from the eye muscle it supplies, the *superior oblique.* It is the *smallest of all the cranial nerves,* and *cell bodies of its motor fibers are located in the mesencephalon.*

TRIGEMINAL NERVE (V) This is the *largest* cranial nerve, and carries *motor, general sensory,* and *proprioceptive fibers.* It has *two large roots, motor* and *sensory.* The sensory root has *three main branches, or divisions: ophthalmic, maxillary,* and *mandibular.* The ophthalmic supplies *sensory fibers* to the *skin of the anterior portion of the scalp,* the *upper eyelid, eyeball, forehead,* and *mucous membrane of the nose,* and carries *autonomic fibers* to the *lacrimal gland.* The *maxillary division* conveys *general sensation* from impulses from the *lower teeth and gums, skin of the lower lip and jaw, teeth and gums,* and *mucosa* (mucous membrane) *of the palate.* It also supplies some of the *autonomic fibers* to the *lacrimal* (tear) *gland.* The *mandibular division* of the sensory root of the trigeminal nerve mediates *sensory* impulses from the *lower teeth and gums, skin of the lower lip and jaw, posterior portion of the scalp, mucous membrane of the mouth,* and *two-thirds of the tongue* (anterior portion). The *motor root* of the trigeminal nerve is associated anatomically with the mandibular division of the sensory root, and supplies the *muscles of mastication* (both pterygoids, masseter, and temporalis) and some of the small *muscles under the floor of the mouth* and *in the upper throat.* Locations of *cell bodies* and

TABLE 7-1

Important features of cranial nerves

Cranial nerve	Number	Functional class	Location of cells of origin	Chief function
Olfactory	I	Sensory	Nasal mucosa	Sense of smell
Optic	II	Sensory	Retina of eye	Visual sense
Oculomotor	III	Motor	Oculomotor nucleus and nucleus of Edinger–Westphal, both in the midbrain	Eye movements, dilation, and constriction of pupil
Trochlear	IV	Motor	Midbrain (mesencephalon)	Eye movements
Trigeminal	V	Mixed	Trigeminal motor nucleus and main sensory nucleus, both in the pons; also, semilunar (Gasserian) ganglion	Movements of chewing, sensation of the head and face
Abducens	VI	Motor	Nucleus in pons	Lateral movement of eye
Facial	VII	Mixed	Motor fibers: inferior portion of pons; sensory (taste) fibers: geniculate ganglion	Movements of facial muscles, secretion of saliva, taste from anterior ⅔ of tongue
Acoustic	VIII	Sensory	Vestibular ganglion in internal acoustic meatus and spiral ganglion of cochlea	Hearing and equilibrium
Glossopharyngeal	IX	Mixed	Sensory neurons (taste): superior and inferior ganglia. Motor neurons: medulla	Secretion of saliva, movements of swallowing, taste from pharynx and posterior third of tongue, reflexes of breathing and blood pressure
Vagus	X	Mixed	Sensory neurons: jugular and nodose ganglia; motor neurons: dorsal motor nucleus	Movements and sensations of heart, digestive organs, and larynx
Accessory	XI	Motor	Spinal portion: anterior gray horn, upper six segments of spinal cord; cranial portion: nuclei in medulla	Movements of head, shoulder, and voice-producing parts of larynx
Hypoglossal	XII	Motor	Hypoglossal nucleus of medulla	Movements of the tongue

courses of the various portions of the trigeminal nerve are as follows: motor-root cell bodies are in the trigeminal motor nucleus, located in the pons. Fibers supply the muscles of mastication, etc., as previously described, by coursing from the side of the pons into the middle cranial fossa, then through the foramen ovale and into the infratemporal fossa, where they are distributed as branch nerves to the appropriate structures. Fibers of the madibular sensory division run along with those of the motor root, and their cells of origin lie in the semilunar or Gasserian ganglion, located in the petrous portion of the temporal bone, along with those of the ophthalmic and maxillary divisions. The ophthalmic nerve courses upward and ante-

riorly, passing into the orbit through the superior orbital fissure, while the maxillary moves almost directly anteriorly through the inferior orbital fissure. A portion of it leaves the orbit via the infraorbital foramen. Although the three sensory divisions or nerves of the trigeminal have their cells of origin in the semilunar ganglion, this ganglion represents only a point of synapse with neuron processes extending from the main sensory nucleus, located in the pons, just lateral to the trigeminal motor nucleus.

ABDUCENS NERVE (VI) Mainly motor, the sixth cranial nerve supplies only one of the external eye muscles, the lateral rectus. It also contains fibers that convey impulses of *proprioception* from the same muscle, and *autonomic* fibers. The *cell bodies of the efferent fibers* of the abducens lie in a *nucleus of the pons,* near the floor of the fourth ventricle. They reach the orbit as a nerve passing through the *superior orbital fissure.*

FACIAL NERVE (VII)   The facial nerve is also called the *nerve of facial expression* because it supplies motor fibers to all the muscles of facial expression (Chapter 6). It also carries fibers for the *special sensation of taste* from the *anterior two-thirds of the tongue.* The *cells of origin* of the motor fibers are found in the *inferior portion of the pons.* After the facial nerve emerges from the brainstem *at the lower border of the pons,* it passes —with the eighth cranial nerve, the acoustic —through the *internal acoustic meatus* to enter the *petrous portion of the temporal bone.* After a winding course through the *facial canal* above the internal ear and behind the middle ear, the facial nerve passes through the *stylomastoid foramen* and finally reaches the side of the face. It *branches* a number of times within the substance of the *parotid gland.* A swelling, the *geniculate ganglion,* is seen on the facial nerve near the *cochlea of the internal ear. Cell bodies* for neurons mediating the *sense of taste* are located in the ganglion. These neurons are located in the *chorda tympani division* of the facial nerve, supplying the *anterior two-thirds of the tongue.* Fibers of the chorda tympani end in the geniculate ganglion; in addition to carrying impulses related to taste, these fibers supply *motor-secretory impulses* to the *submandibular* and *sublingual* salivary glands.

ACOUSTIC NERVE (VIII)   The *dual function* of this sensory nerve is revealed in a new name devised for it—*statoacoustic nerve,* or *nerve of equilibrium and hearing.* Two *divisions,* vestibular and cochlear, mediate the impulses responsible for these two important senses. Coursing just lateral to the facial nerve as it emerges from the brainstem, the acoustic nerve soon enters the *internal acoustic meatus* of the skull and bifurcates into its vestibular and cochlear divisions. *Cell bodies* of the vestibular division are seated in a *vestibular ganglion* within the *internal acoustic meatus.* They extend peripherally

to the specialized endings for *static sense* (balance or equilibrium) located in the semicircular canals of the internal ear, while others run from the ganglion to vestibular nuclei in the pons, medulla, and even the cerebellum. The *cells of origin* of the cochlear division are located in the *spiral ganglion* of the cochlea, and the fibers extend from the *organ of Corti* in the cochlea to the *cochlear nuclei* of the *medulla.* Here they make connection with neurons whose processes reach to the *primary auditory receptive area,* the *transverse temporal gyrus or gyrus of Heschi,* that portion of the cerebral cortex located within the superior portion of the temporal lobe, just inferior to the lateral fissure. The auditory pathway *passes through* the *inferior colliculus* and *medial geniculate body* on its way to the transverse gyrus.

GLOSSOPHARYNGEAL NERVE (IX)   This is a *mixed* nerve. The *cell bodies of its sensory neurons* lie within the *two ganglia* of the nerve—the *superior* and *inferior ganglia*— and these neurons mediate impulses concerned with *taste* from the *posterior third of the tongue and mucous membrane of the pharynx.* The motor fibers belong to the autonomic nervous system, originate in the medulla, and supply the *mucosal glands* of the middle ear, the *stylopharyngeus muscle* (one of the muscles of swallowing), and the *parotid gland.* The nerve emerges laterally from the medulla, enters the *jugular foramen* in company with the *vagus and accessory nerves,* and descends into the neck, giving off, in addition to the above, a branch to the *carotid sinus* (an enlargement at the superior end of the common carotid artery in the neck).

VAGUS NERVE (X)   The vagus nerve might more appropriately be called the *visceral nerve,* in recognition of its distribution to most of the thoracic and abdominal visceral organs and related structures, including the *heart, lungs, pharynx, larynx, palate, trachea, bronchi, esophagus, stomach, intestine, liver, gall bladder, spleen, kidneys,* and *pancreas.* It is a *mixed* nerve, and sends *motor fibers* to the muscles of the *larynx, soft palate,* and *pharynx. Sensory fibers* supply the *pharynx, larynx, bronchi, lungs, esophagus,* and many of the *abdominal organs,* as well as a small number of *taste buds* in the *pharynx and larynx. Autonomic* (parasympathetic) fibers within the nerve reach the smooth muscle in the *walls of the thoracic and abdominal organs.* The vagus *emerges* from the side of the *medulla* and travels with the *internal carotid artery and internal jugular vein* to the thorax, giving off *branches in the neck* along its course. *Cell bodies* for its sensory neurons are grouped within the *jugular* and *nodose ganglia,* near the *jugular foramen.* The *dorsal motor nucleus* of the vagus consists of the cell bodies of the motor neurons, and lies within the *medulla.* Cell bodies of neurons of the parasympathetic division of the nervous system lie in *autonomic plexuses* or ganglia near or within the walls of the organs supplied.

ACCESSORY NERVE (XI)   The eleventh cranial nerve was formerly called the *spinal accessory nerve* because it has a *spinal portion* as well as a *cranial portion.* Its *roots of origin* can be seen emerging from the side of the *lower medulla* and *upper spinal cord.* The spinal portion ascends, joins the cranial portion, and the two together form the *accessory nerve,* which is of course *not completely cranial.* It is the *only one* of the 12 pairs thus formed. The accessory nerve meets the vagus nerve at the jugular foramen and supplies the vagus with some of its *motor fibers* to the *pharynx* and *soft palate.* The spinal portion of nerve XI travels down the neck and supplies the *sternomastoid* and *trapezius* muscles with motor fibers. *Cell bodies of the spinal portion* of the nerve are in the *anterior gray horn* of the *upper half-dozen segments* of the spinal cord; those of the *cranial portion* lie within certain nuclei of the *medulla. Proprioceptive fibers* originate in the sternomastoid and trapezius muscles and terminate in the medulla.

HYPOGLOSSAL NERVE (XII)   Rootlets of the twelfth cranial nerve can be seen springing from the *ventrolateral sulcus of the medulla.* After the nerve proper has been formed from these rootlets, it soon *passes through the hypoglossal canal* and into the neck. Descending to the level of the mandible, the nerve bends anteriorly and supplies the *muscles of the tongue* with *motor fibers. Proprioceptive fibers* are said to be present in

the nerve and *carry muscle sense* from the tongue to the central nervous system. *Cell bodies* of the twelfth cranial nerve lie in the *hypoglossal nucleus* of the medulla.

Spinal nerves

Thirty-one pairs of spinal nerves branch off the spinal cord, beginning just above the *atlas* or first cervical vertebra. These nerves leave the spinal cord in the following manner: the *first pair* emerges between the *occipital bone* and *atlas;* while the remaining thirty pairs pass through *intervertebral foramina,* each of which is formed by a notch in the underportion of the pedicle of a vertebra and the upper surface of the pedicle of the vertebra below it. There are *8 cervical, 12 thoracic, 5 lumbar,* and *5 sacral* pairs of spinal nerves, but only *1 coccygeal* pair. The *first pair* of cervical nerves emerges *above* the first cervical vertebra and the *last pair* of cervical nerves emerges *below* the last cervical vertebra, while all other cervical nerves emerge *above* their respective vertebrae. Beginning with the first thoracic spinal nerves, all remaining spinal nerves emerge *below* their corresponding vertebrae. The long roots of the lower spinal nerves form the *cauda equina* or "horse's tail" described with the spinal cord. At their origins, spinal nerves are *not named,* but merely numbered, *beginning with the uppermost pair in each portion of the vertebral column;* that is, cervical nerves are numbered 1 through 8, thoracic nerves 1 through 12, and so on. Spinal nerves are commonly abbreviated, using a capital letter to represent the portion of the spinal cord in which the nerve is found and an arabic numeral to indicate the exact cord segment: C1, T3, S2, etc.

FORMATION OF SPINAL NERVES   Each spinal nerve is *formed by the junction of a dorsal or posterior root and a ventral or anterior root* (Fig. 7-19). The dorsal root enters the spinal cord at the *dorsolateral sulcus,* and the ventral root leaves the cord at the *ventrolateral sulcus.* Each root is composed of a number of smaller *rootlets.* The roots of each spinal nerve *join* within or near the *intervertebral foramen,* form a spinal nerve, and the nerve divides almost immediately into an

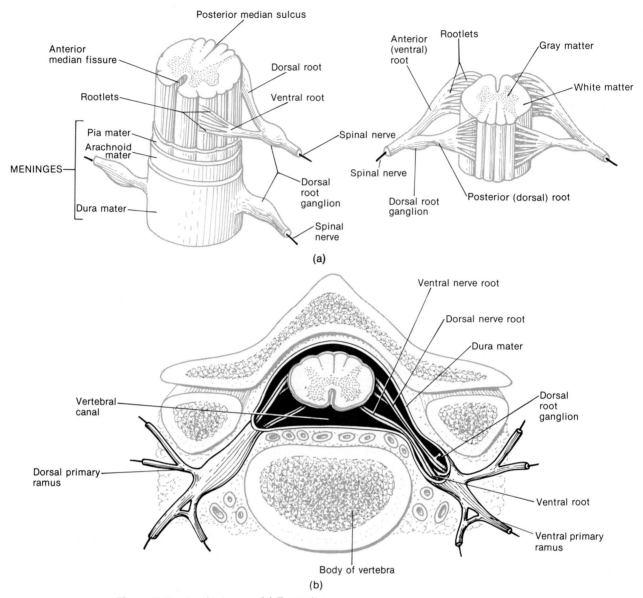

Figure 7-19 A spinal nerve. (a) Formation.
(b) Relation to structures of the vertebral column.

anterior and *posterior ramus*. The *cell bodies* of the *ventral root* are in the *anterior gray-horn substance* of the spinal cord, while those of the *dorsal root* lie within a swelling on that root, the *dorsal-root gaglion.* Neurons in the dorsal root are all *sensory* (afferent), while those in the ventral root are all *motor* (efferent), carrying impulses into the spinal cord and out of the spinal cord, respectively. A thorough *combining* of motor and sensory neurons occurs in the spinal nerve proper, so that the nerve and its rami (major branches) are *mixed,* and carry both motor and sensory neurons. The rami of spinal nerves branch repeatedly, as shown in Fig. 7-20. Two tiny

branches, *gray* and *white rami communicantes,* are given off each spinal nerve in the thoracic and upper lumbar regions, and *connect the nerve with the sympathetic trunk* of the autonomic nervous system (Fig. 7-20). Only the gray ramus communicans is present in the cervical, lower lumbar, and sacral regions. (The autonomic nervous system is discussed in a later section of this chapter.)

HOW SPINAL NERVES ARE DISTRIBUTED By means of their branches and subbranches, the *anterior rami* of spinal nerves *innervate* (supply with nerves) the skin and muscles of the front and sides of the trunk and the upper

172

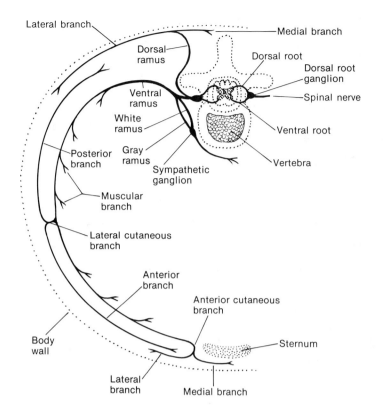

Figure 7-20 A typical spinal nerve and its branches.

The following labels appear in the figure: Lateral branch, Dorsal ramus, Medial branch, Dorsal root, Dorsal root ganglion, Spinal nerve, Ventral ramus, White ramus, Gray ramus, Sympathetic ganglion, Ventral root, Vertebra, Posterior branch, Muscular branch, Lateral cutaneous branch, Anterior branch, Anterior cutaneous branch, Sternum, Body wall, Lateral branch, Medial branch.

clavicle, the trunks bifurcate, resulting in *three anterior* and *three posterior divisions behind the pectoralis minor muscle.* The three posterior divisions unite, forming a *posterior cord.* The anterior divisions of the upper and middle trunks join to form a *lateral cord,* and the anterior division of the lower trunk continues as a *medial cord.* All cords soon bifurcate. *The two terminal branches of the posterior cord are the axillary and radial nerves; the most lateral branch of the lateral cord is the musculocutaneous nerve, and the most medial branch of the medial cord is the ulnar nerve.* The remaining branch of the lateral cord *joins with that of the medial cord to form the median nerve.* The musculocutaneous nerve supplies the *biceps brachii, brachialis,* and *coracobrachialis muscles;* the axillary nerve innervates the *deltoid* and *teres minor;* the radial nerve supplies the *triceps brachii, brachioradialis, extensor carpi radialis longus,* and others; the median nerve innervates the *lateral portion* of the *flexor digitorum profundis,* the *flexor carpi radialis, palmaris longus, flexor digitorum superficialis,* and some of the *small muscles of the hand;* and the ulnar nerve supplies the *flexor carpi ulnaris,* the *medial portion* of the *flexor digitorum profundus* in the forearm, and several *small muscles in the hand.*

THE CERVICAL PLEXUS   In the neck region, the anterior rami of cervical spinal nerves 1 through 4 give rise to the cervical plexus (Fig. 7-21). This plexus is most important because *one of its terminal branches, the phrenic nerve, supplies the main organ of breathing, the diaphragm.* Cutting the pair of phrenic nerves, or injury to the spinal cord above their level of origin, stops the motor impulses to the diaphragm, *paralyzing this organ and resulting in death.* Automobile accidents, poliomyelitis, execution or suicide by hanging, and other causes can bring this about. The *skin and many muscles of the neck and back of the scalp* are also innervated by branches of the cervical plexus. Three of these fan out over the anterior and lateral aspects of the neck, passing over the clavicle: the *anterior, middle,* and *posterior supraclavicular nerves.*

THE LUMBOSACRAL PLEXUS   The lumbosacral plexus is *made up of two plexuses,*

and lower limbs. The *posterior rami* innervate the long back muscles and the skin of the back. All anterior rami except those of the lower 11 thoracic spinal nerves group together into nerve *plexuses,* which in turn send nerves to the structures to be innervated. These include the *cervical, brachial, lumbar, sacral,* and *pudendal* plexuses (Fig. 7-21). The lumbar and sacral are often referred to in combination as the *lumbosacral plexus.* The brachial plexus (Figs. 7-21 and 7-22), perhaps because of its extreme importance in supplying *motor nerves to the muscles of the upper extremity,* is most often studied as a typical plexus. The most important nerves of the upper and lower extremities are illustrated in Figs. 7-23, 7-24, and 7-25 on pp. 175-177.

THE BRACHIAL PLEXUS   The *formation* of the brachial plexus and the *distribution* of its chief *terminal nerves* are as follows: the anterior rami of cervical nerves 5 and 6 unite, forming an *upper trunk;* the ramus of C7 continues on as a *middle trunk;* and the ramus of C8 joins that of T1 to form a *lower trunk.* Formation of trunks occurs in the *base of the neck,* above the first rib. *Deep to the*

173

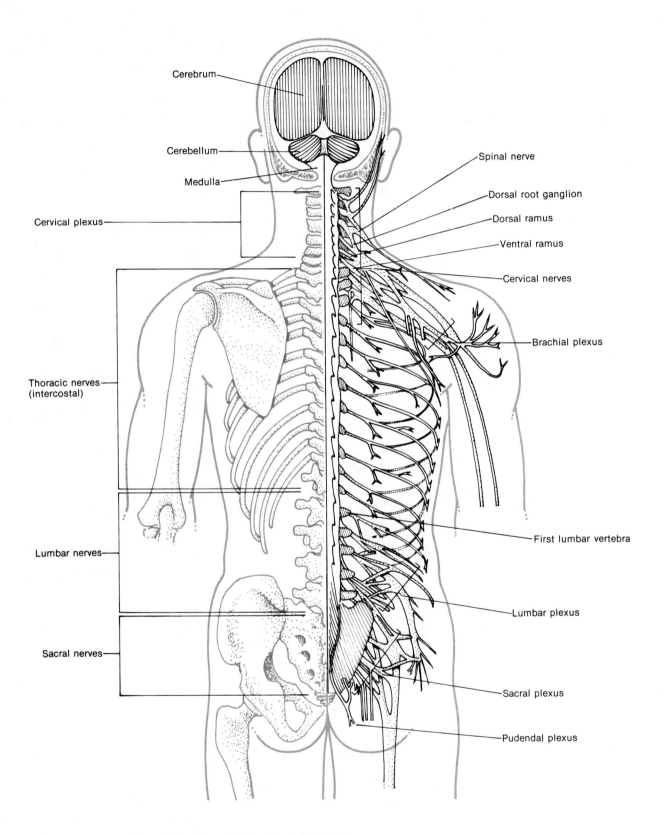

Cerebrum

Cerebellum

Medulla

Cervical plexus

Thoracic nerves
(intercostal)

Lumbar nerves

Sacral nerves

Spinal nerve

Dorsal root ganglion

Dorsal ramus

Ventral ramus

Cervical nerves

Brachial plexus

First lumbar vertebra

Lumbar plexus

Sacral plexus

Pudendal plexus

Figure 7-21   The spinal nerves and plexuses.

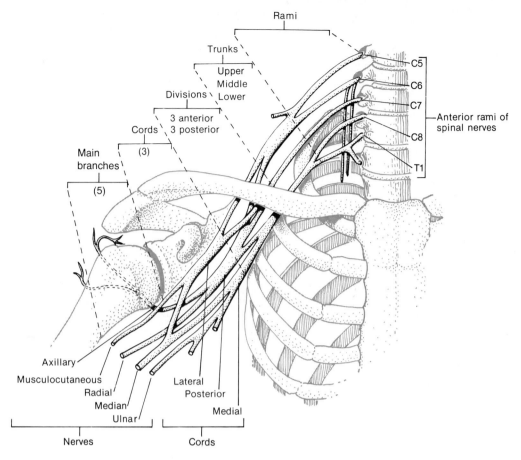

Figure 7-22 Formation and anatomical relationships of the brachial plexus.

Figure 7-23 Certain spinal nerves of the upper extremity, and the position of the brachial plexus.

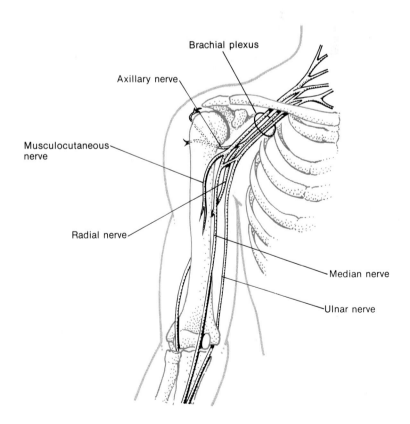

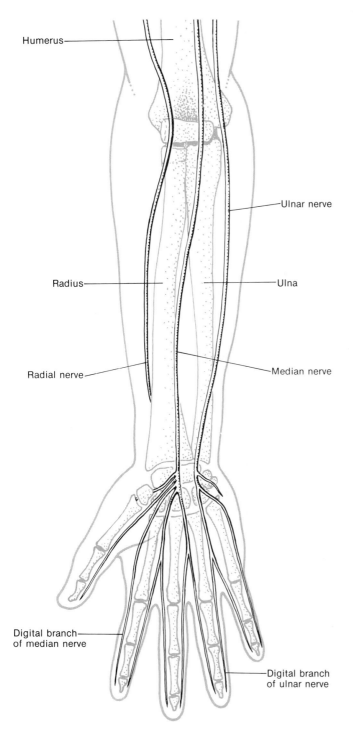

Humerus

Ulnar nerve

Radius

Ulna

Radial nerve

Median nerve

Digital branch of median nerve

Digital branch of ulnar nerve

Figure 7-24 Important nerves of the distal portion of the upper extremity.

medial portions of the thigh, the *skin of the gluteal and hypogastric regions and anterior, lateral, and medial aspects of the thigh,* and the *skin of the anterior and medial sides of the leg.* The skin of the upper portion of the *penis* and *scrotum* in the male, and that covering the *mons pubis* and *labium majus* in the female, is supplied by branches of this plexus. The three nerves that carry most of the sensory fibers for all the above regions are the *iliohypogastric, ilioinguinal,* and *genitofemoral.* That carrying the majority of the *motor fibers* is the *femoral nerve,* formed by the joining together of divisions of the roots of *spinal nerves L2, L3, and L4.* The femoral nerve supplies the *quadriceps muscle* on the front of the thigh (*vastus lateralis, vastus intermedius, vastus medialis and rectus femoris*), *sartorius,* and *pectineus.*

The sacral plexus has among its branches the *largest nerve in the body,* the *sciatic nerve.* The plexus *originates* as a branch of the *fourth-lumbar-nerve* root and one of the *fifth* interweave with the *anterior divisions of S1 through S4.* The sciatic nerve gets its fibers from *L4 through S3.* In the thigh, the sciatic divides into the *tibial nerve* and *common peroneal nerve.* The tibial nerve sends *motor fibers* to the *gastrocnemius, soleus, tibialis posterior, popliteus, long flexors of the toes,* and *muscles of the sole of the foot* (plantar muscles). It furnishes *sensory fibers* to the skin of the *posterior aspect of the leg* and *sole of the foot.* The *common peroneal nerve* divides into *superficial* and *deep trunks,* which supply the skin and some of the muscles of the *front and lateral side of the leg* and *dorsum* (top) *of the foot.* Muscles innervated by the common peroneal nerve include the *peroneus longus* and *peroneus brevis* muscles (by the superficial trunk), and the *tibialis anterior, extensor digitorum brevis* and the *long extensors of the toes* (by the deep trunk). The skin of the *lateral side of the leg* and *dorsum of the foot* is supplied by branches of one or the other of these trunks.

THE PUDENDAL PLEXUS The pudendal plexus is located below and continuous with the sacral plexus, and extends downward far enough to include the *coccygeal nerves.* The *chief nerve* of this plexus is the *pudendal nerve,* which branches to supply the skin

lumbar and *sacral* (Fig. 7-21). The lumbar plexus is formed by the interweaving of the anterior rami of spinal nerves T12 through L4, and *its terminal nerves innervate* some of the *muscles of the anterior, superior, and*

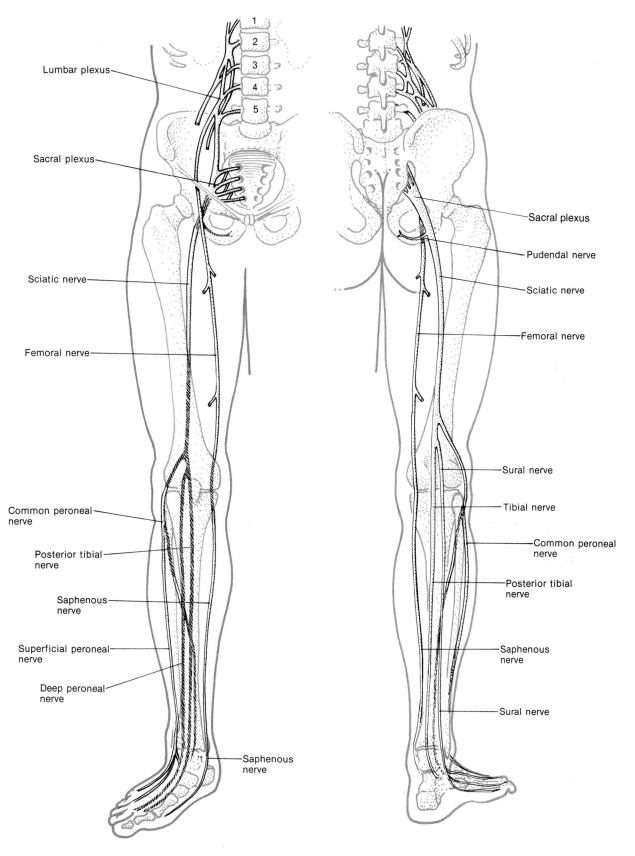

1
2
3
4
5

Lumbar plexus

Sacral plexus

Sciatic nerve

Femoral nerve

Common peroneal
nerve

Posterior tibial
nerve

Saphenous
nerve

Superficial peroneal
nerve

Deep peroneal
nerve

Saphenous
nerve

Sacral plexus

Pudendal nerve

Sciatic nerve

Femoral nerve

Sural nerve

Tibial nerve

Common peroneal
nerve

Posterior tibial
nerve

Saphenous
nerve

Sural nerve

Figure 7-25 Important nerves of the lower extremity, and the plexuses
from which they originate.

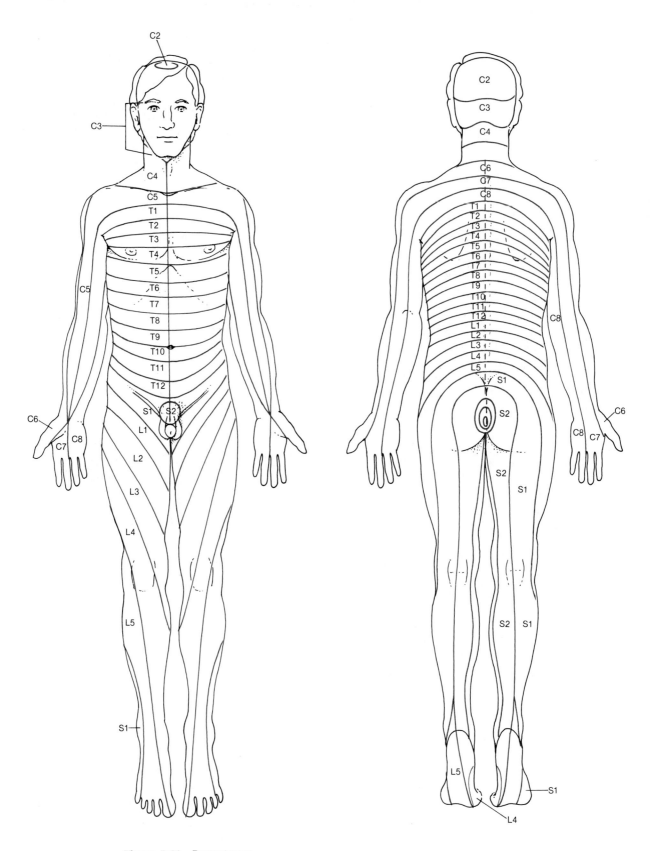

Figure 7-26 Dermatomes.

and muscles of the *anal region,* portions of the *scrotum and penis* (labia majora and clitoris in the female), and skin of the *coccygeal region.*

THORACIC SPINAL NERVES The lower 11 pairs of thoracic spinal nerves do not make significant contributions to plexuses, but rather retain their identities as individual nerves. The *upper 11* thoracic spinal nerves are known as *intercostal nerves,* and extend from the spinal cord around the thorax, between the ribs (Fig. 7-21). The *lowest pair* of thoracic nerves lies below the last pair of ribs, and these are known as *subcostal nerves.* Intercostal and subcostal nerves begin as anterior rami of spinal nerves, and supply the skin and muscles of the *anterior* and *lateral portions* of the *thoracic wall.* The *rear wall* of the chest is innervated by branches of the *posterior rami* of spinal nerves. It should be pointed out that the thoracic nerves, in addition to supplying the structures already mentioned, also supply *sensory branches* to the skin of the *axilla* and *upper arm, parietal pleura* (serous membrane lining the chest cavity), and *parietal peritoneum* (another serous membrane, this one lining the abdomen). *Muscular branches* of the upper intercostal nerves supply the *intercostal muscles, pectoralis major,* and *pectoralis minor* muscles. The *lower nerves* innervate the *external oblique, internal oblique, transversus abdominis,* and *rectus abdominis* muscles.

DERMATOMES It has been found that the skin is supplied with sensory nerves in a *segmental pattern* which is, in general, consistent from one person to the next. This pattern is diagrammed in Fig. 7-26. Each segment or strip of skin outlined in the figure is called a *dermatome.* Sensory nerves of adjacent dermatomes overlap somewhat; therefore, loss of the sensory nerve supply to a single dermatome does not always mean a complete loss of sensation in that segment.

FUNCTIONAL ANATOMY OF THE MAJOR NEURON PATHWAYS

Now that the anatomy of the central and peripheral nervous systems has been discussed, it is possible, by including discussions of specialized nerve endings (receptors) and effectors (such as muscles), to examine the structure and function of the major neuron tracts or pathways. The terms *tract* and *pathway* are interchangeable, and will be used in this manner in the discussion to follow. They serve to carry either motor or sensory impulses between the brain and other structures located in the head region, and between the brain and structures located below the head, a region which includes most of the body. There are even some spinal reflex pathways that never reach the brain.

Sensory or afferent pathways

Neural pathways are made up of *chains of neurons.* In the case of sensory routes, stimulation of *specialized receptors* sends impulses over these pathways to the central nervous system. The *cerebral cortex* usually interprets these impulses as awareness of *cold, heat, pain, light, sound, touch, smell,* and so on; it then sends motor impulses to muscles with instructions to carry out an appropriate response. Some pathways are concerned mainly with *reflex actions,* in which no conscious activity is involved; normal breathing and walking are examples of such activities. The sensory pathways, however, carry impulses that always result in *conscious awareness* of the stimulus. Such sensations as *touch, pressure, pain,* and *temperature* result when stimuli are applied outside the body. Such general sensations are termed *exteroceptive,* while those arising from the body visceral organs are *enteroceptive.* Exteroceptive pathways are better described and more easily understood by first considering those involved in sensations originating below the head—that is, those involving spinal nerves, rather than cranial nerves—and then exploring cranial-nerve pathways, after some degree of knowledge of pathway transmission has been attained. Pathways utilizing the spinal cord consist of chains of *three or more neurons,* one bearing a specialized *receptor* and connecting the periphery (outer portions) of the body with the *spinal cord,* a second connecting this neuron with the *thalamus,* and a third joining the second

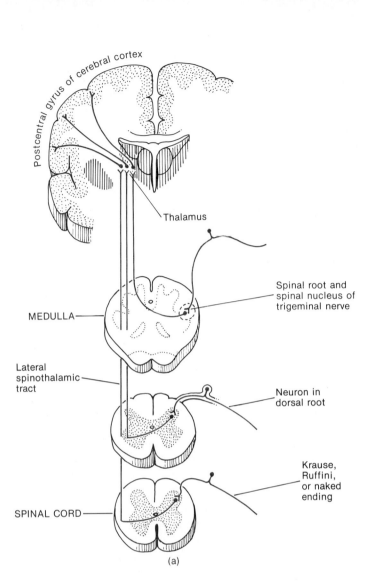

neuron with the *cerebral cortex* (Fig. 7-27). Additional neurons are sometimes interposed at one point or another in the normal 3-neuron pathway, depending upon the sensation mediated; this results in a 4- or 5-neuron tract. The peripheral end of the first neuron in a pathway is specialized to respond to a specific type stimulus; but it must be understood that no matter what type receptor is involved, *nerve impulses are alike,* and it remains for the cerebral cortex to interpret these impulses as those of heat, cold, pain, touch, pressure, and so on. This is possible because all stimuli picked up by a given type receptor are routed to a certain area of the cortex.

One cannot simply slice across a spinal cord and point out well-demarked neuron tracts or pathways, because except for a slight contrast between white and gray substance, the cord material appears homogenous. Location and identification of tracts depend upon reference books and a good imagination. As in the case of the brain itself, the functional areas of the spinal cord have been mapped only after many years of accumulated data involving animal experimentation and study of the effects of disease, injury, and surgery on the human spinal cord. Many of the tracts of the spinal cord make connection with one or more higher centers, and convey impulses from the peripheral nerves to these centers (*ascending tracts*), and from these centers to the peripheral nerves (*descending tracts*).

ASCENDING TRACTS OR PATHWAYS There are *seven major ascending fiber tracts or pathways* in the spinal cord (Fig. 7-27): the *ventral spinothalamic tract* in the *anterior funiculus; lateral spinothalamic tract, dorsal spinocerebellar tract, ventral spinocerebellar tract,* and *spinotectal tract* in the *lateral funiculus;* and the *fasciculus cuneatus* and *fasciculus gracilis* in the *posterior funiculus.* Five afferent pathways, those for pain, temperature, touch, pressure, and proprioception, are illustrated diagrammatically in Figs. 7-27, 7-28, and 7-29.

SENSORY PATHWAYS IN THE HEAD Above those body regions served by the spinal cord, the *first neurons in sensory pathways* are located in cranial nerve V, the *trigeminal nerve.* Both superficial and deep structures of

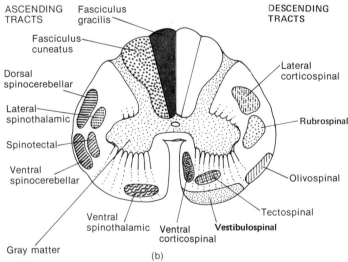

Figure 7-27 Spinal tracts or pathways. (a) A typical three-neuron pathway, the lateral spinothalamic tract, which is the pathway for pain and temperature. (b) Location of the major tracts or pathways of the spinal cord. All are bilateral but are shown on only one side of the drawing for clarity.

the head—including the mucous membranes of the tongue, cheeks, lips, and the cornea of the eye—are supplied with sensory fibers from this nerve. The axons of these neurons enter the pons and form the *spinal root of the trigeminal nerve,* which descends to the *spinal nucleus of the trigeminal nerve,* located in the medulla. Here, synapse is made with *second-order neurons,* whose axons *promptly cross to the opposite side and ascend to the thalamus.* In the thalamus, another synapse is made, and *third-order neurons* carry impulses to the *postcentral gyrus of the cerebrum.*

Motor or efferent pathways

Pathways that convey impulses resulting in conscious awareness are, of necessity, *ascending* pathways, since they must end ultimately in the highest of all brain areas, the cerebral cortex. Motor pathways, on the other hand, are of the *descending* type, simply because they are concerned with im-

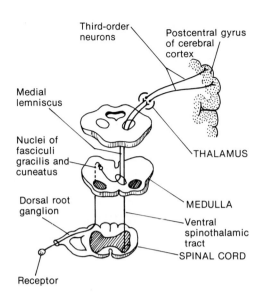

Figure 7-29 Crossed pathways for touch and pressure.

pulses that travel from the brain to the muscles. *Three of the chief motor pathways* are the *corticospinal tract* or pyramidal system, which begins conscious influence of voluntary muscle action (Fig. 7-30); the *extrapyramidal system,* which helps coordinate voluntary muscle action; and the so-called *final common pathway,* which includes the numerous routes by which motor impulses are actually carried to muscles.

VISCERAL MOTOR AND SENSORY PATHWAYS Impulses carrying sensory information from the body visceral organs, and those conveying motor information to the viscera, travel along neurons associated with the autonomic nervous system, which is discussed in detail in a later section of this chapter.

VISCERAL SENSATIONS Visceral sensations such as *appetite, hunger,* and *thirst* begin in the receptors located in the tissues of the visceral organs and travel along fibers that are closely associated with those belonging to one of the divisions—the parasympathetic division—of the autonomic nervous system. Appetite is a rather pleasurable sensation of "empty stomach" coupled with the anticipation of eating. Real hunger, on the other hand, comes when one has gone as long as a few days without eating. The stomach contracts from time to time, and the victim may be weak, tense, and irritable. Usually there is headache, and often even nausea. Thirst in-

Figure 7-28 Pathway for proprioception.

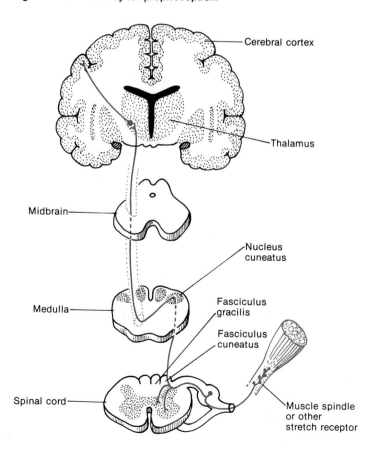

forms us that the body tissues need water. The closer the body gets to a state of *dehydration,* the greater the thirst. Water loss through *profuse perspiration, excessive urination during diabetes, vomiting, diarrhea,* or *hemorrhage* are all capable of producing dehydration. There is a *"thirst center"* in the *hypothalamus,* containing *osmoreceptors* sensitive to the osmotic pressure of the blood. When this center is stimulated by a lowering of the water content of the blood, the hypothalamus secretes *antidiuretic hormone* (ADH); when ADH reaches the kidney via the bloodstream, kidney output is decreased in order to conserve the body's water supply. The amount of saliva secreted during thirst is decreased, with the effect being felt as a dry mouth.

REFERRED PAIN   It should be made clear that pain originating within a visceral organ cannot always be pinpointed or *localized.* Not all organs have separate and distinct afferent tracts to the brain; in fact, many visceral afferent fibers in the lateral spinothalamic tract lie in close association with cells from areas of the skin. The result of this "crossed-wire" situation is that visceral pain is often "referred" (rerouted) to the body surface. For example, in *angina pectoris,* a serious heart condition, pain is felt in the left shoulder and left arm in addition to—or even instead of—pain in the chest region; and abdominal pain is sometimes a sign of pneumonia instead of appendicitis or gall gladder trouble, as one might surmise. Pain originating in the kidney may be felt at the lower lateral portion of the buttock, or across the entire lumbar region. Obviously, it is important for the physician and nurse to bear in mind the phenomenon of referred pain when making a diagnosis or giving patient care. It is interesting to note that even after a limb has been amputated, pain and such sensations as itching and tickling may be felt just as though the limb were still on the body. This often results from stimulation of the proximal portion of a nerve that once supplied the severed portion of the limb. The sensation or combination of sensations that cause an individual to feel as though an amputated limb were still present is called *phantom limb,* and any pain associated with such a condition is dubbed *phantom pain.*

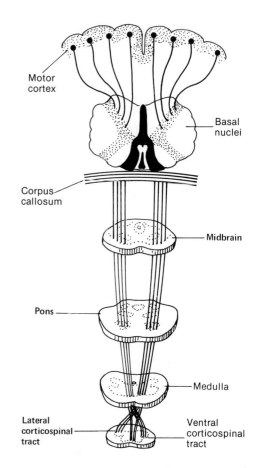

Figure 7-30   The corticospinal tracts.

PAIN OF PSYCHOLOGICAL ORIGIN   Not all pain is due to organic disease or trauma (injury) but may be due to such emotional causes as anxiety and fear—in other words, pain may be *psychogenic* in nature. Psychogenic pain is very real to the victim, and has led to the performance of unnecessary surgery by physicians who may have been misled by it while making a diagnosis.

HEADACHE, THE MOST COMMON PAIN   It is ironical that the head region is the site of frequent, sometimes severe pain, when one recalls that virtually all the brain tissue is insensitive to pain during trauma. Headache cannot be ascribed to any one cause, but in general it can be said to be most frequently caused by *extracranial activity,* such as *constipation* and other *gastrointestinal upsets, sinus and kidney infections, eye fatigue, and fever* (as in the early stages of influenza, pneumonia, and typhoid fever). *Meningitis, high blood pressure* (hypertension), *concussion, brain tumors, drinking alcohol, and anxiety and worry* all bring on headache. Often, the pain of headache may be poorly localized, but is sometimes confined to the area occupied by one lobe of the brain, or may seem to involve only the eyeballs. Often the pain seems to be confined to the skin and muscles on the outside of the head. *Migraine* is a severe, long-lasting headache, difficult to treat successfully. It appears to have deep-seated emotional causes. Most headaches are treated with ordinary aspirin compounds.

THE IMPORTANCE OF REFLEXES

A reflex may be defined as *an involuntary, predictable response to a stimulus.* This response may or may not reach the level of conscious awareness. Normal reflexes are, of course, purposeful and beneficial; they serve to protect and conserve the body and to augment certain body processes, as do reflex movements of the digestive tract and the partial reflex action of the urinary bladder. That reflexes are predictable is shown by the fact that repeating the same stimulus produces the same type of response. Reflex patterns may change or completely disappear during and after disease or injury that damages any portion of a reflex pathway. Some

reflexes are either exaggerated or depressed when lesions of higher brain centers (which normally send impulses that facilitate or inhibit them) are affected.

One of the most convenient ways to study the basic components of a reflex system is to examine the makeup of a spinal reflex arc.

THE REFLEX ARC   (See Fig. 7-31.) Five structures—*receptor, afferent neuron, connecting neuron, efferent neuron,* and *effector* —are the essential components of a spinal *reflex arc.* In a few reflex arcs which lack a connecting neuron, the afferent neuron makes a direct synapse with the efferent neuron. When a spinal reflex pathway is utilized, impulses travel into the cord over neurons having their cells of origin in the dorsal root ganglion. The first neuron makes synapse with a connecting *(association, internuncial)* neuron within the gray matter of the spinal cord, and does not ascend or descend in the cord to do so. Thus impulses travel inward over the afferent neuron, over the connecting neuron, and outward over the efferent neuron, all at one cord level, and even on the same side of the body. The afferent neuron ends in an effector, such as a skeletal muscle. In a spinal reflex pathway such as the one just described, it is not essential that impulses ever reach the level of consciousness; however, connections are made with ascending tracts in the spinal cord, and awareness often accompanies reflex action. Perhaps one of the best demonstrations of the operation of a spinal reflex involves the *scratch reflex* of a dog. A dog is rubbed or "tickled" on his abdomen or other spot where rubbing induces the dog to scratch vigorously. The animal is then anesthetized, and the spinal cord is severed just below the level of the medulla. After the dog has recovered from the shock of surgery (spinal shock), he is again rubbed, and is found to scratch as before. Since there is now *no sensory pathway to the brain* (due to separation of the spinal cord), the animal does not consciously feel the rubbing, and the scratching occurs in a purely reflex manner. The same type reflex is often demonstrated in the laboratory by stimulating the feet of decerebrated frogs by pinching them with forceps or applying heat or chemicals.

Figure 7-31 A three-neuron reflex arc.

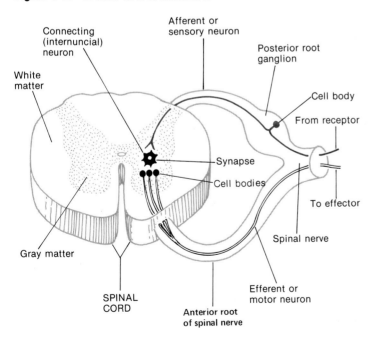

Connecting (internuncial) neuron

Afferent or sensory neuron

Posterior root ganglion

White matter

Cell body

From receptor

Synapse

Cell bodies

To effector

Gray matter

Spinal nerve

SPINAL CORD

Efferent or motor neuron

Anterior root of spinal nerve

Classification of reflexes

There are several ways in which reflexes can be classified. One method is according to the *level of the central nervous system involved.* In this system, reflexes are said to be *spinal, medullary or bulbar,* or of the *midbrain* or *cerebellar type. Clinically,* reflexes are placed in one of four groups: *superficial,* such as those involving the skin, cornea, and mucous membranes; *deep or myotactic,* which depend upon proprioceptive impulses from muscles and tendons; *visceral,* concerned with such organic activities as contraction and dilation of the pupil, speeding and slowing of the heart, emptying of the bladder and the lower intestine or rectum; and *pathological,* or those reflexes seen only after disease or injury has affected neurons at higher centers and has totally or partially removed their influence over lower reflex pathways. Often, reflexes can be *inhibited* at will, as when suppressing a cough, sneeze, or cry of pain. Many are also inhibited by anesthesia. Most reflex actions, such as the reflex of breathing, *cannot be inhibited voluntarily for long periods of time.* The degree to which a reflex action occurs is sometimes dependent upon the *strength of the stimulus;* for example, a slightly painful stimulus applied to one leg may elicit a unilateral reflex, in which only one side of the spinal cord and body are involved, while a very sharp pain may cause the stimulus to cross the cord and bring about an additional response in the *opposite* leg *(bilateral reflex),* and even travel up the cord to the cerebral cortex and trigger a reflex opening of the mouth and a cry of pain. This fanning out of impulses is known as *irradiation* or *divergence.* The converse of divergence is *convergence,* in which several impulses from the CNS are sent through one reflex pathway and produce only one response. The following paragraphs discuss *some reflexes of diagnostic value.*

Deep reflexes

PATELLAR REFLEX Commonly known as the *knee jerk,* this reflex is probably the best known and most widely tested of all reflexes. In testing this reflex, the subject is seated and one leg is crossed over the other at the knee, so that the foot does not touch the floor. (If the patient is unable to sit up, the patellar reflex can often be tested by turning him on his side.) The *patellar tendon* of the uppermost part of the leg is tapped with a percussion hammer (a small rubber hammer) just below the knee, thus slightly stretching the tendon and its muscle, the *quadriceps femoris.* If the stretch reflex pathway is intact, then stimulation of the *stretch receptors* in the tendon and muscle will cause impulses to travel over dendrites of the *first neurons* in the reflex arc, located in the *second, third, and fourth lumbar spinal nerves* and in the *femoral nerve;* the impulses will then pass, via the axons of these neurons, from the sensory root and cross a synapse in the *anterior gray horn of the spinal cord,* and finally move outward over motor neurons to the quadriceps. This muscle group quickly contracts, temporarily extending the leg. It will be seen that this is the simplest type reflex possible. It involves *only two neurons* in a chain, one *motor* and one *sensory.** The impulses enter and leave the spinal cord at one level, without the necessity of traveling up and down it; and there is no crossing over from one side of the cord to the other. How can the physician use the patellar reflex in diagnosis? One way is to use it to help him determine the segmental level at which disease or injury has attacked cell bodies in the anterior gray horn of the spinal cord, or in the anterior or posterior roots of spinal nerves. If the knee jerk is poor or nonexistent in a patient with a history of poliomyelitis or combat wounds, for example, then the physician knows that the anterior gray horn or roots have undergone damage at the level of the cell bodies of the motor neurons supplying axons to spinal nerves L2, L3, L4, and the femoral nerve. With further motor and sensory tests, he can more precisely locate the site and determine the extent of the lesion or injury.

ACHILLES REFLEX In testing this reflex, the patient kneels on a chair with his feet hang-

* It should be understood that single neurons are discussed for the sake of simplicity, and that in any reflex action, impulses pass over *many neurons* lying parallel to one another in the *same nerve.*

ing over, toes pointing downward. The *calcaneous tendon* (tendon of Achilles) is tapped, stretching it and the calf muscles. Normally, the *gastrocnemius* will contract, causing the foot to *plantar flex* or *extend*. The reflex arcs of this mechanism have their *motor neurons in segments S1 and S2 of the spinal cord,* and failure to elicit a satisfactory response when testing it indicates damage at that cord level (provided peripheral portions of both the afferent and efferent neurons are known to be intact).

OTHER DEEP REFLEXES   Included in this group are the *biceps reflex* and *triceps reflex,* in which tapping of these muscles results in flexion and extension of the forearm, respectively. In this way, the integrity of reflex arcs at the level of the motor nerves supplying these muscles is tested.

Superficial reflexes

PLANTAR REFLEX   Testing for this reflex consists of running the handle of a percussion hammer or other instrument along the lateral border of the sole of the foot. A *normal response* includes *curling under* of all the toes and some small degree of *inversion and flexion* of the foot, and indicates an intact *corticospinal* (pyramidal) tract, due to the fact that the reflex is aided or facilitated by impulses which travel down this tract from the cerebral cortex. In an *abnormal response,* the big toe *extends*—and sometimes the other toes do also—and none of them curl under as in the plantar reflex. This abnormal response is given the name *Babinski reflex* and, other things being normal, indicates *lesion or injury involving the corticospinal tract* due to interruption of facilitory impulses from that area.

ABDOMINAL-WALL REFLEX   If the abdominal wall is suddenly and unexpectedly stroked along one of its lateral aspects, the *abdominal muscles will normally contract,* causing the wall to move inward. Neurons of the lower four pairs of spinal nerves are the major components of the reflex arcs involved; but since these are under the influence of neurons in the corticospinal tract, an injury or lesion in the *pyramids* could abolish this reflex as easily as one interrupting the reflex arc proper.

CORNEAL REFLEX   In testing this reflex, the cornea is *lightly* touched with something soft, such as a bit of cotton or dental floss. The normal reflex action is an immediate blinking of the eyelid. The *first neuron* of the arc is in the *ophthalmic branch of the trigeminal nerve.* Synapse is made in the nucleus of the spinal root of the trigeminal with the *second-order neuron,* which in turn synapses with cells in the *nucleus of the facial nerve.* Since the facial nerve sends fibers to the orbicularis oculi muscles, impulses traveling this route cause the eye to close. Actually, because both facial-nerve nuclei receive connecting fibers, both eyes close simultaneously.

Visceral reflexes—pupillary

LIGHT REFLEX   Shining a light into the eye brings about constriction of the iris. The *optic* and *oculomotor* nerves are involved, along with their nuclei and connections in the CNS.

CONSENSUAL LIGHT REFLEX   Shining a light onto the retina of one eye produces constriction of the iris in the other. This illustrates connections between the two halves of the brain and the pathways involved.

ACCOMMODATION REFLEX   Having the subject look at close objects brings on pupillary constriction when the eyes are converged. Cranial nerves II and III and centers in the cortex of the occipital lobe of the cerebrum are involved.

CILIOSPINAL REFLEX   Pinching the skin of the back of the neck or other part of the body produces dilation of the pupil. This reflex is in response to pain and is mediated over somatic and autonomic pathways.

Other visceral reflexes

CAROTID SINUS REFLEX   Pressure on the carotid sinus—a dilation of the internal carotid artery near its point of origin—initiates this reflex. The sinus contains a nerve plexus, and increased blood pressure will cause vasodilation and subsequent slowing of the heart rate and fall in blood pressure, helping to restore the homeostatic state. The *glossopharyngeal and vagus nerves* carry the neurons for this reflex, and lesions involving these nerves abolish it.

RECTAL AND URINARY-BLADDER REFLEXES
The sphincter muscles controlling defecation and urination are supplied with autonomic fibers, and damage to the reflex arc will cause the patient either to be unable to hold back feces and urine or to have no urge to defecate or urinate, depending upon whether the efferent or afferent fibers are involved.

CONDITIONED REFLEXES   It should be noted that although the basic mechanisms for all our reflexes are inborn, many reflexes seen in man and domestic animals are *acquired* during growth and maturity. The latter are known as *conditioned reflexes,* and consist of responses which may not be directly related to the stimuli that bring them about. For example, a factory worker may become so conditioned to eating after he hears the sound of the noon whistle that he begins salivating and his gastric juices flow even when the whistle is blown at some time other than at noon. The scientist Pavlov first demonstrated this by ringing a bell every time he fed his dog. Soon the dog would salivate at the sound of the bell, even though no food was even in the same room. We use acquired reflexes when we perform such skills as driving a car and using a typewriter. Reflexes concerned with such physiological processes as digestion, swallowing, gagging, coughing, portions of the reproductive process, urination, and defecation, on the other hand, are good examples of *inborn* or inherited reflexes.

THE AUTONOMIC NERVOUS SYSTEM

Customarily, the human nervous system is said to consist of three smaller systems: the central nervous system (CNS) or brain and spinal cord; the peripheral nervous system (PNS), consisting of cranial and spinal nerves; and the autonomic nervous system (ANS) or *visceral motor system.* The ANS might more aptly be considered a subdivision of the combined peripheral and central nervous systems, rather than as a system in itself. On the one hand, many of its cell bodies and axons are closely associated with

those of the PNS; and, on the other hand, the ANS is definitely under the influence of higher centers of the brain.

Anatomy of the ANS; divisions

The autonomic nervous system is an *efferent* system. Its fibers carry *involuntary motor impulses* to *smooth muscle, cardiac muscle, and glands.* In some instances, especially where the visceral organs are concerned, afferent fibers are closely associated with the purely efferent fibers of the ANS; however, these afferent fibers do not properly belong to that system, but are in reality *visceral afferent fibers* of the PNS.

Figure 7-32 is a simplified diagram showing the main anatomical features of the autonomic nervous system. It will be noted that *all autonomic innervations* are, by means of the *2-neuron chains,* similar to the arrangement of the somatic motor portion of the peripheral nervous system. In the ANS, one neuron has its cell body in the central nervous system (usually in the spinal cord or medulla); and the axon of this neuron ends in a *ganglion,* where it synapses with the cell body and dendrites of another neuron. The axon of this second neuron then reaches the structure to be innervated. The *neuron extending from the CNS to the ganglion* is called a *preganglionic neuron,* while *that connecting the first neuron with the structure innervated* is a *postganglionic neuron.* Some postganglionic neurons are very short, and many lie within the wall of the organ supplied. There are about 30 postganglionic neurons for every preganglionic neuron, permitting wide areas of distribution with relatively few preganglionic centers in the CNS. Autonomic ganglia are of *three types: vertebral, collateral,* and *terminal.* Vertebral ganglia are arranged in two vertical chains parallel to the vertebral column and are called *sympathetic trunks.* Collateral ganglia are positioned in the thoracic and abdominopelvic cavities close to the aorta and its major branches. The *three most important collateral ganglia* are the *celiac, superior mesenteric,* and *inferior mesenteric,* all lying near major branches of the aorta

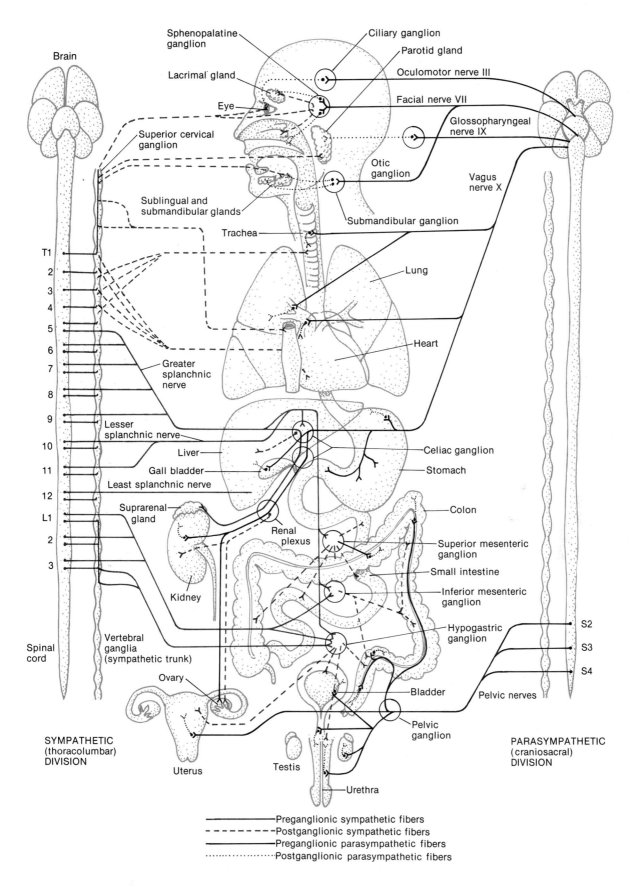

Figure 7-32 The autonomic nervous system.

bearing the same names. Terminal ganglia are found in the great nerve plexuses of the abdomen and thorax, and include among others the *ciliary, submaxillary,* and *spheno-palatine* ganglia of the head. All of the above ganglia are examples of ganglia lying close to the structures innervated by axons spring-ing from them.

SYMPATHETIC DIVISION   It will readily be seen by examining Fig. 7-32 that *the ANS consists of two portions* or *divisions.* That portion whose fibers are indicated by dashed lines (– · – · – · – and – – – –) in the figure is the *sympathetic* or *thoracolumbar division,* while the fibers indicated by solid lines and dots belong to the *parasympathetic* or *cranio-sacral division.* Many visceral organs of the body are supplied by fibers of *both divisions,* and convey impulses having *opposite* or *antagonistic effects.* Depending upon circum-stances, such as physiological requirements and the organ concerned, one division will often override the other; but usually the effects tend to be balanced, playing a major role in maintenance of the homeostatic state.

Cell bodies of *preganglionic neurons of the sympathetic division* of the ANS lie in the *intermediolateral cell column or horn* of *all thoracic and the first three or four lumbar segments of the spinal cord* (Fig. 7-33). They leave the cord in the anterior roots of spinal nerves, form the *white rami commu-nicantes* of the thoracic and lumbar spinal nerves, and enter the ganglia of the sympa-thetic trunk. Here, one of three things hap-pens to the neurons: (1) *they may pass through the ganglia and synapse with post-ganglionic neurons in collateral ganglia;* (2) *they may synapse directly with postgang-lionic neurons that have their cell bodies in one of the 22 sympathetic ganglia;* or (3) *they may either ascend or descend in the sympathetic trunk, and synapse at a level either higher or lower than that at which they entered.* The sympathetic supply to the ad-renal gland is unique in that there is *no post-ganglionic neuron.* Certain cells of the gland are so modified as to conduct the impulses and act as the second-order neuron in the chain.

PARASYMPATHETIC DIVISION   Cell bodies of *preganglionic neurons of this division of the* ANS are located in the nuclei of cranial nerves III, VII, IX, and X in the *brainstem and in the second, third, and fourth sacral segments of the spinal cord.* Axons of these preganglionic neurons are distributed by means of the cranial nerves in which they are found—III, VII, IX, and X—and by means of the sacral spinal nerves. For the most part, these axons reach all the way to the visceral organs supplied before synapsing with post-ganglionic neurons on the surface or within the walls of these organs.

Functions of the ANS

In most cases, viscera and other struc-tures supplied by the ANS are innervated by *both divisions* of the system, and the in-fluences exerted by each division are an-tagonistic to each other, helping to maintain the homeostatic state. In a few instances, however, the influences are *not antagonistic;* for example, stimulation of either sympa-thetic or parasympathetic nerves to the *salivary glands* produces secretion; and the *sweat glands, piloerector muscles* (of the hair), *adrenal medulla* (inner portion of the adrenal gland), *arteries of the digestive sys-tem,* and *coronary arteries* seem to be sup-plied by the *sympathetic division only,* or at least have a very small parasympathetic in-nervation. Sometimes, following an emo-tional upheaval or illness, the two divisions of the ANS seem to get out of balance, and the activity of one division predominates over that of the other. This condition is called either *sympathicotonia* or *parasym-pathicotonia,* depending upon which division is predominant at the time. Normally, the ANS plays a major role in maintaining a state of dynamic equilibrium in regard to *body temperature* (by acting on sweat glands), *body-fluid balance* (by controlling excretion by sweat glands and the kidneys), regulation of the *heart rate* and its *force of beat, blood pressure, enzyme production, blood sugar level, hormone production, di-gestion,* and many other activities. The *chemicals produced at the endings of nerve fibers* no doubt play major roles in helping to carry out an appropriate body function. *Acetylcholine,* for example, which is pro-

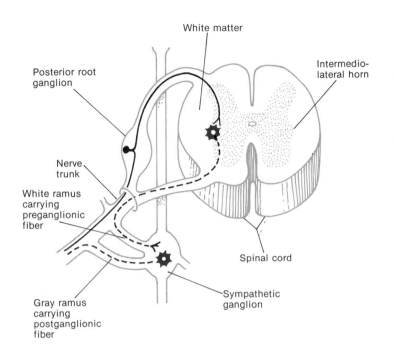

White matter

Posterior root ganglion

Intermediolateral horn

Nerve trunk

White ramus carrying preganglionic fiber

Spinal cord

Gray ramus carrying postganglionic fiber

Sympathetic ganglion

Figure 7-33 Origin of the sympathetic neurons of the autonomic nervous system.

duced at the neuromuscular junctions of skeletal muscles, is also secreted at the *synaptic junctions between preganglionic and postganglionic neurons* of *both divisions* of the ANS, and at the endings of *postganglionic parasympathetic fibers.* All nerve fibers releasing acetylcholine are called *cholinergic fibers.* After production, acetylcholine is soon inactivated by an enzyme secreted by nearby cells, *cholinesterase. Norepinephrine* and minute quantities of *epinephrine* (adrenalin) are released at the endings of *postganglionic sympathetic neurons,* the axons of which are, therefore, called *adrenergic fibers.* The effects of norepinephrine are similar to those of epinephrine in many ways. All chemicals produced at nerve endings are known as *transmitter agents,* because they assist in conveying or transmitting impulses, either from one neuron to another, or from an axon ending to an effector organ, gland, blood vessel, or other structure.

Table 7-2 compares some of the effects of the two divisions of the autonomic nervous system. The autonomic functions outlined in this table were, in general, determined by electrical stimulation of the various portions of the ANS in laboratory animals. Many autonomic activities result from the influence

that this portion of the nervous system has on *smooth muscle*—for example, that in *blood vessels,* the *uterus, urinary bladder, gastrointestinal tract, respiratory system,* and *eye.* It will be seen that the *parasympathetic division* of the ANS tends to *conserve* the body resources, while the *sympathetic division* prepares the body for *emergencies.* In a stressful situation, epinephrine, the so-called *"fight-or-flight" hormone,* is poured into the bloodstream by autonomic action on the adrenal medulla. The heart beats *more forcefully and rapidly,* blood pressure *rises,* and the senses become *more acute.* Blood vessels in the skin and visceral organs *constrict,* shunting more blood to the skeletal muscles. More *immediate energy* is made available to the cells by an increase in the level of *blood sugar,* and this sugar is metabolized at a *much more rapid rate* than usually. Ventilation in the lungs is *increased* by more rapid breathing, and *more oxygen is made available* to the tissues.

It should be clearly understood that the ANS is under the influence of the CNS at all times, especially certain higher centers of the *cerebral cortex, thalamus, hypothalamus, medulla,* and *spinal cord.* Afferent impulses keep these centers informed as to the physiological state of the body and its parts, and efferent impulses are sent from them to the autonomic system to make adjustments as required in order to maintain the homeostatic state.

AUTONOMIC REFLEXES   Most autonomic actions result from reflex activity. Autonomic reflex arcs have *receptors, afferent neurons, internuncial neurons, efferent neurons,* and *effectors,* just like any other reflex arc. The major difference between an autonomic reflex arc and a spinal reflex arc is that autonomic reflexes *always involve two efferent neurons in a chain,* a *preganglionic* and a *postganglionic* neuron. The afferent neurons of autonomic reflex arcs do not actually belong to the ANS, but to the PNS; and connections within the CNS permit the autonomic system to utilize these neurons during autonomic reflex activity. A much better understanding of autonomic reflexes will be obtained as such physiological processes as heart action, respiration, digestion, and excretion are studied in later sections of this book.

TABLE 7-2

Functions of the autonomic nervous system (ANS)

Function or effector	Sympathetic supply	Parasympathetic supply
Heart (cardiac muscle)	Increases rate and strength of contraction	Decreases rate
Glands		
Sweat	Causes secretion	No innervation
Lacrimal	No secretion	Causes secretion
Salivary *	Slight secretion	Abundant secretion
Gastric *	Slight secretion	Causes secretion
Liver *	Promotes glycogen breakdown, raising blood sugar level	No effect
Pancreas *	Decreases secretion	Increases secretion both of digestive juices and the hormone insulin
Adrenal medulla	Produces secretion of epinephrine, which in turn raises blood pressure, heart rate, and blood sugar level	Little or no effect
Blood vessels		
In skeletal muscle	Causes dilation	No effect
In skin	Causes constriction	No effect
Coronary	Causes dilation	Causes constriction
In viscera of abdomen and pelvis	Causes constriction	Causes dilation
Of salivary glands	Causes constriction	Causes dilation
Of external sex organs	Causes constriction	Causes dilation
Of brain	Causes constriction	Causes dilation
Pulmonary	Causes constriction	Causes dilation

* These are all digestive glands.

Pharmacology of the ANS

Since transmission of autonomic impulses depends upon chemical transmitting agents at synapses and *neurovisceral junctions,* it is possible to modify visceral function using drugs that act at ganglia or at autonomic effectors. These drugs must either *imitate the effect* produced by sympathetic or parasympathetic stimulation, or *inhibit the action* of one or the other division, in order to produce the desired effect. Transmission by preganglionic cholinergic neurons is *stimulated* by moderate doses of *acetylcholine* and *nicotine,* and *inhibited* by massive doses of the same drugs and moderate doses of *cholinesterase;* postganglionic cholinergic neurons are *stimulated* by moderate doses of *acetylcholine* and *muscarine* and *inhibited* by *atropine, scopolamine, belladonna,* and *belladonnalike synthetics;* adrenergic neurons are *stimulated* by *norepinephrine, epinephrine, ephedrine,* and *amphetamines,* and *inhibited* by *ergotamine, phentolamine, benzodioxane, phenoxybenzamine,* and others. These are only a few of the agents affecting autonomic transmission.

Function or effector	Sympathetic supply	Parasympathetic supply
Eye		
Iris	Causes contraction of radial muscle, dilating pupil	Causes contraction of circular muscle, constricting pupil
Ciliary muscle	Causes relaxation, permitting distant vision	Causes contraction and accommodation for near vision
Gastrointestinal tract		
Stomach wall	Decreases motility	Increases motility
Sphincters	Constricts	Relaxes
Intestine wall		
Anal sphincter (internal)	Decreases motility Constricts	Increases motility Relaxes
Respiratory system		
Bronchi	Dilates	Constricts
Secretions in air passages	Inhibits	Increases
Urinary bladder		
Wall	Relaxes	Contracts
Sphincter	Constricts	Relaxes
Uterus		
Pregnant	Contraction	No effect
Nonpregnant	Relaxes	No effect
Piloerector muscles (of body hair)	Contraction, producing "goose pimples"	No effect
Penis	Causes ejaculation	Brings about erection
Mental activity	Increases	No effect
Blood clotting	Accelerates	No effect
Overall rate of metabolism	Greatly increases	No effect

PROTECTION OF THE BRAIN AND SPINAL CORD

Membranes covering the brain and spinal cord

(See Figs. 7-34 and 7-35.) Three membranes called *meninges*—the *dura mater, arachnoid mater,* and *pia mater*—cover the two large structures that comprise the central nervous system. The dura is the *outermost, is the most fibrous and thickest, and hence the toughest* of the three. It can be preserved intact when dissecting a cal-varia ("skull cap") from a laboratory specimen. The *arachnoid layer,* as its name implies, is a *webby, delicate, almost diffuse* structure. *Cerebrospinal fluid* (CSF) forms a cushion for the brain and spinal cord by filling the *subarachnoid space.* The *pia mater* is the *thinnest* of all the meninges, and is so intimately adherent to the gyri and sulci of the brain surface that it cannot be dissected away except by means of special techniques. Double-layered folds of the inelastic dura mater extend into several clefts of the brain. One of these, the *falx cerebri,* (color plate VI) penetrates deep into the longitudinal

191

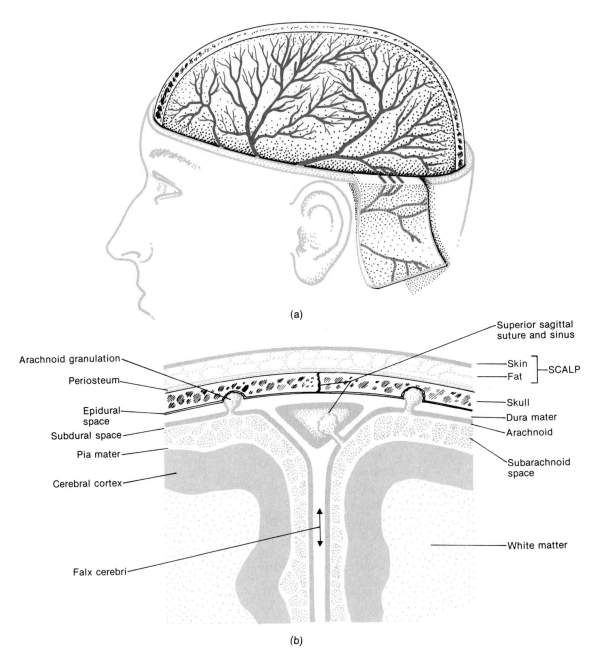

(a)

Arachnoid granulation

Periosteum

Epidural space

Subdural space

Pia mater

Cerebral cortex

Falx cerebri

Superior sagittal suture and sinus

Skin
Fat
}SCALP

Skull

Dura mater

Arachnoid

Subarachnoid space

White matter

(b)

Figure 7-34 (a) The dura mater and its blood vessels. (b) Frontal section through the meninges, showing relationships to other structures.

fissure *between the cerebral hemispheres;* another, the *falx cerebelli,* occupies a similar position *between the hemispheres of the cerebellum.* Separating the cerebellum below from the cerebrum above is the *tentorium cerebelli.* A small, disc-shaped portion of dura, the *diaphragma sella,* roofs the *pituitary gland* and is penetrated by its stalk, the *infundibulum.* At various points, the arachnoid mater develops outpouchings that push their way into the *large blood sinuses* (which carry venous blood from the brain); cerebrospinal fluid enters the bloodstream at these points, called *arachnoid villi* or granulations. Often, such projections are seen on the surface of the cerebral hemispheres. The pia

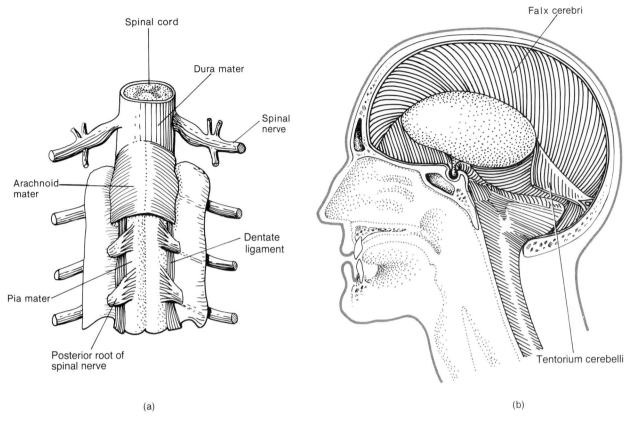

Figure 7-35 Special functions of the meninges. (a) The dentate ligament, which helps hold the spinal cord in place. (b) The falx cerebri and tentorium cerebelli, which separate the cerebral hemispheres from each other and separate the cerebrum from the cerebellum, respectively.

mater is the *most delicate* and the *most vascular* of the meninges. Within it lie the blood vessels supplying the brain and spinal cord. Dentate (tooth-edged) ligaments of pia mater connect the spinal cord proper to the dura mater in the spinal canal (Fig. 7-35).

Cerebrospinal fluid:
its formation and circulation

Cerebrospinal fluid, or CSF, is found within four spaces, *ventricles,* within the brain (Fig. 7-36). It is also present in the tiny *central canal* of the spinal cord, and fills the subarachnoid space around both the brain and cord. CSF acts as a *shock absorber* for the entire CNS. An average of some 150 cc of this rather clear, watery liquid is usually

present within the fluid spaces of the adult nervous system. It is formed by *choroid plexuses* of tiny blood vessels located in all the brain ventricles, then circulated through these ventricles, the subarachnoid space, and the central canal, and returned to the bloodstream via the arachnoid villi that invaginate (push into) into the large blood sinuses of the brain (Figs. 7-34 and 7-37).

The four ventricles of the brain are customarily numbered I, II, III, and IV. *Ventricle I* is the space within the *right cerebral hemisphere, II* is in the *left hemisphere, III* is the cavity of the *diencephalon,* and *IV* is situated on the dorsal aspect of the *pons and medulla.* A small channel, the *interventricular foramen* (of Munro), connects each lateral ventricle with ventricle III; while this latter cavity is joined below with ventricle IV by a narrow channel, the *cerebral*

193

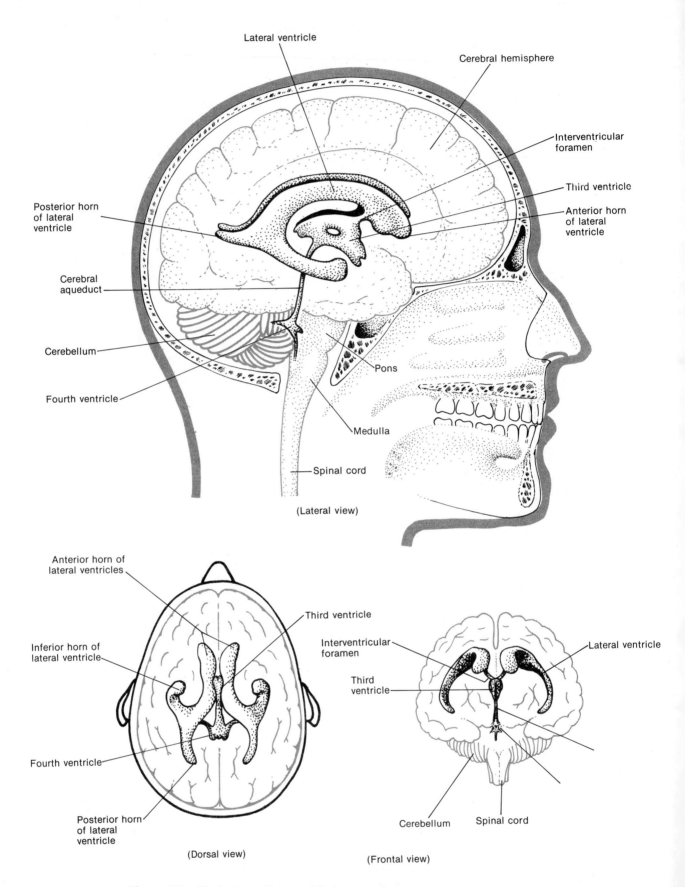

Lateral ventricle

Cerebral hemisphere

Interventricular foramen

Third ventricle

Anterior horn of lateral ventricle

Posterior horn of lateral ventricle

Cerebral aqueduct

Cerebellum

Fourth ventricle

Pons

Medulla

Spinal cord

(Lateral view)

Anterior horn of lateral ventricles

Third ventricle

Inferior horn of lateral ventricle

Fourth ventricle

Posterior horn of lateral ventricle

(Dorsal view)

Interventricular foramen

Third ventricle

Lateral ventricle

Cerebellum

Spinal cord

(Frontal view)

Figure 7-36 The brain ventricles and their connections.

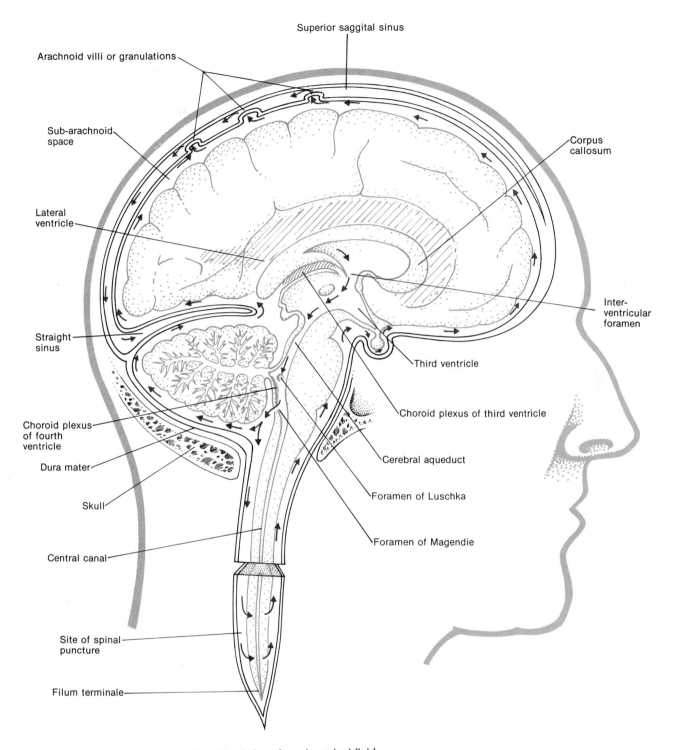

Superior saggital sinus

Arachnoid villi or granulations

Sub-arachnoid space

Lateral ventricle

Straight sinus

Choroid plexus of fourth ventricle

Dura mater

Skull

Central canal

Site of spinal puncture

Filum terminale

Corpus callosum

Inter-ventricular foramen

Third ventricle

Choroid plexus of third ventricle

Cerebral aqueduct

Foramen of Luschka

Foramen of Magendie

Figure 7-37 Circulation of cerebrospinal fluid.

aqueduct (aqueduct of Sylvius). Ventricle IV is continuous inferiorly with the central canal of the spinal cord. This ventricle also has three "holes" in it—two *foramina of Luschka,* one in each lateral portion of the ventricle—and one *foramen of Magendie* in

the ventricle roof. All these openings permit cerebrospinal fluid to flow out into the sub-arachnoid space. One way to trace the circulation of CSF would be to begin at one of the lateral ventricles, follow it through the inter-ventricular foramen into ventricle III, from

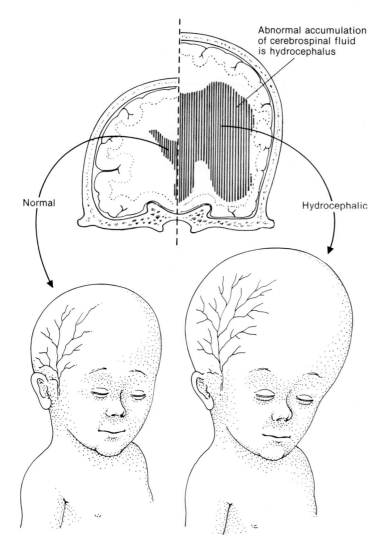

Figure 7-38 Hydrocephalus.

this space via the cerebral aqueduct to ventricle IV, and from ventricle IV into the subarachnoid space and down the central canal of the spinal cord (Fig. 7-37). The fluid in the subarachnoid space is *reabsorbed* at *arachnoid villi,* while that moving down the central canal slowly moves back upward, perhaps due to action of the cilia found on the ciliated columnar epithelium that lines a portion of it. Examination of the spinal cords of cadavers reveals that the central canal is often plugged with dead *ependymal (lining) cells* and other cellular debris, but apparently this is of little or no consequence.

FORMATION OF CSF Cerebrospinal fluid is slowly but continuously formed by seeping or diffusing through the walls of tufts of

arterioles (small arteries) and capillaries of the choroid plexuses, present in all the brain ventricles. Circulation of the fluid is due chiefly to the constant formation processes and constant reabsorption into the venous system, but is aided by ciliated cells in the ventricles. Blockage of the ventricular system can result in a backing up of CSF and enlargement of the head, a condition called *hydrocephalus* (Fig. 7-38). Blockage can be present at birth, or acquired later as a result of injury or disease, such as a brain tumor. Hydrocephalus is of two major types, *internal* and *external*. The internal type is characterized by *collection of CSF within the brain ventricles,* while external hydrocephalus consists of excess CSF *in the subarachnoid space,* outside the brain proper.

BLOOD SUPPLY OF THE BRAIN AND SPINAL CORD

The arterial network

The brain cannot do without oxygen for more than five minutes without suffering permanent damage. A good blood supply carrying this oxygen is, therefore, vital to its very existence. Figure 7-39 and color plate VIII illustrate the major arterial vessels of the brain and spinal cord. It will be seen that all the arteries supplying the brain are *either direct or indirect branches of two large paired vessels,* the *internal carotid artery* and the *vertebral artery.* The internal carotid is one of the two terminal branches of the *common carotid artery,* and the vertebral springs from the *subclavian artery.* Note that the two vertebral arteries give off *posterior inferior cerebellar arteries* laterally and two other branches that join to form an *anterior spinal artery* before the vertebral arteries themselves join, forming the *basilar artery* on the ventral surface of the medulla and pons. The first branches off the basilar artery are the *anterior inferior cerebellar arteries,* followed shortly by the *internal auditory branches.* Several *pontine branches* are applied to the inferior surface of the pons. Near the anterior end of the basilar artery, a pair of *superior cerebellar* and *posterior cerebral arteries* are given off. Two *posterior communicating arteries,* branches of the internal carotids,

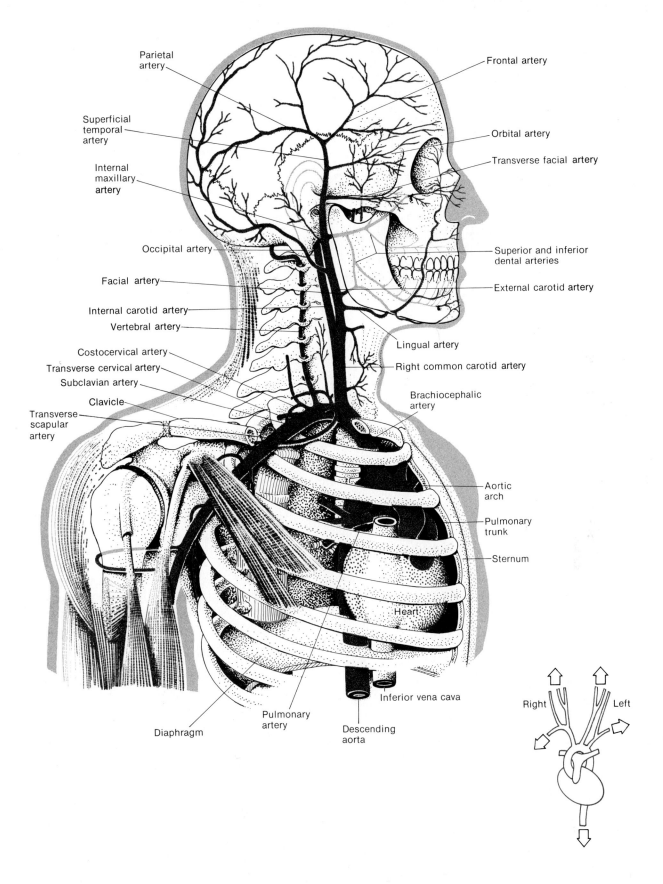

Figure 7-39(a) Origin of the internal carotid and the vertebral artery.

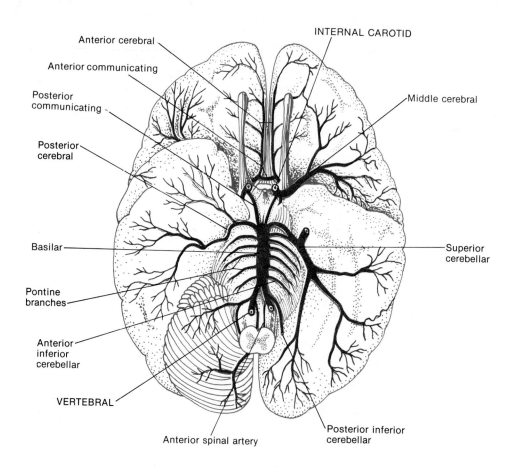

Anterior cerebral

Anterior communicating

Posterior communicating

Posterior cerebral

Basilar

Pontine branches

Anterior inferior cerebellar

VERTEBRAL

Anterior spinal artery

INTERNAL CAROTID

Middle cerebral

Superior cerebellar

Posterior inferior cerebellar

Figure 7-39(b)   The internal carotid and the vertebral artery give origin to the arteries that supply the brain. (See also Fig. 7-40.)

link their parent vessels with the posterior cerebral arteries. Two more branches of the internal carotids, the *anterior cerebral arteries,* are joined by a short *anterior communicating artery.* The ring around the hypophysis and optic chiasm—formed by portions of the posterior cerebral arteries, the posterior communicating arteries, portions of the internal carotids and anterior cerebral arteries, and the anterior communicating artery—is called the *circle of Willis.* The most important branches of the internal carotids are the large *middle cerebral arteries* and *anterior cerebral arteries.*

Figures 7-39 and 7-40 illustrate the *arterial supply of the cerebral hemispheres.* The *anterior cerebral artery* carries blood to outer and medial portions of the frontal and parietal lobes; the *middle cerebral artery* supplies the lateral portions of these same lobes and the lateral and medial portions of

the temporal lobe; while the *posterior cerebral artery* feeds the occipital lobe (and hence the visual cortex), and the underside of the temporal lobe. The *chief arteries of the spinal cord* are the *anterior spinal artery,* lying near the anterior median fissure of the cord, and two *posterior spinal arteries,* one near each dorsal nerve root. Both the anterior and posterior spinal arteries arise from the vertebral artery, and give off numerous branches to the spinal cord.

Venous drainage of the CNS

Venous blood of the brain is drained by *veins accompanying the arteries of the brain,* and then enters the *superior sagittal, inferior sagittal, sigmoid, straight, petrosal, and transverse blood sinuses.* From these, most of it flows downward in the internal

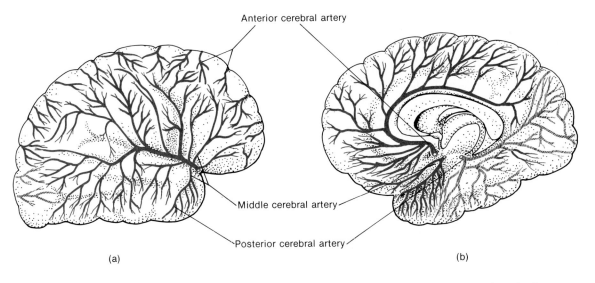

Anterior cerebral artery

Middle cerebral artery

Posterior cerebral artery

(a)

(b)

Figure 7-40 Distribution of the three cerebral arteries. (a) Lateral aspect of cerebral hemisphere. (b) Medial and inferior aspects of cerebral hemisphere.

jugular to the brachiocephalic veins (Fig. 10-14). *Spinal veins* accompany the spinal arteries and, after joining the *vertebral veins,* drain blood from the spinal cord into the *inferior cerebellar veins.*

Degeneration and regeneration of nervous tissues

Once a neuron dies, it is *never replaced.* Once a tract or pathway in the brain or spinal cord is damaged by disease or injury, the function of that tract or pathway is altered or lost forever. Some regeneration of peripheral nerve fibers does take place, under very exacting conditions. For example, if the motor nerve to a muscle is cut, the distal portions of its severed axons undergo a breakdown process called *Wallerian degeneration;* but within less than a day, the proximal portions of these axons begin a process of regeneration by *budding,* and in the distal portions a tube is formed by proliferation of Schwann cells. If the new buds from the proximal portion of the severed nerve are successful in entering the tubes formed by the distal portion, they will reinnervate the muscle, restoring partial or complete function. Such regeneration is, unfortunately, the exception rather than the rule. It can often be encouraged by a neurosurgeon who can sometimes approximate the ends of severed

nerves and suture them together; however, because there is no way in which motor neurons may be matched with motor neurons, or sensory fibers with sensory fibers, at best it is a procedure of possibilities rather than probabilities as far as recovery is concerned.

LEARNING, MEMORY, AND SLEEP

Learning and memory are thought to be seated in those portions of the cerebral cortex other than the motor and sensory portions—*association areas.* Special names are given to many of the association areas. There are strong indications that the *seat of memory* may be in the temporal lobe, just below the auditory area. Electrical stimulation of this portion of the brain in conscious subjects often results in vivid recall of the past in great detail. Many theories have been advanced regarding the memory process; nevertheless, its mechanisms are not yet completely understood. Short *association fibers* connect the association areas on one side of the cerebrum with each other, while still more fibers join those of one hemisphere with those of the other. Learning processes involve these fibers, which occur in rather loosely arranged groups and as tracts and pathways of the brain. The electrical type

199

nerve impulses which follow the application of outside stimuli, plus certain chemical changes in the *ribonucleic acid* and brain proteins, point to possible ways in which learning, memory, and even "thinking" take place. Neurons are extremely rich in RNA, and the concentration of this nucleic acid, as well as that of brain protein, builds up if a neuron is stimulated repeatedly. It is currently thought that stimuli bring about not only an increase in the amount of RNA in brain neurons, but an alteration in the configuration (shape) of the molecule such as to imply that the learning process and memory are theoretically limitless (the components of an RNA molecule having the potential of being arranged in an infinite number of different ways). Some support for the *RNA hypothesis* has been provided by recent experiments involving flatworms called *planarians*. A number of these tiny animals were conditioned to respond to a light by being subjected to a mild electrical shock every time the light came on. These worms were then cut up and fed to untrained specimens, with the result that the latter worms acquired the conditioned response much faster than did the trained cousins they had eaten for lunch.

The physiology of sleep

We spend one-third of our lifetime asleep. Sleep is essential for our well-being; psychological and physical disorders and even death can result from the prolonged lack of it; yet exactly what sleep is, and the mechanism by which we fall into this state of somnolence, are still mysteries to us. During sleep, body functions slow down, and some of them—such as digestion—may even stop for a short period of time. During restful sleep, the central nervous system, heart, skeletal muscles, and other body organs have a chance to relax and rejuvenate, making ready for another day. Many are the theories that have been advanced in attempts to explain sleep, including the idea that a "sleep hormone" is produced and accumulates during the waking hours, or that some of the waste products of metabolism, attacking the CNS, bring on the condition. It is known that impulses relayed from the thalamus and reticular formation of the medulla to the cerebral cortex help to maintain wakefulness and alertness; so a state of sleep may depend upon the slowing or cessation of these impulses, thereby making sleep possible. What could bring this about, no one knows. When sleep is extremely light, difficult to attain, or lasts for only short periods of time, we say that an individual has *insomnia*. Almost everyone experiences occasional periods of sleeplessness, but chronic insomnia may have underlying organic or psychologic causes, and should be treated accordingly.

Freud and many other psychologists have spent much time investigating the causes and significance of dreams. One-fifth of the time we spend sleeping is devoted to dreaming. Everyone dreams about every $1\frac{1}{2}$ hours, for short periods lasting from a few minutes to three-quarters of an hour. Dream periods get longer as sleep becomes lighter, toward the end of the night's rest. During dreaming, the eyes move rapidly, the heart rate increases, and an *electroencephalogram* shows that brain waves resemble those of an individual who is wide awake. Investigators have found that if a person stops dreaming, he is headed for severe psychological disturbance, thereby indicating that dreams are important and necessary manifestations of our complex personalities, and are necessary to the release of normal psychic tensions.

OUTLINE SUMMARY

1. The nervous system: consists essentially of the brain, spinal cord, and nerves
   The most important functions of this vital system are the following
   A. It enables us to perceive many of the changes that take place in our external and internal environments, and to respond to those changes. Vision, hearing, tasting, smelling, and experiencing touch, pressure, pain, and temperature changes are examples of perception
   B. It enables us to "think," "reason," "remember," and carry out other abstract activities

C. It makes possible body movements by the skeletal muscles, by supplying them with nerve impulses which bring about contraction

D. It works closely with the endocrine glands in correlating and integrating body functions such as digestion and excretion

All actions of the nervous system depend upon the transmission of nerve impulses over neurons or nerve cells, the functional units of the nervous system. The chief parts of a neuron are the cell body, axon, and dendrites. Many of the activities of the nervous system are purely reflex in character, and never reach the level of consciousness

2. The nerve impulse: a self-propagating wave of electrical negatively (not a simple electrical current) carried by the conducting elements (neurons) of the nervous system

A. Some characteristics of the nerve impulse

a. Since it is self-regenerating, it does not lose strength with distance traveled, as does an ordinary electrical current

b. Impulses are much slower than common electrical currents

c. Impulses are initiated in response to a variety of stimuli, such as electricity, changes in pH and temperature, and such physical trauma as pinching

d. The impulse is due to the inward movement of sodium ions and outward movement of potassium ions through the nerve-cell membrane, following alterations in membrane permeability brought on by a stimulus. A resting potential is converted to an action potential, which moves along the neuron at high speed. The neuron is rapidly depolarized and repolarized during the process. An active-transport mechanism, such as the sodium–potassium pump, may aid in repolarization

e. Neurons, like muscle cells, exhibit relative and absolute refractory periods

B. Facilitation and summation

a. Facilitation: increase in the excitability of a neuron by subthreshold impulses

b. Summation: the "addition" of two or more subthreshold impulses, causing a neuron to discharge an impulse of its own

1. Spatial summation: summation caused by impulses converging from different neurons

2. Temporal summation: summation in time. Impulses may be

from only one source, but arrive rapidly enough to cause the recipient neuron to fire

C. Inhibitory neurons: neurons which act to prevent others from discharging an impulse. Many are present in the CNS. They are especially important in the reciprocal actions of muscles, and in the inhibition of certain reflexes, such as those of urination and defecation

D. Synaptic transmission: movement of the nerve impulse across the synaptic gap, via such chemical transmitter agents as acetylcholine, which is released by the terminal buttons of axons. Synaptic transmission occurs in one direction only: from axon to dendrite; therefore, the synapse determines the direction of impulse transmission. Transmission at neuromuscular junctions is similar to that at the synapse

3. Subdivisions of the nervous system

a. The central nervous system or CNS, consisting of the brain and spinal cord. The brain includes the cerebrum, cerebellum, and brainstem, the latter consisting of the pons, medulla, and associated structures

b. The peripheral nervous system or PNS, made up the cranial and spinal nerves which branch off the brain and cord

c. The autonomic nervous system or ANS, consisting of some independent nerves and nerve cells that travel along with those of the PNS

A. The cerebrum

a. The largest, most complex part of the brain

b. Consists of two hemispheres, connected by four commissures: the corpus callosum, fornix, and anterior and posterior commissure. The hemispheres are almost completely separated by the longitudinal fissure

c. From the lateral aspect, resembles a large mitten

d. Can be divided into lobes, five in each hemisphere: frontal, parietal, temporal, occipital, and insular. The central sulcus and lateral fissure are important boundaries of the frontal, parietal, and temporal lobes

1. Frontal lobe: here are located much of the brain tissues concerned with voluntary movements (motor areas) and personality. Body movements are represented in inverse fashion on the precentral gyrus

2. Parietal lobe: this lobe is concerned with general sensations such as temperature, touch, pressure, pain and proprioception, many of them represented in inverse order in the postcentral gyrus
3. Occipital lobe: this is the cerebral lobe in which visual sense reaches the level of consciousness
4. Temporal lobe: the temporal lobe houses the cells that bring to consciousness the sensations of hearing and smell
5. Insular lobe: this lobe may assist the frontal, parietal, and temporal lobes in carrying out their functions

  e. Cerebral white and gray matter
1. Gray matter: consists chiefly of neuron cell bodies and forms a thin, outer cerebral cortex of some 12 billion neurons. It is also found in the basal nuclei, deep within the cerebral hemispheres
2. White matter: made up mostly of axons and lies deep to the cortical substance

B. The cerebellum
  a. Consists of two hemispheres connected by a central vermis
  b. Has a cerebellar cortex of gray matter, and internal aggregations of cell bodies, cerebellar nuclei
  c. Has numerous narrow gyri
  d. Has two types of neuron fiber tracts
1. Association fiber tracts, connecting the cells of the cortex with those of the cerebellar nuclei
2. Projection fibers, connecting the cerebellum with the medulla, pons, and thalamus, and called the inferior, middle, and superior cerebellar peduncles, respectively
  e. Controls smooth, precise body movements by "computer action"

C. The brainstem: a "stalk" for the brain consisting of the medulla, pons, mesencephalon, diencephalon, and basal nuclei
  a. The medulla
1. Continuous below with the upper end of the spinal cord, and above with the pons
2. Main external features: anterior median fissure, posterior median sulcus, dorsolateral sulci (2), ventrolateral sulci (2), pyramids (2), fasciculi gracili (2), fasciculi cuneati (2), olives (2), and the emerging roots of

cranial nerves VI, VII, VIII, IX, X, XI, and XII. The medulla helps the pons to form the fourth ventricle of the brain
3. Main internal features: nuclei of several cranial nerves; reflex centers concerned with the control of breathing, heart rate, and blood-vessel diameter; centers for swallowing, coughing, vomiting, sneezing, and hiccupping; white-matter fiber tracts that convey impulses between brain and spinal cord, and vice versa; and a reticular formation of intermingled white and gray matter

  b. The pons
1. Connects the medulla and cerebellum with the mesencephalon, and joins the two cerebellar hemispheres
2. Contains the roots of cranial nerves V (the pair), and is adjacent to cranial nerves VI, VII, and VIII as they emerge from the medulla at its junction with the pons
3. Has the nuclei of origin of cranial nerves V, VI, VII, and VIII
4. Consists mostly of white matter and reticular formation, and contains the cells of the pneumotaxic center
5. Traversed by respiratory reflex pathways
6. Helps the medulla to form the fourth ventricle

  c. The mesencephalon
1. Joins the pons and cerebellum to the diencephalon and cerebrum
2. Has two superior colliculi, concerned with visual reflexes, and two inferior colliculi, involved in auditory reflexes
3. Has a small canal, the cerebral aqueduct
4. Contains the nuclei of cranial nerves III and IV, and a portion of the nucleus of V; also contains the red nucleus

  d. The diencephalon
1. Consists of the thalamus, epithalamus, subthalamus, and hypothalamus

The epithalamus consists of the pineal body, habenular trigone, and posterior commissure

The subthalamus consists of the nucleus of Forel and Field of Forel

The hypothalamus consists

of the hypophysis or pituitary gland, infundibulum (pituitary stalk), tuber cinerum (base of the infundibulum), mamillary bodies, and optic chiasm

The thalamus proper consists of gray-matter nuclei, covered by a thin layer of white matter. The nuclei are arranged in five groups

2. Has a wide variety of functions, described in this chapter
3. Has a cavity, the third ventricle

e. The basal nuclei: lie within each cerebral hemisphere inferior and lateral to the thalamus. They include the putamen, globus pallidus, and caudate nucleus, all of which consist of gray matter; and the internal and external capsules, which are made of white matter that penetrates the nuclei. The nuclei and their capsules form a corpus striatum on either side of the brain

D. The spinal cord
   a. External features
      1. Begins at the foramen magnum, and is continuous with the lower end of the medulla
      2. About 43 cm long, but is only two-thirds as long as the vertebral canal
      3. Gives rise to 31 pairs of spinal nerves
      4. Has two enlargements, cervical and lumbar, formed by cell bodies of neurons leading to the extremities
      5. Has a tapering lower end, the conus medullaris, attached to the coccyx by the filum terminale
      6. Has an anterior median fissure, posterior median sulcus, dorsolateral and ventrolateral sulci, and dorsal intermediate sulci in the cervical and lumbar portions
      7. Divided by its sulci into anterior, lateral and posterior funiculi; a fasciculus gracilis; and fasciculus cuneatus
      8. Has a cauda equina consisting of the long roots of the lumbar and sacral spinal nerves
   b. Internal features
      1. Has central gray matter shaped like an H or butterfly, consisting chiefly of neuron cell bodies
      2. Gray matter is surrounded by white matter, consisting of neuron processes which form fiber tracts

      3. The dorsal roots of spinal nerves enter the dorsal horn of the spinal-cord gray matter, and have their cell bodies in the dorsal-root ganglia
      4. The ventral roots of spinal nerves have their cells of origin in the anterior horns of the cord gray matter
      5. A reticular formation is formed by the intermingling of white and gray matter in the cord
      6. The major tracts or pathways of the spinal cord are classed as ascending or descending, depending upon whether they carry impulses up the cord or down it

4. The peripheral nervous system (PNS) consists of cranial and spinal nerves, and joins the CNS with all parts of the body
  A. Cranial nerves: 12 pairs, emerging from beneath the brain near the pons, medulla, and diencephalon. Superficial origins do not necessarily indicate deep origins
    a. Cranial nerves and their numbers
      I Olfactory
      II Optic
      III Oculomotor
      IV Trochlear
      V Trigeminal
      VI Abducens
      VII Facial
      VIII Acoustic
      IX Glossopharyngeal
      X Vagus
      XI Accessory
      XII Hypoglossal
    b. Distributions and functions of cranial nerves are discussed in the text
  B. Spinal nerves—31 pairs branch off the spinal cord: 8 cervical, 12 thoracic, 5 lumbar, 5 sacral, and 1 coccygeal
    a. Spinal nerves are formed by the junction of anterior and posterior roots, then are distributed by means of rami and smaller branches, some of which group together into plexuses. Some of the more important plexuses include: the cervical plexus, brachial plexus, lumbar plexus, sacral plexus, and pudendal plexus
    b. Dermatomes: areas of skin that are supplied by individual sensory nerves

5. Functional anatomy of the major neuron pathways
  A. Sensory or afferent pathways of the spinal cord
    a. Ventral spinothalamic
    b. Lateral spinothalamic
    c. Dorsal spinocerebellar

  d. Ventral spinocerebellar
  e. Spinotectal
  f. Fasciculus gracilis
  g. Fasciculus cuneatus
 B. Sensory pathways in the head: involve the trigeminal nerve, thalamus, and postcentral gyrus of the cerebrum, as well as neuronal connections between these structures
 C. Motor or efferent pathways: are of the descending type, as opposed to afferent pathways, which are ascending. Three of the chief motor pathways are these:
  a. Corticospinal tract or pyramidal system
  b. Extrapyramidal system
  c. Final common pathway
 D. Visceral motor and sensory pathways: utilize neurons associated with the autonomic nervous system
6. Reflexes: involuntary responses to a stimulus, which may or may not reach the level of conscious awareness
 A. The structural and functional unit of a reflex is the reflex arc, which always has at least four components: receptor, afferent neuron, efferent neuron, and effector. One or more internuncial, or connecting, neurons are also present in many reflex arcs
 B. Classification of reflexes
  a. According to the level of the CNS involved: spinal, medullary, midbrain, cerebellar
  b. Clinically: superficial, deep, visceral, pathological
 C. Some reflexes of diagnostic value
  a. Deep: patellar, achilles, biceps, triceps
  b. Superficial: plantar, abdominal-wall, corneal
  c. Visceral: pupillary, carotid sinus, rectal, urinary
7. The autonomic nervous system (ANS): a purely efferent system, carrying involuntary motor impulses to cardiac muscle, smooth muscle, and glands
 A. Divisions
  a. Sympathetic or thoracolumbar
  b. Parasympathetic or craniosacral
 With one exception (the adrenal gland), each structure served by the ANS is supplied with nerves containing bundles of 2-neuron chains. The neuron connected with the CNS is the preganglionic neuron; that joining the organ innervated is the postganglionic neuron
 B. Functions: impulses traveling over the ANS influence heart action, diameter of blood vessels, digestion, breathing, excretion, hormone and other glandular secretions, and other processes
 C. Chemical transmitter agents released at endings of ANS neurons

  a. Acetylcholine: at synapse of preganglionic and postganglionic autonomic neurons, and at the endings of postganglionic parasympathetic neurons. Only cholinergic fibers release acetylcholine
  b. Norepinephrine and epinephrine: at endings of postganglionic sympathetic neurons, which are termed adrenergic fibers
 D. Autonomic reflexes: utilize afferent fibers of the PNS. The efferent portion of the reflex arc always contains two neurons: preganglionic and postganglionic
 E. Pharmacology of the ANS: many drugs and other chemical agents affect the ANS, and in a variety of ways
  a. Two agents stimulating transmission by preganglionic cholinergic neurons are acetylcholine and nicotine. Massive doses of these drugs and moderate doses of cholinesterase inhibit these neurons
  b. Examples of agents stimulating postganglionic cholinergic neurons include acetylcholine and muscarine. Some agents inhibiting these neurons are atropine, scopolamine, and belladonna
  c. Some agents stimulating adrenergic neurons include norepinephrine, epinephrine, and the amphetamines. These neurons are inhibited by erogotamine, phentolamine, and other agents
8. Protection of the brain and cord
 A. Three membranes, the meninges, cover the CNS
  a. Dura mater: the outermost, toughest coat
  b. Arachnoid mater: intermediate layer; filmy, weblike
  c. Pia mater: innermost, most vascular, thinnest; dips into gyri and sulci, adheres tightly to brain and cord
 B. Double folds of dura separate various portions of the brain (examples: falx cerebri, falx cerebelli, tentorium cerebelli, diaphragma sella)
 C. Cerebrospinal fluid (CSF)
  a. Present in the subarachnoid space and brain ventricles
  b. A shock absorber for the CNS, and a medium of nutrient and waste exchange
  c. Formed by choroid plexuses (of blood vessels) in all brain ventricles and circulates through the ventricles, their connecting channels, the central canal of the spinal cord, and the subarachnoid space. It reenters the circulation through arachnoid villi

d. The brain ventricles
   1. Ventricle I: right lateral ventricle
   2. Ventricle II: left lateral ventricle
   3. Ventricle III: cavity of the diencephalon
   4. Ventricle IV: cavity of the pons and medulla
e. Connections between ventricles and other channels
   1. Interventricular foramina (of Munro)
   2. Cerebral aqueduct (of Sylvius)
   3. Foramen of Magendie
   4. Foramina of Luschka
f. Blockage of the flow of CSF produces an accumulation of CSF called hydrocephalus

9. Blood supply of the brain and spinal cord
   A. Arteries: direct and indirect branches of the paired internal carotid and vertebral arteries
      a. The anterior, middle, and posterior cerebral arteries supply the cerebral hemispheres
      b. The circle of Willis surrounds the hypophysis and optic chiasm
      c. Cerebellar and pontine arteries supply the cerebellum, pons, and medulla, while spinal arteries supply the spinal cord
   B. Venous drainage of the brain: into the superior sagittal, inferior sagittal, sigmoid, straight, petrosal, and transverse blood sinuses, then into the internal jugular and brachiocephalic veins. Venous drainage of the spinal cord is via spinal veins into the inferior cerebellar veins

10. Degeneration and regeneration of nervous tissue: regeneration of degenerated or injured neurons is extremely limited. In some cases budding of the proximal portion of an injured neuron occurs, but these buds must enter tubes formed by the distal portion of the severed neurilemma, if even partial function of the neuron is to return

11. The learning process and memory
    A. Learning involves possible changes in the RNA, and other chemicals of association areas of the cerebrum
    B. Memory is closely linked to learning, and the processes involved may be located in the temporal lobe, below the auditory area

12. The physiology of sleep:
    A. Sleep may possibly be due to the depression or the reflex slowing of waking activities by the thalamus and reticular formation of the medulla
    B. Sleep may be due to the accumulation of a "sleep hormone"

STUDY QUESTIONS AND PROBLEMS

1. What are the two specialties of nervous tissue? What is an impulse? Describe its origin and propagation.

2. Define: *facilitation, spatial summation,* and *temporal summation.* What are inhibitory neurons?

3. Discuss nerve-impulse transmission at the synapse and at neuromuscular junctions.

4. Outline the organization of the nervous system, listing the components of the central nervous system, peripheral nervous system, and autonomic nervous system.

5. In what large structure of the central nervous system does an activity reach the level of conscious awareness? Make a sketch showing the various lobes of the cerebrum, and list the most outstanding functions of each.

6. Mr. K. is admitted to the hospital, and it is immediately noted by the nurse that most of the body movements of the patient are incoordinated and lacking in smoothness. What large structure of the central nervous system would you suspect as the site of a possible lesion or injury?

7. What small portion of the central nervous system, continuous with the spinal cord, is the seat of several important reflexes, such as those of breathing, swallowing, coughing, and heart rate?

8. What gyrus of what lobe of the cerebrum is primarily concerned with voluntary motor activity? With the conscious awareness of the sensations of temperature, pain, touch, and pressure?

9. What kind of nervous tissue makes up the gray matter of the central nervous system? The white matter?

10. Define a nervous-system nucleus. What is a ganglion? A plexus?

11. List the parts of the mesencephalon and diencephalon. What are the major functions of these portions of the brain? What is the pons and what is its function?

12. List the structures that comprise the basal nuclei. What is the corpus striatum?

13. Describe the structure of a typical spinal nerve. List the components of a typical reflex arc that involves the spinal cord. List the major ascending and descending tracts of the spinal cord.

14. List the cranial nerves, their numbers, and general distribution. State the functional components of each.

15. List the different classes of reflexes, and give examples of each.

16. Briefly describe the most outstanding structural and functional features of the autonomic nervous system.

17. Why can the autonomic nervous system be called a visceral motor system?

18. Locate the cell bodies of preganglionic parasympathetic neurons.

19. What is the effect of the sympathetic division of the ANS on the blood vessels of skeletal muscles? On vessels of the brain? On the diameter of the pupil? On the diameter of the bronchi? On the pregnant uterus? On blood clotting?

20. What is the effect of the parasympathetic division of the ANS on the overall metabolic rate? On the wall of the urinary bladder? On the ciliary muscle? On the coronary blood vessels? On the pancreas? On the gastric glands?

the special senses

Ｔhe senses of *sight, smell, hearing,* and *taste* are the *special senses.* Closely associated with hearing is another highly important sense, *equilibrium.* We now turn our attention to the anatomy and physiology of the organs concerned with the special senses. All of them have highly specialized receptors that enable them to respond to the appropriate stimuli. Both structurally and functionally, the organs of special sense are intimately associated with the nervous system, and are completely dependent upon it for conscious interpretation of the environmental changes which they detect.

VISUAL SENSE, OR SIGHT

The ability to see depends upon highly specialized receptors in the eye—receptors that have the unique ability to distinguish between different degrees of light and dark, and even between different colors and hues of color.

Anatomy of the eye

The eye (Fig. 8-1 and Color Plate IV) is a fluid-filled, somewhat movable sphere, continuous with the anterior end of cranial nerve II—the *optic nerve,* an extension of the brain. Visual impulses initiated by receptors in the retina of the eye travel over this nerve, then the *optic tract,* and finally the *optic radiation* (in the *visual cortex*), where

they are interpreted as vision or sight. The eye or more precisely, the eyeball, is a little longer than it is wide, and the anterior portion seems to be a sort of bump growing on a larger sphere. The wall of the eye is made up of three layers or coats: and outer, tough, fibrous coat, consisting of the *cornea* and *sclerotic coat* or *sclera;* a middle, highly vascular coat, consisting of the *choroid layer, iris,* and *ciliary body;* and an inner coat, the *retina,* which bears the receptors of sight. A longitudinal section through the eye reveals three fluid-filled cavities: an *anterior chamber,* filled with thin, watery, *aqueous humor;* a *posterior chamber,* also containing *aqueous humor;* and a large *vitreous chamber,* filled with a jellylike substance called *vitreous humor.* The anterior chamber lies *between the cornea and the iris,* the posterior chamber *between the iris and lens,* and the vitreous chamber *between the lens and retina.* The gelatious mass filling this largest of all the cavities of the eyeball is usually referred to as the *vitreous body.* Running through the vitreous body from the lens to the optic-nerve area is a tiny channel—the *hyaloid canal,* all that remains of the hyaloid artery of the embryo. The hyaloid canal is often completely obliterated during development. At the anterior end of the canal is a slight depression, the *hyaloid fossa,* in which fits the lens; while at the posterior end is an area of the retina known as the *optic disc,* positioned directly over the anterior end of the optic nerve. Just anterior to the vitreous body lies the *crystalline lens,* and in front

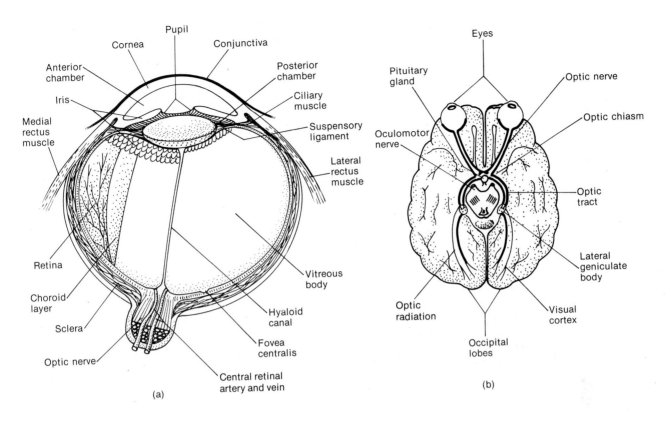

Figure 8-1 The visual apparatus. (a) Structure of the eyeball. (b) Relationship of the eyeballs, optic nerves, and optic tracts to the brain.

of it, the *pupil,* or opening in the iris. The pupil is not a structure, but merely a variable-sized space. The lens is a transparent, biconvex disc of fibrous protein material (so-called *lens-substance fibers*) built up in concentric layers or *lamellae.* An elastic *lens capsule,* lined with a layer of *lens epithelium,* encloses the lens and offers some degree of protection to it. The lens is firmly attached to the *ciliary body* by the *suspensory ligament* (Fig. 8-1). Most of the ciliary body consists of the *ciliary muscle,* which has its origin on the sclerotic coat near the cornea and its insertion on the choroid coat. Two layers of smooth muscle comprise the iris: a *sphincter layer,* which constricts the pupil and makes it smaller, and a *dilator layer,* that makes the pupil larger. As might be expected, the fibers in the sphincter-muscle layer are arranged in a *circular pattern* around the iris, while those of the dilator layer are arranged *radially.* Both of these muscle layers of the iris as well as the ciliary muscle are innervated by the autonomic nervous system. Around its periphery, the iris

joins the ciliary body; the remainder extends inward between the cornea and the lens. The color of a person's eyes depends upon the *color of the pigments in the iris.* The "white" of the eye is the *visible portion of the sclera* around the cornea. The innermost layer of the wall of the eyeball is the retina. It does not cover the entire inner surface of the wall, however, but extends anteriorly only as far as the posterior aspect of the ciliary body. The border of the retina at this point has a zigzag appearance, and is called the *ora serrata.*

LAYERS OF THE RETINA Two main layers comprise the retina: an *outer pigmented layer,* which is adherent to the choroid layer of the wall of the eyeball; and an *inner nervous layer,* or so-called *retina proper.* The nervous layer itself consists of three layers of neurons: (1) a *layer of visual receptor neurons,* some 100 million rods and 7 million cones, so-called because of their characteristic shape; (2) a *layer of bipolar neurons,* the first nerve cells to receive the impulse

209

that is initiated by the rods and cones when they are struck by light; and (3) an inner *layer of ganglion neurons,* which are directly attached to the fibers of the optic nerve (Fig. 8-2).

BLOOD SUPPLY OF THE RETINA   The *central artery and vein to the retina* enter the eye *inside the optic nerve* and spread out in the substance of the retina by means of many branches. The central retinal artery is a branch of the *ophthalmic artery.* By using an ophthalmoscope (an instrument containing a lens and a source of light) to examine the retina (Fig. 8-2), the physician can note the condition of the retinal artery branches and gain valuable information concerning the health of the patient. These vessels take on characteristic appearances in diabetes mellitus, hypertension, and other pathologic conditions. Examination of the optic disc—the point at which the optic nerve leaves the eye—is also a diagnostic aid. If the disc is indented in the direction of the optic nerve (*"cupped disc"*), high *intraocular pressure*

—pressure within the eyeball—such as that seen in *glaucoma,* a serious disease of the eye, is indicated; if, on the other hand, the disc protrudes anteriorly (*"choked disc"*), *extraocular* high pressure is suspected—posterior to the eyeball—which may be caused by a brain tumor or be due to other conditions.

THE FORMATION OF AQUEOUS HUMOR Aqueous humor probably is filtered out of the blood in the capillaries of the ciliary body and may also be actively secreted by these vessels. Once it is produced, aqueous humor moves into the posterior chamber, and from there moves between the lens and iris, through the pupil, and into the anterior chamber. From the anterior chamber, it normally moves into a narrow channel that passes like a ring through the anterior part of the sclera, the *canal of Schlemm* (Fig. 8-3). This canal acts as a venous sinus, draining the humor into numerous small veins. If the canal becomes blocked or closed due to swelling or other source of pressure

Figure 8-2   (a) Diagram of the various layers of the retina.
(b) The retina as seen with an ophthalmoscope.

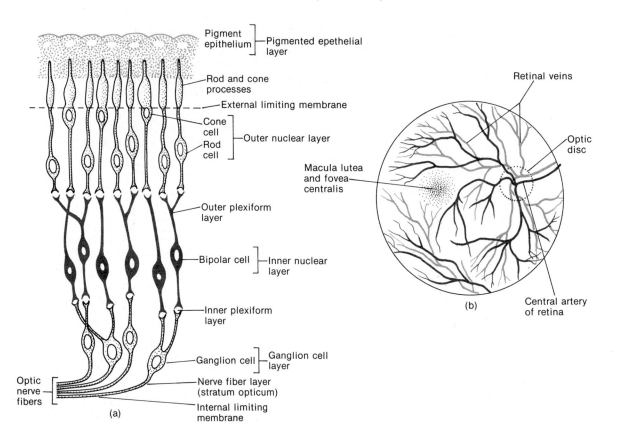

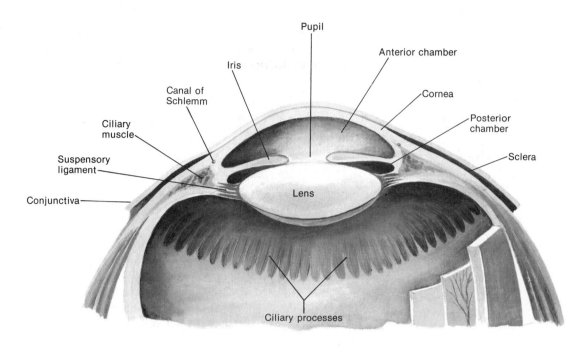

Figure 8-3 Location of the canal of Schlemm.

within the eyeball, aqueous humor cannot drain away, and a condition of high pressure in the anterior chamber exists. This condition is known medically as *glaucoma,* and may result in damage to retinal cells and blindness. A decrease in the rate of absorption or an increase in the rate of formation of aqueous humor may contribute to this condition.

PROTECTION OF THE EYE   It is vital that an organ so important as the eye be preserved from injury. Under ordinary circumstances, the eye is protected by the rim of the *bony orbit,* by the *blinking reflex,* by the constant formation of *tears* (which prevent drying and subsequent degeneration of the eyeball), and by shock-absorbing *fat* that is deposited between the eyeball and the walls of the orbit.

ACCESSORY STRUCTURES OF THE EYE   The *eyebrows, eyelids, eyelashes, conjunctiva,* and *lacrimal apparatus* constitute the accessory structures of the eye. Each has its own purpose; for example, the brows are considered to be necessary to a pleasing appearance, as are the lashes. The lashes offer a small amount of protection against the entrance of foreign particles. The eyelids are, of course, the great protectors of the anterior portion of

the eye. They are made of skin and striated muscle, and are covered on their deep surfaces by conjunctiva, the name given to a mucous membrane that is reflected (folded) over part of the eyeball. The anatomical name for the eyelids is *palpebrae,* and the slitlike opening between the upper and lower lids is the *palpebral fissure.* Each "corner" of the palpebral fissure is called a *canthus.* The *medial canthus* is next to the nose, while the opposite corner is the *lateral canthus.* A small red bump, the *caruncle,* is located within the medial canthus. The free borders of the eyelids are thickened by connective tissues to form rather firm ridges, the *tarsal plates,* or simply *tarsi.* The lacrimal apparatus (Fig. 8-4) is extremely important to the wellbeing of the eye. It constantly forms tears which bathe the eyeball and keep it moist. Each lacrimal apparatus consists of a *lacrimal gland* ("tear gland") with about 12 *excretory ducts;* a *lacrimal sac* with two side branches, the *lacrimal ducts;* and a *nasolacrimal duct.* Everyone knows that during crying, tears overflow from the medial corner of the eye; students are, therefore, often surprised to learn that these tears are produced in glands located above the *lateral* portion of the eye. Normally, tear formation is not excessive, but an irritant to the eye or an emotional upset brings about copious secre-

211

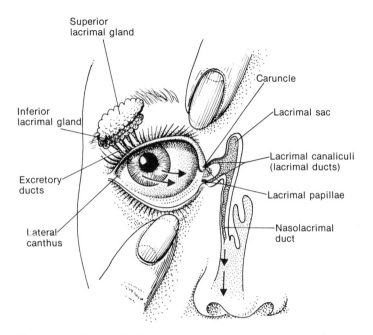

Superior lacrimal gland

Inferior lacrimal gland

Excretory ducts

Lateral canthus

Caruncle

Lacrimal sac

Lacrimal canaliculi (lacrimal ducts)

Lacrimal papillae

Nasolacrimal duct

Figure 8-4 The lacrimal apparatus.

tion by the lacrimal glands. The resulting flow is mostly in an inferiomedial direction across the eyeball to the medial canthus, where much of it is picked up by the lacrimal ducts and carried to the lacrimal sac, where it is then emptied into the nasal cavity by the nasolacrimal duct. Excess secretion overflows, mostly at the medial canthus. During colds and such allergenic reactions as "hay fever," the mucous membrane lining the lacrimal papillae and nasolacrimal duct becomes inflamed, the passageways swell shut, and the tear secretion overflows, producing "watery eyes."

The functioning of the eye

The physiology of vision, like that of many other body processes, is not completely understood. We do know, however, that *rod-like receptors* of the retina are concerned with perceiving *silhouettes or outlines* in poor light (so-called twilight vision), and can quickly detect *movements*. The visual pigment, *rhodopsin* ("visual purple"), helps carry out this function. When there is sufficient light to permit *close, detailed vision,* the *cones* are most active ("daylight vision").

These receptors also enable us to see *detail,* and are responsible for *color vision.* The *fovea centralis,* a small dent near the posterior portion of the center of the retina, consists entirely of cones; much of our detailed vision and color perception begins in this area. There are fewer and fewer cones in points more peripheral to the fovea; but the number of rods increases from a few around the fovea to their greatest numbers at the outer edge of the retina. Obviously, the peripheral portion of the retina is associated with *detection of movements and twilight vision.* The area surrounding the fovea centralis is yellowish in color, and is called the *macula lutea* or "yellow spot."

When light energy stimulates the rods and cones of the eye, certain chemical changes take place in these visual receptors with lightning speed. Just as rapidly, these changes cause nerve impulses to "happen" and to travel over the optic nerve and optic tract into the optic radiation and the visual cortex, where they are interpreted as sight (Fig. 8-5). Nerve fibers originating in the medial half of each retina cross to the opposite side in the optic chiasm, while those originating in the temporal half remain on the same side. Because of this arrangement of fibers, visual abnormalities called *hemi-anopsiae* are possible. These abnormalities are discussed in a later section of this chapter.

When light strikes rod cells, rhodopsin breaks down into a compound called *lumi-rhodopsin,* which in turn is converted to *meta-rhodopsin.* The latter compound is converted to *scotopsin* and *retinene,* which in darkness combine to reform rhodopsin. Scotopsin is a protein, and retinene is a yellow pigment that is formed in sufficient quantities only when there is an adequate amount of vitamin A in the diet. When light strikes cone cells, another visual pigment, *iodopsin,* breaks down. Light of higher intensity is necessary for the breakdown of iodopsin; therefore, cones are responsible for daylight and color vision.

Before impulses travel over the optic pathway, a visual image is formed on the light-sensitive areas of the retina. There are

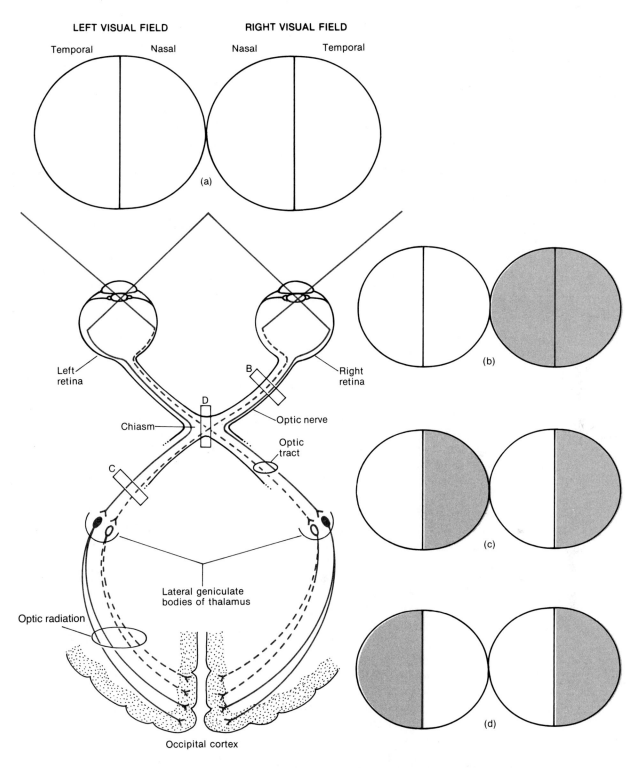

Figure 8-5   The visual pathways and the visual fields. (a) Normal visual fields (actually, they overlap considerably). (b) Blindness of the right eye following disease or injury of its optic nerve. (c) The type of hemianopsia resulting from interruption of the visual pathway at C in the diagram. (d) Hemianopsia resulting from the particular type of interruption indicated at D in the optic chiasm portion of the diagram.

no visual receptors to be found at the optic disc; thus no portion of the visual image is formed in this area, and it is commonly called the *"blindspot."* Cameras are similar to the eye in construction. The camera has an iris diaphragm to regulate light, a lens to focus the image clearly, and light- or color-sensitive film upon which the image is focused, just as it is on the retina of the eye. This image reaches both the retina and the film in an *inverted* position, due to the optical properties of the lens, and is *righted* by the cortex of the occipital lobe or, in the case of the film, by simply holding the developed photographic print so that the image appears in an upright position. Some years ago, two scientists decided to see if they could "retrain" the neurons of their occipital lobes so that they saw upright images while wearing glasses that inverted these images. After wearing the glasses for a prolonged length of time, objects no longer appeared upside-down, but right-side-up; and just as the researchers had predicted, when they removed their spectacles, objects appeared to be inverted! Several weeks were required before the visual cortex became reoriented so that images were again right-side-up when no glasses were worn.

When light rays enter the eye, they must be focused—so that sharp, clear images may be formed on the retina—during a process called *accommodation.* This process also includes the adjustment of the amount of light entering the eye, and the convergence or divergence of the eyeballs for near or distant vision, respectively. The size of the pupil varies directly with the distance of the object being viewed. The pupil becomes smaller when the object is moved close and larger when it is moved farther away.

The lens is the principal structure of the focusing portion of accommodation. If the lens is normally elastic, accommodation does not usually present a problem. When the object to be focused is a *distant* one, the shape of the lens becomes *flattened;* focusing upon *near* objects requires that the lens become *more convex.* How does the lens manage to change its shape? Chiefly by means of the ciliary muscle, acting on the suspensory

ligament. When accommodating for *distant vision,* the *ciliary muscle relaxes* and the *tension of the elastic suspensory ligament increases.* When this happens, the lens is drawn out into its most flattened shape. During accommodation for *near vision,* the *ciliary muscle contracts, releasing tension on the suspensory ligament;* the lens becomes more convex, due to its own natural elasticity and inherent tendency to assume the shape of a sphere. During focusing of the eye, the pupil changes size, the eyes either *converge* (turn medially) or *diverge* (turn laterally), and entering light rays are bent or *refracted* as they pass through the cornea, aqueous humor, lens, and vitreous humor, each of which represents a *refracting medium.* Refraction is easily demonstrated by placing a soda straw in a glass of clear water. The straw seems to be broken, due to bending of light rays by the water (Fig. 8-6). After light rays have passed through the four refracting media, they converge on the fovea of the retina, where the image is formed. When the object being observed is a distant one, the *anteroposterior axes* of the eyes are *parallel,* but the closer the object is brought to the observer, the more the eyeballs converge; and at extremely close range, the *anteroposterior axes point toward each other* at their anterior ends, and the individual has a typical "cross-eyed" appearance. Convergence and divergence are, of course, dependent upon the *extrinsic muscles* of the eye, with the medial and lateral rectus muscles playing the major roles in these movements, respectively. These two synchronized movements of the eyes insure that we see a single, three-dimensional or *stereoscopic* image. Persons having a *strabismus,* a condition in which one eye is directed either more medially or laterally than the other, see two images unless they are able to ignore one of them or do away with it by squinting one eye. A strabismus is said to be either of the *medial* or *lateral* type, depending upon the direction in which the affected eye is out of line. A strabismus may be present in only one eye (*unilateral*) or in both (*bilateral*). True three-dimensional vision depends upon the use of both eyes, and requires that they be so aligned that no

is responsible for the ability to form a single, three-dimensional image. The area of the retina upon which visual images are formed is the *internal visual field,* and is often the object of examination by ophthalmologists. A visual field may be conveniently divided into a *lateral or temporal half* and a *medial or nasal half* (Fig. 8-5). For the most part, light entering from one half of the external visual field reaches the opposite half of the internal visual field; that is, light rays entering the lateral half of the external visual field fall on the medial half of the internal visual field, and vice versa.

VISUAL DEFECTS   Two of the most common disorders of the eye are nearsightedness, or *myopia,* and farsightedness or *hyperopia.* In the former condition, the image does not quite reach the retina, and comes to focus slightly anterior to it, due to elongation of the eyeball or a lens that does not adjust sufficiently during accommodation to near vision (Fig. 8-7). Glasses with *biconcave lenses* (concave at both surfaces) focus the image where it belongs. In farsightedness, the image reaches the retina but is blurred because the eyeball is too short or the lens too flat for near vision. Theoretically, the image comes to a focus posterior to the retina (Fig. 8-7). This defect is almost inevitable as the lens loses its elasticity with age (*presbyopia*). Eyeglasses with *biconvex* lenses (convex at both surfaces) remedy this disorder. *Astigmatism* is an eye disorder brought about by an *irregularly curved lens or cornea,* resulting in refraction of light rays so that they fall on *separate areas* of the retina, thereby blurring the visual image. There is an inability to separate two closely spaced points. It is likely that most people have some degree of astigmatism. Serious astigmatism is corrected by the use of cylinder-shaped lenses.

One of the most common visual defects is *color blindness;* nevertheless, almost everyone has some degree of color vision, and the person who has none is rare indeed. Color blindness results from the *lack of cones sensitive to a few or (rarely) all the colors of the spectrum.* For example, a significant percentage of people have *red–green color blindness,* and do not distinguish these two colors

Figure 8-6   A demonstration of light refraction. (Science Photographics, Ltd.)

strabismus is present. A *bilateral medial strabismus* is known as cross-eye, while a *lateral strabismus* is called cockeye or walleye. Individuals having *monocular* vision— that is, sight in only one eye—often find it difficult to judge distances. Sight in both eyes is called *binocular* vision.

THE VISUAL FIELDS   The area included or "seen" by an eye is called its *external visual field.* The external visual field of one eye somewhat overlaps that of the other, and this

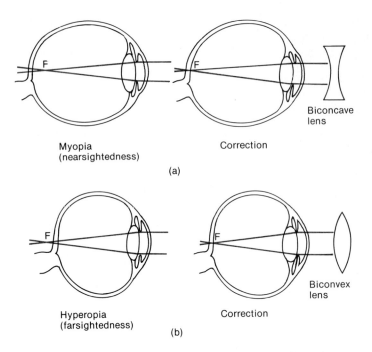

Myopia
(nearsightedness)

Biconcave
lens

Correction

(a)

Hyperopia
(farsightedness)

Biconvex
lens

Correction

(b)

Figure 8-7 Myopia and hyperopia, and how they are corrected. In (a), it is seen that in myopia the eyeball is longer than it would be normally, and light rays focus some distance anterior to the retina. In (b), the short eyeball of hyperopia is shown. In this instance, if light rays could pass through the retina, they would come to a focus behind it. The letter F indicates the focal point in all the drawings.

because of lack of red- and green-sensitive cones in the retina. About eight times more men than women have some degree of color blindness, because of the sex-linked genetic pattern of the trait. The few people with *total* color blindness see everything in *different shades of gray.* Those with partial color blindness may not even know that they have the defect unless they are tested, usually by means of a color chart. Such charts as this reveal many cases of color blindness among military inductees.

Blindness, or loss of visual sense, may be *partial* or *complete,* and may result from a number of diseases—such as tumors and other lesions—and injuries affecting the eye or optic pathway. Among the injuries are the following:

1. Injury to the *optic nerve.* This results in partial or complete blindness *on the affected side* (Fig. 8-5).

2. Injury to the *optic chiasm.* This produces blindness in the *lateral half of the ex-* ternal visual field, or in the *medial half of the internal visual field,* of *both eyes,* due to the crossing of fibers in the chiasm.

3. Injury to the *optic tract.* Because of the crossing of neurons in the optic chiasm, injury to the optic tract affects those going to the *lateral internal visual field on the affected side* and those supplying the *medial internal visual field of the opposite side,* with resulting blindness in these portions of the retina.

4. Injury to the *visual cortex.* The result in this case is *similar to that produced by injury to the optic tract,* but will be more apt to result in *partial blindness,* due to the fanning out of the fibers in the *optic radiation.*

5. Injury to the *retina.* Many injuries to the eye or visual pathway affect the retina; for example, if a brain tumor affects an optic nerve or optic tract, visual cells in the retina degenerate. In some injuries to the eyeball, the retina separates from the choroid layer. If this detached retina is not repaired by an eye surgeon, blindness will result.

It will be noted that in many cases of blindness, only one-half of the visual field is affected (Fig. 8-5); this is called *hemianopsia,* and can occur in one eye (*unilateral hemianopsia*) or in both eyes (*bilateral hemianopsia*).

Frequently, blindness may result from *opaqueness of the refracting media* of the eye, and especially of the lens and cornea. If these media are no longer transparent, vision is impossible. Often, they may remain *translucent* and admit a certain amount of light, but clear images do not form on the retina. A clouded lens is a *cataract,* and follows the breakdown of protein in the lens substance in old age, overexposure to bright sunlight, trauma, and other conditions, including such diseases as *diabetes.* In treating cataract, the lens is usually removed and the patient fitted with suitable glasses. Clouded corneas may be removed (in part) and replaced with clear "patches" of cornea material obtained from individual donors or eye banks.

ARGYLL ROBERTSON PUPIL Often a *complication of syphilis,* this condition is manifested when the pupil fails to constrict or dilate in response to light while retaining the ability to do so during accommodation. The reason for these differing responses is that the pathway for the pupillary light reflex differs from that of the pupillary accommodation reflex.

OTHER DISORDERS OF THE EYE AND ASSOCIATED STRUCTURES *Blepharitis* is an inflammation of the hair follicles and glands along the borders of the eyelids. *Conjunctivitis* is inflammation of the lining (conjunctiva) of the eyelids. *Endophthalmos* is a condition in which the eyeball sinks deep into its socket during extreme old age, malnutrition, certain diseases, blindness, and may even result from wearing eyeglasses. The pad of fat normally present behind the eyeball virtually disappears. *Exophthalmos* is a classic indication of *hyperthyroidism*—oversecretion of thyroid hormone. The eyeballs protrude as a result of the increased width of the palpebral fissure (slit between the upper and lower lids) and are pushed forward when large amounts of fat accumulate behind them (Fig. 9-7). An individual with *nyctalopia,* commonly called night blindness, cannot see in dim light. The pigment of the rods, rhodopsin or *"visual purple,"* is necessary for twilight vision. Vitamin A is essential for the continued formation of rhodopsin; therefore, a person with a dietary deficiency of vitamin A may suffer from nyctalopia. Occasionally, there is a congenital lack of rhodopsin, in which case nyctalopia cannot be remedied by administration of vitamin A. *Ptosis* is a drooping of the upper eyelid and may range from mild to very severe. It may be due to interruption of the nerve supply to the levator palpebrae muscles (the facial nerve) or to hereditary factors. *Stye* is an inflammation involving one or more sebaceous glands of the eyelid; it is also called *hordeolum.* A person suffering from *tunnel vision* sees objects as though through a long, narrow tube or tunnel. The field of vision is severely limited, and the eyes and even the entire head must constantly be moved about if the victim is to see enough to carry out normal, everyday activities. Hysterical individuals sometimes acquire this symptom, and tunnel vision can also result from pressure of enlarged internal carotid arteries on the optic nerves (*bilateral internal carotid aneurysm*)

or even breathing pure oxygen for prolonged periods of time. Such visual disorders or defects as myopia, hyperopia, astigmatism, cataract, night blindness, color blindness, and 20 different kinds of blindness (including that caused by glaucoma) may be *inherited.* Ptosis, *microphthalma* (undersized, nonseeing eyes), and many other abnormalities are also known to be congenital in certain forms.

TESTS OF VISUAL ACUITY *Visual acuity* is the degree of *sharpness* of the eyesight, and is greatest in that portion of the retina containing a large number of cones but no rods: *the fovea.* It varies from person to person, due to differences in the refractory media and the retina. One common test for visual acuity is the *Snellen test.* This test determines the smallest standard-sized printed letter of the alphabet that can be clearly seen by an individual at a distance of 20 feet (Fig. 8-8); or, alternatively, how near a person must be to letters of one size in order to read them. A person with *normal vision* is defined to be one who can read standard-sized letters at a distance of 20 ft, and normal visual acuity is recorded as a fraction, 20/20; that is, anyone who can see clearly at 20 ft what a person with "normal" visual acuity can see at 20 ft is said to have normal, or 20/20, vision. If he must move to a distance of 10 ft from the chart (or can only read a comparably larger-sized line of letters), his acuity is 20/40, or *only one-half normal;* in other words, at 20 ft he sees what a person with normal vision would see at 40 feet. If, on the other hand, he can see the letters at a distance of, say, *one-quarter greater than normal,* his acuity is recorded as 20/15; that is, he can see at a distance of 20 ft what people with normal vision see only at 15 ft.

THE EFFECT OF DRUGS ON THE PUPIL Ophthalmologists often use drugs to adjust the size of the pupil so that they may more efficiently examine and treat disorders of the eye. *Epinephrine, atropine, cocaine,* and several other drugs cause the pupil to *dilate,* and are called *mydriatic drugs; morphine, pilocarpine,* and *physostigmine* bring about *constriction* of the pupil, and are known as *miotic drugs.*

THE SENSES OF TASTE AND SMELL

Taste

The sense of taste, or *gustatory sense,* tells us less than any of our other special senses. In man, taste is so poorly developed that it requires reinforcement from the senses of smell, sight, and even tactile sense if we are to know exactly what we are eating. Blindfold a person and place a clamp on his nose, and he cannot distinguish between grapefruit juice and orange juice, or between a slice of apple and a slice of potato. Taste is a *chemical sense;* and due to the nature of the end organs of taste—taste buds—*substances must be dissolved and in molecular form* (in saliva, water, or other liquid) before they can be tasted. On the upper surface of the tongue, many tiny elevations or "bumps" called *papillae*—which contain *taste buds*—can be seen. The largest, or *vallate papillae,* are arranged to form a V-shape on the posterior part of the tongue. The smaller, more numerous papillae of the tongue are of two types, *filiform* and *fungiform.* Some papillae are present also on the soft palate, walls of the pharynx, and surrounding regions, but they are of minor importance. The four basic or *primary tastes—sweet, sour, bitter,* and *salt*—are not all sensed uniformly on the surface of the tongue. The *posterior* portion is most sensitive to *bitter* stimuli, the *anterior lateral* portion to *sour, posterior lateral* to *salt,* and the *extreme anterior* portion to *salt and sweet* (Fig. 8-9). Molecules of the substance to be tasted enter *taste pores* of the papillae and stimulate specialized *gustatory cells* of the taste buds, which in turn send impulses over a branch of the *facial nerve* (anterior two-thirds of the tongue) or over the *glossopharyngeal nerve* (posterior one-third of the tongue). Neurons in these nerves extend to the *gustatory nucleus of the medulla,* near the lower portion of the fourth ventricle, where they synapse with other neurons leading to the *thalamus.* Third-order neurons lead from the thalamus to the *cerebral cortex* (temporal lobe). It is in the cortex that impulses are interpreted as taste. The sense of taste varies widely be-

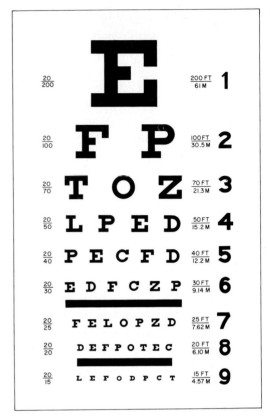

Figure 8.8 The Snellen test chart for visual acuity. The individual with normal vision can read line 8 of the full-sized chart at a distance of 20 feet.

tween individuals; for example, some people can taste *sodium benzoate,* but most people cannot; some describe the taste of *phenylhydrazine* as *bitter,* others as *sweet,* while still others affirm that it has *no taste* whatever. So far, no significant anatomical differences have been found among the 9000-odd taste buds on the tongue, and exactly why some are sensitive to sour substances, others to sweets, and so on, is still a mystery.

Smell

The sense of smell, or *olfactory sense,* like taste, is a chemical sense, and requires physical contact between receptors and fine particles of the substance to be sensed. True, we can smell many substances at a distance but, as opposed to the cases of sight or hearing, contact must still be made. With the exception of a few surviving Indian tribes, man has all but lost his sense of smell; and some smells, like some tastes, are not sensed by some people. During the actual process of detecting odors, fine particles of odorous substances enter the nose and stimulate *special*

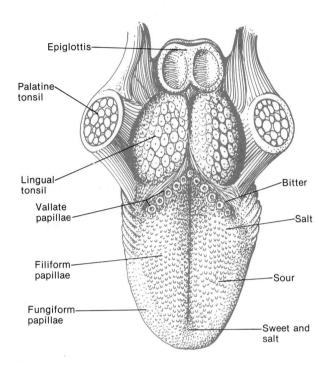

Epiglottis

Palatine tonsil

Lingual tonsil

Vallate papillae

Filiform papillae

Fungiform papillae

Bitter

Salt

Sour

Sweet and salt

Figure 8-9 The various types of papillae found on the tongue, and the areas of the tongue where the different kinds of tastes are projected.

Figure 8-10 Sound waves. (a) Waves demonstrating pitch. (b) Waves indicating intensities.

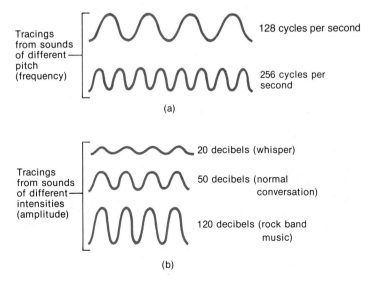

Tracings from sounds of different pitch (frequency)

128 cycles per second

256 cycles per second

(a)

Tracings from sounds of different intensities (amplitude)

20 decibels (whisper)

50 decibels (normal conversation)

120 decibels (rock band music)

(b)

receptors (olfactory cells), present only in the mucous membrane of the uppermost portion of this organ. Nerve fibers leave the olfactory cells and *enter the skull through the cribriform plate of the ethmoid bone,* then disappear into the *olfactory bulb* located at the anterior end of the *olfactory tract,* which in turn possibly leads to the *frontal*—or, eventually, the *temporal lobe*—of the cerebrum. At present, there is no satisfactory explanation for the mechanism of olfaction. It is known that olfactory cells are easily fatigued, and this explains why we soon become so accustomed to odors that we are no longer aware of them.

HEARING AND EQUILIBRIUM

Hearing or audition

Hearing is the perception of sound. Sound consists of *waves* and is produced by the *vibration* of an object, and it can travel through solids, liquids, and gases, as well as around corners, and through a wall or other obstacle. Sound travels must *faster* through water and many solids *(such as bone)* than it does in gases, but it is the transmission of sound in a gas—air—with which we are most concerned here. Sound waves (Fig. 8-10) travel at a speed of about 1100 ft/sec (330 m/sec). The most important properties of sound are *pitch* or *frequency*—that is, the number of vibrations per unit of time, usually expressed as *cycles per second,* cps, or hertz (Hz) units; *intensity* or *strength,* which varies directly with the height or amplitude of the sound wave and is usually expressed in *decibels* (db); and *timbre* or *quality,* which depends upon a single tone's extra constituents called *overtones,* which vary with the object that is producing the sound. For example, a flute, violin, and trumpet can all produce the musical note A (440 Hz); but if they do it separately, one does not even have to look in order to determine which instrument is making the sound. The particular overtones that give a sound its timbre are caused by *secondary vibrations* within the

* The normal range of human hearing is approximately 20 to 20,000 Hz.

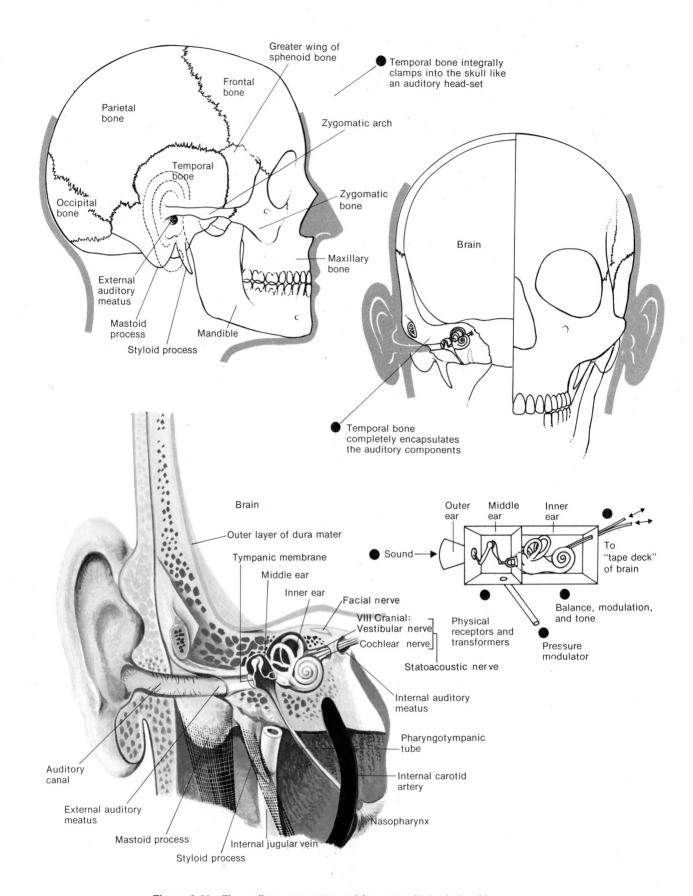

Figure 8-11 The auditory apparatus and its anatomical relationships.

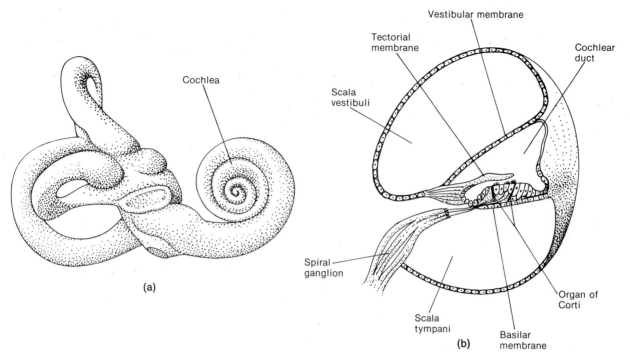

Figure 8-12   The cochlea. (a) External appearance. (b) Internal structure.

object producing the *primary sound,* and follow closely the production of the latter. The anatomy of the ear is illustrated in Figs. 8-11 and 8-12. The reader is urged to refer frequently to these drawings while studying the physiology of the ear.

THE PHYSIOLOGY OF HEARING   Whereas the senses of sight, smell, and taste depend first upon chemical activity and then a nerve impulse, the sense of hearing involves *mechanical action* followed by the nerve impulse. After the pickup of sound waves by the *pinna* or earflap, these waves travel inward over the other portion of the external ear—the *external acoustic meatus*—to the first structure of the middle ear, the *tympanic membrane* or eardrum (Fig. 8-11). The energy of traveling sound causes this delicate membrane to vibrate ever so slightly, and this vibration is transferred directly to the outermost of the three tiny linked *ossicles* or bones of the middle ear, the *malleus* or "hammer." The malleus vibrates the *incus* ("anvil"), which in turn moves the *stapes* or "stirrup." This last little bone, the innermost of the ossicles, is attached directly to a membrane covering an oval window of the large snail-like *cochlea,* the outermost structure of the inner

ear. It should be noted at this point that the cavity of the middle ear communicates with the pharynx by means of the long, slender *pharyngotympanic (Eustachian) tube.* It is this tiny canal that permits us to *equalize the pressure on both sides of the eardrum* when traveling to higher or lower altitudes. This can usually be accomplished by yawning or swallowing, as either of these acts will often open the Eustachian tube and send air up it to the inner side of the tympanic membrane. The entire middle-ear cavity is lined with mucous membrane and is *located within the temporal bone.*

After sound energy has reached the stapes and caused it to vibrate, the delicate membrane of the *oval window* also moves, sending vibrations through fluid (perilymph) in a portion of the cochlea called the *scala vestibuli* (Fig. 8-12).

Vibrations of this perilymph are transmitted through the roof * of the *cochlear duct* to the endolymph that fills the duct, then to the *organ of Corti* within the duct. Den-

---

* The roof of the cochlear duct is known also as the *vestibular membrane* or *Reissner's membrane.*

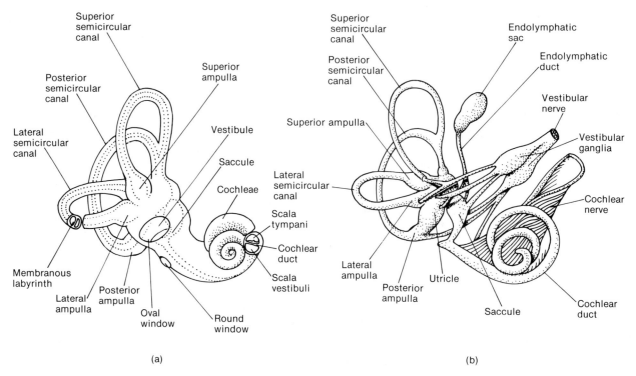

Superior semicircular canal

Posterior semicircular canal

Lateral semicircular canal

Superior ampulla

Vestibule

Saccule

Cochleae

Scala tympani

Cochlear duct

Scala vestibuli

Membranous labyrinth

Lateral ampulla

Posterior ampulla

Oval window

Round window

(a)

Superior semicircular canal

Posterior semicircular canal

Superior ampulla

Lateral semicircular canal

Endolymphatic sac

Endolymphatic duct

Vestibular nerve

Vestibular ganglia

Cochlear nerve

Lateral ampulla

Posterior ampulla

Utricle

Saccule

Cochlear duct

(b)

Figure 8-13   The labyrinths. (a) Osseus labyrinth. (b) Membranous labyrinth. The position of the membranous labyrinth within the osseus labyrinth is indicated by the phantom lines in (a).

drites of neurons that form the cochlear division of the acoustic nerve are arranged around the *hair cells* of the organ of Corti. The upper surfaces of these hair cells adhere to a gelatinous structure called the *tectorial membrane.* When vibrations cause these hair cells to move against the membrane, the dendrites clustered around their bases are stimulated to initiate impulses that travel over the cochlear nerve to the brainstem. Enroute to the cortex of the temporal lobe of the cerebrum, these impulses pass through nuclei in the medulla, pons, midbrain, and thalamus. The cochlear nerve takes origin from bipolar neurons in the *spiral ganglion* of the cochlea.

Equilibrium or balance

The inner ear or *labyrinth* is essentially a series of tortuous passageways or canals, and is the most complex structure in this portion of the temporal bone. These canals are concerned with the senses of *balance* or *equilibrium* as well as hearing. The labyrinth (Fig. 8-13) is customarily divided into two portions—a *membranous labyrinth* enclosed

by a *bony labyrinth.* The bony labyrinth is filled with a fluid, *perilymph;* the membranous labyrinth is, therefore, bathed in this fluid. The membranous labyrinth also contains its own fluid, *endolymph.* Three looped structures—the *superior, lateral,* and *posterior semicircular canals,* connected to the cochlea by a *vestibule**—lie within the bony or osseus labyrinth. It should be understood that all these structures are *membranous,* and are surrounded by the various parts of the bony labyrinth, which takes the same shape as the structures it contains. Suspended in perilymph within the vestibule are *two dilations,* the *utricle* and the *saccule;* a tiny *canal* joins them together. The utricle and semicircular canals are concerned with the sense of balance or equilibrium, and with the closely related *proprioceptive sense*—the knowledge of position of body parts in space.

---

* The vestibule is an oval cavity in the middle of the bony labyrinth. The vestibule communicates anteriorly with the cochlea and posteriorly with the semicircular canals, and contains the utricle and saccule. The oval and round windows of the middle ear and the semicircular canals of the inner ear all open into the vestibule.

Each of the semicircular canals lies at right angles to the others, and each connects with the utricle. At its connection with the utricle, each canal has an enlarged portion or dilation, the *ampulla,* containing a cluster of sensory hair cells, the *crista,* which is concerned with *dynamic equilibrium* during movements of considerable range. When the position of the head is changed, movement of the endolymph in the canals stimulates the hair cells, and these promptly cause impulses to be set up which travel along the vestibular division of the acoustic nerve to the brain.

Both the utricle and saccule contain tiny structures called *maculae.* Each macula is made up of hair cells and a gelatinous membrane containing extremely small bits of calcium carbonate, *otoliths,* commonly called "ear stones." A change in the position of the head, changes the pressure on the gelatinous membrane of the macula, and causes the otoliths to pull on the hair cells, which in turn initiate impulses that travel over the vestibular division of the acoustic nerve. The utricle is concerned mostly with smaller degrees of movement, such as those involved in maintaining posture—that is, maintaining *static equilibrium.* The function of the saccule is not known. There is some evidence that it may somehow be involved in the sense of hearing.

Disorders of hearing and equilibrium

The relative "sharpness" or acuity of a person's hearing can be determined accurately by employing an electronic *audiometer,* which can produce musical tones of variable pitch and amplitude, and comparing the resulting *audiogram* with accepted standards. Less accurate methods—such as deliberately speaking softly to a subject, or determining the distance at which he can hear the ticking of a watch or the hum of a vibrating tuning fork—are not as conclusive, but useful during routine clinical examinations.

DEAFNESS   Any loss of hearing ability, no matter how slight, is *deafness* of some sort. It may range from the inability to hear sounds of certain pitch or intensity to *complete deafness,* in which case no sounds are heard. Many persons with total deafness can detect sounds—or at least vibrations—made by a tuning fork if the handle of the instrument is held against the skull—an example of *bone conduction* of sounds.

Any case of deafness can be placed in one of three categories: *conduction deafness, nerve deafness,* or *central deafness.* Conduction deafness results when the ear ossicles "freeze" stiff by *ankylosis* (fusing of the ossicles at their joints), or when the Eustachian tube becomes plugged and the pressure can no longer be equalized on both sides of the tympanic membrane. Conduction deafness can often be corrected by means of a hearing aid or surgery. Nerve deafness involves *degeneration or lesions of the cochlear portion of the inner ear or of the cochlear division of the acoustic nerve,* and hearing cannot be improved. This type of deafness may be either *partial* or *complete,* and it often occurs in extreme old age. Central deafness results when degeneration or lesions involve the *acoustic center* in the cerebral cortex (temporal lobe). There is no cure or remedy for this type of deafness.

OTITIS AND TINNITUS   Two other disorders that commonly produce difficulty in hearing are *otitis* and *tinnitus.* Otitis means an inflammation of the ear, and is called variously *otitis externa, otitis media,* or *otitis interna,* depending upon the portion of the ear affected. Otitis media is the most common of these, and the infection that causes it may spread to the *mastoid air cells* and eventually to the *brain meninges* if not checked by antibiotic drugs. Tinnitus is a noise in the ear, usually a ringing or cricket sound. It may result from *acoustic-nerve degeneration,* from an *overaccumulation of wax * in the external meatus,* from *otitis media,* or as a side effect of taking a medication such as *quinine* or a large dose of *aspirin.*

VERTIGO AND MOTION SICKNESS   The chief disorders of the apparatus of equilibrium are *vertigo* and *motion sickness.* Neither of these is synonymous with "dizziness," although this symptom is often present in both conditions. In vertigo, the subject may feel that he is going round and round in space, or that the room is revolving about him. Diseases

---

* Tiny *ceruminous glands* in the ear canal produce this protective wax, called *cerumen.*

involving the *brain, eyes, heart, stomach, kidneys,* and *inner ear,* as well as *toxic drugs* or a *general toxemia* of the body itself, may produce vertigo. During *motion sickness—* carsickness, seasickness, airsickness, etc.— the subject feels "bad" or "rough" (*malaise*), and is usually *nauseated.* The nausea may or may not be accompanied by vomiting. The inability of the equilibrating mechanism to keep pace with the constant motion of the body during a rough ride on a plane, ship, amusement-park ride, or even in an automobile, brings on this condition. In some instances, motion sickness seems to have a *psychogenic* basis; for example, some people claim that they cannot ride in the rear seat of an automobile without becoming carsick. When these people are blindfolded and do not know whether they are riding in front or back, there is no correlation between the incidence of their motion sickness and the particular seat in which they ride.

Aerospace considerations and deep-sea diving

Traveling in a modern aircraft at high altitudes, man is reasonably safe, and also comfortable. Air pressure inside the passenger compartment is maintained near that of the atmosphere at about 5000 ft, and oxygen is supplied so that he may breathe with ease. Riding in a space vehicle, however, is an entirely different matter. During takeoff, the astronaut is subjected to tremendous vibrations; during flight, there is *weightlessness* and the possibility of *pitching,* even *rolling* and *tumbling;* and during reentry into the earth's atmosphere, there is more rolling.

SOME EFFECTS OF GRAVITY AND WEIGHT-LESSNESS Some of the effects of these conditions are already known, and can be demonstrated experimentally in the laboratory. In certain instances, great stress is placed upon the heart; after many spins in a specially constructed centrifuge, a man may be completely disoriented as to equilibrium and position of body parts in space, due to the traumatic effect on the delicate structures of the inner ear. If he breathes too much oxygen, he may develop *tunnel vision,* and

soon lose consciousness unless the situation is corrected. In certain attitudes that a high-speed aircraft or spacecraft may assume, the inner-ear mechanism may feed false information to the brain, resulting in *spatial disorientation.* Vision plays an important role in equilibrium. If an airplane pilot is flying in fog or clouds heavy enough to obscure the horizon, he may *"feel"* that the plane is not maintaining a straight and level course, in spite of instrument readings. The illusion of turning or banking may be so strong as to cause him to "straighten out," often with disastrous results. The importance of vision to equilibrium can also be illustrated by considering the example of a circus tight-wire walker. He must look constantly at the wire in order to maintain balance (except for brief intervals when he may somersault or perform other tricks). When such a performer blindfolds himself and successfully walks the wire, he "cheats" by peeking down the sides of his nose or by using a fake blindfold.

Many of the physiological effects resulting from riding in an airplane or spacecraft are due to *acceleration* (speeding up) and *deceleration* (slowing down). There are two kinds of acceleration, *linear* and *angular.* Any increase in straight-line speed is linear acceleration, while a change in direction (as when a military aircraft attempts to evade a missile, or when a spacecraft is rolling or pitching) is of the angular type. The immediate effect of angular acceleration of an airplane on the body may often be more pronounced than that of a spacecraft in orbit, due to the pull of gravity on the persons riding in the airplane. For example, a man weighing 170 lb in straight and level flight (the same as he would weigh on the ground) can in effect weigh 1020 lb when pulling out of a steep dive—six times his normal body weight. During the pullout, his blood is slung downward away from the head and thorax by *centrifugal force,* and the arterial blood pressure in the upper portion of his body drops sharply, from (for example) 120 mm Hg (millimeters of mercury) to as low as 40 mm Hg or even lower. There is a good chance that the subject will lose consciousness due to lack of blood (and subsequently, oxygen) in the brain, especially if the dive is particularly steep and the speed high.

Cardiac output can cease entirely during such a dive. On the other hand, linear acceleration is of minor importance in aircraft, but can be critically important in spacecraft. A man taking off vertically in a spacecraft thus lies on his back in order to avoid the experience of having the blood rush from his head and thorax to his abdomen and legs during takeoff. Once in orbit, he is weightless, and gravity cannot put undue stress upon body organs.

Deceleration is not dangerous unless it is too abrupt—as when an airplane crashes into a mountain, or when an elevator falls. Deceleration is important to parachutists: parachutes must be designed so that the shock upon opening will not be too great, but still offer enough resistance to fall to prevent a person from hitting the ground too fast and hard (and thereby decelerating too quickly).

DECOMPRESSION SICKNESS IN AVIATION AND DEEP-SEA DIVING Decompression sickness, or "the bends," is an extremely painful condition brought about by the expansion of nitrogen in the body fluids. It can cause permanent damage to the central nervous system and other neural tissues. The mechanism of its cause is discussed in the following chapter, which is concerned with the circulatory system.

OUTLINE SUMMARY

The special senses: sight, smell, hearing, taste, and equilibrium

1. Sight, or visual sense
   A. Depends upon highly specialized neurons in the retina of the eye—rods and cones—and visual pigments
   B. Anatomy of the eye—structural features
      a. The eyeball is a fluid-filled globe, with a wall consisting of sclerotic, vascular, and retinal coats
      b. The most anterior portion of the eyeball is the clear cornea
      c. Just posterior to the cornea is the iris, which regulates the amount of light entering the eye
      d. Posterior to the iris is the lens, which focuses light rays upon the retina, the most posterior portion of the eyeball
      e. The retina is continuous with the optic nerve, which leads to the optic tract and eventually to the occipital lobe of the cerebrum. The two major layers of the retina include a pigmented layer and a nervous layer. The nervous layer contains the rods and cones and bipolar neurons. There are actually ten minor layers in the retina
      f. The retina is supplied by the central artery and vein
   C. Accessory structures of the eye include the eyebrows, eyelids, eyelashes, conjunctiva, and lacrimal apparatus
   D. Functioning of the eye: light energy stimulates the rods and cones of the retina, rapid chemical changes occur within these cells, and an inverted visual image is formed. Impulses travel via the optic nerve, optic tract, and optic radiation to the occipital lobe of the cerebrum, where the impulses are interpreted as an upright image. The ciliary muscle, acting on the suspensory ligament of the lens, brings about focusing. The iris constricts and dilates as necessary, regulating the size of the pupil, and hence the amount of light, that enters the eye. The visual fields of the two eyes overlap somewhat
   E. Visual defects: there are many different disorders of the eyesight, including myopia, hyperopia, astigmatism, color-blindness, and varying degrees of blindness, such as hemianopsia. Some of the other disorders of the eye and associated structures, not necessarily associated with visual defects, include blepharitis, conjunctivitis, endophthalmos, exophthalmos, nyctalopia, ptosis, stye, tunnel vision, and microphthalmia
   F. Tests of visual acuity: two of the most common are the Snellen test and Jensen grid test
   G. Some drugs which affect the size of the pupil: epinephrine, atropine, and cocaine cause dilation; morphine, pilocarpine, and physostigmine cause constriction
2. Taste, or gustatory sense
   A. In man, it is poorly developed, but adequate
   B. Substances in solution stimulate gustatory cells in taste buds of papillae, mainly on the tongue
   C. Impulses originate at the gustatory cells, and travel over the facial and glossopharyngeal nerves to the medulla and, eventually, the cerebral cortex

3. Smell, or olfaction
   A. Poorly developed in man
   B. Olfactory cells of the nasal mucosa are stimulated by chemical particles suspended in the air
   C. Impulses are conveyed over the olfactory nerves and tracts to the cerebral cortex (frontal or temporal lobe)
4. Hearing, or audition
   A. Fairly well developed in man
   B. Sound waves striking the eardrum cause it to vibrate, bringing about the vibration of the malleus, incus, and stapes, in that order
   C. As the stapes vibrates, so does the fluid of the cochlea
   D. Impulses are set up by these vibrations in the organ of Corti, and travel over the cochlear division of the acoustic nerve to the acoustic center in the temporal lobe of the cerebrum

5. Equilibrium: change in position of the head brings about movement of endolymph in the membranous labyrinth. Sensory hair cells in the ampullae are stimulated, and impulses are conveyed to balance centers in the brain
6. Some of the disorders of hearing and equilibrium
   A. Conduction deafness
   B. Nerve deafness
   C. Central deafness
   D. Otitis
   E. Tinnitus
   F. Vertigo
   G. Motion sickness
7. Some effects of gravity and weightlessness
   A. Proprioceptive disorientation
   B. Tunnel vision
   C. General spatial disorientation
   D. Vertigo
   E. Loss of consciousness

STUDY QUESTIONS AND PROBLEMS

1. List the special senses. What body system do the special sense organs depend upon for interpretation of environmental changes?

2. Briefly describe the eyeball. What structure of the eye regulates the size of the pupil? The shape of the lens? List the layers of the retina.

3. An ophthalmologist examines his patient's eyes, and finds that the optic disc is cupped in both eyes. This is an indication of high intraocular pressure, such as that resulting from what disease of the eye?

4. List the accessory structures of the eye and the functions of each.

5. Mrs. Z. tells her nurse that an ophthalmologist has told her that she has a choked disc in one eye. What is one condition that might cause this protrusion of the optic disc anteriorly?

6. What is the cause of myopia? Hyperopia? What is presbyopia? What is astigmatism? Red–green color blindness? Hemianopsia? Is it possible to inherit very many kinds of visual disorders?

7. What does "20/20" mean, with regard to an eye examination?

8. What are the effects of epinephrine, atropine, cocaine, morphine, pilocarpine, and physostigmine on the size of the pupil?

9. What is the scientific term for taste? Describe a taste bud, and the distribution of papillae on the tongue. What are the four basic primary tastes, and where are they sensed on the tongue?

10. What is the scientific term for the sense of smell? At what lobe of the cerebrum does it reach conscious awareness?

11. What are the common and scientific names of the ear ossicles? To what is each attached?

12. An otolaryngologist found that one of his patients had a deafness that resulted from degeneration of the "eighth nerve." What does this mean?

13. A hearing test revealed that one patient heard poorly in the low-frequency range. Would this involve high-pitched sounds, or low-pitched sounds?

14. Describe the pathway of hearing from tympanic membrane to cerebrum.

15. Describe the mechanism of equilibrium as it involves the ear.

16. What are otitis, tinnitus, vertigo, and motion sickness?

17. What is the chief function of the Eustachian tube?

hormonal control by the endocrine glands

The second *great regulatory system of the body* is made up of the **endocrine or ductless glands**—glands which lack excretory ducts, and therefore pour their secretions directly into the bloodstream—and associated tissues, the one previously considered being the *nervous system*. The endocrine tissues assist the nervous system in correlating and integrating the activities of the body cells, thereby helping to maintain the homeostasis of the internal environment. The chief distinction between the two systems lies in the relative speed with which they do their work. The nervous system has the power to act rapidly, and is often involved in quick adjustments of the body in response to changes in its external or internal environment. Often, its action is of short duration. The endocrine system, on the other hand, influences processes that require much longer periods of time—body growth and sexual maturation, for example. However, there are exceptions to this general rule, and the secretion of *hormones*—protein or proteinlike chemicals (see Fig. 9-1) produced by the endocrine tissues—does in some instances produce rapid changes in body functions. From birth until death, hormones play vital roles in metabolism. They do this by acting upon the body tissues and upon each other, in a manner so complex as to defy complete explanation, at least until now. The glands that secrete these powerful chemicals include the *pituitary* or *hypophysis, thyroid, parathyroids,* a portion of the *pancreas,* the *adrenals* or *suprarenals,* and the *gonads* (testes and ovaries, Fig. 9-2). Hormones are also secreted by cells in the *stomach, duodenum, kidneys,* and, during pregnancy, the *placenta.* In early life, the pineal gland and the thymus produce hormones. All endocrine secretions discharge directly into the blood and lymph, by which they are carried throughout the body. Either directly or indirectly, hormones exert at least some control over *every basic physiological process,* including growth and development, reproduction, the conversion of energy, and even the functions of the nervous system, including behavior. Currently, it is believed that hormones do this by affecting the actions of the innumerable cellular enzymes. Chemically, some hormones are relatively simple, while others are extremely complex. *Epinephrine* (adrenalin), secreted by the adrenal gland, is one of the simpler hormones (Fig. 9-1). The molecular structures of many have not yet been determined. Some, such as those secreted by the adrenal gland and the gonads,

Figure 9-1 Chemical structure of epinephrine.

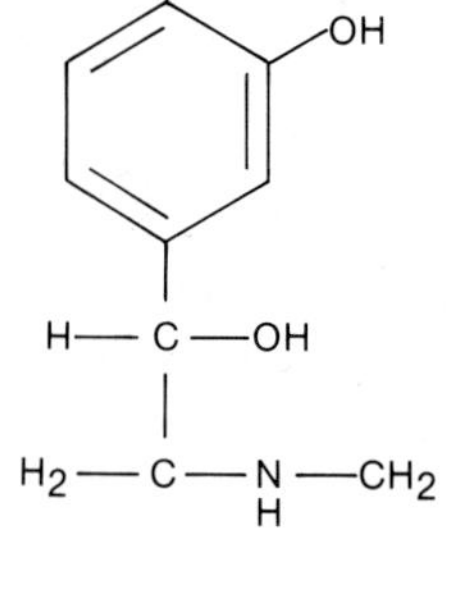

228

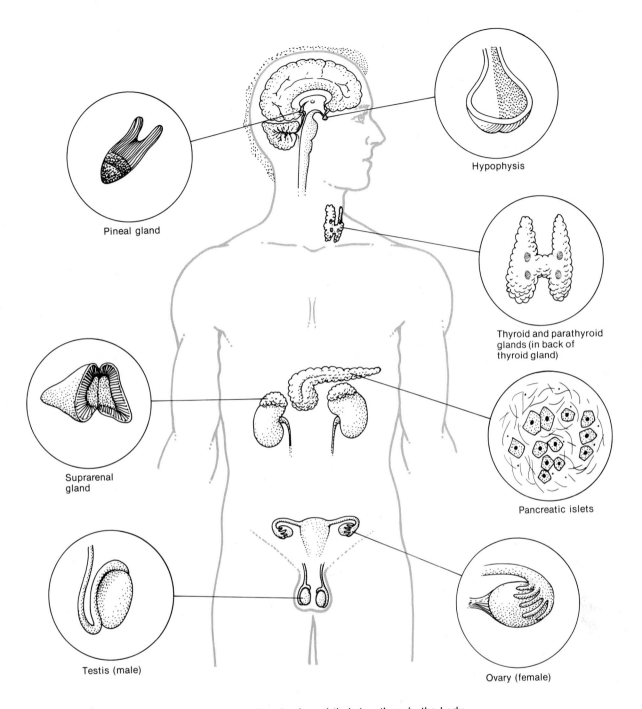

Figure 9-2 The endocrine glands and their locations in the body.

Pineal gland

Hypophysis

Thyroid and parathyroid glands (in back of thyroid gland)

Suprarenal gland

Pancreatic islets

Testis (male)

Ovary (female)

are *steroids;* that is, they are either sterols or are closely related to these compounds. It is possible that the sterols are derived from a parent compound, *cholesterol,* which is always present in the body in varying amounts. Other hormones are *proteins, polypeptides, amino acids,* or other *nitrogenous compounds.* All hormones are extremely potent, and are produced in astonishingly small amounts.

Factors that regulate the secretion of hormones

The secretion of hormones is controlled by two kinds of factors, *nervous* and *chemical.*

NERVOUS FACTORS   One of the most outstanding examples of the control of endocrine secretion by the nervous system is seen in the relationship between the *hypothalamus* and the *pituitary gland*. Nerve impulses from the former greatly influence the activity of the latter. Some endocrine tissues are either stimulated or inhibited by impulses traveling to them via the *autonomic nervous system*. A classic example of this is the control over the medullary portion of the adrenal gland by the sympathetic division of the ANS; the amount of epinephrine secreted by this endocrine tissue is in direct proportion to the number of sympathetic impulses it receives per unit of time.

CHEMICAL FACTORS   Various chemical substances, both *hormonal* and *nonhormonal*, are highly important in regulating the production of hormones by the various endocrine tissues. For example, when fats or acids enter the duodenum, the hormone *secretin* is produced by certain cells in the mucosa of this portion of the intestine. Other examples include the secretion of *insulin* by the pancreas in response to an increase in blood sugar level, and the production of hormones by the gonads, adrenals, and thyroid in response to hormone action of the pituitary.

INTERRELATIONSHIPS   The endocrine system is composed of glands and tissues which are dependent upon each other in varying degrees; that is, the secretions of some quickly and directly affect the actions of others, and reciprocally, in so-called *feedback mechanisms;* but among some, there is little if any interrelationship. The interworkings that do exist between the various endocrine glands and tissues* make the subject of *endocrinology* a complex one; therefore, the various endocrine glands and other hormone-producing tissues will be considered separately, with some of their relationships to other parts of the system included in the discussion of each, wherever applicable.

Recent evidence has shown that neuron tracts extend from the cerebral cortex to the hypothalamus. It is therefore evident that the

cortex can affect the activities of the hypothalamus; and since the hypothalamus directs much of the activity of the pituitary gland, which in turn exerts great influence over the body, both directly and by influencing the activities of other endocrine glands, it is apparent that our state of mind can and does influence physiological processes throughout the body, which in turn influence brain activity. This cyclic pattern between brain and body processes is known as the *circular theory of mind and body relations,* or *somatopsychosomatic theory.*

THE ENDOCRINE GLANDS

The hypophysis

Commonly called the pituitary gland, the hypophysis is only about 1 cm in diameter and rests in the shallow *sella turcica* of the sphenoid bone, at the base of the brain. It is attached to the hypothalamus by means of a stalk called the *infundibulum* (Fig. 9-3 and Color Plate VIII). The gland consists of an *anterior lobe* or *adenohypophysis,* and a *posterior lobe* or *neurohypophysis.*

HORMONES OF THE ADENOHYPOPHYSIS   The anterior lobe of the pituitary gland has the microscopic structure of endocrine tissue and produces several hormones, all called *tropic* hormones because they act mainly on other endocrine glands. Of those to be considered in the following list, *growth hormone* and *lactogenic hormone* are secreted by cells called *acidophils.* The other hormones of the adenohypophysis are secreted by *basophil* cells.

1. *Somatotropin, or Growth Hormone* (GH). Promotes growth, especially of bones and muscles by speeding protein anabolism until the age of puberty. *Hypersecretion* of somatotropin due to pituitary tumors or other causes results in *gigantism* in the young and *acromegaly* in adults (Fig. 9-4). *Hyposecretion* produces *dwarfism* and a state of general ill health called *pituitary cachexia* or *Simmonds' disease.* GH also acts to promote *fat catabolism and mobilization.* The rate of fat deposition is thereby decreased. Somatotropin has a *hyperglycemic* or *diabe-*

---

* The *hypophysis, adrenal, thyroid,* and *parathyroids* are *exclusively endocrine* in function. The *pancreas, gonads, stomach,* and *duodenum* are *combination endocrine–exocrine* (heterocrine) organs. Exocrine glands all have excretory ducts through which their secretions are carried to the appropriate body area or part.

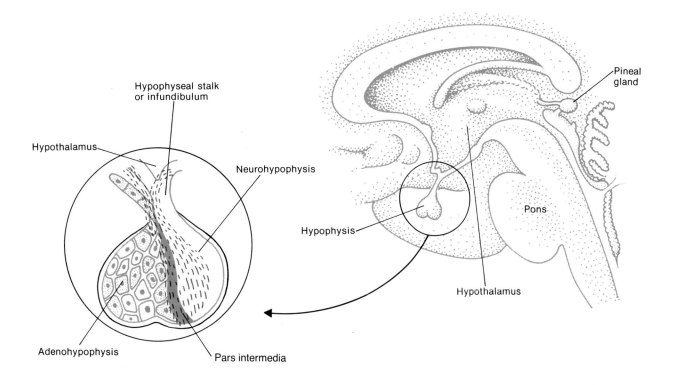

Figure 9-3 Location of the hypophysis or pituitary gland, and its microscopic structure.

Figure 9-4 Effects of abnormal secretion of pituitary growth hormone. (a) A pituitary giant stands with a dwarf and a man of normal height. Gigantism is due to hypersecretion of GH in the young, while dwarfism follows hyposecretion in the young. (b) Acromegaly, the result of pituitary hypersecretion in adults.

(a)   (b)

togenic effect by acting against insulin as the latter hormone attempts to promote the utilization of carbohydrate. Secretion of GH is regulated by a *somatotropin-releasing factor* (SRF), secreted by the hypothalamus and transported to the anterior pituitary by the *hypophyseal portal system of vessels.*

2. *Adrenocorticotropic Hormone* (ACTH, adrenocorticotropin). Stimulates the outer or the cortical portion of the adrenal gland to secrete its hormones. A drop in the blood level of adrenal cortical hormones triggers the production of ACTH, and conversely; that is, when the level of the adrenal cortical hormones is adequate, ACTH secretion is curtailed. ACTH is *essential to the growth and maintenance of a healthy adrenal cortex,* and can be given by injection in cases of adrenal insufficiency. The hormone also promotes the *mobilization of fats.*

A *corticotropin-releasing factor* (CRF), produced by the hypothalamus, aids in the regulation of the secretion of ACTH. When ACTH reaches normal blood levels, production of CRF is inhibited by the hormone that it stimulates the pituitary to secrete (ACTH). This is a clear example of a feedback system.

3. *Thyrotropin* (*Thyroid-Stimulating Hormone, TSH*). Promotes growth and devel-

opment of the thyroid gland, and directs the gland to produce two hormones, *thyroxin* and *triiodothyronine*. The same reciprocal relationship that exists between the pituitary and the adrenals exists between the pituitary and the thyroid; in fact, this type of relationship with the pituitary is common to all endocrine glands that are stimulated by pituitary secretions. *Thyrotropin-releasing factor* (TRF), produced in the hypothalamus, regulates the secretion of TSH.

4. *Follicle-Stimulating Hormone* (FSH). Promotes the growth of ovarian follicles in the female and the growth of the seminiferous tubules in the male during spermatogenesis. Any pituitary hormone affecting the gonads, such as this one, is called a *gonadotropic hormone*. It is likely that an FSH-*releasing factor* (FSH-RF), produced in the *hypothalamus*, regulates the secretion of FSH. When the blood levels of *androgens* in the *male* and *estrogens* in the *female* are within the normal range, the production of FSH and other gonadotropins is inhibited.

5. *Luteinizing Hormone* (LH). After the FSH has acted, this hormone stimulates the development of ovarian follicles and the corpus luteum, and stimulates ovulation and the production of estrogens. The hypothalamus produces a *luteinizing-hormone–releasing factor* (LRF) which apparently regulates the secretion of LH. A comparable hormone, *interstitial-cell–stimulating hormone* (ICSH) is produced in the male. It promotes the secretion of *testosterone* and other androgens by the interstitial cells of the testes. The secretion of ICSH is inhibited by testosterone.

6. *Lactogenic Hormone or Prolactin*. Promotes the production of milk by the mammary glands (after ovarian hormones have brought about the development of the secretory tubules of the glands) and general development of the breasts during pregnancy. Lactogenic hormone was formerly referred to as luteotropic hormone (*luteotropin* or LTH). Recent research indicates that a *prolactin-inhibiting factor* (PIF), secreted by the hypothalamus, suppresses the secretion of prolactin until it is time for lactation to begin.

7. *Melanocyte-Stimulating Hormone* (MSH)—Promotes the deposition of melanin in the skin, following exposure to sunlight or atrophy of the adrenal cortices as in Addison's disease. The hypothalamus probably regulates the secretion of MSH.

HORMONES OF THE NEUROHYPOPHYSIS The posterior lobe of the pituitary gland has the microscopic structure of nervous tissue, and secretes two hormones:

1. *Oxytocin*. Stimulates the smooth muscle of the uterus to contract during childbirth, and stimulates the smooth muscle of the mammary glands during nursing after the baby has been born. The sucking action of the infant triggers the production of oxytocin in the latter case. Oxytocin is actually secreted in the hypothalamus, but moves through neuron protoplasm into the posterior lobe of the pituitary before being released.

2. *Antidiuretic Hormone* (ADH, or vasopressin). Promotes reabsorption of water by the kidney tubules, with the result that less urine is formed. ADH is produced in the hypothalamus and stored in the posterior lobe of the pituitary. It is released when *osmoreceptors* in the hypothalamus detect an increase in osmotic pressure of the blood, following body water loss. ADH acts to conserve water by decreasing urine output.

It should now be clear that the pituitary operates on a feedback system with the other endocrine tissues. It releases its hormones into the bloodstream upon receiving signals following actions of the other endocrine glands and tissues affected by its secretions. The master regulator of the pituitary is the hypothalamus, most significantly so during those periods of most rapid growth. The pituitary, like all other endocrine glands, is highly vascular in nature, and its secretions quickly enter the blood by passing through the walls of its many capillaries. There is abundant evidence that the two hormones of the posterior lobe of the pituitary (oxytocin and ADH) are actually produced in the hypothalamus and travel along nerve fibers to the pituitary, where they are stored until needed. The disease *diabetes insipidus*, in which copious amounts of urine of low specific gravity are excreted, is caused by deficient production of ADH, or by the inability of the pituitary to store or release it. The urine of diabetes insipidus does not contain sugar.

The thyroid and its hormones

The thyroid gland lies on the upper anterior and lateral aspects of the trachea, at the level of the second and third tracheal rings (Fig. 9-5 and Color Plate IV). It is essentially bilobed, though its central portion, or *isthmus,* sometimes becomes elongated superiorly and inferiorly, forming a third or middle lobe. Not infrequently, upward extensions of the lateral lobes are present, and are called *pyramidal lobes.* The thyroid averages about 5 cm long by 3 cm wide, and weighs about 30 g. The substance of the thyroid is amber in color, and is made up of *follicles* or *alveoli,* some macroscopic, and all lined with a layer of *cuboidal epithelium.* Between the follicles lies a network of *connective tissue* and numerous *blood* and *lymph vessels.* The thyroid is supplied by the paired *superior* and *inferior thyroid arteries,* and by both divisions of the autonomic nervous system. The follicles contain a rather thick, translucent fluid called *colloid,* a protein material which may store the two major thyroid hormones, *thyroxin* or T_4, and *triiodothyronine* or T_3. About 95% of the total

thyroid hormone consists of thyroxin. Two layers of connective tissue invest the thyroid gland: an outer fibrous capsule and an inner elastic layer. Inward extensions of the capsule, *trabeculae,* divide the gland into *lobules.* There are numerous follicles in each lobule. The thyroid hormones are actually *amino acids,* and are combined with a colloidal protein, *thyroglobulin,* and are released into the bloodstream only when thyroglobulin is hydrolyzed, under the influence of TSH from the anterior pituitary. Only about 0.35 mg of thyroid hormones is secreted each day. They act chiefly on the *rate of metabolism,* increasing the rate of oxidation of foods within the tissue cells. The thyroid hormones are also necessary for normal growth. *Thyrocalcitonin,* a hormone substance recently determined to be produced by the thyroid, homeostatically regulates the *blood calcium level* and the *phosphate level of bone.* It was formerly thought to be produced exclusively by the parathyroid glands.

Figure 9-5 (a) The thyroid gland, its location and blood supply. (b) Follicles.

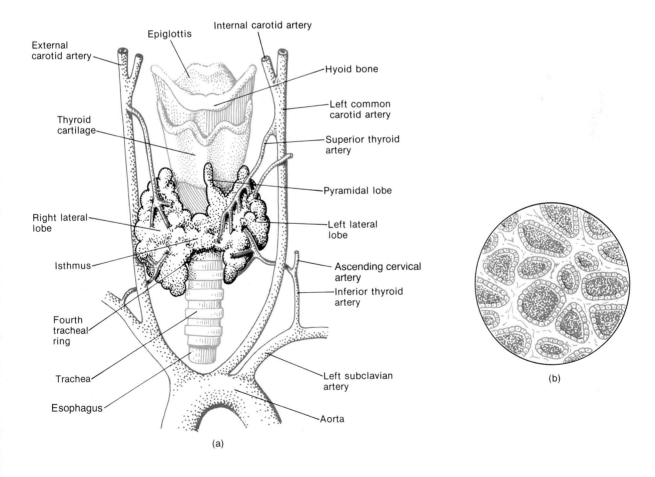

External carotid artery

Epiglottis

Internal carotid artery

Hyoid bone

Thyroid cartilage

Left common carotid artery

Superior thyroid artery

Pyramidal lobe

Right lateral lobe

Left lateral lobe

Isthmus

Ascending cervical artery

Inferior thyroid artery

Fourth tracheal ring

Trachea

Esophagus

Left subclavian artery

Aorta

(a)

(b)

Figure 9-6 Cretinism. This condition is due to hypothyroidism in the very early growing years.

Secretion of hormones by the thyroid is regulated by the pituitary hormone *thyrotropin* or TSH (see item 3 under "Hormones of the Adenohypophysis" in the section on the pituitary gland).

HYPOTHYROIDISM The metabolic action of thyroid hormones is extremely important during growth and development—so important that a deficiency of thyroid hormones (*hypothyroidism*) during the very early growing years results in *cretinism* (Fig. 9-6), typified by arrested growth, mental retardation, low metabolic rate, slow heart rate, bloated face, and dry, yellowish skin. Hypothyroidism occurring after several years of normal development but still during the growing years is called *juvenile myxedema*. This condition is characterized by dwarfism, bloating of the face, chronically open mouth with protruding tongue and drooling, and a generally listless, "stupid" expression. Preparations of dried thyroid gland, if administered early and with regularity, bring about re-

markable improvement in both cretinism and juvenile myxedema.

Hypothyroidism occurring after adulthood has been reached is called *myxedema*. The face is pale, puffy, and without expression. The metabolic rate drops, and mental and physical activities become sluggish. The hair may fall out and the teeth loosened. Treatment of myxedema, which is often caused by unexplained atrophy of the thyroid gland, consists of the administration of thyroid hormones. This treatment is usually highly successful in alleviating all symptoms, often within a few weeks.

HYPERTHYROIDISM Oversecretion of thyroid hormones is called variously *hyperthyroidism, thyrotoxicosis, Grave's disease,* or *exophthalmic goiter.* One of the most outstanding signs of the disease is *exophthalmos,* or protrusion of the eyeballs, due to the increased deposition of fat behind them (Fig. 9-7). The patient is nervous and irritable, moves about restlessly, and tires easily. There is an increase in metabolic rate, heart rate, and body temperature, and the face may be flushed. The cause of hyperthyroidism is unknown, but a tendency to acquire the disease seems to be inheritable. Severe hyperthyroidism may require the use of various antithyroid drugs; if the enlargement of the gland is due to malignant growth, surgical removal may be resorted to.

SIMPLE GOITER Another type of disorder of the thyroid gland is *simple* or *endemic*

Figure 9-7 Hyperthyroidism with exophthalmos.

Figure 9-8 Simple goiter.

goiter. It is caused by a dietary deficiency of *iodine.* The gland enlarges in an attempt to compensate for lack of iodine, essential to the manufacture of its hormones. Although an enlarged thyroid gland creates an undesirable appearance (Fig. 9-8) it is not particularly injurious to health until it becomes large enough to cause undue pressure upon the trachea and other nearby structures. In its early stages, simple goiter can be successfully treated by the administration of iodine preparations. Gross enlargement of the thyroid, however, may necessitate the removal of at least a major portion of the gland. Simple goiter is prevalent in areas in which the amount of iodine in the soil and drinking water is low. This situation has been remedied in the United States by the addition of small amounts of iodine to table salt and, in some cases, to drinking water.

The parathyroid glands

The four yellowish-brown parathyroids are the smallest of the endocrine glands, each averaging about 5 mm in diameter and weighing only about 0.033 g. Two of them lie on the posterior aspect of each lateral lobe of the thyroid gland (Fig. 9-9). They are deep to its capsule, but separated from the substance of the thyroid by a layer of connective tissue. The substance of the parathyroids consists of a *reticulum of connective tissue,*

interspersed with numerous *principal or chief cells* and *oxyphil cells.* The principal cells, which secrete the parathyroid hormone parathormone (PTH), are arranged in *cords* and *compact masses* and have a clear, *nongranular cytoplasm.* The function of the oxyphil cells, which have a granular cytoplasm, is not known. Blood courses through the parathyroid glands in innumerable *capillaries* and *sinusoids.* Lymph vessels are also abundant.

Parathormone is intimately concerned with the *metabolism* of *calcium and phosphorus,* and exerts control over the calcium–phosphorus ratio in the blood. It promotes *absorption* of calcium from the intestine, *deposition* of calcium in bone and *mobilization* of calcium from bone, as well as the *reabsorption* of calcium ions by the kidney tubules. Removal of the parathyroids in experimental animals produces a *rise* in the *blood phosphorus level* and a *decrease* in the level of *calcium.* Within a few days, muscular tremors and spasms develop, followed by tetany and death, unless parathyroid extract or calcium is administered, in which case tetany does not occur. Abnormalities of parathyroid function, although rare, do occur.

The secretion of PTH is not influenced by the pituitary, but depends on the *blood*

Figure 9-9 Location and relative size of the parathyroids.

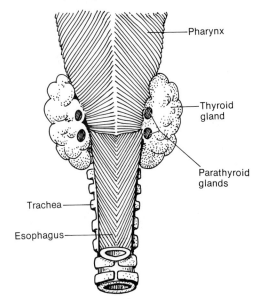

Pharynx

Thyroid gland

Parathyroid glands

Trachea

Esophagus

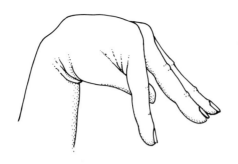

Figure 9-10 Tetany. Typical of parathyroid disorder that produces hypoparathyroidism.

level of calcium ions. When the serum calcium level rises, secretion of PTH is suppressed; conversely, a fall in serum calcium promotes increased secretion of PTH.

HYPOPARATHYROIDISM   Hypoparathyroidism, or *parathyroid insufficiency,* most commonly occurs following injury to the parathyroids during surgery involving the thyroid gland. It is possible for the parathyroids to be completely removed—accidentally—during this surgery. But whether hypoparathyroidism is caused by an accident of surgery or is due to a degeneration of the parathyroid tissue, the result is the same: *tetany* (Fig. 9-10) develops, especially in the muscles of the hand and wrist, there is general muscular weakness throughout the body, and the peripheral neuromuscular system becomes hyperexcitable. Tapping on the facial nerve causes the muscles of facial expression to contract, producing an expression of sadness. The administration of parathyroid preparations in cases of hypoparathyroidism brings about a *rise in the blood calcium level* and a *fall in blood phosphates;* however, they must be injected (the preparations are digested by gastrointestinal enzymes), and begin to lose effectiveness when used for long periods of time. One successful treatment of hypoparathyroidism is the oral administration of *calcium lactate* and *vitamin D.*

HYPERPARATHYROIDISM   An enlargement of or tumor of one or more of the parathyroid glands is a sign of oversecretion of parathyroid hormone; that is, *hyperparathyroidism.* The calcium blood level rises, and as greater-than-normal amounts of calcium are withdrawn from the skeleton, the bones become

weak , deformed, and *susceptible to fracture.* Kidney stones may form, and the blood phosphate level rises, even though the excretion of both calcium and phosphate is increased. Surgical removal of a portion of the enlarged parathyroid helps to restore calcium–phosphate metabolic balance.

The adrenal (suprarenal) glands

An adrenal gland sits on the upper medial pole of each kidney (Fig. 9-11 and Color Plate VIII). Although they are loosely attached to the kidneys by connective tissue and fat, the adrenals have their own fibrous, connective-tissue capsules. In longitudinal section, an adrenal is seen to consist of an inner *medullary portion* and an outer *cortical portion.* These portions are quite different histologically, and produce entirely different hormones. The adrenal medulla consists chiefly of so-called *chromaffin cells,* which stain a characteristic dark brown with chromic acid.

THE ADRENAL MEDULLA   The medulla is highly dependent upon the hypothalamus and autonomic nervous system for regulation, and secretes the important hormone *epinephrine* (adrenalin), which has essentially the same effects upon certain body functions as the sympathetic division of the autonomic nervous system: *constriction* of *peripheral arterioles,* bringing about an *increase in peripheral resistance* and a *rise in blood pressure; an increase in heart rate; dilation of the bronchial tubes* and *pupils;* and *inhibition of intestinal movements.* A closely related hormone, *norepinephrine* (formerly called sympathin), is also secreted by the adrenal medulla. It acts to *constrict peripheral blood vessels* and promote a *rise in blood pressure.* In addition to being produced in the adrenal gland, norepinephrine is also released at *postganglionic sympathetic-nerve endings,* and is present in the brain and spinal cord. Synthesized forms of both hormones of the adrenal medulla are used as vasoconstrictors in dentistry and surgery, and epinephrine is used as a heart stimulant and to raise blood pressure after a precipitous drop such as that seen in shock. Epinephrine and norepinephrine are known chemically as

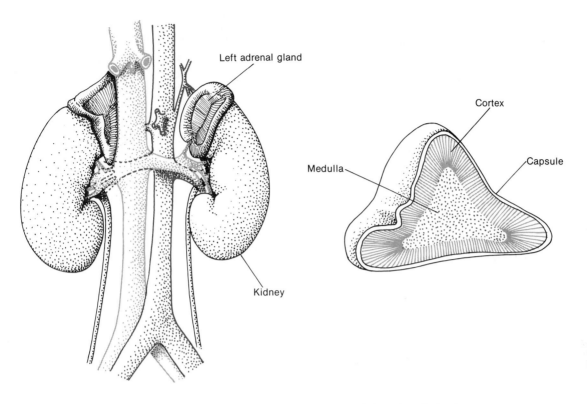

Figure 9-11 Location and internal structure of the adrenal glands.

catecholamines. Both can speed the conversion of glycogen to glucose and raise the blood sugar level. Although epinephrine has quite appropriately been termed the "emergency hormone"—because it is released into the blood in greater quantities during highly emotional states, such as fear and anger—the adrenal medulla is not essential to life, as is the adrenal cortex. Complete removal of the medullary substance of both adrenals seems to cause predisposition to infection, but epinephrine is probably also secreted elsewhere in the body (perhaps by the sympathetic division of the ANS) and its production by the adrenal medulla is not vital.

MEDULLARY HYPERSECRETION Rarely, an adrenal medulla may exhibit hypersecretion due to tumor. When this happens, the *blood pressure becomes elevated,* accompanied by *glucosuria, hyperglycemia,* and *highly elevated metabolic rate.* If the condition is not remedied, such complications as *coronary insufficiency* and *pulmonary edema* may result. Treatment of a tumorous adrenal medulla is often by surgical removal.

REGULATION OF MEDULLARY SECRETION There is evidence to indicate that the hypothalamus sends impulses along preganglionic sympathetic neurons to the adrenal medulla, causing it to produce epinephrine. It is postulated that stress situations greatly increase the rate of impulse transmission from the hypothalamus to the adrenal medulla, and this brings about an increase in the production of epinephrine.

THE IMPORTANCE OF THE ADRENAL CORTEX The adrenal cortex (Fig. 9-11) is *essential to life,* and the loss of the cortical portions of both adrenals is fatal unless cortical hormones are administered regularly. Over three dozen hormones, all steroids, are apparently produced by the adrenal cortex, but only seven of these are known to have direct effects upon body functions. These *corticosteroids* —or *corticoids,* as they are called—can be grouped into three classes: *glucocorticoids,* such as cortisone and hydrocortisone (cortisol); *mineralocorticoids,* including corticosterone, deoxycorticosterone, and aldosterone, and *sex hormones* (androgens, estrogens, and progesterone). The last are produced in only the most minute amounts, and for all practical purposes are thought to be insignificant. The glucocorticoids assist in the synthesis of glycogen from proteins in the liver; glycogen can then be broken down to glucose, with the result that the glucose blood level is increased. The glucocorticoids also somehow help to prevent inflammation of wounds.

The mineralocorticoids are important in the regulation of water balance and in helping to maintain a homeostatic equilibrium of electrolytes. By promoting the retention of sodium salts by the kidneys, these hormones prevent the amount of water excreted by them from abnormally increasing, and thus tend to keep the plasma volume up to its normal level. If the adrenal cortices are removed from an experimental animal, that animal becomes highly prone to infection and hemorrhage, and cannot easily tolerate high altitudes or extremes of temperature. Even mild trauma often produces shock. All these again attest to the importance of the hormones produced by the adrenal cortex.

UNDERSECRETION AND OVERSECRETION BY THE ADRENAL CORTEX The adrenal cortex is subject to a degenerative disorder causing adrenocortical insufficiency and called *hypoadrenocorticalism* or *Addison's disease*. Symptoms and signs of Addison's disease include hypotension, general weakness, loss of appetite and weight, and a characteristic pigmentation of the skin, gums, and mucous membranes of the mouth. Treatment is by means of cortical steroid preparations, such as cortisone and deoxycorticosterone acetate (DOCA).

On occasion, the adrenal cortex will become hyperactive, due to overproduction of ACTH by the pituitary or because of a tumor in the cortex itself. Such cortical hyperfunction is known as *hyperadrenocorticalism,* and produces several physical alterations. *Cushing's disease,* typified by obesity, hypertension, and weakness of the muscles and skeletal system, is one of the most common syndrome in mature individuals suffering from cortical hyperfunction. In the female, hyperadrenocorticalism after puberty can bring about great growth of body hair, even on the face and chin. The voice deepens, and the body becomes more masculine in form.

In young boys, hyperfunction of the adrenal cortex can often result in abnormally rapid growth, muscular development, and aging. Pubic hair and an enlarged penis may develop even in very young boys. In the case of very young girls, sexual development takes place, and they tend to be rather masculine in appearance; axillary and pubic hair may grow (even as early as age three), chin hair may be prominent, and the clitoris enlarges. This maturity far in advance of the usual age of puberty is known as *sexual precocity*.

HOW ADRENAL-CORTICAL FUNCTION IS REGULATED Recent research indicates that the anterior lobe of the pituitary regulates the secretion of hydrocortisone and corticosterone, but little if any aldosterone. ACTH apparently promotes the production of the glucocorticoids, which then may inhibit the secretion of corticotropin–releasing factor by the hypothalamus, or perhaps inhibit the secretion of ACTH directly. In either instance, there is a negative-feedback relationship.

The secretion of aldosterone is thought to be chiefly under the control of the hormonal substance *renin,* produced by *juxtaglomerular* cells in the kidney. This again is not a direct relationship, as renin acts to convert other substances which act on still other agents that finally bring about aldosterone production by stimulating the adrenal cortex.

The pancreas

The exocrine function of the pancreas, involving the production of digestive enzymes, is discussed in Chapter 12. The location of the pancreas is shown in Color Plate VI. The *endocrine tissue of the pancreas* consists of discrete clusters of cells which are dispersed throughout the substance of the pancreas and well supplied with blood vessels. Because these groups of cells reminded early histologists of tiny islands scattered about in an ocean, they were named the *isles of Langerhans* in honor of the German pathologist Paul Langerhans, who carried out research involving the islet tissue. Islet cells are of two kinds, designated *alpha* and *beta* (Fig. 9-12). The beta cells are the smaller of the two, and

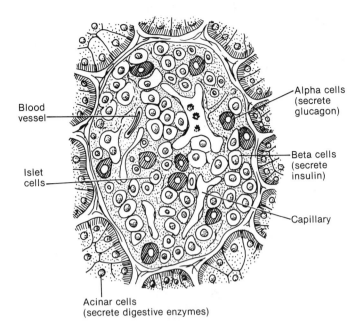

Blood vessel

Islet cells

Alpha cells (secrete glucagon)

Beta cells (secrete insulin)

Capillary

Acinar cells (secrete digestive enzymes)

Figure 9-12 Islet tissue of the pancreas (acinar cells belong to the exocrine tissue).

produce the hormone so important to the metabolism of carbohydrates, *insulin.* The larger alpha cells secrete another hormone, *glucagon,* which also helps to regulate the blood sugar level.

THE IMPORTANCE OF INSULIN Insulin is a complex protein substance, first prepared in extract form about 1922. Although glucagon and the digestive enzymes of the pancreas are not essential to life, insulin *is.* Insulin lowers the blood glucose level by promoting the passage of glucose into the cells, increasing the conversion of glucose to glycogen in the liver and skeletal muscles, increasing oxidation of glucose by the tissues, helping to increase the rates of conversion of carbohydrates to fats, and aiding in the synthesis of proteins from amino acids. Insulin *must* be present in the blood in order for carbohydrates to be utilized by the tissues. If it is not, the blood sugar level rises (*hyperglycemia*), and sugar accumulates in the kidneys and "spills over" into the urine (*glycosuria*) instead of being metabolized; also, urine is produced in copious amounts. This syndrome —consisting of hyperglycemia, glycosuria, and polyuria—is called *diabetes mellitus,* or (erroneously) "sugar diabetes." The normal blood glucose level is about 80–120 mg per 100 cc. In diabetics, the level may soar to 200 and even 300 mg per 100 cc. Sugar can be detected in the urine when the blood glucose level reaches about 160–180 mg per 100 cc. Just why the pancreas ceases to produce insulin in diabetes mellitus is not known. In some cases, it appears that the islet cells are simply nonfunctional, while in others, these cells may be few in number. There seems to be a hereditary tendency to acquire the disease, since some 25% of patients have a family history of diabetes. At autopsy, the pancreas of a large number of diabetics shows degeneration or atrophy of islet tissue. Today, diabetes can be controlled (but not cured) by the regular administration of insulin, given by injection. Several oral hypoglycemic preparations have been developed, but in general have not proven to be entirely satisfactory for all patients. Diabetics are often obese and consume large quantities of carbohydrates and fats, and are most often in middle or old age. After the disease has progressed for a while, the diabetic may become weak and often lose weight. He is continually drinking water (*polydipsia*) and eating (*hyperphagia*). The liver produces more ketone bodies (such as acetone) than normally, resulting in *ketonuria* and *ketosis,* and eventually *acidosis.* There is loss of sodium and, if acidosis develops to a significant degree before treatment, there is danger of coma and death. Ketones give the breath a fruitlike odor, and there is danger of dehydration due to polyuria. Polyuria, dehydration, and loss of sodium result when excessive glucose in the renal filtrate brings on an *osmotic imbalance* that severely curtails the reabsorption of water. The diabetic is highly susceptible to infection and predisposed to diseases of the heart and remainder of the circulatory system. Therapy utilizing insulin must be carefully regulated according to the patient's individual needs. There must be a balance between the carbohydrate intake and the amount of insulin used. Too little insulin in relation to the amount of carbohydrate consumed can result in diabetic coma, and too much insulin can produce *insulin shock,* characterized by unconsciousness and convulsive muscular seizures. Insulin shock has been induced deliberately in some mental patients as a substitute for electric-shock treatment.

239

On occasion, the islet cells of the pancreas exhibit *hyperinsulinism* or overproduction of insulin, usually due to tumorous growth in these tissues. The general effect is just the opposite of that of the hypoinsulinism of diabetes: *hypoglycemia,* instead of hyperglycemia as in diabetes.

GLUCAGON Glucagon, known as *hyperglycemic–glycogenolytic* (HCG) factor, is secreted by the alpha cells of the pancreatic islet tissue. As the blood sugar level falls below a certain point between meals, glucagon is secreted. The hormone then stimulates the conversion of glycogen to glucose in the liver, and the blood sugar level *rises.* The effect of glucagon is directly opposite to that of insulin, which brings about a drop in blood sugar.

REGULATION OF PANCREATIC ENDOCRINE SECRETION The secretion of insulin and glucagon is dependent upon the *blood sugar level.* If this value drops, glucagon is produced and the amount of blood sugar level increases; if the level increases, *insulin* is secreted, and there is a decrease in blood sugar. Homeostatic control of the amount of glucose in the circulating blood is thus maintained by this mechanism. The pituitary gland does not secrete a hormone that stimulates the pancreas to produce either insulin or glucagon. Adrenocorticotropic hormone indirectly causes the secretion of insulin by stimulating the production of cortisone and hydrocortisone (the glucocorticoids), which results in an increase in the blood sugar level. Growth hormone has the same effect.

OTHER HORMONES AFFECTING THE BLOOD-SUGAR LEVEL Several hormones not secreted by the pancreas have a hyperglycemic effect: epinephrine of the adrenal medulla, and TSH, ACTH, and GH of the anterior lobe of the pituitary gland. Thyroid hormone has a hypoglycemic effect.

THE GONADS

The testes

The hormones produced by the testes are *androgens*—that is, substances that have masculinizing effects on the body. The principal androgen of the testes is *testosterone.* Chemically, testosterone is a steroid, and is probably produced in the *intertubular cells* of the testis. These irregularly shaped cells, known also as *interstitial cells* or *cells of Leydig,* are found as clusters among the seminiferous tubules. The appearance of secondary sex characteristics—such as the beard, growth of hair in the axillary and pubic regions, deepening of the voice, and development of the psychological sex drive, or libido—all depend upon the secretion of testosterone.

Occasionally, complete loss of the testes (castration) occurs, following injury or due to necessary surgery. If castration takes place *before* the age of sexual maturity, the secondary sex characteristics never develop; if it happens *after* puberty, the sex drive is gradually lost. Production of testosterone is under the influence of the gonadotropic hormone of the pituitary gland, interstitial-cell–stimulating hormone (ICSH). The production of ICSH is depressed or even arrested by a certain concentration of testosterone in the blood.

The ovaries

Four principal hormones are produced by the ovaries. Three of these belong to a class of compounds called *estrogens,* which are extremely important in the development of secondary sex characteristics and regulation of the menstrual cycle. They also increase the libido and influence the metabolism of electrolytes and nitrogen. The estrogens include *estradiol, estrone,* and *estriol,* all of which, like testosterone, are *steroids.* Estradiol is probably produced by *cells of the Graafian follicles,* while estriol and estrone may be derived from estradiol.

The fourth principal hormone of the ovaries is *progesterone.* It, too, is a steroid, chemically similar to the estrogens. Although it also, like the estrogens, helps to regulate the changes that take place during the menstrual cycle, more significantly, it aids in preparing the endometrial lining of the uterus for implantation of a zygote. During pregnancy, progesterone influences the development of the fetal membranes and mammary glands. *Three gonadotropic hormones* of the pituitary gland regulate the secretion of the estrogens and progesterone: follicle-stimulating hormone (FSH), luteinizing hormone (LH), and lactogenic hormone or prolactin.

In spite of the fact that the male and female sex hormones have tremendous influence upon the development and functioning of the respective reproductive systems as well as the development of the respective secondary sex characteristics, at least *some* male and female hormones are *secreted by members of both sexes.* Androgenic hormones are found in the urine of women, while estrogens are present in the urine of men. Apparently, male hormones are secreted in greater quantities and are of greater potency when produced by the male, and conversely insofar as female hormones are concerned. The *adrenal glands* of both sexes may also produce a certain amount of sex hormones that are normally associated with the opposite sex.

OTHER ORGANS THAT PRODUCE HORMONES

The placenta

During pregnancy, the placenta acts as an endocrine gland, producing estrogens, progesterone, and a gonadotropic hormone, *chorionic gonadotropin.* This last hormone is necessary for the maintenance of the corpus luteum, while the estrogens and progesterone seem to function as supplements to those produced by the ovaries.

The stomach

The stomach produces at least one hormone, tentatively called *gastrin,* which is secreted in response to the presence of partially digested foods. The hormone is released into the bloodstream and circulates throughout the body and back to the stomach, where it stimulates gastric glands to produce their enzymes and hydrochloric acid.

The intestine

Intestinal hormones are produced by cells in the duodenal mucosa. Three of these

hormones have been named: *secretin,* which stimulates the production of bile and pancreatic enzymes; *pancreozymin,* which aids secretin in stimulating the pancreas and regulates the ejection of bile by the gallbladder; and *enterogasterone,* which helps in the regulation of secretion by the gastric glands.

The kidneys

The hormonal substance renin, produced by the kidneys, probably controls the secretion of aldosterone by the adrenal cortex and acts as a catalyst in the production of angiotensin from angiotensinogen, a product of the liver. In excess, angiotensin may cause widespread vasoconstriction and hypertension.

The thymus

The *thymus* is located in the mediastinum, and at its greatest size, extends to the lower border of the thyroid gland. It is largest at puberty. It is believed that in early childhood, the thymus produces a hormone that aids the conversion of lymphocytes into *plasma cells.* Plasma cells manufacture antibodies that attack foreign protein substances; so, indirectly, the thymus is important in rendering the body immune to attack by microorganisms. Before birth, the thymus manufactures lymphocytes. After puberty, the gland gradually atrophies until at old age it may almost disappear.

The pineal body

The *pineal body* or gland is located just posterior to the midbrain, and is attached to the roof of the third ventricle. It begins to degenerate at about age 7, and by adulthood, is made up mainly of fibrous tissue. However, there is evidence—from experimentation with rats—that suggests that a hormone produced by the pineal gland, *melatonin,* may help to regulate ovarian activity and the menstrual cycle. An increase in the production of melatonin slows the estrus cycle of rats, while a decrease in production of this hormone accelerates the cycle. The pineal body may also secrete *serotonin,* which seems to be essential to the normal functioning of the brain, and *adrenoglomerulotropin,* which stimulates the glomerular zone of the adrenal cortex to produce aldosterone.

The endocrine system: assists the nervous system in homeostasis, and plays important roles in growth and sexual maturation

1. The endocrine glands include
   A. Pituitary or hypophysis
   B. Thyroid
   C. Parathyroids
   D. Pancreas (islet tissue)
   E. Adrenals
2. Other hormone-secreting tissues include
   A. Cells in the stomach and intestine
   B. Placenta
   C. Kidneys
   D. Thymus
   E. Pineal body
3. Chemistry of hormones
   A. Some are relatively simple, some complex
   B. Categories of hormones include steroids, proteins, polypeptides, amino acids, and various other nitrogenous compounds
   C. Hormones are potent and, therefore, are produced in very small amounts
4. Factors that regulate hormone secretion
   A. Nervous factors—examples
      a. Influence of the hypothalamus over the pituitary
      b. Control of the adrenal medulla by sympathetic autonomic impulses
   B. Chemical factors—examples
      a. Production of secretion by cells in the duodenal mucosa in response to the presence of fat or acids in the duodenum
      b. Secretion of insulin by the pancreas in response to an increase in blood sugar level
5. Interrelationships: the secretions of some endocrine glands and tissues are dependent upon the secretions of others and reciprocally, in feedback relationships
6. Individual endocrine glands and tissues
   A. The hypophysis
      a. About 1 cm in diameter; located in the sella turcica
      b. Attached to the hypothalamus by the infundibulum
      c. Two portions: the anterior lobe or adenohypophysis, and posterior lobe or neurohypophysis
      d. Hormones of the adenohypophysis: called tropic hormones because they act mainly upon other endocrine glands
         1. Somatotropin or growth hormone (GH)
         2. Adrenocorticotropic hormone (ACTH)
         3. Thyrotropin (thyroid-stimulating hormone, TSH)
         4. Follicle-stimulating hormone (FSH)
         5. Luteinizing hormone (LH)
         6. Lactogenic hormone or prolactin
         7. Melanocyte-stimulating hormone (MSH)
      e. Hormones of the neurohypophysis
         1. Oxytocin
         2. Antidiuretic hormone (ADH or vasopressin)
      f. Effects of pituitary disorder: because of its many hormones and interrelationships with the other endocrine glands, disorders of the pituitary can cause a variety of effects, such as abnormal growth and development, malfunction of the thyroid and adrenal glands, and failure of lactation
      g. Control and regulation of the pituitary: dependent upon its relationship with the hypothalamus and to feedback mechanisms with other endocrine glands
   B. The thyroid
      a. Bilobed; located on the anterior aspect of the trachea at the second and third rings; about 5 cm long by 3 cm wide
      b. Consists of follicles lined with cuboidal epithelium, connective tissue, and blood and lymph vessels
      c. Hormones of the thyroid
         1. Thyroxin: makes up 95% of thyroid hormone production
         2. Triiodothyronine (T_3): constitutes the remaining 5%
      d. Disorders of the thyroid
         1. Hypothyroidism
         2. Hyperthyroidism
         3. Simple goiter
      e. Regulation of the thyroid: largely by the pituitary
   C. The parathyroids
      a. Smallest of the endocrine glands; about 5 mm in diameter
      b. Two positioned on the back of each lobe of the thyroid, deep to its capsule
      c. Consists of a reticulum of connective tissue, interspersed with nu-

merous principal cells and oxyphil cells

d. Hormones of the parathyroids
   1. Parathormone
   2. Calcitonin
e. Disorders of the parathyroids
   1. Hypoparathyroidism
   2. Hyperparathyroidism
f. Control or regulation of secretion by the parathyroids: depends upon the blood concentration of calcium ions

D. The adrenals
   a. One positioned on the upper medial pole of each kidney, but loosely attached and having their own capsules
   b. Have an outer cortex and inner medulla, which differ histologically
   c. Hormones of the adrenal medulla
      1. Epinephrine
      2. Norepinephrine
   d. Hormones of the adrenal cortex: at least seven have direct effects upon body functions. They are called corticosteriods, and are grouped in three classes
      1. Glucocorticoids, such as cortisone and hydrocortisone
      2. Mineralocorticoids, including corticosterone, deoxycorticosterone, and aldosterone
      3. Sex hormones
   e. Disorders of the adrenal gland
      1. Cortical hyposecretion or hypersecretion
      2. Medullary hyposecretion or hypersecretion
   f. Regulation and control of the adrenal glands: by the hypophysis and kidney

E. The pancreas
   a. Endocrine tissue consists of clusters of cells called islet tissue
      1. Alpha cells: produce glucagon

   2. Beta cells: produce insulin
   b. Disorders of the endocrine portion of the pancreas
      1. Hypoinsulinism: causes hyperglycemia
      2. Hyperinsulinism: causes hypoglycemia
   c. Regulation of pancreatic endocrine secretion: dependent upon the blood sugar level

F. The testes—hormones are produced as androgens, the principal one of which is testosterone, produced in the intertubular cells. Regulation of testosterone production is by the pituitary gland

G. The ovaries—produce four principal hormones
   a. Estrogens
      1. Estradiol
      2. Esterone
      3. Estriol
   b. Progesterone
   c. Regulation of ovarian endocrine function: by three hormones of the pituitary

H. The placenta—produces
   a. Estrogens
   b. Progesterone
   c. Chorionic gonadotropin

I. The stomach—produces gastrin

J. The intestine—produces four hormones in the duodenal mucosa
   a. Secretin
   b. Pancreozymin
   c. Cholecystokinin
   d. Enterogasterone

K. The kidneys—produce renin and angiotensin

L. The thymus—produces a hormone that helps to convert lymphocytes into plasma cells

M. The pineal body—secretes melatonin, serotonin, and adrenoglomerulotropin

STUDY QUESTIONS AND PROBLEMS

1. Contrast the speed of the regulatory action of the endocrine system with that of the nervous system.

2. Name the glands which are totally endocrine in function, then other organs that secrete hormones, but not exclusively.

3. Discuss the nervous and chemical factors that act to regulate the secretion of hormones.

4. What is the adenohypophysis? The neurohypophysis? List the hormones produced by each.

5. What is the result of hyposecretion of growth hormone? Of hypersecretion of this hormone?

6. What is the function of follicle-stimulating hormone in the male?

7. What is the action of melanocyte-stimulating hormone?

8. What are the functions of oxytocin and antidiuretic hormone, respectively?

9. What is the major hormone of the thyroid gland?

10. Discuss the control of thyroid secretion.

11. You learn of a patient that is suffering from hypothyroidism. The patient is six years old. Describe the signs and symptoms you would expect to see in such a case.

12. What outstanding change from the normal in a patient's facial expression is a clasical sign of hyperthyroidism?

13. What is the difference between exophthalmic goiter and simple or endemic goiter?

14. Where are the parathyroid glands located? What is their major function? What is the effect of their removal?

15. What does the secretion of parathormone and calcitonin depend upon?

16. What acts to control insulin and glucagon secretion by the pancreas? Which cells of the pancreas secrete glucagon, and which secrete insulin? Which of these two hormones is hyperglycemic in its action, and which is hypoglycemic?

17. Describe the typical patient with hypoparathyroidism. With hyperparathyroidism.

18. Discuss the hormones of each portion (cortex and medulla) of the adrenal gland.

19. Discuss the hormones produced by the digestive tract.

20. Discuss the hormones produced by the thymus and the pineal gland.

the circulation of body fluids

Until some three hundred years ago, man did not realize that blood circulated in his body. For hundreds of years, he thought that only veins contained blood, and that arteries were filled with air. The blood was supposed to ebb and flow from the heart through the veins and back again, in the manner of a tide. It was indeed a long while before men of science began to accept the idea that blood *left the heart in arteries, circulated throughout the body tissues, and returned to the heart in veins.* In the seventeenth century, the Englishman William Harvey did more to clarify the problem of circulation than any man who had preceded him. Like his predecessors and contemporaries, Harvey had never seen the microscopic vessels, *capillaries,* that connect arteries with veins in the tissue; but he performed a series of ingenious experiments that proved his theory of circulation. Perhaps the best known of these experiments was the one demonstrating the direction of flow of blood in the veins (Fig. 10-1). By occluding (stopping the flow of blood) in a vein on the forearm, Harvey showed that blood left the vein above the blockage and distended (swelled) that portion of the vein below it. He showed also that if a finger pressing on the *distal end* of the collapsed (emptied) portion were removed, the vein would *immediately refill,* but if only a finger at the *proximal end* of the collapsed portion were removed, refilling would not occur. Blood, it thus became obvious, moves *toward the heart in veins,* and not in the other direction. To-

day, we can trace the circulation of the blood with great precision and accuracy; and we know that the circulation of the blood within its system of tubes is necessary to the maintenance of the homeostatic state of the body. The circulatory system makes its contribution to homeostasis by **transporting** *food, water, electrolytes, enzymes, hormones, antibodies, and oxygen and carbon dioxide either toward or away from the body cells and tissues as required.* The gross anatomy of the circulatory system is shown in Color Plates III, IV, V, VI, VII, & VIII.

Overall plan of the circulatory system

One of the best ways to learn how something works is to first get a general idea of its construction and the responsibility of its component parts, then to examine each of these parts and their functions in detail. We can apply this method to the circulatory system by tracing a drop of blood from the heart to a distant portion of the body and back again. A sectional view of the heart (Fig. 10-2) reveals that its muscular walls surround four *chambers:* two *atria* and two *ventricles.* The atria send blood into the ventricles, and when the ventricles squeeze (*contract*) and wring the blood from themselves, it travels by *two routes: that from the left ventricle travels to all parts of the body except around the air sacs of the lungs; that leaving the right ventricle goes to these air*

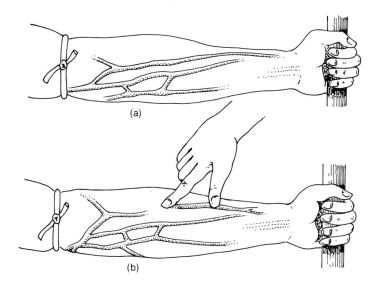

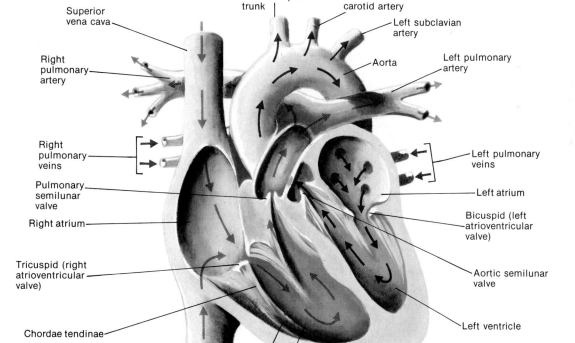

Figure 10-1 One of Harvey's experiments. (a) A tourniquet around the arm causes the veins of the forearm to be distended. (b) If the tourniquet is slightly loosened and a vein compressed by a finger, blood remains in the portion of the vein distal to the compression, but leaves the proximal portion. This technique can be used to demonstrate the position of the valves.

sacs, where it picks up oxygen and leaves carbon dioxide. The first pathway is called the **systemic circulation,** while that concerned with carrying blood around the air sacs of the lungs is the **pulmonary circulation.** It is now apparent that we are going to have to follow our drop of blood—destined for the right big toe, let's say—through *both* these circuits in order to make the trip complete. We can begin tracing the flow of blood anywhere we choose; arbitrarily, we shall begin in the *left ventricle of the heart.* When the left ventricle contracts, blood leaves the heart through the largest artery in the body, the *aorta* (Fig. 10-3), and travels through its *arch* and down its *descending portion* until the great vessel *bifurcates* (divides by branching) into *right and left common iliac* arteries. In order to get to the right big toe, our drop of blood goes down the right common iliac artery, and moves within this vessel until it branches into *external iliac* and *internal iliac* arteries. At this point, the drop must con-

Figure 10-2 Internal structure of the heart.

Superior vena cava

Brachiocephalic trunk

Left common carotid artery

Left subclavian artery

Right pulmonary artery

Aorta

Left pulmonary artery

Right pulmonary veins

Left pulmonary veins

Pulmonary semilunar valve

Left atrium

Right atrium

Bicuspid (left atrioventricular valve)

Tricuspid (right atrioventricular valve)

Aortic semilunar valve

Chordae tendinae

Left ventricle

Inferior vena cava

Descending aorta

Right ventricle

Papillary muscle

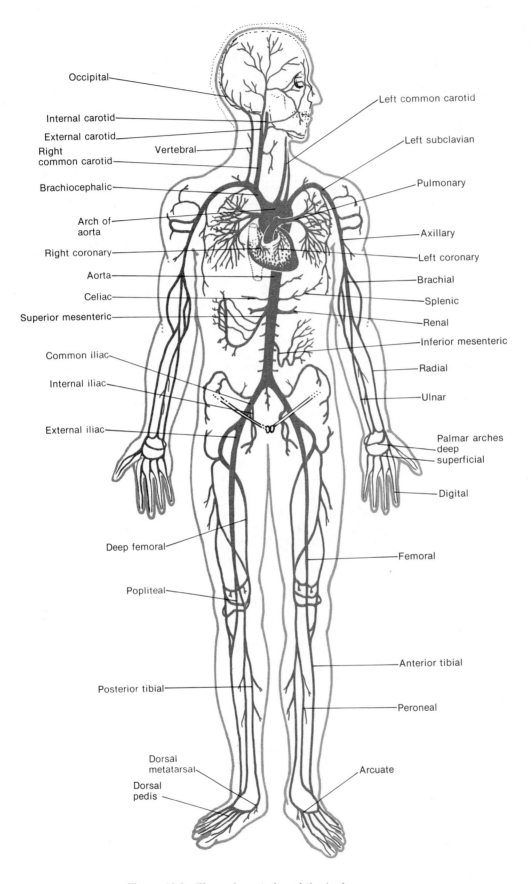

Figure 10-3 The major arteries of the body.

tinue in the external iliac if it is ever to reach the big toe. The external iliac artery soon branches into *femoral* and *deep femoral* arteries, and this time the femoral must be followed. Just behind the knee, the femoral artery is known as the *popliteal* artery, which soon branches or bifurcates into *anterior and posterior tibial* arteries. The blood in the anterior tibial eventually reaches the big toe via a branch of the *dorsalis pedis* artery. The drop of blood has at last reached the toe. Here, it will enter a very small vessel called an *arteriole,* then a capillary—one of thousands in a network or capillary "bed" (Fig. 10-4)—and after *giving up oxygen and nutrients* and *picking up carbon dioxide and other wastes* by diffusion exchanges between the capillary and body cells, will enter a slightly larger vessel called a *venule.* The venule soon empties our drop of blood into a *small vein of the leg* (Fig. 10-5). Eventually it will reach the *right external iliac vein,* then the *right common iliac,* and finally the large *inferior vena cava.* The inferior vena cava connects directly with the *right atrium* of the heart. From the right atrium, the blood moves to the *right ventricle,* which promptly contracts and sends it through the *pulmonary trunk* and one of its two large branches—the *right and left pulmonary arteries*—to the *lungs.* In the lungs, the capillaries surround tiny air sacs, *alveoli,* which connect with *air passages* leading eventually to the *trachea* or "windpipe." A drop of blood passing through the *alveolar capillaries* gives up its carbon dioxide and picks up oxygen, then returns to the left atrium of the heart via one of the four *pulmonary veins.* From the left atrium, the oxygenated drop of blood enters the *left ventricle,* and is ready to again begin its journey to the big toe or to other parts of the body, such as the muscles, internal organs, brain, etc., including the *tissue cells* of the lungs.

At this point, it might be well to define the terms artery, vein, and capillary. An *artery* is a blood vessel that carries blood away from a heart chamber while a *vein* is a vessel that carries blood toward a heart chamber. A *capillary* is a microscopic vessel that connects the *arterial portion* of the circulatory "tree" with the *venous portion.* It is often said that arteries always carry *oxygenated* ("arterial") blood, while veins transport only *deoxygenated* ("venous") blood. This is not precisely true, because the pulmonary trunk and its arteries are *arteries* transporting *deoxygenated* blood; also, the four pulmonary *veins* carry *oxygenated* blood to the heart.

Cross-sections of arteries and veins reveal three layers in their walls (Fig. 10-6): an endothelial lining backed by elastic connective tissue, the *tunica intima;* an intermediate layer of smooth muscle and elastic tissue, the *tunica media* (the thickest layer); and an outer layer of loose white fibrous tissue, the *tunica externa* or *adventitia.* Veins are relatively thin-walled and more easily collapsed because the tunica media in them is poorly developed. Arteries range in cross-sectional diameter from 0.5 to 25 mm, while veins are somewhat larger. Capillaries are so small in diameter as to require the passage of red blood cells in single file. These smallest of all the vessels in the circulatory system have walls which usually consist of a *single layer of endothelial cells* (squamous epithelium) plus a cementing material (Fig. 10-6). Oxygen, carbon dioxide, water, and certain other substances diffuse easily through capillary walls.

THE ANATOMY OF THE HEART

The heart is positioned in the central portion of the thoracic cavity, just above the diaphragm (Fig. 10-7). It hangs within the

Figure 10-4 A diagrammatic drawing of the capillary network.

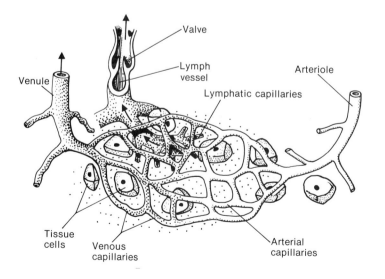

Valve

Lymph vessel

Arteriole

Lymphatic capillaries

Venule

Tissue cells

Venous capillaries

Arterial capillaries

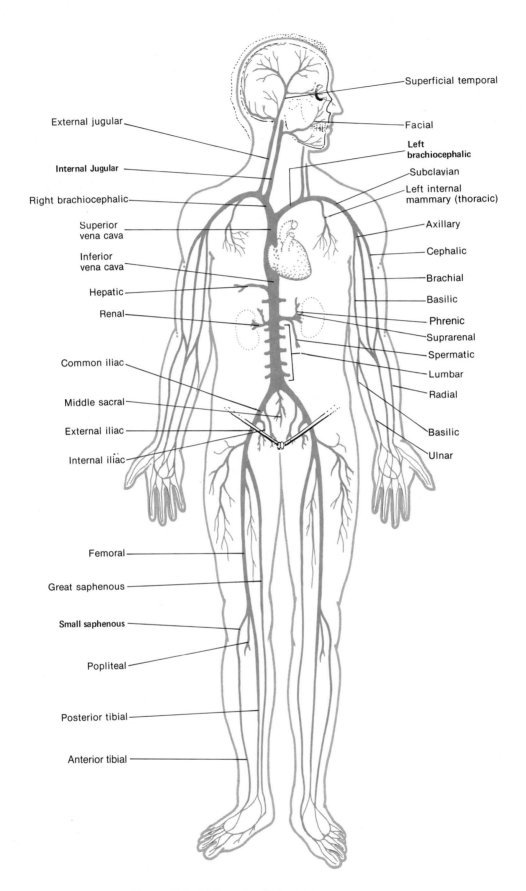

Superficial temporal

Facial

Left brachiocephalic

Subclavian

Left internal mammary (thoracic)

Axillary

Cephalic

Brachial

Basilic

Phrenic

Suprarenal

Spermatic

Lumbar

Radial

Basilic

Ulnar

External jugular

Internal Jugular

Right brachiocephalic

Superior vena cava

Inferior vena cava

Hepatic

Renal

Common iliac

Middle sacral

External iliac

Internal iliac

Femoral

Great saphenous

Small saphenous

Popliteal

Posterior tibial

Anterior tibial

Figure 10-5 Major veins of the body.

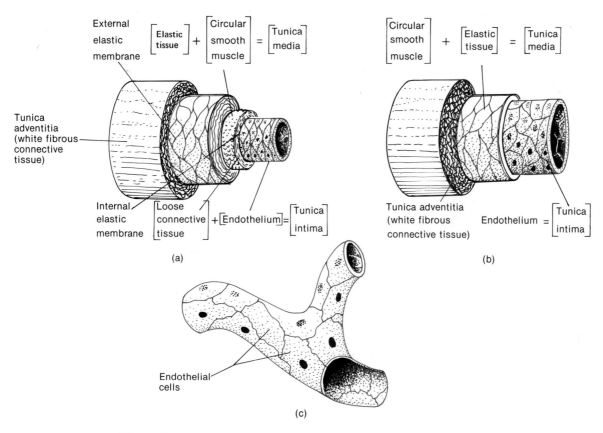

Figure 10-6 Structure of blood vessels. (a) Artery. (b) Vein. (c) Capillary.

Figure 10-7 Position of the heart and its valves.

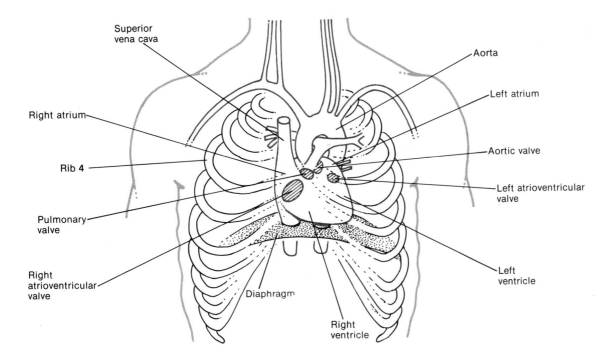

chest in such a way that *most of the anterior surface consists of the right ventricle, while the left atrium makes up most of the posterior surface.* During embryonic development (early development of an unborn infant) the heart invaginated its way into a serous sac much as though one would push a hand into an inflated balloon, until the inner layer of membrane tightly covered the organ and a portion of the great vessels that spring from it. A tough, fibrous coating formed on the outer layer of serous membrane, and a fluid-containing space remained between the two serous layers (Fig. 10-8). That layer of membrane that is intimately adherent to the heart is called the *visceral pericardium, or epicardium;* while the fibrous portion with its serous lining is the *parietal pericardium.* The fluid in the *pericardial space* (between the two serous layers) acts as a lubricant during the heart beat. The entire muscle mass of the heart is called the *myocardium;* it is much thicker in the walls of the ventricles than in those of the atria, and is lined with a layer of *endothelium,* here given the special name

endocardium. The walls of the ventricles are reinforced by interlaced ridgelike structures, *trabeculae carnae. Musculi pectinati,* or "pectinate muscles," serve the same purpose in the walls of the atria, but they are not so large and tough as the trabeculae of the ventricles. The four cavities or chambers of the heart are the *right and left atria and the right and left ventricles.* The earlike appendage on the outside of either atrium is called the *auricle.* Unfortunately for students, this term is often used interchangeably with the word *atrium.* Normally, the chambers are separated from each other by *interatrial, interventricular,* and *atrioventricular septa,* with the right atrium communicating with the right ventricle by means of the *right atrioventricular (tricuspid) valve,* and the left atrium communicating with the left ventricle by way of the *left atrioventricular (bicuspid) valve.* During embryonic and a part of fetal life, before birth, the left atrium communicates with the right atrium by means of an opening, the *foramen ovale.* Occasionally, this opening fails to close, leaving a *septal*

Figure 10-8 The pericardium. (a) Reflection of the parietal pericardium (visceral pericardium sticks tightly to the heart). (b) Detail drawing showing layers of the pericardium and the pericardial space.

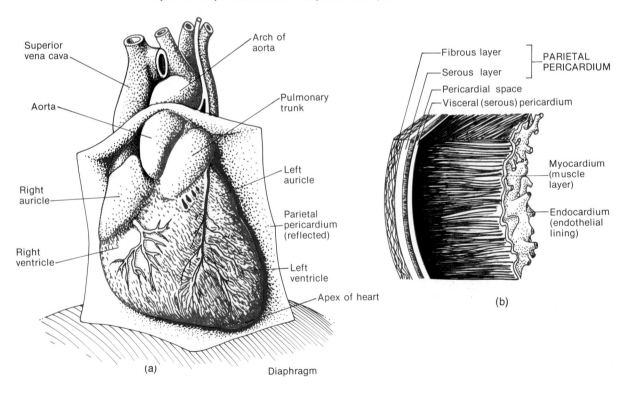

defect known as *patent foramen ovale.* It usually does close, however, and only a depression, the *fossa ovalis,* remains in the interatrial septum. An *interventricular foramen* also sometimes fails to close during development, producing an *interventricular septal defect.*

The heart valves

The heart has two kinds of valves, *flap valves* and *semilunar valves.* The atrioventricular valves are of the flap type, and are prevented from turning inside-out during contraction of the ventricles by stringlike *chordae tendinae,* themselves attached to elevations of the ventricular wall, *papillary muscles* (Fig. 10-2). During contraction of the ventricles, these valves are forced shut by moving blood, and the blood rushes out through the only two openings available, *the semilunar valves guarding the openings of the aorta and the pulmonary trunk. Whereas the flap valves prevent the upward flow of blood from the ventricles back into the atria, the semilunar valves keep blood from flowing downward, back into the ventricles.* The construction of the semilunar valves is interesting (Fig. 10-9). Each consists of three little pouches, reminiscent of a cartoonist's conception of kangaroo pouches, half-moon

shaped at the upper border. After blood has rushed through these valves following ventricular contraction, it tends to go back down into the ventricles due to gravity and backpressure of the blood in the aorta and pulmonary trunk. The cusps of the semilunar valves quickly become filled with blood and force the free borders together, preventing backflow. The two atria contract virtually simultaneously, sending blood into the two ventricles, which then contract almost in unison, sending the blood out the two great vessels, one leading to the lungs (*pulmonary trunk*), the other to the rest of the body (*aorta*). The very first of the body organs supplied with oxygenated blood is, appropriately, *the heart itself.*

The coronary circulation

Two *coronary arteries* branch off the wall of the ascending portion of the aorta, their openings inside two of the pouches of the *aortic semilunar valve.* These two arteries and their branches form a crown or *corona* around the heart, and many smaller branches and capillaries make the heart one of the most *vascular* (literally, "full of blood vessels") of the organs in the body (Fig. 10-10). The *left coronary artery* gives off an *anterior interventricular branch* that lies in the groove over the *interventricular septum* (*interventricular sulcus*) and a *circumflex branch* seated in the *atrioventricular groove or sulcus.* The *right coronary artery* bends around the heart in the atrioventricular groove and eventually connects with the *circumflex branch of the left coronary artery* on the posterior surface of the heart. Such a connection of larger blood vessels without an intervening capillary network is called an *anastomosis.* Like the left coronary artery, the right one gives off several branches which branch repeatedly into smaller and smaller vessels until they become capillaries that ramify throughout the heart muscle. The major branches of the right coronary artery include several *atrial branches* to the right atrium, a *posterior descending branch* running down the *posterior interventricular groove,* and a *marginal branch* that sends

Figure 10-9 The heart valves.

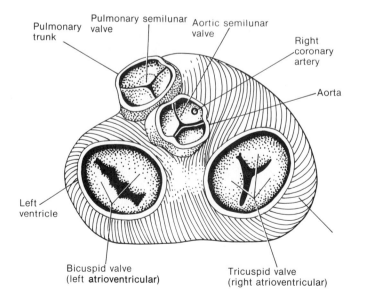

Pulmonary trunk

Pulmonary semilunar valve

Aortic semilunar valve

Right coronary artery

Aorta

Left ventricle

Bicuspid valve (left atrioventricular)

Tricuspid valve (right atrioventricular)

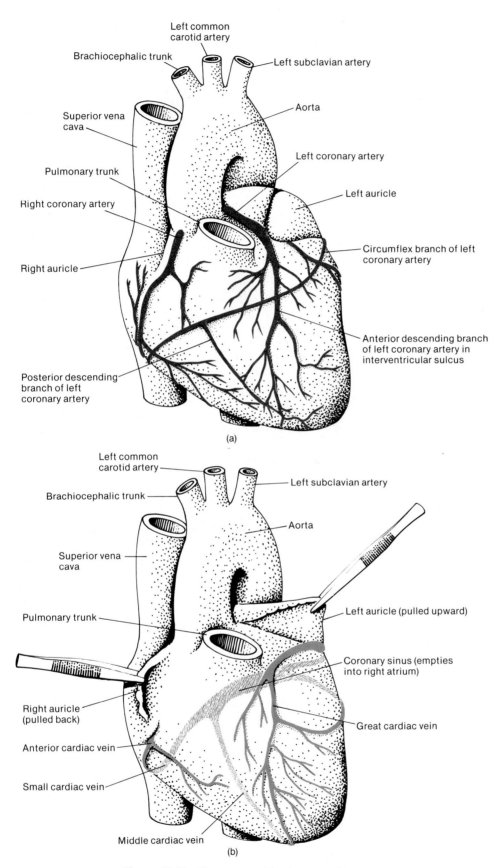

Figure 10-10 The coronary blood vessels. (a) Coronary arteries. (b) Coronary veins and coronary sinus.

smaller branches to the anterior and posterior surfaces of the right ventricle. After blood has circulated through the heart muscle, it is picked up by a network of *coronary veins* and carried mostly to the *great cardiac vein* and the largest venous structure draining the heart muscle, the *coronary sinus*. This latter vessel empties its blood directly into the right atrium, between the opening of the inferior vena cava and the valve opening from the right atrium into the right ventricle (*right atrioventricular valve*).

The great vessels of the heart and blood supply of the lungs

The aorta, pulmonary trunk, superior vena cava, and inferior vena cava are the *largest blood vessels in the body*. All of them can be said to either originate or terminate at the heart, depending upon the direction of blood flow. Under this criterion, *the aorta and pulmonary trunk begin at the heart, and the superior and inferior venae cavae terminate there*. It has already been pointed out that the aorta is concerned with *systemic circulation,* the pulmonary trunk with *pulmonary circulation*. The blood from the head, neck, and upper limbs returns to the right atrium of the heart by way of the *superior vena cava,* while that from the remainder of the body enters the same chamber via the *inferior vena cava*. Oxygenated blood returns to the heart through *four pulmonary veins,* and *enters the left atrium* as it does so. So far in this discussion, no mention has been made as to how the lung tissue gets its supply of oxygenated blood. Since the pulmonary arteries carry venous blood to the lungs to be oxygenated, and the pulmonary veins carry this oxygenated blood directly back from the lungs to the left atrium for distribution throughout the body, just where does the lung's tissue get its blood? There are *two and usually three bronchial arteries* that nourish the lungs, *two on the left side branching off the back of the aorta* and *one on the right coming off the first intercostal artery,* which runs between the upper pair of ribs and is also a branch of the aorta. These bronchial arteries and various smaller vessels supply the lung tissue and *bronchi* (branches of the "windpipe" or trachea).

THE MAJOR BLOOD VESSELS, FETAL CIRCULATION

The major arteries of the body

The *first arteries to branch off the aorta* are the *right and left coronary arteries*. After the aorta has given off these two branches, it courses upward for a few centimeters, as the *ascending aorta;* then it begins to curve to the left and posteriorly in a shepherd's crook, the *aortic arch,* or arch of the aorta (Figs. 10-3 and 10-11). The *first vessel to spring from this arch* is the large *brachiocephalic trunk,* which soon bifurcates into the *right subclavian* and *right common carotid artery*. The *second* branch of the aortic arch is the *left common carotid artery,* the *third* the *left subclavian*. After the aorta has completed its arch, it courses downward as the *descending aorta,* which is customarily divided into *thoracic* and *abdominal* portions. The *thoracic aorta* gives off ten pairs of *intercostal arteries* that course between the ribs in company with the *intercostal nerves and veins, two left bronchial arteries,* branches to the *esophagus* and back of the *pericardium,* and finally *two superior phrenic arteries* to the upper surface of the *diaphragm*. After passing through the diaphragm and becoming the *abdominal aorta,* the vessel gives off two *inferior phrenic branches* to the undersurface of the diaphragm, a *celiac trunk* that immediately divides into *gastric, hepatic,* and *splenic branches,* then a *superior mesenteric artery, two renal arteries, a pair of genital arteries* (*testicular* or *ovarian,* depending upon sex), and an *inferior mesenteric artery. Four pairs of lumbar arteries* arise from the posterior aspect of the abdominal aorta, and a small *median sacral artery* is given off as the aorta bifurcates into *right and left common iliac arteries* at the level of the *fourth lumbar vertebra*.

The arterial supply of the head and neck (Fig. 10-12) is made up of the *two common carotid arteries* and a pair of *vertebral arteries,* the latter being branches of the *subclavian vessels*. Below the angle of the jaw the *common carotid arteries* bifurcate into *internal and external branches*. The *internal carotid artery* and *vertebral artery* both enter the skull and supply the *brain* and *meninges*. The *external carotid arteries* sup-

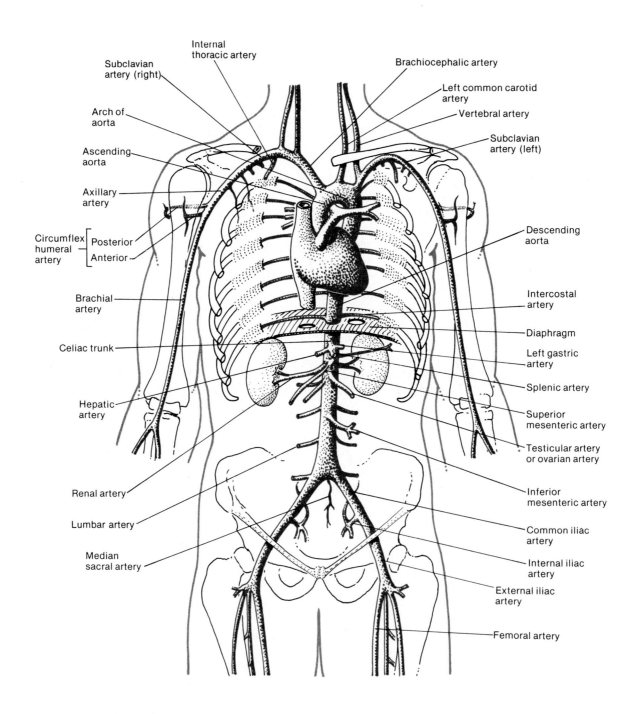

Figure 10-11 The aorta and its branches.

256

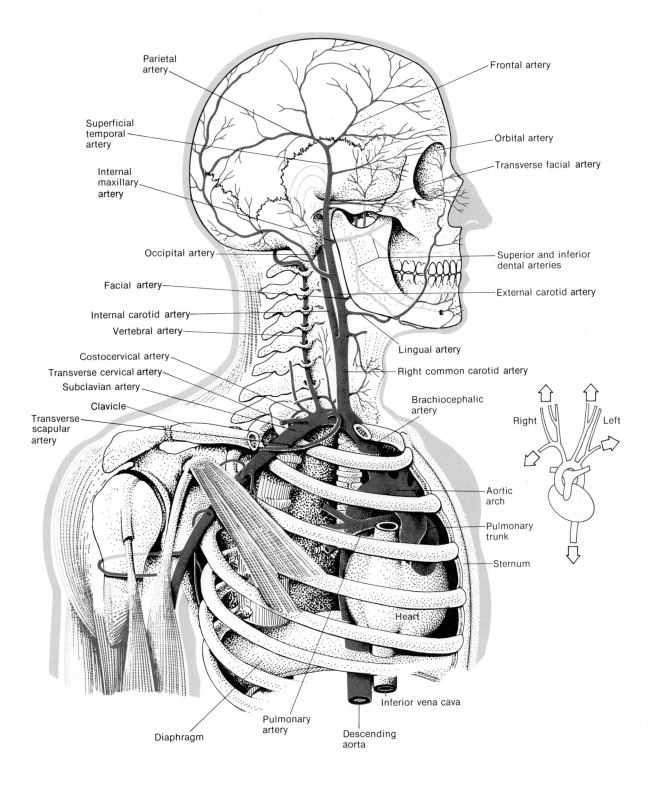

Parietal artery

Frontal artery

Superficial temporal artery

Orbital artery

Internal maxillary artery

Transverse facial artery

Occipital artery

Superior and inferior dental arteries

Facial artery

External carotid artery

Internal carotid artery

Vertebral artery

Lingual artery

Costocervical artery

Right common carotid artery

Transverse cervical artery

Subclavian artery

Brachiocephalic artery

Clavicle

Right

Left

Transverse scapular artery

Aortic arch

Pulmonary trunk

Sternum

Heart

Inferior vena cava

Diaphragm

Pulmonary artery

Descending aorta

Figure 10-12 Principal arteries to the head and neck.

ply the *skin and muscles of the head and face.* As it passes through the axilla, the *subclavian artery* becomes the *axillary artery;* and as it leaves this region it is named the *brachial artery* (Figs. 10-13 and 10-14), the vessel commonly occluded when taking blood-pressure measurements. At the elbow, the brachial artery bifurcates, giving origin to the *radial* and *ulnar* arteries. Both the radial and ulnar arteries enter into anastomoses and formation of *arches in the hand* which, by means of their branches, supply the *palm of the hand and the digits.* The radial artery is commonly used for feeling the pulse—the "throbbing" caused by the surge of blood resulting from each contraction of the heart—at the wrist. The pulse may also be felt over the *temporal artery* at the temple, *facial artery* over the mandible, *carotid artery* on the anterolateral aspect of the neck, *brachial artery* on the medial side of the upper arm, *femoral artery* in the lateral pubic

region, *popliteal artery* behind the knee, and the *dorsalis pedis artery* of the foot. A good rule to remember is that the pulse may be felt at virtually any point at which an artery lies near the body surface.

ARTERIES OF THE BRAIN   The major arteries of the brain and the areas supplied by each are shown in Fig. 10-15. The view of the undersurface of the brain shows that *the two vertebral arteries unite at the base of the brain, forming the basilar artery.* Two small *posterior communicating arteries* springing from the anterior end of the basilar artery join with the *internal carotid arteries,* and these in turn are joined anteriorly by *anterior cerebral arteries* connected by an *anterior communicating artery* to form what is known as the *arterial circle of Willis. Superior cerebellar* and *anterior cerebellar* arteries branch off the basilar artery, along with several *pontine branches* (which supply the pons).

Figure 10-13   Main arteries of the shoulder and upper arm.

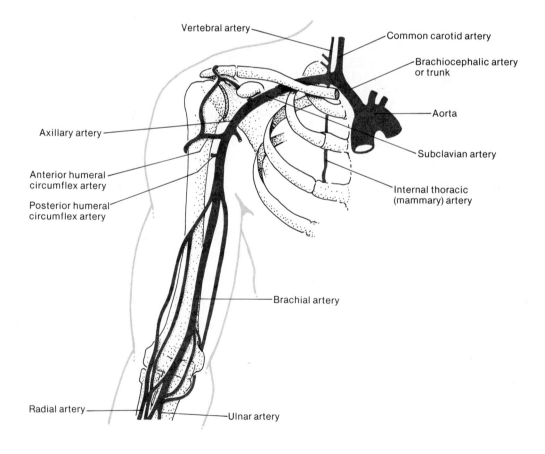

Posterior inferior cerebellar arteries branch one each from the lateral aspect of a vertebral artery just prior to the junction of the two

Figure 10-14 Main arteries of the forearm and hand.

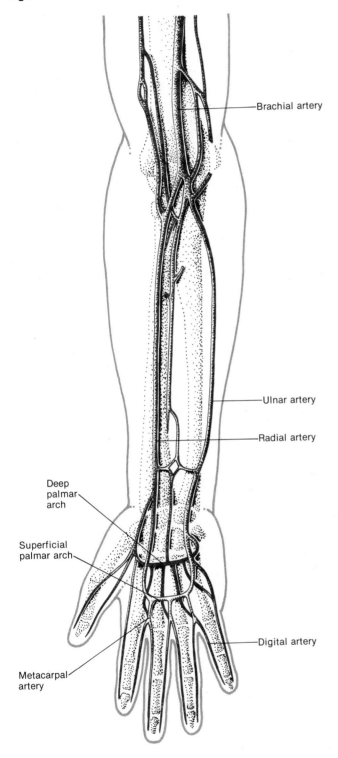

Brachial artery

Ulnar artery

Radial artery

Deep palmar arch

Superficial palmar arch

Digital artery

Metacarpal artery

vertebral arteries to form the basilar. Two smaller branches, these originating on the medial aspect of the vertebral arteries, join to form an artery that lies in the ventral median fissure of the spinal cord, the *anterior spinal artery.* The dorsal aspect of the spinal cord is supplied by two *posterior spinal arteries.* The cerebrum is supplied with arterial blood carried by the *anterior, middle,* and *posterior cerebral arteries.* The anterior vessel supplies the most anterior, upper, and medial portions of the *frontal lobe* and the uppermost and medial portions of the *parietal lobe* of the cerebrum. The middle cerebral artery supplies lateral portions of the *parietal and temporal lobes* and ramifies (spreads by branching) over the medial surface of the anterior portion of the *temporal lobe.* The branches of the posterior cerebral artery extend to the undersurface of the *temporal lobe* and all surfaces of the *occipital lobe.* The brain *meninges* are supplied by the *middle meningeal artery* and *meningeal branches of other arteries.* The middle meningeal is a branch of the *internal maxillary artery,* itself a branch of the *external carotid artery.*

The venous circulation

The blood returning to the heart does so by traveling through the *venous network* (Fig. 10-5). In much of the body, venous flow is sluggish, and depends a great deal upon *valves* within the veins, which prevent the blood from going the "wrong way" (Fig. 10-27). Venous patterns are not so regular as those of the arteries—a vein found in one individual may be absent in the next, or the pattern of branching may be different—so only the major (and more constant) veins will be considered here. Blood drains from the head and neck into the *internal jugular, external jugular,* and *vertebral veins* (Fig. 10-16). The internal jugular and *subclavian vein* (from the upper extremity) unite, forming the *brachiocephalic* (old name, *innominate*) vein. The union of the two brachiocephalic veins forms the *superior vena cava.* In most instances, the external jugular vein connects with the subclavian vein on each

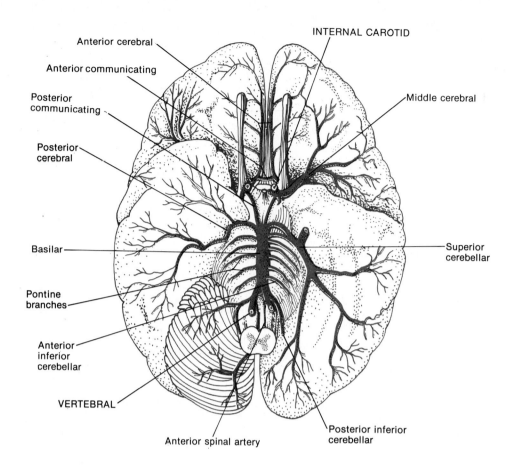

Anterior cerebral

Anterior communicating

Posterior communicating

Posterior cerebral

Basilar

Pontine branches

Anterior inferior cerebellar

VERTEBRAL

Anterior spinal artery

INTERNAL CAROTID

Middle cerebral

Superior cerebellar

Posterior inferior cerebellar

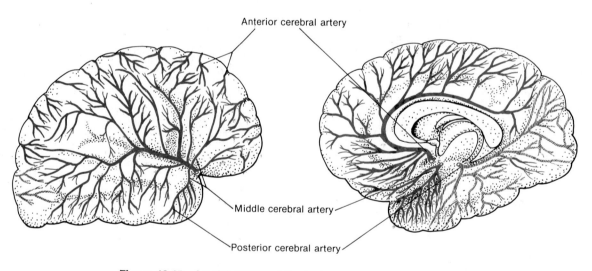

Anterior cerebral artery

Middle cerebral artery

Posterior cerebral artery

Figure 10-15 Arterial supply of the brain.

side, while the vertebral veins empty into the posterior aspect of the brachiocephalics. The major veins of the head are shown in Fig. 10-

16. The internal jugular and vertebral veins receive the blood from inside the head and some of the superficial areas, while the ex-

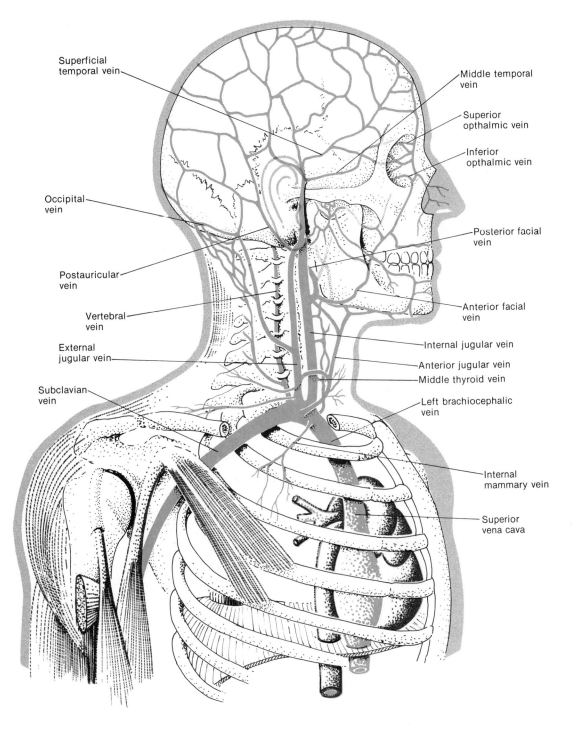

Figure 10-16 Major veins of the head and neck.

ternal jugular drains the superficial areas of the side and posterior aspect of the head. The *ophthalmic, angular, anterior facial, maxillary, retromandibular, external jugular,* and *vertebral veins drain the regions indicated in*

Fig. 10-16. The brain and meninges are drained by veins that empty their blood into large venous structures, the *blood sinuses of the head;* their names and positions are shown in Fig. 10-17. These sinuses drain into

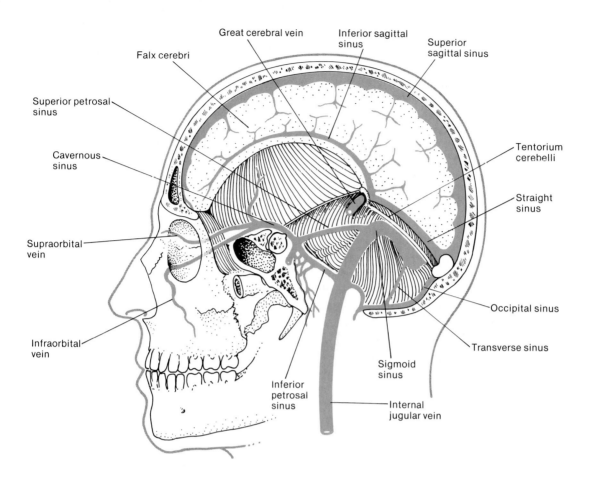

Superior petrosal sinus

Falx cerebri

Great cerebral vein

Inferior sagittal sinus

Superior sagittal sinus

Cavernous sinus

Tentorium cerebelli

Straight sinus

Supraorbital vein

Infraorbital vein

Occipital sinus

Transverse sinus

Inferior petrosal sinus

Sigmoid sinus

Internal jugular vein

Figure 10-17   Venous sinuses draining the brain and meninges.

the *internal jugular vein,* and are discussed in a later section of this chapter.

The major veins of the thorax include the venae cavae, azygous, hemiazygous, intercostals, and internal thoracic.

The most important *veins of the upper extremity* are shown in Fig. 10-18. The *venous network of the hand* drains chiefly into the *cephalic, median, and basilic veins.* The cephalic and basilic continue into the brachium or upper arm, and are often united at the elbow by a *median cubital* vein, commonly used as a site of intravenous ("within a vein") injections and the withdrawal of blood. The cephalic vein stays rather superficial throughout most of its course and eventually joins the subclavian vein near the point at which the subclavian becomes the *axillary* vein. The basilic vein, on the other hand, goes deep about halfway up the brachium and contributes to the formation of the axillary vein. The *main veins of the lower*

extremity are illustrated in Fig. 10-5. Those of the leg are the *anterior and posterior tibial* veins and the *peroneal* vein. The peroneal and posterior tibial commonly unite, forming the popliteal vein, which in turn becomes the femoral vein. The femoral and another large vein of the thigh, the *great saphenous vein,* join to form the *external iliac vein.* After it receives the internal iliac vein, the external iliac is known as the common iliac vein. Junction of the two common iliacs forms the *inferior vena cava,* the blood vessel that has the largest diameter of any in the body. Into this great structure drain the *hepatic, renal,* and *genital veins.* One might ask: what happens to the venous blood of the stomach, intestines, pancreas, and spleen? These structures all have veins that join a large vein that leads into the liver, the *portal vein;* and the blood, therefore, passes through the liver for "processing" before entering the inferior vena cava via the *hepatic veins.* This arrange-

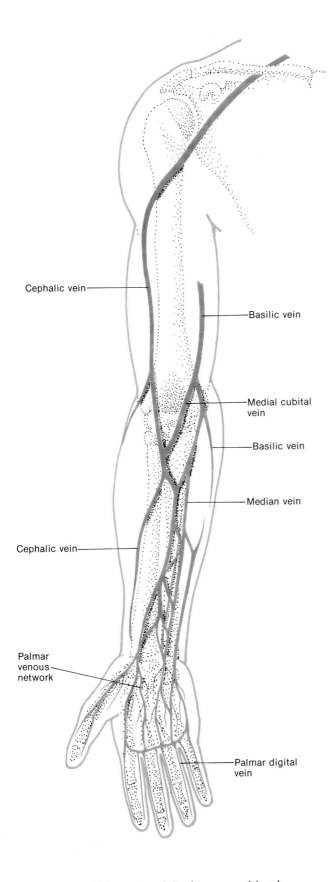

Figure 10-18 Major veins of the forearm and hand.

Cephalic vein

Basilic vein

Medial cubital vein

Basilic vein

Median vein

Cephalic vein

Palmar venous network

Palmar digital vein

ment of veins to the adbominal visceral organs is often called the **hepatic portal system** (Fig. 10-19).

PORTAL CIRCULATION   The circulation in the liver is unusual because both *arterial* and *venous* blood enter the liver. Arterial blood enters in the *hepatic artery,* and venous blood by way of the *portal vein,* which brings this blood from the abdominal viscera. Within the liver, arterial blood mixes with venous blood. All blood eventually leaves the liver via the right and left *hepatic veins,* which drain into the inferior vena cava. Usually, but not always, the portal vein is formed by the union of the *superior mesenteric* and *splenic* veins. The *inferior mesenteric, gastric,* and *pancreatic* veins empty their blood into the splenic vein before it joins the superior mesenteric vein. Blockage of hepatic circulation by *cirrhosis* (during which growth of fibrous tissue in the liver constricts blood vessels), or by clots in the vessels of the portal system can cause increased pressures in the portal system and loss of fluid from the liver into the abdominal cavity (*ascites* or "dropsy").

VENOUS DRAINAGE OF THE BRAIN   After circulation through the brain, blood empties from veins into large *venous sinuses,* previously mentioned (Fig. 10-17). They are the *cavernous sinus,* deep beneath the base of the brain; the *superior sagittal sinus,* lying within the dura mater over the superior and posterior surfaces of the cerebrum; the *straight sinus,* extending anteriorly from the lowermost end of the superior sagittal sinus; the *inferior sagittal sinus,* draining into the straight sinus; the paired *transverse sinuses,* continuations of the superior sagittal sinus; the paired *sigmoid sinuses,* continuations of the transverse; and the *superior and inferior petrosal sinuses,* both paired, and both draining into the sigmoid sinuses. The large sigmoid vessels are continuous with the upper ends of the *internal jugular veins.*

Circulation in the fetus

During the nine-month prenatal period, the developing baby neither breathes nor eats; yet his body cells must be supplied with

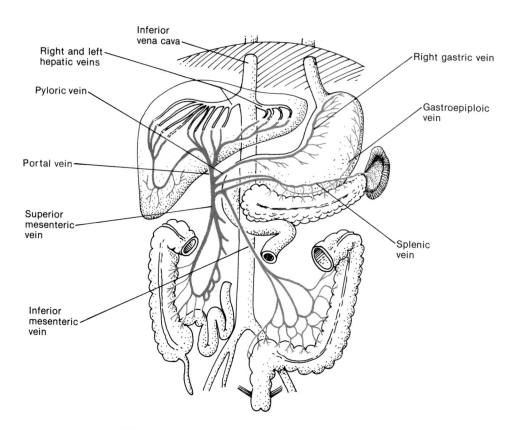

Figure 10-19 The hepatic portal system.

food and oxygen if he is to be born alive. Because a special circulatory "system" exists before birth, the fetus is able to obtain nutrients and oxygen from maternal blood. He is also able to eliminate wastes such as carbon dioxide by utilizing this special *fetal circulation.*

There is no direct connection between the blood vessels of the mother and those of the developing fetus; but a special organ that is present in the mother's uterus ("womb") only during pregnancy serves as an *indirect* connection between these vessels. This organ is the *placenta* (Fig. 10-20). Oxygen and nutrients diffuse from capillaries of the uterus into capillaries of the placenta, and are carried to the fetus via an *umbilical vein.* This vein gives off a few branches to the liver and then joins the inferior vena cava. Between the liver and the inferior vena cava, the vein is known as the *ductus venosus.* The inferior vena cava leads to the beating fetal heart, which pumps blood throughout the tiny body.

Once blood has circulated throughout the fetus, it has lost its oxygen and nutrients and has picked up carbon dioxide. The deoxygenated blood leaves the fetal body via two *umbilical arteries,* which are branches of the internal iliac arteries. The umbilical arteries plus the umbilical vein make up the *umbilical cord,* which enters the fetus at the *umbilicus,* or naval.

It should be made clear that *the body of the fetus makes its own blood, and that this blood moves to the placenta in the umbilical arteries, loses its carbon dioxide and picks up oxygen and nutrients, and returns to the fetus via the umbilical vein.*

In addition to the placenta, umbilical arteries, and umbilical vein, three other structures are important to fetal circulation: the *foramen ovale, ductus arteriosus,* and the previously mentioned *ductus venosus.* Only a small amount of the blood traveling in the umbilical vein is detoured to the liver, and most of it continues on to the inferior vena cava via the ductus venosus. The foramen

264

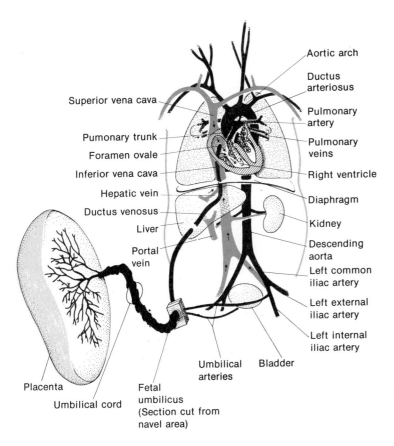

Labels on figure:
Superior vena cava
Pumonary trunk
Foramen ovale
Inferior vena cava
Hepatic vein
Ductus venosus
Liver
Portal vein
Placenta
Umbilical cord
Fetal umbilicus (Section cut from navel area)
Umbilical arteries
Bladder
Aortic arch
Ductus arteriosus
Pulmonary artery
Pulmonary veins
Right ventricle
Diaphragm
Kidney
Descending aorta
Left common iliac artery
Left external iliac artery
Left internal iliac artery

Figure 10-20 The fetal circulation.

ovale is an opening in the interatrial septum of the fetal heart. A valve within the inferior vena cava shunts most of the incoming blood through the foramen ovale into the left atrium, thereby bypassing the (nonbreathing) fetal lungs. The ductus arteriosus is a temporary blood vessel that connects the pulmonary trunk with the aorta, soon after the latter vessel has left the heart. By means of the ductus arteriosus, some of the blood that is not shunted away from the lungs by the valve of the inferior vena cava and the foramen ovale is detoured into the aorta (and therefore, away from the lungs).

It will readily be seen by careful examination of Fig. 10-20 that virtually all fetal blood is a mixture of oxygenated and deoxygenated blood. Once birth has occurred

and the newly born infant requires a more direct supply of oxygen to the body cells, certain changes take place which separate the blood into oxygenated ("arterial") and de-

oxygenated ("venous") types. These changes are as follows:

1. The umbilical cord is tied and cut; so the umbilical vein and the two umbilical arteries no longer function. During the first week, the remaining portion of the umbilical vein becomes the *ligamentum teres* (round ligament) of the liver, helping to hold that organ in place. The umbilical arteries become fibrous tissue.

2. The ductus venosus becomes the *ligamentum venosum,* another ligament of the liver.

3. The foramen ovale disappears, usually within nine months. Only a depression, the *fossa ovalis,* remains.

4. The ductus arteriosus soon withers and becomes a nonfunctional bit of fibrous tissue, the *ligamentum arteriosum.* If the foramen ovale fails to close (*patent foramen ovale*) or the ductus arteriosus remains open (*patent ductus arteriosus*), as happens on occasion, oxygenated blood mixes with deoxygenated blood, and a "blue baby"—one with a bluish tinge of the nails, lips, and mucous membranes—results. Both conditions are now routinely corrected surgically.

THE PHYSIOLOGY OF THE HEART

Origin of the heartbeat and the cardiac cycle

The *heart rate,* or number of times the heart beats per minute, is regulated by its autonomic nerve supply. *Sympathetic fibers* to the heart, located in the *superior, middle, and inferior cardiac nerves,* act as *cardioaccelerator nerves,* and impulses traveling over them insure that the heart beats fast enough to maintain good circulation during any activity. *Parasympathetic fibers,* traveling in the *vagus nerves,* tend to *slow* the heart, and serve as *cardioinhibitor nerves.* Because of this nerve supply, the heart does not beat too fast or too slowly—whether the individual is resting or taking part in vigorous physical activity. Various factors (such as exercise, drugs, smoking, alcohol, and food) that affect the heart rate are discussed in a later section of this chapter. For the present, let us consider the *origin of the heartbeat,* and the manner in which the impulse that follows it *spreads over the entire heart.* The impulse that causes the heart to contract does not arrive over the cardioaccelerator and cardio-inhibitor nerves; these merely act to control its rate. *The heartbeat originates within the heart muscle itself,* and is therefore said to be *myogenic.* In the wall of the right atrium, near the superior vena cava, is a small bit of modified cardiac-muscle tissue, the *sino-atrial (SA) node* (Fig. 10-21). Here is where the impulse that brings about the contraction of the heart, or *systole,* begins. Once started, this impulse spreads as a *wave of excitation* over fibers radiating outward from the SA node, causing both atria to contract simultaneously. As some of these impulses reach a second patch of modified cardiac-muscle fibers—the *atrioventricular*

or *AV node*—located in the wall of the right atrium near the upper end of the interventricular septum, the wave of electrical excitation spreads downward over the two branches of the ventricular conducting system, the *bundle of His.* Both the *right-bundle branch* and the *left-bundle branch* divide repeatedly, giving rise to tiny fibers that ramify throughout the ventricular walls, *Purkinje fibers.* It is over these Purkinje fibers—which comprise a *Purkinje system*—that the impulses travel in order to bring about ventricular contraction, shortly after atrial systole. Since contraction begins at the sinoatrial node, that atypical bit of heart muscle is called the *pacemaker* of the heart. Even small, isolated pieces of the heart will beat if kept in a nutrient solution and supplied with sufficient oxygen.

A condition known as *heart block* results if the excitatory wave is interrupted at any point along the conducting system of the heart (for example, during such infections as rheumatic fever). Two common

Figure 10-21 Conducting system of the heart.

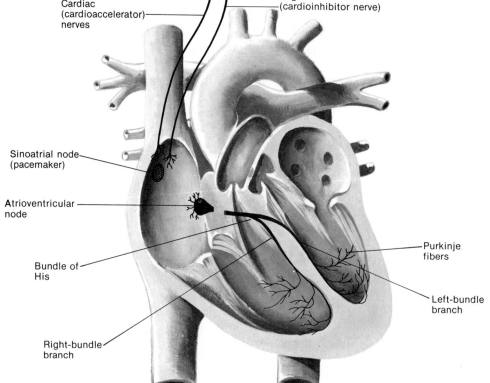

types of heart block are *AV block,* occurring at the atrioventricular node, and *bundle-branch block,* involving one of the branches of the bundle of His. Heart block may be *complete* or *incomplete.* For example, if only a portion of the bundle of His is diseased, the block is incomplete, and each ventricular beat may occur significantly later than usual. This is called *first-degree heart block.* In *second-degree heart block,* the ventricles contract at a much slower rate than the atria —but in a *definite ratio,* such as 2:1, 3:1, or even 4:1. *Third-degree heart block* is complete heart block. In this instance, the beats of the atria and the ventricles are completely independent of each other, but the ventricles still contract much more slowly than the atria, and apparently receive no impulses from the atria, but have enough automaticity to beat slowly on their own. This illustrates the importance of the SA node as a pacemaker. Heart block may sometimes be brought on by overdose of such a drug as *digitalis,* which is sometimes used in giving support to a failing heart.

ELECTRICAL ACTIVITY OF THE HEART; THE ELECTROCARDIOGRAM It has long been known that the heartbeat is associated with changes in electrical potential, which can be demonstrated by using an instrument sensitive to such changes, the *galvanometer.* Today, a modern version of this apparatus, the *electrocardiograph,* is used to demonstrate this electrical activity and to assist in the diagnosis of heart disease, especially heart ailments involving malfunction of the myocardium or the conducting system; the record obtained is called an *electrocardiogram* (ECG or EKG).

Electrical activity originating in the heart passes over the entire body (due to the conducting ability of the electrolytes in protoplasm), and a satisfactory tracing of this activity can be made by attaching the electrocardiograph to the patient by means of *electrodes* (metal plates) fastened to the wrists and ankles (using rubber straps) or to the chest wall (using a suction cup). The placing of *two* electrodes on a patient constitutes a *lead* (Fig. 10-22). Three *standard leads* have been established, as well as several leads employing chest electrodes. The three standard leads are designated *Lead I, Lead II,* and *Lead III.* In the case of Lead I, electrodes are fastened to the *right wrist and left wrist;* in Lead II, they are attached to the *right wrist and left ankle;* and in Lead III,

Figure 10-22   Placement of electrodes for the three standard leads of the electrocardiogram.

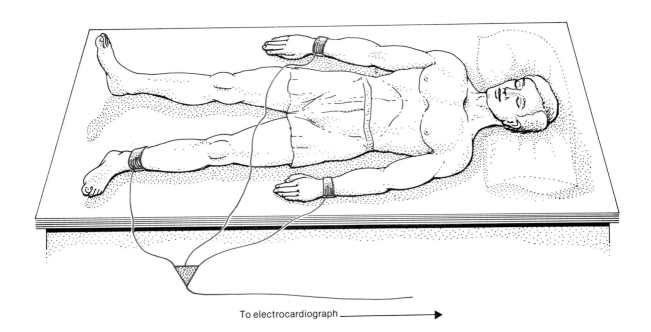

To electrocardiograph ⟶

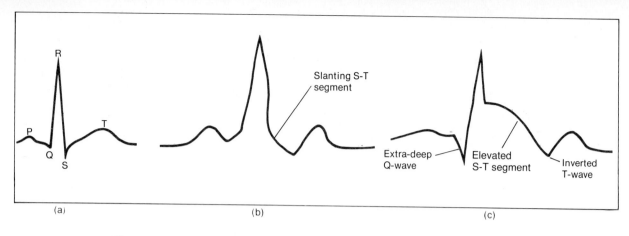

Figure 10-23 Three electrocardiograms. (a) Normal tracing, Lead I. (b) Bundle branch block. (c) Myocardial infarction.

to the *left wrist and left ankle.* Each of the standard leads produces a tracing that has its own characteristics, and the use of chest leads results in the production of still different tracings.

A "typical" electrocardiogram can perhaps be best exemplified by examining a tracing made from Lead I (Fig. 10-23). It will be seen that *five waves constitute a tracing:* a *P-wave, Q-wave, R-wave, S-wave, and T-wave.* The P-wave results when the electrical wave of the heartbeat passes over the atria—that is, *when the atria are depolarized,* much as a neuron or skeletal-muscle cell is depolarized when their impulses travel over them. Abnormal or missing P-waves indicate disease of the SA node, where the contraction impulse normally begins. The Q-wave is not extremely important as such, but is part of the *QRS-complex,* consisting of the Q-, R-, and S-waves collectively. The complex represents *depolarization of the ventricles* and the time required for the impulse to move down the branches of the bundle of His. If the QRS-complex requires too much time, bundle-branch block may be suspected.

That period of time between the beginning of the P-wave and the start of the Q-wave is called the *P–R interval.* (It is not called the P–Q interval because not infrequently, the Q-wave is missing from the ECG tracing.) The P–R interval indicates the *time necessary for the wave of contraction to arrive at the ventricles.* A prolonged P–R interval points to a possible conduction problem in the AV node.

The *time interval between the end of ven-*

tricular depolarization and the beginning of repolarization is called the *S–T time segment.* Damage to the myocardium following a *coronary thrombosis*—clot in a coronary artery—(for example) results in an S–T segment that tends to be either longer or shorter than normal.

Completion of repolarization of the heart immediately after contraction is best indicated by the T-wave. An inverted T-wave indicates possible damage to the myocardium. It should be made clear that a person may have a normal electrocardiogram and still have heart disease. The ECG is useful in pointing out abnormalities in the conducting system and in the electrical activity of the heart, as well as certain abnormal conditions of the myocardium; but otherwise, its usefulness is limited. Some examples of abnormal electrocardiograms are shown in Fig. 10-23.

SOME ABNORMAL RHYTHMS OF THE HEART An unusual heart rate, such as that seen in heart block, is known as an *arrhythmia.* Some arrhythmias include *tachycardia,* in which the heart beats too rapidly; *bradycardia,* or slow heart; and *fibrillation,* characterized by small areas of the heart beating weakly and independently of each other. There is little or no pumping of blood during fibrillation, and death is usually soon forthcoming. Another arrhythmia which indicates serious cardiac damage is *"gallop rhythm,"* in which the heart beats in a manner similar to that of the hooves of a running horse.

The heart, being composed of a fused mass of contractile cells, *obeys the all-or-*

none principle as an entity; that is, under any given set of conditions, the heart, when stimulated by a threshold stimulus, will contract maximally or not at all. Conditions (such as blood pressure and the blood levels of ions, oxygen, carbon dioxide, and hormones) vary, and a contraction of the heart at any given time is a maximal one only for the conditions of the moment. The heart *cannot be tetanized.* Its muscle has an *extra-long refractory period* (about 0.3 sec, which is some 65 times as long as that of skeletal muscle), and stimuli applied during systole will not produce an additional response. An *extrasystole* can be demonstrated, however, by stimulating a heart during the last portion of diastole (relaxation and rest). Such pre-

mature beats are common in certain diseases, and are always followed by a long *compensatory pause.*

REFLEXES AFFECTING THE HEART RATE
There are several ways in which reflex activity can speed or slow the heart. Specialized nerve endings called *pressoreceptors* or *baroreceptors,* located in the arch of the aorta, inside a swelling of the internal carotid artery—the *carotid sinus*—and in the walls of the venae cavae and right atrium are sensitive to changes in blood pressure and initiate impulses that indirectly affect the heart rate (Fig. 10-24). For example, a rise in venous blood pressure following strenuous exercise causes pressoreceptors in the venae

Figure 10-24 Nervous connections responsible for nervous control of the heart. Connections between the central nervous system and the sympathetic trunk are not shown (see Chapter 7).

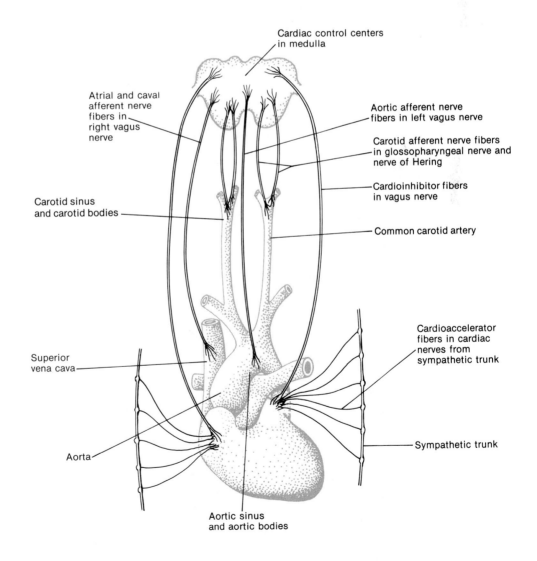

Cardiac control centers in medulla

Atrial and caval afferent nerve fibers in right vagus nerve

Aortic afferent nerve fibers in left vagus nerve

Carotid afferent nerve fibers in glossopharyngeal nerve and nerve of Hering

Cardioinhibitor fibers in vagus nerve

Carotid sinus and carotid bodies

Common carotid artery

Cardioaccelerator fibers in cardiac nerves from sympathetic trunk

Superior vena cava

Sympathetic trunk

Aorta

Aortic sinus and aortic bodies

cavae and right atrium to be stimulated, and the resulting impulses travel to the medulla over afferent fibers in the vagus nerve. Here, they either *stimulate the cardioaccelerator center or inhibit the cardioinhibitor center,* or both. Impulses then travel from the cardiac control centers thus activated over sympathetic fibers in cardioaccelerator nerves. The heart promptly beats faster, more blood is sent to the lungs to pick up oxygen, and more oxygenated blood is delivered to the muscles and other body tissues. This automatic increase in heart rate following physical activity is known as the *Bainbridge reflex.*

Eventually, an increase in blood pressure will bring about a reflex slowing of the heart. As the arterial blood pressure increases during exercise, pressoreceptors in the carotid sinus and aortic sinus are stimulated and in turn stimulate cells in the cardioinhibitor center, meanwhile inhibiting those in the cardioaccelerator center. Impulses travel from the carotid sinus over afferent fibers in the carotid sinus nerve (nerve of Hering) and glossopharyngeal nerve, while those from the aortic sinus travel over afferent fibers of the vagus. Impulses are then sent from the cardioinhibitor center via efferent fibers of the vagus to the heart, which then slows. The principle governing such action, which states that *the heart rate is inversely proportional to the arterial blood pressure,* is known as *Marey's law of the heart.*

In close association with the carotid and aortic sinuses are the carotid and aortic *bodies* (Fig. 10-24). These are *chemoreceptors* and are sensitive to changes in the *oxygen level and pH of the blood,* but apparently not to the carbon dioxide content of the blood unless this gas is present in sufficient quantity to cause a change in pH. If the oxygen level of the blood falls to a certain point, or the pH falls too low, the carotid and aortic body receptors send impulses over the nerve of Hering to the cardiac centers of the medulla. The cardioaccelerator center is stimulated and the cardioinhibitor center is inhibited. The result is an increase in the number of sympathetic impulses that arrive at the heart each second, which produces an increase in heart rate. Apparently, low levels of oxygen in the blood (*hypoxia*) can stimulate cells of the cardioaccelerator

center directly as the blood flows through the medulla; this is yet another mechanism by which the heart can be speeded up.

The heart can be reflexly slowed by stimulating sensory nerves in various parts of the body, such as when one steps into a cold shower, undergoes surgery (during which the visceral organs are handled), or applies pressure to the eyeballs. Many sensory nerves are indirectly connected with the autonomic nervous system (via the brain), or with the cardioinhibitor and cardioaccelerator centers.

THE CARDIAC CYCLE The *sequence of events that occurs during one heartbeat, or contraction and subsequent relaxation, is called the cardiac cycle.* At an average 72 beats per minute, each cycle must be completed in 0.8 sec. A convenient way to illustrate the cycle and its components is by means of a circular diagram, divided into eight equal wedges, like a pie (Fig. 10-25). Each piece of the "pie" represents a time interval of only 0.1 sec. It will be seen that the time required for each event of the cycle

Figure 10-25 The cardiac cycle. The heart rate can be assumed to be 72 beats per minute. Each "piece of pie" in the diagram then represents 0.1 sec, and the entire cycle lasts 0.8 sec. The outer circle indicates atrial events; the inner circle, ventricular.

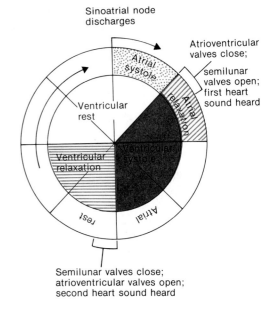

to occur can be determined simply by counting the pieces of pie it covers and multiplying by 0.1; thus *ventricular systole* requires 0.3 sec, *ventricular diastole* 0.5 sec, *atrial systole* 0.1 sec, *atrial diastole* 0.7 sec, and so on. It will be noted also that relationships between atrial events and ventricular events are easily determined by use of the chart; for example, atrial systole and 0.4 sec of atrial diastole occur during ventricular diastole. Another example: 0.3 sec of the atrial-diastolic period occur during ventricular systole. Diastole can be further broken down into *periods of relaxation and rest.* During the first 0.1 sec of atrial diastole, the atria are relaxing, while during the remaining 0.6 sec, they are resting. Two-tenths of a second are spent on ventricular relaxation, 0.3 sec on rest. During most of ventricular rest, the heart is in a relatively quiescent state known as *diastasis.*

Action of the heart valves;
heart sounds

It will be seen by examining Fig. 10-25 that the *aortic and pulmonary semilunar valves open* at the *onset of atrial diastole,* and that the *bicuspid and tricuspid valves close* at the same time. At the *end of ventricular systole,* the *atrioventricular valves open* and the *semilunar valves close.* During both these periods, the *snapping shut of valves* and *vibrations set up within the walls of the heart* produce two sounds which are heard distinctly with a stethoscope: the so-called *first heart sound,* commonly written as *"lub,"* which is heard near the beginning of ventricular systole; and the *second heart sound, "dup,"* heard at the end of ventricular systole. Repeated over and over in sequence, they produce a chain of *lub-dup* combinations as long as normal heartbeat continues. A rather dull, low-pitched, *third heart sound* can sometimes be heard immediately after the second heart sound. It may be caused by vibration of the walls of the ventricles following the inrush of blood from the atria. The first heart sound is thought to be due mainly to *closure of the AV valves and contraction of the ventricles,* while the second heart sound is due chiefly to *closure of the aortic and pulmonary semilunar valves.* If

one or more of the heart valves become diseased, abnormal sounds called *heart murmurs* may be heard. Many people have nonpathological heart murmurs, however; that is, they have abnormal heart sounds which apparently are not caused by heart disease. Pathological or disease-caused murmurs may be due to *stenosis* or narrowing of the opening between valve parts due to valvular disease and scarring, or to regurgitation of blood as it flows backward through a valve that does not close completely. During diagnosis of abnormal heart sounds, the cardiac cycle must be kept in mind. As examples, an *aortic stenosis* would result in a murmur during *systole,* while a murmur caused by a *mitral stenosis* would be heard during *diastole.*

CARDIAC DYNAMICS AND
BLOOD PRESSURE

The efficiency with which the blood circulates throughout the body, other factors being constant, depends upon *the amount of blood pumped by the left ventricle during each beat or stroke of the heart, and the number of beats that occur per minute or other unit of time.* Normally, the left ventricle ejects about 70 cc (or ml) of blood per stroke or contraction. This is the *stroke volume.* (The right ventricle pumps the same amount of blood, but it is concerned with pulmonary rather than systemic circulation.) Multiplying the stroke volume by 70 gives the appropriate volume of blood pumped by the ventricle in 1 minute (min), at rest. This value is the *cardiac minute volume,* perhaps better known as the *cardiac output* or *C.O.;* it can be expressed as:

$$\begin{pmatrix} \text{Cardiac} \\ \text{output} \\ \text{(C.O.)} \end{pmatrix} = \begin{pmatrix} \text{Heart} \\ \text{rate} \end{pmatrix} \times \begin{pmatrix} \text{Stroke} \\ \text{volume} \end{pmatrix}$$

At rest, the average cardiac output would be

$$70 \times 70 = 4900 \text{ cc } (or \text{ ml})$$

This means that some 5 liters of blood (which may represent the entire blood volume of the individual) are pumped each minute by the heart when the level of physical activity is no more strenuous than sitting in a chair. Several factors affect the stroke volume and rate (and hence the C.O.) of the heart. It will be recalled that the *amount of stretch placed upon muscle fibers* determines (up to a point) just how vigorously those muscle fibers will contract (*Starling's law*); therefore, it might be assumed that the more fully the ventricles fill with blood during their diastolic period, the more stretch will be placed on the myocardium, and the more vigorously will its muscle fibers contract. Ventricular filling does indeed influence the stroke volume; but the *chief* forces that act to regulate heart action are supplied by the nervous and endocrine systems. Impulses from the sympathetic division of the autonomic nervous system, reaching the heart via the cardiac nerves, act to speed the heart and make it contract more vigorously. Epinephrine (adrenalin), a hormone secreted by the adrenal glands and poured into the bloodstream during periods of high excitement, accomplishes the same result. The parasympathetic division of the ANS, acting through fibers in the vagus nerves, sends impulses that slow the heart and decrease its force of contraction.

Arterial and venous blood pressures and factors affecting them

If an artery is cut, blood will come from the wound in *powerful spurts.* In contrast, the flow of blood from a vein is rather even and sluggish. In both instances, the blood is obviously *under pressure,* with the arterial pressure by far the greater of the two. Arterial blood pressure must be maintained at a relatively high level so that blood can reach all the body tissues. This pressure, created by the pumping action of the heart, falls precipitously by the time the blood reaches the veins. Perhaps it would be well to consider at this time the major factors contributing to the maintenance of a blood pressure sufficiently high (and also low enough) for good health.

Arterial blood pressure is *the force exerted by the blood against the walls of the arteries, and is a direct function of those factors that affect the flow of blood in the arteries.* The *more freely blood can move, the lower* will be the pressure; and *the more resistance to flow* encountered by the blood, the *higher* the pressure. A simple experiment will serve to illustrate this principle: if a hypodermic syringe is filled with water and a large rubber tube is attached, comparatively little effort is required to force the water through the tube, at a rate of, say, 10 cc every 20 sec, and the water will exit from the tube as a comparatively slow, low-pressure stream; but if the tube is removed and replaced by a small-diameter hypodermic needle, much greater pressure will be required to force the water from the syringe at the same speed as before, and the water will come out of the needle as a narrow, high-speed, higher-pressure stream. One factor affecting the flow of blood, then, is the *diameter of the blood vessels.* When other things—such as cardiac output—are constant, it is apparent that *the smaller the diameter of the vessel, the higher the pressure.*

The most commonly encountered resistance of this type in the body is not caused by flow through capillaries, as one might surmise, but through *arterioles,* those vessels which might be said to be too small to be called arteries, and too large to be capillaries. The walls of arterioles are well supplied with smooth muscle, which in turn is innervated by the autonomic nervous system. In order to help maintain normal blood pressure—and hence the homeostatic state of the body—arterioles are dilated and constricted by the ANS as required. The more *constricted* the arterioles, the *greater* the resistance to flow and the *higher* the pressure, and conversely. The impedance to flow offered by the arterioles makes up a portion of what the physiologist calls *peripheral resistance,* or resistance to flow encountered distal to the heart and arteries. Other major factors contributing to peripheral resistance include the extremely *small diameter and large number of the capillaries* (about $8.0\ \mu$), *constriction and dilation of the arteries themselves, and friction encountered by the blood as it moves against the walls of the blood vessels.* Other factors affecting the arterial blood pressure include *cardiac output, velocity or speed of the flow, elasticity and distensibility of the arteries, total blood volume,* and the *viscosity of the blood.* The effect exerted by each of these factors on blood pressure can be summarized as follows:

1. *The Effect of Cardiac Output.* The greater the cardiac output, the higher the pressure, other factors being constant.

2. *Effect of Blood Velocity.* Blood pressure varies directly with the velocity—speed —at which the blood moves, other things being equal.

3. *Elasticity of Arteries.* The elastic layers in the walls of arteries cause these vessels to tend to squeeze or constrict, thereby increasing the pressure.

4. *Distensibility of Arteries.* Helping to balance the squeezing effect of the arteries is the fact that healthy arteries can distend or expand—they are stretched by increasing blood pressure—and help to buffer or keep the arterial pressure lower, especially during systole of the ventricles (systolic pressure).

5. *Total Blood Volume.* The more blood an individual has in his circulatory system, the higher his blood pressure, and conversely. In one blood disorder, *polycythemia,* too many red blood cells are produced by the bone marrow. The result is that the total blood volume increases, with an attendant rise in blood pressure. The patient must be bled periodically. Usually, the blood viscosity greatly increases in polycythemia, and this also contributes to a rise in pressure.

6. *Blood Viscosity.* The more viscous or "thick" the blood becomes, the more it resists flow; hence the rise in pressure described in the foregoing paragraph.

Regulation of arteriole diameter

The diameter of the arterioles is one of the two most important determinants of peripheral resistance, the other being blood viscosity. Arteriole diameter is regulated by a *vasomotor control mechanism,* which involves pressoreflexes, chemoreflexes, a medullary reflex, and control by higher brain centers.

VASOMOTOR PRESSOREFLEXES Vasomotor centers in the medulla, consisting of vasodilator and vasoconstrictor centers, regularly send impulses to the smooth muscle in the walls of arterioles via the autonomic nervous system. These impulses help the body to maintain a degree of peripheral resistance that is consistent with normal blood pressure. An increase in arterial blood pressure will cause pressoreceptors in the carotid and aortic sinuses to send impulses over the glossopharyngeal and vagus nerves to the vasomotor center, inhibiting the vasoconstrictor center. The result is immediate vasodilation of the arterioles of the skin and abdominal organs. This occurs because few vasoconstrictor impulses are now being sent over sympathetic fibers to the arterioles of these regions. With vasodilation, there is a decrease in peripheral resistance and in venous return to the heart. Both of these events contribute to a lowering of arterial blood pressure, since a decrease in venous return brings about a decrease in cardiac output. The relative importance of the vasodilator center in this reflex is not known.

A decrease in arterial blood pressure somehow causes the pressoreceptors in the carotid and aortic sinuses to send impulses which *stimulate* the vasoconstrictor center in the medulla, which in turn sends more impulses per unit of time over sympathetic fibers to the arterioles, causing them to constrict. The result is an increase in arterial pressure. Normal vasomotor tone of the smooth muscle of arterioles is maintained by a steady stream of sympathetic impulses that are sent by the vasoconstrictor center at a moderate rate. When arterioles in the skin and viscera constrict, blood is shunted to the skeletal muscles and heart; this makes the vasoconstrictor reflex an important mechanism during physical exercise.

VASOMOTOR CHEMOREFLEXES Chemoreceptors of the carotid and aortic bodies are sensitive to low blood oxygen levels (hypoxia), high blood levels of carbon dioxide (hypercapnia), and low blood pH values. Any one of these conditions will cause the chemoreceptors to send impulses to the medullary vasoconstrictor centers, and this will result in the vasoconstriction of arterioles.

MEDULLARY ISCHEMIC REFLEX Although all reflexes utilizing centers located in the medulla can be classed as medullary reflexes, the medullary ischemic reflex is the only one of the group under consideration that actually originates in the medulla. The word *ischemia* means inadequate blood supply; and when, for one reason or another, the blood supply to the medulla is reduced, the resulting hypoxia and hypercapnia in the medulla stimulates the vasoconstrictor center, and vasoconstriction of arterioles soon follows. The medullary ischemic reflex is the most powerful of the vasoconstrictor reflexes.

Systolic and diastolic pressures; pulse pressure

While the blood is traveling in arteries, it is under relatively high pressure—about 115 to 150 mm Hg and higher, depending upon age, physical activity and condition, and other factors. But as the arteries divide into smaller and smaller branches and then into arterioles, the pressure drops to about 35 mm Hg due to the increased area of flow now available. This is a mean or "normal" value, and assumes that the arterioles are neither greatly constricted nor overdilated. As the blood spreads out even more into the great space afforded by the capillary bed, the pressure drops to only a few millimeters of mercury. All the foregoing pressures represent readings taken immediately following contraction of the ventricles, and are known as *systolic* pressures. Another reading is customarily taken during ventricular relaxation and rest; this is the *diastolic* pressure, and averages about 70 mm Hg. When a physician or nurse measures the blood pressure of a patient, both the systolic and diastolic readings are recorded. As an example, if the systolic pressure were 120 and the diastolic pressure 70, the readings would be recorded as 120/70, which is customarily read, "120 over 70." Still another pressure value can be determined, one that is important in physical diagnosis: *pulse pressure*. It is determined by subtracting the diastolic pressure from the systolic pressure. In the foregoing example, the pulse pressure would be 120 − 70, or 50 mm Hg.

HOW ARTERIAL BLOOD PRESSURE IS DETERMINED CLINICALLY   There are two ways to measure blood pressure: *directly* and *indi-*

rectly. The former method requires that a tube or cannula be inserted into an artery and connected to the base of a graduated cylinder. The blood is allowed to flow into the tube, and the height reached by the column of blood gives an indication of the blood pressure. Whereas this is the most accurate method of determining blood pressure, it is also the most impractical, except perhaps in the research laboratory. Today, blood pressure is measured clinically by indirect methods, by noting how many millimeters a column of mercury rises as a result of pressure applied when occluding an artery, usually the brachial artery. The mercury manometer *—in this case called a *sphygmomanometer*—is connected to an inflatable cuff that can be fastened around the upper arm. The cuff is pumped up until the reading is well above the normal value for an individual of the age being examined, or until the radial pulse can no longer be felt. The examiner then places a stethoscope over the brachial artery at the cubital fossa (front of the elbow), and while listening carefully, slowly releases the pressure from the occluding cuff. The height of the mercury column on the sphygmomanometer is noted at the instant at which pulse sounds can be heard as the blood begins to rush through the brachial artery. This is the *systolic pressure*. The examiner continues to listen and watch. The pulse sounds get louder and louder as the pressure of the cuff is decreased, then they start to fade. Just as they are fading another reading is taken, and this is considered to be the *diastolic pressure*. Several readings may be taken and the mean or average used as the blood pressure of the person being examined. The sounds heard in the brachial artery are known clinically as the *sounds of Korotkoff*.

The mercury-column sphygmomanometer is somewhat cumbersome, especially in busy hospital wards. A more convenient instrument is the popular *anaeroid* apparatus, which utilizes a coiled spring and simple clocklike dial, the latter calibrated in mm Hg. Any indirect method of blood-pressure determination has an expected error of

---

* An instrument used to measure the pressure of liquids or gases. It consists of a movable column of mercury contained in a glass tube calibrated in millimeters. The tube is connected to the source of pressure.

from 5–10 mm Hg. Any method involving listening is called an *ausculatory method*. Less popular is a system requiring feeling the pulse, known as the *palpatory method*.

VENOUS PRESSURE Capillary pressure is about 30 mm Hg near the arterioles and 12 mm Hg near the venules. In a person at rest, the blood pressure is virtually zero in most of the large veins. The pressure in venules is about 12 mm Hg, but decreases to about 4.5–5.0 mm Hg in the inferior vena cava near the heart. The *"milking" action of muscles, suction provided by diastole of the right atrium, increases and decreases in intrathoracic and intraabdominal pressures during breathing,* and the *valves of the veins* (which permit blood to flow only in one direction— see Fig. 10-26) must all be relied upon to maintain venous circulation during periods of relative inactivity. While we are asleep or otherwise resting in a reclining position, venous return is much easier, since the force of gravity no longer works against the flow as it does when the blood must move "uphill" (as when we are in the upright position). During vigorous activity, the venous pressure rises considerably.

The foregoing pertains to venous pressures below the level of the heart. When the body is in the erect position, venous pressure in veins above the heart drops to zero and even to below zero. The venous return is so

facilitated by gravity that the venous pressure in the veins of the neck is zero, for example, while that in the large blood sinuses that drain the brain may fall to −10 ("minus ten") mm Hg. Clearly, venous return from the head is normally not a problem. There is no quick, practical, indirect method of measuring venous pressure; it is too low to be measured accurately by a sphygmomanometer.

*Miscellaneous factors
affecting blood pressure*

It has already been pointed out that, normally, blood-pressure values depend upon the construction of the circulatory system and the combined functions of its various components. Cardiac output, blood volume, blood viscosity, peripheral resistance, and various other factors were considered. Such things as *disease, age, amount of sleep, physical activity, body weight, sex,* and *emotional factors* also have direct bearing upon the blood pressure. At birth, the average systolic blood pressure is only about 40 mm Hg, while at age 65, it is not uncommon for the reading to climb to 150 mm Hg and even higher. A systolic pressure above 160 mm Hg is usually considered to be a state of *hypertension,* or "high blood pressure." Average blood pressure values at various ages are indicated in Table 10-1. During vigorous exercise, the blood pressure may rise 75 mm Hg or more above the normal resting pressure, and may remain at this level for a period of time after exercise has ceased. Before menopause, women have lower blood pressures—by about 10 mm Hg—than men. At about 60 years of age, however, the blood pressure of a women often equals or exceeds that of a man of the same age. *Obesity* (a state of being greatly overweight) causes a rise in blood pressure for two reasons: first, because of the extra workload placed on the heart in carrying extra weight around; and second, because adipose tissue is abundantly supplied with blood vessels, and the peripheral resistance is thereby greatly increased. Such emotions as *fear, excitement,* and *worry* tend to bring on an *increase* in systolic pressure, but *depression, loneliness, grief,* and similar emotional states are often asso-

Figure 10-26 Venous valves and their actions.

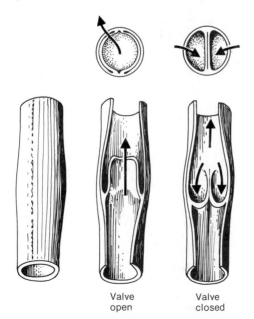

Valve
open

Valve
closed

ciated with a *fall* in pressure. It was pointed out in Chapter 7 that *shock* causes the blood pressure to *drop*. This is also the case when the heart is diseased in such a manner that the *cardiac output is decreased*. Other diseases of the heart and certain diseases of the liver and kidneys bring on hypertension. *Arteriosclerosis* or "hardening of the arteries" is probably the disease most often associated with high blood pressure, since the arteries are no longer as elastic and extensible as normally.

pulse include the *radial* artery at the wrist, the *temporal* artery on the lateral side of the head anterior to the ear, the *common carotid* artery lateral to the thyroid cartilage, the *facial* artery at the lower margin of the mandible (about a third of the way anterior to the angle), the *brachial* artery in the cubital fossa, the *posterior tibial* artery just posterior to the medial malleolus (at the ankle), and the *dorsalis pedis* artery on top of the foot. Clinical consideration of the pulse is presented on p. 285.

TABLE 10-1

Average arterial blood pressures at different ages (mm Hg)

Age	Systolic	Diastolic
Newborn	40	20
1 Month	75	50
2 Years	85	60
4 Years	90	65
10 Years	105	70
15 Years	110	70
20 Years	120	80
30 Years	130	85
40 Years	140	90
50 Years	145	90
60 Years	150	90

The pulse and pressure points

Pulse may be defined as a series of surges of blood in the arteries, resulting from contraction of the left ventricle. The distensibility and elasticity of the arterial walls bring about the expansion and contraction of the arteries following each ventricular systole. Each pulse travels as a *pulse wave* as blood moves away from the heart. It takes a considerable amount of time for a surge of blood leaving the left ventricle to reach a distant portion of the body; therefore, the pulse felt at these distant points does not coincide exactly with ventricular systole.

WHERE TO FEEL THE PULSE   The pulse is best palpated at points where arteries are rather superficial and lie over bones or other firm structures. Common sites for feeling the

THE BLOOD

If one were asked to state a single outstanding function of blood, the question might easily be answered with one word: **transportation.** Blood transports *oxygen, water, nutrients* (such as glucose), *hormones, antibodies,* and *phagocytic* (engulfing) *cells* throughout the body, mostly to the cells and tissues. It also carries *carbon dioxide, urea, lactic acid,* and other wastes from the cells. Blood transports some of the *heat of metabolism* throughout the body, helping maintain its temperature, and some to the lungs and skin for dissipation, thereby helping to prevent the body temperature from rising too high. Blood is also necessary for *effective heart action.* It will be recalled from an earlier section of this chapter that vigorous ventricular systole depends a great deal upon the stretching of cardiac-muscle fibers during ventricular filling. The heart muscle also requires oxygen and nutrients, which are carried to it only in the blood. In addition to all the foregoing functions, the blood helps in the *maintenance of acid–base balance* in all cells of the body. It is able to do this because of the *buffers* present in the blood.

Composition and physical features of blood

Blood is a fluid tissue and is unique in that its cells do not remain in one place as do those of other tissues, but move throughout the body, *contained in the blood vessels,* which in turn comprise a *closed circulatory system.* Blood is *bright red when oxygenated, dark red when deoxygenated.* Oxygenated blood is found in *systemic arteries,* deoxygenated blood in *systemic veins.* About 7% of the body weight is made up of blood. This amounts to about 10 lb or 5 liters in the average 150-lb individual. Blood has a specific gravity of about 1.060, and is about 5 times as viscous as water. It is only slightly alkaline, with an average pH of 7.4. If blood in a laboratory test tube is prevented from clotting (by the addition of a chemical *anticoagulant),* the cells will settle to the bottom of the container. The speed with which this settling occurs is called the *sedimentation rate,* and is increased during certain infections. It is possible to obtain both the sedimentation rate and the *hematocrit*—the percentage of formed elements (blood cells) by volume—by the use of a special container, the *Wintrobe tube* (Fig. 10-27). Measured by this method, the normal sedimentation rate amounts to about 5 to 10 millimeters per hour, the hematocrit about 45%. The hematocrit is determined by centrifuging the

Figure 10-27 The hematocrit. (a) Wintrobe tube. (b) A centrifuge tube, showing the percentage of formed elements or cells in whole blood.

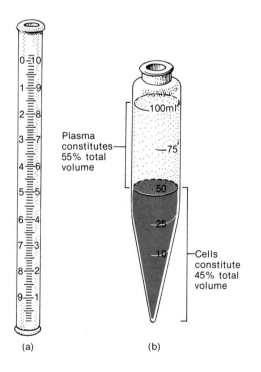

Plasma constitutes 55% total volume

Cells constitute 45% total volume

(a)   (b)

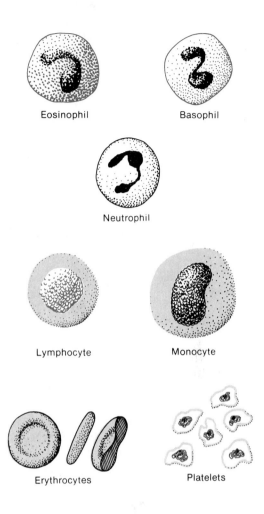

Eosinophil   Basophil

Neutrophil

Lymphocyte   Monocyte

Erythrocytes   Platelets

Figure 10.28 The formed elements of blood.

Wintrobe tube after the sedimentation rate has been obtained.

Blood can be separated into two portions: a *fluid fraction,* the straw-colored *plasma;* and a *solid fraction,* the *formed elements* or *blood cells.* The cells (or *corpuscles,* as they are sometimes called) include *erythrocytes* or red blood cells (RBC's), *leucocytes* or white blood cells (WBC's), and *thrombocytes* or platelets, which are actually only cell fragments (Fig. 10-28). Normally, plasma comprises about 55% of the blood volume and the formed elements about 45%. The percentage of blood volume occupied by all the formed elements actually represents the hematocrit, but since the numbers of white cells are very small compared to those of red cells, the hematocrit is commonly spoken of clinically as the *percentage of blood volume occupied by the red cells.*

The hematocrit is important in diagnosing cases of *anemia,* which in some instances is due to an insufficient number of erythrocytes, and in others to a decrease in the amount of the oxygen-carrying pigment, *hemoglobin,* present in all red cells. It is also valuable in diagnosing *polycythemia,* in which case there is an overproduction of red blood cells.

RED BLOOD CELLS OR ERYTHROCYTES Red blood cells are flattened discs, averaging 7.5 μ in diameter. They are about 2.2 μ thick near the periphery, but are *biconcave,* so that they are only about 1 μ thick in the central portion. The size of red cells is clinically important; for example, in one type of anemia they are smaller than normal, while in a second type, they are larger. Their thin (150 Å) membrane is extremely flexible, and permits them to bend and twist their way through capillary networks. Men have about 5 million erythrocytes in every cubic millimeter of their blood—women have about 4½ million—and, therefore, there are billions of erythrocytes in the body. Once they have reached maturity, erythrocytes can no longer be classed as true cells, because during the process of maturation they *lose their nuclei.* They may then be spoken of as *anucleate* cells. Red blood cells can be counted by using a *hemacytometer* or counting chamber. After the cells in a small volume of blood are counted, numerical factors are applied which give a calculated estimate of the number of erythrocytes present in 1 mm³ (cubic millimeter) of blood. (It should be mentioned that there are 1000 mm³ in 1 cc, in order to emphasize how small a volume 1 mm³ actually represents.)

HEMOGLOBIN Hemoglobin is a pigment found in the red cells. It is called a respiratory pigment because it carries the *respiratory gases, oxygen and carbon dioxide. Hemoglobin,* an internal network or *stroma* of protein and lipid, and the *cell membrane* comprise the entire red blood cell. Hemoglobin is a complex *iron-plus-protein substance* that transports most of the oxygen carried by the blood. (A small amount of oxygen travels dissolved in the plasma.) Oxygenated hemoglobin, in blood leaving the lungs and headed for the tissues, is *bright red;* while deoxygenated hemoglobin, in venous blood after having given up its oxygen to the tissues, is *dark red.* Normally, blood contains about 15 g of hemoglobin per 100 cc of blood. An adult whose blood contains less than 12 g of hemoglobin per 100 cc of blood is said to be anemic. Each gram of oxygenated hemoglobin carries about 1.34 cc of oxygen held in *loose*—not strongly bonded—combination. Deoxygenated hemoglobin is also called *reduced hemoglobin.* If reduced hemoglobin is in large enough quantities in the blood—about 5 g per 100 cc or more of arterial blood—the nails, lips, and mucous membranes appear bluish in color, and a condition of *cyanosis* is said to exist. Various cardiovascular and respiratory disorders can bring on cyanosis, which in turn indicates inadequate oxygenation of blood.

Hemoglobin that has been oxygenated is called *oxyhemoglobin.* Oxygenation of hemoglobin occurs when blood passes through the capillaries surrounding the microscopic air sacs (*alveoli*) that comprise most of the lung tissue. As the blood travels through these capillaries, *oxygen diffuses into the blood* from the alveoli, and *carbon dioxide diffuses out of the blood* and into the alveoli, ready to be expelled during the breathing out process of *expiration* (or *exhalation*) (Chapter 11). The oxygen picked up by the hemoglobin in the red cells is carried to the body cells and released for their use in the processes of metabolism. At the same time, carbon dioxide is picked up by the blood and carried to the lungs for exhalation. The process is carried out over and over again, for as long as we live and breathe.

Hemoglobin has an *affinity* (attraction) for oxygen, but it has a greater affinity for *carbon monoxide,* a poisonous gas. It combines with carbon monoxide much more firmly than it does with oxygen or carbon dioxide. In breathing air that is contaminated with a large amount of carbon monoxide, oxygen is crowded out of the blood cells, and suffocation by carbon-monoxide poisoning results. The single most important function of hemoglobin is the *transport of the respiratory gases, oxygen and carbon dioxide,* although hemoglobin is also an important *blood buffer.*

FORMATION AND LIFE SPAN OF ERYTHROCYTES Although red blood cells have no nuclei at maturity, they develop in red bone

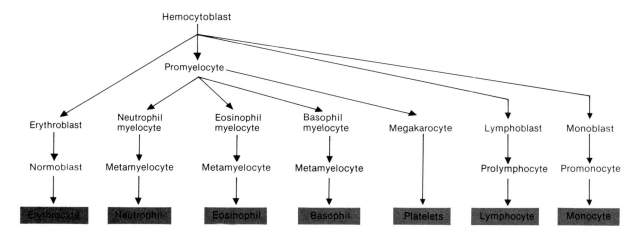

Figure 10-29 Diagram of blood cell formation.

marrow from primitive cells which do have nuclei, *erythroblasts,* which in turn develop from *hemocytoblasts,* or "stem cells" (Fig. 10-29). A few erythroblasts develop into *reticulocytes,* which in turn become *normoblasts,* which develop into erythrocytes. If the reticulocyte count of an individual is less than $\frac{1}{2}\%$ of the red cell count, red cell production is said to be slow. On the other hand, a reticulocyte count greater than $1\frac{1}{2}\%$ indicates an accelerated red cell formation.

After the long bones stop growing at about age 20 or 25, red cells are produced only in the *proximal portions of the femora and humeri,* and in the *membranous bones,* such as the *sternum* and *bones of the skull.* The nucleus of an erythrocyte is usually extruded ("squeezed out") before the cell enters the circulation. By the use of radio-isotope tagging, it has been determined that a red blood cell has an *average life span of only 120 days.* An astonishing fact is that *about $2\frac{1}{2}$ million red cells are formed and destroyed every second!* The rate of erythrocyte formation seems to be under the control of a substance produced by the kidneys, *erythropoietin.* As red cells disintegrate, or for some reason hemoglobin production slows, the oxgen-carrying capacity of the blood falls, and this condition (called *anoxemia*) seems somehow to stimulate the kidneys to secrete erythropoietin, which in turn is carried to the bone marrow, where it stimulates the production of greater numbers of red cells, thereby raising the oxygen capacity of the blood back to normal levels. This is a remarkable but poorly understood

homeostatic mechanism. The formation of blood cells is called *hemopoiesis,* and the formation of erythrocytes in particular, *erythropoiesis.* The formation of leucocytes is *leucopoiesis.* Hemorrhage, pulmonary diseases, even high altitudes act to trigger erythropoiesis.

For bone marrow to produce and maintain the normal number of erythrocytes, it must be supplied by the blood with several raw materials—e.g., iron and amino acids—and catalysts (copper, cobalt, and vitamin B compounds). Also, the mucous membrane lining of the stomach (*gastric mucosa*) must supply the marrow with an *intrinsic factor,* which is necessary for absorption of an *extrinsic factor,* vitamin B_{12}. The latter is one of several vitamin B compounds that stimulate the bone marrow to produce red cells.

If the gastric mucosa does not produce enough intrinsic factor, *pernicious anemia* develops. Vitamin B_{12} is then poorly absorbed and the bone marrow produces fewer (but larger) erythrocytes than normal.

Such factors as bone marrow **injury** (perhaps by X ray or other radiation) and increased destruction of erythrocytes (as in infections and leukemia) produce anemia.

When "old" erythrocytes disintegrate, their fragments are engulfed by reticulo-endothelial cells in the bone marrow, liver, and spleen. The hemoglobin is broken down into two bile pigments (*bilirubin* and *biliverdin*) and an iron-protein pigment, *hemosiderin.* The iron of hemosiderin is used in the production of new hemoglobin, and the bile pigments are excreted in bile.

ROLE OF THE SPLEEN   Although the *spleen* does not normally produce erythrocytes except in the unborn child, it is a center for their *storage* and *destruction.* Up to 1 pt of concentrated blood may be released into the circulation by contraction of the spleen during severe hemorrhage. This is a safety-reflex mechanism that helps to prevent shock due to loss of blood. Many circulating red cells are destroyed in the spleen each day; so many, in fact, that the spleen has been called the "cemetery" of red blood cells.

WHITE BLOOD CELLS OR LEUCOCYTES White blood cells are generally larger than erythrocytes, and *all have nuclei.* There are five different kinds of leucocytes, and each has a characteristically shaped nucleus (Fig. 10-28). Leucocytes are customarily divided into *two groups,* depending upon whether or not small, dark-staining particles called *granules* are present in the cytoplasm. Those cells having such granules are called *granulocytes,* and include *neutrophils, eosinophils,* and *basophils.* Those lacking granules in the cytoplasm are called *agranulocytes,* and include *lymphocytes* and *monocytes.* Characteristic staining reactions and shape or form of the nucleus serve to differentiate one type of white blood cell from another. Neutrophils are so named because their granules and nuclear material are colored by *pH-neutral stains;* basophils show an affinity for *basic or alkaline stains;* while eosinophils stain well with *eosin and other acid-type stains.* The nuclei of neutrophils often have three or more enlarged sections or *lobes,* held together by strands of nuclear material. About 70% of all WBC's are neutrophils, and some 4% are eosinophils. Eosinophils have nuclei similar in form to those of the neutrophils, but their *cytoplasmic granules are very coarse,* and acid stains color these granules a *deep red.* The basic stain *methylene blue* is often used to color the granules in the cytoplasm of basophils. After this treatment, they appear as *coarse blue-black dots.* The lobes of the nuclei of basophils are not nearly so pronounced as those of the nuclei of the other two types of granulocytes. Very few basophils are found in the bloodstream.

Two types of *lymphocytes* are present in the circulation, *large* and *small.* They originate in the *lymph nodes, spleen,* and *tonsils. Wright's stain,* commonly used for coloring lymphocytes, produces a *light-blue cytoplasm* and *deep-purple nucleus,* the latter being *large* and often *bean-shaped.* Monocytes are very large cells that originate in *bone marrow.* The *large, oval nucleus* appears to be made up of small *lobules.* Both the *nucleus* and *cytoplasm* of monocytes stain *pale blue,* but the cytoplasm stains more faintly than the nucleus.

FORMATION AND LIFE SPAN OF LEUCOCYTES The granulocytes—neutrophils, basophils, and eosinophils—are formed in the bone marrow. Most of the lymphocytes and (probably) monocytes originate in lymphatic or lymphoid tissues (discussed later in this chapter), particularly in the lymph nodes, but also in the tonsils and spleen. It is difficult to determine the life span of leucocytes because they move from the blood into the tissues, and perhaps even back again. It is known that granulocytes may move into the tissues after only 10 or 12 hours (hr) in the bloodstream, and that lymphocytes may move from the lymphatic system into the blood and back again, repeating this process for as long as three months before they disintegrate. It is likely that most leucocytes have a maximum life span of only a few days, but there is evidence to indicate that lymphocytes may live as long as 300 days. The total number of WBC's per cubic millimeter of blood ranges from 5000 to 10,000 at any given time. This fluctuation is due to the migratory habits of white blood cells, just explained. In *differential counts* * of the leucocytes in, say, 1 mm³ of blood, it is found that, on the average, neutrophils comprise up to 75% of the total, eosinophils up to 5%, basophils 0.5%, lymphocytes up to 25%, and monocytes up to 8% of the total. The numbers of leucocytes in the bloodstream increase markedly during infections, except during some of the virus infections, when their number may actually decrease. During infection, leucocytes migrate through

---

* In differential counts, the number of *each kind* of white blood cell is determined, as opposed to a total count, during which no distinction is made between one kind of leucocyte and another.

capillary walls and enter the infected tissue, in an *ameboid process* called *diapedesis.* Some degree of diapedesis goes on even when no infection is present. Leucocytes appear to be attracted to a site of infection or inflammation by chemical substances that are released by tissue cells which have been attacked by disease organisms. The process in which leucocytes respond to chemicals in the blood is called *chemotaxis.* Pus consists chiefly of such living pathogenic organisms as bacteria plus living leucocytes, and many dead bacteria and leucocytes, as well as their decay products. *Inflammation* is a reaction of tissues to the invasion of such microorganisms as bacteria. Capillaries in the invaded area dilate, and lymph collects, with the result that there is localized swelling, redness of the skin, an increase in temperature (due to increased quantities of blood and accelerated rate of cellular metabolism in the infected region) and pain.

THE FUNCTIONS OF LEUCOCYTES The most outstanding role played by leucocytes is that of *phagocytosis,* the engulfing and destroying of harmful microorganisms and small foreign particles that might happen to get into the tissues or blood. During infections, the numbers of leucocytes sometimes reach staggering proportions; for example, each cubic millimeter of blood may contain as many as 50,000 to 60,000 WBC's. This great proliferation of white cells is called *leucocytosis.* Its opposite is *leucopenia,* which means a decrease in the number of white blood cells. All the different types of leucocytes except eosinophils have the ability to phagocytize invading microorganisms and other foreign matter. The *basophils* multiply rapidly in *chickenpox, smallpox, sinus infections, asthma,* and *Hodgkin's disease,* but their exact functions are not known. *Eosinophils* increase in number in *bronchial asthma,* and in *trichinosis* and certain other types of infestation by animal parasites, but here again, the exact function is not known. The *agranulocytes*—especially the *lymphocytes*—may take part in *tissue repair.* Lymphocytes may also produce *antibodies* (chemical substances which form in response to the presence of other chemicals called antigens) and other immunizing substances.

THE FORMATION AND FUNCTION OF PLATELETS Platelets are not cells at all, but rather fragments of *megakaryocytes,* large cells formed in the bone marrow. Platelets have no nuclei and their average diameter is only 3 μ—a little less than one-half the size of a red cell. There are from 300,000 to 400,000 platelets in each cubic millimeter of blood. They function to initiate the clotting or coagulation process, and to seal holes and tears in small blood vessels—especially capillaries—so that blood is not permitted to seep into the surrounding tissues. During the occurrence of a wound, thousands of platelets are ruptured and promptly release a substance that triggers a chain of reactions that produces a blood clot.

Blood plasma

Plasma, the fluid portion of blood, is *mostly water* (about 90%). The solutes constituting the remaining 10% are *proteins; electrolytes, such as mineral salts;* and *nonelectrolytes, such as glucose, fats, and the waste products of metabolism,* including *creatinine, lactic acid, urea, and uric acid. Antibodies, enzymes, and hormones* are also present in plasma, and small amounts of *oxygen* and *carbon dioxide* are dissolved in it. Plasma is important as a *suspension medium for the formed elements of blood,* and in maintaining *osmotic relationships with the blood cells. Hemolysis* or laking of blood cells occurs if the plasma becomes *hypotonic* to the cells. In this case, *water diffuses into the cells* (from a region of greater concentration to one of lesser concentration of water molecules) until they swell and burst. A shrinking or *crenation* of erythrocytes, on the other hand, indicates that *water has diffused outward* through their membranes, into a surrounding *hypertonic* plasma.

PLASMA PROTEINS The major proteins of blood plasma make up 6% to 8% of its volume and include *albumin, fibrinogen, prothrombin,* and *three globulins—alpha, beta,* and *gamma.* These and other proteins make up a floating storage system of proteins that are used by the tissues as required. Some of the proteins present in plasma are made *in the liver,* while others originate in processes in other sources, such as in the breakdown of old erythrocytes. The protein found in the plasma in the greatest quantity is *albumin.* It is important in the regulation of osmotic pressure between the plasma and the formed elements and of that between the plasma and the tissue cells. *Fibrinogen* is essential to the coagulation of blood. Both this plasma protein and albumin are synthesized in the liver from *amino acids. Prothrombin* is another plasma protein that is synthesized *in the liver,* and it, too, is important in the clotting process. Adequate amounts of *vitamin K* in the diet are necessary to the formation of prothrombin in the liver. For the most part, the globulins are formed *in the liver,* although most gamma globulin is made in small, spherical plasma cells found *in the connective tissues of the digestive tract and in lymphatic tissues. Alpha and beta globulins* assist in the transport of proteins and other substances throughout the body, while gamma globulin has immunizing properties and acts as an antibody in fighting disease. All plasma proteins help to maintain the viscosity and normal volume of the blood.

PLASMA NUTRIENTS   Also present in plasma are *glucose, lipids, amino acids,* and other nutrients. Glucose is the most important nutrient in blood plasma, and is commonly called *"blood sugar."* It is used by all tissues as their major source of fuel in carrying out the metabolic processes essential to life. The blood sugar level must remain within relatively narrow limits in order for good health to be maintained. Lipids as *fats, phospholipids, cholesterol,* and in other forms are commonly stored as *reserve energy sources,* to be used if available *carbohydrate* (blood sugar level) falls too low. *Amino acids* are used in the growth and repair of tissues—especially muscles and other tissues rich in protein.

PLASMA ELECTROLYTES   Much of the electrolyte balance of the body tissues depends upon the presence of the *salts of sodium, potassium, magnesium,* and *calcium* in the plasma, especially as *sulfates, phosphates, chlorides,* and *carbonates.* Electrolytes are important in *nerve-impulse transmission, acid–base balance,* and in *nutrition.*

MISCELLANEOUS SUBSTANCES IN PLASMA   Grouped in this category are the *metabolic waste products, antibodies, enzymes,* and *hormones,* as well as small amounts of *oxygen* and *carbon dioxide.* Waste products are carried to the kidneys for *elimination;* antibodies are essential in the constant *fight against infection;* enzymes are necessary in the processes of *digestion* and in the large number of reactions that constitute *cellular metabolism;* and hormones are required for the *maturation and maintenance of the reproductive system* and for other functions.

THE CLINICAL SIGNIFICANCE OF PLASMA   Diagnosis of various disorders and diseases is often aided by laboratory examination of blood plasma. As examples: high levels of nitrogenous wastes in the plasma may indicate a kidney disease such as *nephritis;* high blood glucose levels point to *diabetes mellitus;* and variations in the plasma calcium levels suggest *parathyroid-gland disorders.* On occasion, it is desirable to know the *plasma volume.* One method of determining this value is to inject a dye, *Evans blue* (T1824), into a vein. This dye forms a complex with plasma protein molecules and then, because it cannot diffuse through capillary walls, is retained within the circulation. After allowing time for the dye to become equally distributed throughout the circulatory system, blood samples are taken, and the concentration of Evans blue in the plasma is determined. By use of the following formula, the plasma volume can then be calculated:

$$\frac{\left(\begin{array}{c}\text{Concentration}\\ \text{of dye injected}\end{array}\right) \times \left(\begin{array}{c}\text{Volume}\\ \text{injected}\end{array}\right)}{\left(\begin{array}{c}\text{Concentration}\\ \text{in plasma}\end{array}\right)} = \left(\begin{array}{c}\text{Plasma}\\ \text{volume}\end{array}\right)$$

In order to determine the *entire blood volume,* the hematocrit is determined and the blood volume calculated by simply multiplying the plasma volume by a factor obtained during determination of the hematocrit.

Bleeding and the clotting of blood

When an artery is cut or punctured, brilliant red blood comes forth in spurts, pulsating with each beat of the heart. If a vein is similarily injured, the blood is dark red, and flows slowly from the wound in a more or less even manner. The forceful manner in which arterial blood leaves a wound is due to the relatively high pressure of blood in the arteries. Bleeding should be stopped quickly, in order to prevent excess loss of blood and *possible shock*. If the wound that opens a blood vessel is not too extensive, and if the subject and his blood are normal and healthy, bleeding can be stopped permanently (or will stop of its own accord) within a short time. How soon bleeding from a small wound will cease of its own accord depends upon the *bleeding time* and *clotting time* of the blood of the individual concerned. Once bleeding has stopped, damaged blood vessels undergo a process of natural repair.

BLEEDING TIME   When the body receives a wound, vessels in the area normally tend to undergo *vasoconstriction* in order to help stem the flow of blood; and if the wound is not too extensive, a *clot* will form and the bleeding will stop. If, on the other hand, a large artery or vein has been opened, or if the individual suffers from *hemophilia*—"bleeder's disease"—the flow of blood does not cease, and prompt action is necessary in order to save a life. If a patient is scheduled to undergo surgery, a *test for bleeding time* may be performed. This consists of making a puncture or small incision in the earlobe or elsewhere and noting how much time is required for the bleeding to stop.

CLOTTING TIME   If blood did not have the capacity to clot or coagulate, life as we know it would not be possible. Everyday nicks and abrasions, which often open thousands of capillaries, would produce bleeding or hemorrhage so extensive as to be fatal. Even the constriction of vessels in the wound area by tourniquets would not suffice to permanently arrest the flow, because as soon as the tourniquets were removed, the flow of blood would

begin all over again. During clotting, blood forms a dark red, jellylike mass. If blood is placed in a test tube and allowed to stand for 5 minutes or a little longer, *coagulation* will take place, and the blood is no longer in the liquid state. About 25 minutes after that, it will be seen that the clot has "tightened up" or *retracted* into a compact, rubbery mass, surrounded by a pale yellow fluid—blood *serum*. Serum is essentially *blood plasma minus the major plasma proteins*. Microscopic examination of a clot of blood reveals that it consists of red and white blood cells trapped in a *reticulum* or meshwork of the blood protein *fibrin,* which is formed from the protein substance *fibrinogen.* The process by which formation of a blood clot or *thrombus* takes place is worthy of our consideration.

THE MECHANISM OF COAGULATION   There has long been much speculation and controversy regarding the detailed reactions occurring during the coagulation of blood. Only the most widely accepted basic features of the process will be considered here.

Four substances are known to be essential to the formation of a blood clot: *calcium, thrombokinase, prothrombin,* and *fibrinogen;* furthermore, it is necessary that two reactions take place: (1) *prothrombin must be converted to thrombin;* and (2) *fibrinogen must be converted to fibrin.*

Once fibrin has been formed, cells are trapped, and a clot buildup results. Calcium is present in the plasma in the form of *calcium ions;* thrombokinase is more or less a general term, used to represent any such substance as *cephalin* or *thromboplastin* which helps calcium ions convert prothrombin to thrombin; and prothrombin and fibrinogen are both proteins found in the plasma. It is thought that thromboplastin (or cephalin) is released by the cells of injured tissues and is formed (in the presence of calcium ions) from a "factor" released by broken-up platelets, rather than being released directly from the platelets themselves. In all, some one dozen *clotting factors* have been identified, but some are controversial.

A brief summary of the chief events taking place during coagulation can be diagrammed as follows:

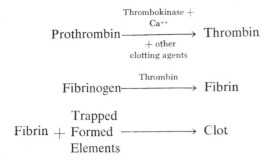

Vitamin K indirectly influences the ability of blood to clot, as it is *necessary to the formation of prothrombin,* which takes place in the *liver.* An individual who is a "bleeder" may be deficient in this vitamin, which is found in green plants and is also normally synthesized by microorganisms in the large intestine. Vitamin K is a fat-soluble vitamin, and since the digestion and absorption of fats require bile, the absorption of vitamin K indirectly requires bile. So an obstruction of the bile duct brings about a vitamin K deficiency, which in turn causes a prothrombin deficiency to develop, because this vitamin is necessary to the formation of prothrombin in the liver. Since persons with a prothrombin deficiency have a strong tendency to hemorrhage, they are routinely given a vitamin K preparation prior to surgery. Obstructive jaundice due to a gallstone in the common bile duct is a case in point. Fibrinogen, as well as prothrombin, is synthesized in the liver.

While it is absolutely necessary that the blood coagulate whenever blood vessels are opened, it is just as necessary that this mechanism *not* be extended to include the blood circulating *within the vessels;* that is, *intravascular clotting must not occur.* The presence of *anticoagulants* such as *antithrombin* and *heparin* insures that this is the case. Anticoagulants probably inhibit in some manner the formation of thrombin from prothrombin. At the site of a wound, the large number of platelets that become broken up or fragmented release enough *"platelet factor"* to carry thrombin formation to completion. This is not to say that intravascular clotting (thrombosis) *never* occurs. If the inner surfaces of blood vessels become roughened—as during *atherosclerosis* (a condition in which the connective tissues of the arterial walls become involved in the

buildup of fatty "plaques" made up of cholesterol and other substances) or following infection—platelets may be broken up, and a clot may form, especially in the veins of an individual who is bedridden and whose circulation is particularly sluggish (a condition known as *venous stasis*). If an *intravascular clot* remains in one place, it is called a *thrombus;* a moving clot is an *embolus.* Both can be extremely dangerous. For example, an embolus may stop in a pulmonary artery, and so prevent blood from entering one of the lungs. This condition is called *pulmonary embolism,* and on occasion such clotting is massive enough to occlude both pulmonary arteries, thereby cutting off all pulmonary circulation. A clot in one of the coronary arteries is a *coronary thrombosis* or *myocardial infarction.* Unless the clot is a small one, lodging in one of the smaller branches of the artery, or unless collateral circulation (new pathways for the blood) can be established within a relatively short period of time through anastomosing vessels or the formation of new capillaries, a complete *cardiac arrest* (stoppage) may occur. Such drugs as *dicumarin* and *heparin* are used to extend the clotting time in patients whose circulation is sluggish due to long periods of rest or other reasons. Dicumarin (dicumarol) is long-acting, but requires about two days to bring about its desired result. Heparin is usually injected into a vein and acts almost at once, but its effect lasts only a fraction of the time of orally administered dicumarin. *Heparin attacks thrombin,* and *dicumarin prevents prothrombin formation in the liver.* It should be realized that the use of anticoagulants is accompanied by increased risk of hemorrhage.

Hemorrhage

Technically, any bleeding whatever constitutes a *hemorrhage,* which can be rated as slight, moderate, or severe, according to the amount of blood that escapes from the opened blood vessels. Commonly, the term hemorrhage is used to indicate severe or excessive bleeding; but there are several notable exceptions, such as hemorrhage following rupture of one or more tiny vessels in the eye or brain, the latter being designated *cerebral hemorrhage* or *cerebral vascular accident* (CVA).

There are various ways in which hemorrhage can be controlled. Large vessels can be *ligated* or "tied off"; they can also be clamped, using *hemostats* or other surgical clamps; *tourniquets* can be applied to vessels on the upstream side of the wound; and *"pressure pads"* made of cotton gauze can be applied directly over wounds that are not too large. Firm hand pressure on *pressure points* (where arteries lie near the surface and over a bone or other firm structure) is often a good emergency procedure for controlling hemorrhage. Six of the most important pressure points are as follows:

1. *Temporal Artery.* Anterior to the ear; press against skull.

2. *Facial Artery.* Lower margin of mandible, where pulse is felt; press against mandible.

3. *Common Carotid Artery.* Lateral to thyroid cartilage. Depending upon exact location of wound, pressure should be applied over thyroid cartilage or over vertebral column.

4. *Subclavian Artery.* Behind medial third of clavicle, pressure being applied to the first rib.

5. *Brachial Artery.* Three to four inches above elbow on medial side of arm; artery is pressed against humerus.

6. *Femoral Artery.* In central portion of the groin, with pressure against the pubic bone.

It will be noted that the first three points in the above list correspond to three locations where the pulse may be felt. The pulse may also be taken over the femoral artery.

Laboratory preparations of *thrombin* and *fibrin* are also used in the control of hemorrhage, especially if tests indicate that the patient's clotting mechanism is less than adequate.

The amount of time required for a victim of hemorrhage to regain his lost blood depends upon the amount he has lost (if we assume that he is in good health otherwise, and that his body has normal blood-forming ability). Within about 24 hr after 1 pt of blood has been lost, the original *volume* of blood has been restored by the osmotic movement of tissue fluid into the bloodstream; but an additional 45 to 50 days are required for restoration of the full complement of *formed elements.* During the period when *the number of circulating red blood cells is low,* the *total amount of hemoglobin will aslo be low,* since the latter is carried in the red cells.

It is worthy of mention that following the rapid loss of a large amount of blood, *the blood pressure drops sharply* and the *pulse and breathing rate increase.* An individual may lose about *one-fourth his total blood volume* and still survive.

BLOOD SUBSTITUTES After the loss of a large amount of blood, it is important for the original blood volume to be restored as quickly as possible so that the blood pressure will rise to its normal level and help to prevent shock (or aid in the recovery from shock, if this state already exists). It was previously mentioned that the spleen can release as much as a pint of blood into the circulation following hemorrhage, but often this is not enough to prevent or overcome shock. Ideally, a victim of hemorrhage should receive *whole blood* during a transfusion, not only to restore blood volume, but to elevate the oxygen-carrying capacity of the blood to its normal level; however, blood of all types is not always immediately available, especially in military-combat zones; therefore, various fluids are used to restore the blood volume and provide a source of energy, including *plasma, reconstituted plasma* (dried plasma to which water is added), *serum, saline–glucose solutions,* and preparations made from a *carbohydrate and water,* such as *dextran.* The blood substitute should exert the *same osmotic pressure as the blood itself;* that is, the blood and the blood substitute should be of the *same tonicity,* in order to prevent *hemolysis or crenation* of the blood cells in the patient's circulatory system.

*The grouping of blood;
blood types; transfusion*

During the seventeenth century, an enterprising French physician named Jean Baptiste Denis performed the first recorded

TABLE 10-2

Blood typing or grouping

Type or group	Percentage occurrence	Antigens (agglutinogens) in red cells	Antibodies (agglutinins) in plasma	Agglutination when mixed?			
				A	B	AB	O
A	41	A	Anti-B	No	Yes	No	Yes
B	10	B	Anti-A	Yes	No	No	Yes
AB	4	A & B	None	Yes	Yes	No	Yes
O	45	None	Anti-A & anti-B	No	No	No	No

* Where mixing is concerned, the type or group in the left-hand column is that of the donor, while the type or group at the upper right is that of the recipient.

successful blood transfusion in which the recipient of the blood was a human—in this case, a young boy. Lamb's blood was injected into the veins of the youth, who miraculously survived. Elated, the good doctor attempted a second transfusion. This time the recipient was an older man, who promptly died. Transfusions were outlawed for 100 years. Today, it is common knowledge that the blood of one person cannot be mixed indiscriminately with that of another person, much less that of a lower animal. An individual's blood is said to fall within one of four groups or types, according to an *international system of blood grouping:* O, A, B, or AB; and if his blood contains a protein substance, *"Rh factor,"* he is said to be *"Rh-positive";* or if his blood does not contain the factor, he is *"Rh-negative."* Rh factor is also referred to as *"D-antigen."*

Blood is grouped according to the presence or absence of one or more proteins—*agglutinogens or antigens**—in the red blood cells, designated A and B. If antigen A is the only one present, the blood is type A; if antigen B is the only one, the type is B; if *both* antigens A and B are present, the blood is placed in type AB; and if *neither* antigen is present in the red cells, the type is O. Still other proteins, those in plasma, are called *agglutinins or antibodies.* These can bring about clumping or *agglutination* of red cells

* An antigen is a protein that stimulates the formation of other proteins called antibodies.

that contain an incompatible antigen. These antibodies are designated *anti*-A and *anti*-B, or simply a and b. Obviously, the blood of an individual *never* contains antigens and antibodies that are incompatible; otherwise, agglutination would occur. Blood of group A does not contain anti-A antibodies in its plasma; it contains anti-B antibodies. Group-B blood contains anti-A antibodies; AB has *no* antibodies; and O has *both* anti-A and anti-B antibodies (Table 10-2).

In preparation for a *transfusion,* blood must be *cross-matched* and examined with reference to type or group and Rh factor. Assuming that the bloods of donor and recipient are *compatible*—that is, that no clumping occurs when the blood of the donor and recipient are mixed during cross-matching—and that they are compatible with respect to Rh factor as determined by laboratory test, blood may be safely transfused under any one of the following conditions:

1. If the blood types of donor and recipient are *identical.*

2. If the blood type of the *donor* is O—the blood cells of these individuals are *not agglutinated by any plasma,* and they are known as *universal donors.*

3. If the blood type of the *recipient* is AB—there are *no antibodies in the plasma* of these individuals, who are called *universal recipients.*

In actual practice, the universal-donor or -recipient principle is not used except in cases of dire emergency. It has been found that *many subtypes of blood exist,* and that agglutination can and occasionally does occur when blood of similar types—according to the A, O, B, AB classification—are mixed. The only safe method is to carry out *individual cross-matching,* in which cells from a donor blood sample are suspended in plasma or serum from the recipient, and vice versa. If no agglutination of cells is observed in either case, a transfusion can be safely performed.

Always to be avoided in transfusions is the agglutination of the red cells of the donor by the plasma of the recipient. Since the donor's plasma is greatly diluted by the recipient's plasma, the agglutination of the recipient's red cells by the donor's plasma does not present a problem.

THE IMPORTANCE OF Rh FACTOR   Like the A and B factors, the Rh factor is a blood protein. It is an antigen present in the red cells of 85% of caucasians and over 95% of the nonwhite population. It was first discovered in the blood of the rhesus monkey—hence the designation Rh. An Rh-positive (Rh$^+$) individual has the protein in his red blood cells, while an Rh-negative (Rh$^-$) person does not. *Anti-Rh proteins* or agglutinins are *absent* from the plasma of Rh-negative individuals, unless their blood has been stimulated to build these agglutinins by exposure to Rh proteins. There are two ways in which this exposure can come about: *by transfusion with Rh-positive blood* (which is very unlikely to happen) and in the *blood of a mother whose husband has Rh-positive blood.* In the latter instance, larger and larger amounts of anti-Rh agglutinins are built up in the mother's blood in response to the Rh-positive blood of the unborn children (children can inherit the Rh-positive blood from the Rh-positive father). The Rh protein diffuses from the placenta into the blood vessels of the uterus.

When the mother's blood is Rh$^-$ and that of the father is Rh$^+$, a disease called *erythroblastosis fetalis* can develop in their second or third child. The mother's blood builds up anti-Rh agglutinins following exposure to Rh proteins from an Rh$^+$ first child, as previously described. These agglu-

tinins may reach sufficient levels to endanger a second child, since they diffuse from the uterus to the placenta and thus enter the bloodstream of the developing embryo. If the level is high enough, the red cells of the fetus will agglutinate, and its blood vessels will be blocked. Eventually the clumps and even the cells themselves disintegrate, and the hemoglobin thus set free in the circulation converts to the yellow bile pigment, *bilirubin.* The decrease in hemoglobin drastically reduces the oxygen-carrying capacity of the blood, and the resulting *anemia* may be severe enough to prove fatal (if the clumping of red cells in itself has not already proven so). The skin of the newborn with this severe anemia is yellow, due to the deposition of bilirubin. If the baby is to be saved, all of its blood must be replaced with Rh-negative blood, in order to arrest the agglutinogen–agglutinin reaction. Gradually, the Rh-negative blood thus transfused will be replaced by Rh-positive blood; and while this is going on, the agglutinins that came from the mother are disintegrating, and clumping and destruction of red cells will cease.

It is now possible to prevent the formation of anti-Rh agglutinins in the mother's blood by means of drugs if treatment is instigated soon enough.

The buffers of the blood

It was previously mentioned that the pH of the blood remains remarkably close to 7.4. Maintenance of this near-neutral pH is possible due to the presence of *buffers* in the blood. A buffer is *a chemical substance which can prevent a change in pH of a solution when acids or bases are added.* Most of the buffers found in the blood—as well as those in other body tissues—consist of two substances: a *weak acid,* and the corresponding *salt of that acid.* Together, they comprise *buffer pairs,* the members of which work together in carrying out their neutralizing action. One of the most important buffers in the blood is the *bicarbonate buffer,* which consists of *sodium bicarbonate* ($NaHCO_3$) and the weak acid of which it is a salt, *carbonic acid* (H_2CO_3). If a moderate amount of a strong acid, such as hydrochloric acid (HCl), is added to this buffer, the acid is converted to ordinary sodium chloride (NaCl) in the following manner:

$$NaHCO_3 + HCl \rightarrow NaCl + H_2CO_3$$

The chloride ion of the hydrochloric acid (Cl^-) has been replaced by the bicarbonate ion (HCO_3^-).

Instead of a strong acid, suppose that a strong base, such as sodium hydroxide (NaOH), is added to the bicarbonate buffer pair:

$$H_2CO_3 + NaOH \rightarrow NaHCO_3 + H_2O$$

In this instance, it is the *carbonic-acid portion of the buffer* which takes part in the buffering. It changes the strongly alkaline sodium hydroxide into sodium bicarbonate and water.

The products of buffer action can easily be eliminated from the body by the lungs or kidneys, or they may be utilized in one or more of the myriad of chemical reactions that go on in the body. For example, the carbonic acid (H_2CO_3) which is produced along with sodium chloride when hydrochloric acid is added to bicarbonate buffer is in a volatile form, and is quickly eliminated by the lungs.

Hemoglobin, disodium phosphate, and the *plasma proteins* are other buffers of importance which are found in the blood. These and the bicarbonate buffer are particularly useful as sources of *alkali reserve,* standing ready to help prevent a drastic change in the blood pH by strong acids. The respiratory and urinary systems are also of great importance in the maintenance of a constant body pH. The roles of these and the circulatory system in the acid–base balance of the body are discussed in Chapter 15.

THE LYMPHATIC SYSTEM

There is a plasmalike fluid that circulates throughout the body, a fluid that has several different names, depending upon where it is found. As the external fluid environment of individual cells, it is called *intercellular or interstitial fluid;* in lymph vessels, which carry the collected interstitial fluid to the venous circulation, it is known simply as *lymph;* and lymph that is leaving the intestines following a meal (and which is milky white due to finely dispersed fat particles) is called *chyle.* Lymph is not exactly like plasma. Its protein content is low compared to that of plasma, and there are other minor differences. Lymph is formed as interstitial fluid that leaves plasma, filtering through capillary walls by a process called *transudation.* This involves the passage of certain substances—mostly water—through the walls of capillaries and into tissue spaces. Lymph contains *leucocytes,* mostly *lymphocytes.* It functions to return water and proteins from the interstitial spaces to the blood, thus helping to maintain blood osmotic pressure and body fluid balance. After remaining for a time in the interstitial spaces, lymph enters the venous circulation after passing through four different types of structures: (1) *lymph capillaries,* (2) *lymph vessels,* (3) *lymph nodes or glands,* and (4) *lymph ducts.* A good idea of the histological makeup of lymphatic tissue can be obtained by slicing through a lymph node lengthwise with a laboratory instrument called a *microtome* and examining the slice with a microscope.

LYMPH NODES   Lymph nodes are the bean-shaped structures found along lymph vessels throughout the body. Some are as big as large beans, while others are much smaller; but they all have the same *basic internal structure* (Fig. 10-30. Covering the node is a sheath of white fibrous connective tissue, or *capsule.* Tiny connective-tissue partitions—*trabeculae*—penetrate the node, dividing it into a number of sections or *lymph sinuses.* The inner portion of the node is the *medulla,* while the outer portion is the *cortex. Reticular connective tissue* is found throughout the medulla. Lymphocytes can be seen in both cortex and medulla, and are often grouped together in the cortical region in clusters called *nodules.* Several lymph vessels enter the outer or convex surface of a lymph node. They carry lymph *into* the node, and are given the name *afferent vessels.* Two larger vessels are seen at the depression or hilum of the lymph node; these are *efferent vessels,*

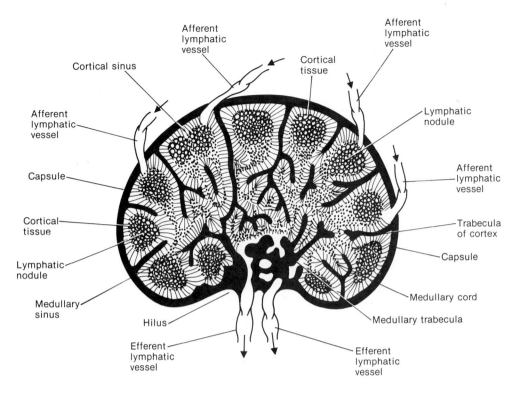

Figure 10-30 Structure of a lymph gland or node.

and transport lymph *out* of the node. All lymph vessels have little "trapdoors" or *valves* which prevent the backflow of lymph and, therefore, permit it to go in only one direction.

LYMPH CAPILLARIES AND VESSELS Like the capillaries of the blood-vascular system, *lymph capillaries* are microscopic and are structured mainly of one layer of endothelial cells. They are located in the intercellular spaces throughout the body. Lymph leaves the interstitial areas and makes its way via lymph capillaries to the larger, three-layered *lymph vessels*. Lymph capillaries in the mucosal lining of the intestine are given the special name *lacteals*. There is a lacteal in each microscopic *villus* of the intestine (Fig. 12-8). Digested lipids are absorbed through the walls of the lacteals and are then on their way to the bloodstream. Lymph capillaries end blindly and have no valves; but the largest lymph vessels have valves similar to those of veins.

LYMPH DUCTS Eventually, *all lymph collected by the lymph vessels enters one of two large lymph ducts:* the *thoracic duct,* which drains the entire body except the right half above the level of the diaphragm; and the *right lymph duct,* which drains this latter portion of the body (Fig. 10-31). The thoracic duct has an enlargement at about the level of the first lumbar vertebra, the *cysterna chyli.* The cysterna chyli receives lymph from several large vessels draining the lower extremities and the pelvis and abdomen. Both lymph ducts join the venous system at the angle formed by the *junction of the internal jugular and subclavian vein* on either side of the body.

The circulation of lymph

Lymph returning to the large lymph ducts from the head and neck does so easily, due to the force of gravity; but that moving from those portions of the body below the entrance of the lymph ducts into the circulatory system depends upon the *milking action of skeletal muscles,* the *lowered pressure within the thorax which results from breathing in,* the *movements of the heart and abdominal organs,* and the *prevention of backflow by the valves of the lymph vessels.*

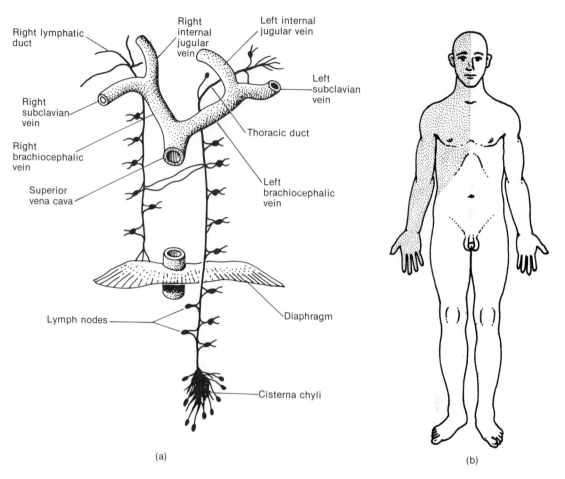

Right lymphatic duct

Right internal jugular vein

Left internal jugular vein

Left subclavian vein

Right subclavian vein

Thoracic duct

Right brachiocephalic vein

Superior vena cava

Left brachiocephalic vein

Diaphragm

Lymph nodes

Cisterna chyli

(a)

(b)

Figure 10-31 The two large ducts that carry lymph into the venous circulation near the point at which the subclavian veins join the internal jugular veins. (a) The thoracic duct and the right lymphatic duct. (b) Areas of drainage of each duct. The shaded area is drained by the right lymphatic duct; the unshaded area is drained by the thoracic duct.

The lymphoid organs

Lymph *glands* or nodes represent only one type of structure made of lymphatic tissue; others include the *thymus gland, spleen, tonsils,* and aggregations of lymphoid cells that form small nodules called *Peyer's patches.* These patches are particularly abundant beneath the mucous membrane of the *ileum,* the lower portion of the small intestine. All lymphatic tissue is essentially a connective-tissue *stroma* (a reticulum or network), in which is found *lymphocytes* (including the immature form, lymphoblasts), *phagocytic leucocytes,* and antibody-producing cells called *plasma cells.* Large numbers of *erythrocytes* are found in the spleen, and many of them disintegrate there.

FUNCTIONS OF LYMPH NODES Lymph nodes produce lymphocytes and serve to filter out microorganisms and other debris that gets into the lymphatic system. During infection, phagocytes in the lymph nodes engulf and destroy many of the bacteria or other infecting organisms. *Lymphadenitis,* an inflammation of the lymph nodes, may occur if the infection is severe.

Most of the lymph nodes of the body are arranged in clusters in the *cervical, axillary, pectoral, abdominal, pelvic,* and *inguinal* regions (Fig. 10-32), with smaller aggregations in various other locations, such as the *popliteal* regions. As will be noted in the figure, an elaborate system of vessels connects the nodes of these regions. An infection in one part of the body may produce soreness in the area into which the lymph from the infected area drains; for example, an infected finger may cause tenderness in the axilla, due to inflammation and swelling of the axillary nodes. *Carcinoma* (cancer) may spread—*metastasize*—via lymphatic routes. Surgeons operating for breast cancer routinely remove the axillary nodes as well as those in the pectoral region, in the hope of

arresting the possible spread of the disease to the arm and even up the neck. During an infection, the lymph vessels themselves may become inflamed, a condition called *lymphangitis.* Blood poisoning or *septicemia* may result if the infection goes untreated, or if treatment is begun too late. Lymphangitis involving deep lymph vessels is sometimes difficult to detect, but if superficial vessels are involved, long red marks or streaks can often be seen on the skin.

TONSILS   Three pairs of lymphoid structures help to prevent the entrance of bacteria into the upper respiratory and digestive tracts: the *pharyngeal tonsils or adenoids,* located in the posterior wall of the nasopharynx; the *palatine tonsils,* lying embedded in the posterior lateral walls of the throat (these are the tonsils so often removed in childhood); and the *lingual tonsils,* situated on the posterior portion of the tongue. Removal of the tonsils (*tonsillectomy*) and adenoids (*adenoidectomy*) is not so routine an operation as it was some 25 years ago. Today, inflamed tonsils (*tonsillitis*) can often be successfully treated by the use of antibiotics, thereby saving the tonsils to help protect the respiratory and digestive tracts. Tonsils may be involved in the *formation of lymphocytes* (they release these leucocytes into the blood from time to time) and of *immune substances* important in the overall resistance of the body to disease.

THE SPLEEN   The spleen is just below the diaphragm in the upper left portion of the abdomen (Fig. 12-7). It is about $5\frac{1}{2}$ in. long by 3 in. wide, and well supplied with blood spaces (*sinusoids*). Vessels enter and leave the spleen at its concavity, the *hilum.* In addition to filtering blood, acting as a cemetery for old erythrocytes and as a storage organ for an emergency blood supply, the spleen also *produces antibodies* and even produces a substance that seems to *stimulate the production of blood cells* in the bone marrow.

THE THYMUS   Somewhat of a mystery organ, the thymus is located in the superior portion of the thorax, *anterior to the aortic arch and superior vena cava.* The gland has

Figure 10-32   The major lymphatics of the body.

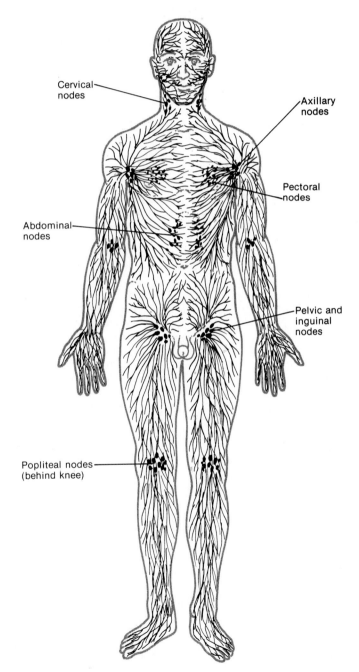

Cervical
nodes

Axillary
nodes

Pectoral
nodes

Abdominal
nodes

Pelvic and
inguinal
nodes

Popliteal nodes
(behind knee)

two *lobes* and is gray to pinkish gray in color. Up until about age 12, the thymus is relatively large; but after sexual maturity, it begins to atrophy (shrink), and by middle age may hardly exist. It seems to be a *source of lymphocytes* before birth, and a temporary producer of cells that bring about the formation of antibodies.

B. Thorax
    a. Superior vena cava
    b. Inferior vena cava
    c. Azygous
    d. Hemiazygous
    e. Intercostals
    f. Internal thoracic

C. Upper extremity
    a. Venous network of the hand
    b. Cephalic
    c. Median
    d. Basilic
    e. Median cubital
    f. Axillary

D. Lower extremity
    a. Anterior tibial
    b. Posterior tibial
    c. Peroneal
    d. Popliteal
    e. Femoral
    f. Great saphenous

E. Abdomen and pelvis
    a. External iliac
    b. Internal iliac
    c. Common iliac
    d. Inferior vena cava
    e. Hepatic
    f. Portal
    g. Renal
    h. Genital

F. Venous drainage of the brain
    a. Cavernous sinus
    b. Superior sagittal sinus
    c. Inferior sagittal sinus
    d. Straight sinus
    e. Transverse sinus
    f. Sigmoid sinus
    g. Superior petrosal sinus
    h. Inferior petrosal sinus
    i. Internal jugular vein

6. Circulation in the fetus
  A. Only indirectly connected with that of the mother, by means of the vessels of the placenta and umbilical cord
  B. Special features of fetal circulation
    a. Connection of fetal internal iliac arteries with placenta by means of umbilical arteries
    b. Connection of inferior vena cava and liver to the placenta by means of the ductus venosus and umbilical vein
    c. Communication of atria by means of the foramen ovale
    d. Joining of aorta and pulmonary trunk by the ductus arteriosus, which later becomes the ligamentum arteriosum
  C. A persisting foramen ovale is called patent foramen ovale, and a persisting ductus arteriosus is called patent ductus arteriosus (or simply patent ductus)
  D. The umbilical vein becomes the ligamentum teres, and the ductus venosus becomes the ligamentum venosum. Both help hold the liver in place

7. Physiology of the heart
  A. Origin of the heartbeat: within the heart itself (myogenic)
    a. Sinoatrial (SA) node, the pacemaker
    b. Atrioventricular (AV) node
    c. Bundle of His
    d. Purkinje system
  B. Control of the heart rate: by the autonomic nervous system
    a. Cardioacceleration is by sympathetic fibers in the superior, middle, and inferior cardiac nerves
    b. Cardioinhibition is by parasympathetic fibers in the vagus nerves
  C. Heart block: interruption of the excitatory wave at any point within the conducting system; may follow rheumatic fever or other infectious diseases, or drug overdose
    a. AV block: occurs at AV node
    b. Bundle branch block: involves a branch of the bundle of His
    c. Complete block: third-degree block (atria and ventricles beat independently)
    d. Incomplete block: first- and second-degree block; ventricles contract slower than atria, often in a definite ratio to the contraction of the ventricles
  D. Electrical activity of the heart
    a. The electrocardiogram (ECG or EKG): a visual record of the electrical activity of the heart, produced by the electrocardiograph
    b. Leads: each requires that two electrodes be placed on the subject, in the following manner
      1. Lead I: right wrist and left wrist
      2. Lead II: right wrist and left ankle
      3. Lead III: left wrist and left ankle
    c. Parts of the electrocardiogram
      1. P-wave: represents depolarization of the atria
      2. Q-wave ⎫ Form the QRS-complex, representing
      3. R-wave ⎬ plex, representing
      4. S-wave ⎭ depolarization of the ventricles
      5. T-wave: indicates completion of repolarization of the heart
      6. P–R interval: time period between the beginning of the P-wave and beginning of the Q-wave; indicates time required for wave of contraction to arrive at the ventricles
      7. S–T time segment: time period between the end of ventricular

depolarization and beginning of repolarization

E. Cardiac arrhythmias: abnormal heart rates
   a. Tachycardia: rapid heart
   b. Bradycardia: slow heart
   c. Fibrillation: contraction of small areas of the heart, independently of each other
   d. Extrasystole: a contration of "premature beat" following stimulation of the heart during the last portion of diastole
   e. Compensatory pause: an extra period of rest following extrasystole
F. Reflexes affecting the heart rate
   a. Aortic sinus reflex: pressoreceptors in the aortic arch send impulses to cardioinhibitor and cardioaccelerator centers, which return impulses over cardioaccelerator and cardioinhibitor neurons
   b. Carotid sinus reflex: similar to aortic sinus reflex, but pressoreceptors in common carotid arteries are utilized
   c. Carotid and aortic body reflex: depends upon chemoreceptors which are sensitive to changes in the oxygen level and pH of the blood
   d. Venous pressure reflex: depends upon pressoreceptors in the superior and inferior venae cavae
   e. Bainbridge reflex: increase in heart rate following physical activity
   f. Marey's law of the heart: reflex slowing of the heart following an increase in arterial blood pressure
G. The cardiac cycle: the sequence of events occurring during one complete heartbeat. At 72 beats per min, each cycle lasts 0.8 sec. An 8-slice pie chart reveals these (and other) features of the cardiac cycle:
   a. Ventricular systole requires 0.3 sec
   b. Ventricular diastole requires 0.5 sec
   c. Atrial systole lasts 0.1 sec
   d. Atrial diastole lasts 0.7 sec
   e. Atrial systole and 0.4 sec of atrial diastole occur during ventricular diastole
   f. Three-tenths of a second of atrial diastole occur during ventricular systole
   g. During the first 0.1 sec of atrial diastole, the atria are relaxing, while during the remaining 0.6 sec, they are resting
   h. Two-tenths of a second are devoted to ventricular relaxation, 0.3 sec to rest
H. Heart sounds and action of the heart valves
   a. At the beginning of atrial diastole: semilunar valves open, bicuspid and tricuspid valves close
   b. At the end of ventricular systole: atrioventricular valves open, semilunar valves close
   c. "Lub," the first heart sound, is heard near the beginning of ventricular systole, and is due to closure of the AV valves and contraction of the ventricles
   d. "Dup," the second heart sound, is heard at the end of ventricular systole, and is due to closure of the SL valves
   e. Third heart sound: low-pitched, dull, heard just after second heart sound; may be due to ventricular vibration during rapid filling phase; not always present
   f. Murmur: an abnormal heart sound; may be nonpathological or pathological, and caused by such factors as valvular stenosis, for example, mitral stenosis
8. Cardiac dynamics and blood pressure
   A. Cardiac output (C.O.) = heart rate × stroke volume
      a. Concerns the left ventricle, because it pumps blood through the systemic circulation
      b. Averages 4900 cc in the adult
      c. Varies with ventricular filling, and influences of the autonomic nervous system and endocrine system
   B. Arterial blood pressure
      a. Arterial pressure represents the force exerted by the blood against the walls of the arteries. It varies with the following factors
         1. Frictional resistance offered by the walls of the arteries
         2. Peripheral resistance offered by arterioles, which can constrict and dilate
         3. Cardiac output
         4. Blood volume
         5. Blood velocity, or speed of flow
         6. Elasticity of the arteries
         7. Distensibility of the arteries
         8. Blood viscosity
      b. Systolic, diastolic, and pulse pressures
         1. Systolic: results from the force of ventricular contraction; averages about 115 to 150 mm Hg
         2. Diastolic: blood pressure existing during ventricular relaxation and rest; averages 70 mm Hg

3. Pulse pressure: the arithmetical difference between systolic and diastolic pressures; averages 50 mm Hg
   c. Clinical measurement of arterial blood pressure
      1. Direct method, by cannulation, rarely used
      2. Indirect method, by determining the pressure required to occlude an artery with an inflatable cuff
   C. Venous pressure
      a. Averages 12 mm Hg in venules, 4.5–5.0 mm Hg in the inferior vena cava near the heart, and is almost unmeasurable in most large veins; may be —10 mm Hg in the venous sinuses of the brain
      b. Depends upon the milking action of muscles, suction by the right atrium, and variations in intrathoracic and intraabdominal pressures during breathing
   D. Miscellaneous factors affecting arterial blood pressure
      a. Disease
      b. Age
      c. Amount of sleep
      d. Physical activity
      e. Body weight
      f. Sex
      g. Emotional factors
   E. Control of blood-vessel diameter by the autonomic nervous system
      a. The circular smooth muscle of small arteries and arterioles is supplied by sympathetic vasoconstrictor fibers and parasympathetic vasoconstrictor and vasodilator fibers
      b. Vasoconstrictor centers in the medulla and spinal cord send impulses over the vasoconstrictor fibers
      c. A vasodilator center may exist in the medulla. If not, all vasodilation results from inhibition of the vasoconstrictor centers
9. The blood
   A. Function: acts as the transportation medium of the circulatory system, aids in body-temperature regulation, efficient heart action, and in the homeostasis of acid–base balance
   B. Composition and physical features
      a. A fluid tissue, with cells in suspension
      b. Bright red when oxygenated, dark red when deoxygenated
      c. Comprises about 7% of the body weight (an average of 10 lb or 5 liters)

d. Specific gravity about the same as water (1.06)
e. Slightly alkaline (pH about 7.4)
f. Consists of two portions or fractions
   1. Plasma, or fluid fractions (55%)
   2. Formed elements, or solid fraction (45%): the hematocrit
C. Plasma
   a. About 90% water
   b. Has solutes consisting of proteins, electrolytes, glucose, fats, and such metabolic wastes as creatinine, lactic acid, urea, and uric acid. Plasma also contains antibodies, enzymes, and hormones, as well as small amounts of dissolved oxygen and carbon dioxide
   c. Plasma is important in osmotic relationships with blood cells
   d. Plasma has these major proteins: albumin, fibrinogen, prothrombin, and alpha, beta, and gamma globulins. Their chief functions are as follows
      1. Albumin—osmotic relationships of plasma and formed elements
      2. Fibrinogen—coagulation or clotting
      3. Prothrombin—coagulation
      4. Alpha and beta globulins—protein transport
      5. Gamma globulins—immunization
   e. Nutrients of plasma
      1. Glucose
      2. Lipids
      3. Amino acids
      4. Miscellaneous nutrients
   f. Electrolytes of plasma: salts of sodium, potassium, magnesium, and calcium, as sulfates, phosphates, chlorides, and carbonates. They are important in nerve impulse transmission, acid–base balance, and nutrition
   g. Clinical importance of plasma: high blood plasma nitrogen levels indicate kidney disease; high blood glucose, diabetes mellitus; and variations in plasma calcium, parathyroid malfunction
D. The blood cells
   a. Red blood cells (RBC's) or erythrocytes
      1. Anucleate, biconcave discs, 7.5 μ in diameter, and 2.2 μ thick near the periphery
      2. Have a flexible membrane only 150 Angstroms thick
      3. Average $4\frac{1}{2}$ to 5 million per mm^3 of blood

4. Consists of an internal stroma, cell membrane, and the respiratory pigment, hemoglobin. About 15 g of hemoglobin is present in every 100 cc of blood, and each gram carries about 1.34 cc of oxygen in loose combination

5. Formed from erythroblasts in bone marrow, and remain in circulation about 120 days. 2½ million are formed and destroyed every second. Formation may be controlled by erythropoietin, produced by the kidneys

6. Formation of blood is hemopoiesis; that of red cells in particular, erythropoiesis; and that of white cells, leucopoiesis

7. The spleen is a center for the storage and release or destruction of erythrocytes

b. White blood cells (WBC's) or leucocytes: these are larger than erythrocytes, have nuclei, and may live only a few days. They are extremely important in phagocytosis, and also take part in tissue repair and antibody production. They wriggle through capillary walls (diapedesis) and move in response to chemical substances in the blood (chemotaxis). There are five kinds: neutrophils, basophils, eosinophils, monocytes, and lymphocytes. The first three are called granulocytes because of granules present in the cytoplasm. All except lymphocytes are formed in bone marrow. Lymphocytes are formed in the lymphoid tissues. Important features of the different kinds of leucocytes are as follows

1. Neutrophils: nuclei colored by neutral stains; three or more lobes in nuclei; make up 60% of all WBC's

2. Eosinophils: nuclei colored by eosin and other acid stains; make up 4% of all leucocytes; have lobulated nuclei, coarse cytoplasmic granules

3. Basophils: have affinity for basic stains, such as methylene blue; nuclei only partially lobulated

4. Monocytes: large, with large, oval, unlobulated nuclei

5. Lymphocytes: two types, large and small; comprise up to 25% of the total circulating leucocytes; have unlobulated nuclei

c. Platelets, or thrombocytes: anucleated fragments of megakaryocytes, about half the size of an erythrocyte. There are 300,000 to 400,000 per mm³ of blood. Platelets initiate clotting when they are damaged by releasing thromboplastin into the wound

E. Bleeding and coagulation

a. Arterial bleeding is forceful, and pulsates with each beat of the heart; venous bleeding is much less forceful, and does not pulsate

b. Bleeding time: the time required for cessation of bleeding from a small wound, such as the puncture of an earlobe

c. Clotting time: the time required for whole blood to coagulate when placed in a test tube

d. Mechanism of coagulation

1. Four substances are essential to clot formation: calcium, thrombokinase, prothrombin, and fibrinogen

2. Two reactions must take place if a clot is to be formed
   i. Prothrombin must be converted to thrombin
   ii. Fibrinogen must be converted to fibrin

3. A summary of the chief events of coagulation is as follows

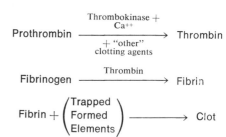

Vitamin K is essential to the formation of prothrombin in the liver

e. Hemorrhage: literally, any internal or external bleeding. Can often be controlled by pressure, ligation, or administration of thrombin and fibrin preparations. The rapid loss of a large quantity of blood results in a sharp drop in blood pressure and an increase in breathing and heart rates. In severe hemorrhage, there is danger of shock

f. Blood substitutes: restore blood volume and provide an emergency source. Some examples: whole and reconstituted plasma, serum, saline–glucose solutions, and carbohydrate–water preparations. The blood substitutes must be isotonic to the blood

F. Blood typing and transfusion
   a. International system of blood grouping includes four types or groups: O, A, B, and AB. Rh-positive blood contains a certain protein, Rh-negative blood does not
      1. Type A: contains a certain blood protein or antigen of the "A" variety in the red cells
      2. Type B: contains "B" antigen
      3. Type AB: contains antigens "A" and "B"
      4. Type O: contains neither "A" nor "B" antigens
   b. Agglutinins or antibodies present in the plasma: bring about agglutination of red cells containing an incompatible antigen
      1. Type A: contains anti–B antibodies
      2. Type B: contains anti–A antibodies
      3. Type AB: contains no antibodies
      4. Type O: contains both anti–A and anti–B antibodies
   c. General conditions for transfusion
      1. If blood types of donor and recipient are identical
      2. If blood type of donor is O. Cells of this blood are not agglutinated by any plasma ("universal donor")
      3. If blood type of recipient is AB. Plasma of this blood does not contain antibodies ("universal recipient")
   d. Cross-matching: cells of donor blood are suspended in plasma of the recipient, and vice versa. No agglutination of cells must occur if transfusion is to be safely performed.
      e. The importance of Rh factor: poses potential problems during second or succeeding pregnancies, if the blood of the child is Rh+, and that of the mother is Rh−
G. Blood buffers: most consist of buffer pairs made up of a weak acid and the salt of that acid. Some important buffers of the blood include the bicarbonate buffer ($NaHCO_3 + H_2CO_3$), hemoglobin, disodium phosphate, and the plasma proteins

10. The lymphatic system
    A. Lymph is a plasmalike fluid that circulates in lymph capillaries, lymph vessels, and lymph ducts. It is named variously lymph, interstitial fluid (between the cells), and chyle (as it leaves the intestine). Its function is to return water and proteins from the interstitial spaces to the blood
    B. Lymph cells (lymphocytes) are formed in the lymphatic or lymphoid tissues (lymph nodes, tonsils, and spleen)
    C. Eventually, all lymph enters the thoracic duct or right lymph duct, then enters the venous circulation at the junctions formed by the internal jugular and subclavian veins
    D. Most of the lymph nodes of the body are located in aggregations in the cervical, axillary, pectoral, abdominal, pelvic, and inguinal regions
    E. The lymphatic system offers a route for the spread of infection and metastasis of cancer
    F. The tonsils, spleen, and thymus are all associated with the circulatory or lymphatic system at some time during a normal life span

**STUDY
QUESTIONS
AND
PROBLEMS**

1. Briefly discuss the contribution of the circulatory system to the body homeostasis.

2. Make a general-outline plan of the circulatory system, including the heart and its four chambers. Discuss the microscopic structure of arteries and veins.

3. Sketch a diagram of the heart as seen on frontal section, and label all chambers, valves, and other structures.

4. Jenny, a patient in a children's hospital, has a mitral stenosis. This is narrowing of what atrioventricular valve?

5. What great blood vessels of the heart have semilunar valves? Describe a typical semilunar valve and tell how it works.

6. Name the arteries that supply the myocardium. Where do they originate?

7. Make a diagram of the major arteries and veins of the body. The radial and ulnar arteries are branches of what artery?

8. Discuss the arterial supply to the brain. Name the major venous structures that drain the brain.

9. Describe features of the fetal circulation that are not present in the adult.

10. What is meant by the statement that the heartbeat is myogenic? What is the "pacemaker" of the heart? The bundle of His? The Purkinje system?

11. What is the name given to a cardiac disorder that involves the conducting system of the heart to the extent that the contraction impulse is interrupted? Discuss reflex control of the heart.

12. Define: *stroke volume, cardiac output, extrasystole, tachycardia, fibrillation,* and *coronary thrombosis* or *myocardial infarction.*

13. Discuss the electrocardiogram and its three standard leads. Draw and label a "pie chart" of the cardiac cycle.

14. List the factors that affect arterial blood pressure. How is blood pressure commonly determined clinically?

15. Describe the composition and physical features of the blood. What is the hematocrit? What is another name for platelets?

16. Discuss blood grouping, transfusion, agglutination, and coagulation. Write equations showing the major steps in coagulation.

17. What is Evans blue? Write the formula for calculating plasma volume.

18. Briefly discuss the lymphatic system and its functions. In what ways does this system act to spread infection and cancer?

the breathing mechanism and gaseous exchange

Human life on earth is dependent upon (among other things) our ability to *utilize* one gas, **oxygen,** and to *eliminate* another gas, **carbon dioxide.** Oxygen, present in the amount of about 21% in the air, must enter the blood and reach every body cell so that foods may be burned—more precisely, *oxidized*—and so that the cells, therefore, may continue to live. Many cells, notably those of the central nervous system and heart, are extremely sensitive to low blood levels of oxygen, or *hypoxia,* and of course to complete lack of oxygen, *anoxia.* Without oxygen, *most brain cells are dead within 3 to 5 minutes.*

Oxygen reaches the cells, and CO_2 (carbon dioxide) is eliminated from these cells, all by a complicated physiologic process called *respiration*. Clinically, respiration and *breathing* are synonymous; but from a purely physiological standpoint, this identification is not a valid one. The physiologist knows that there are two major types of respiration—one involving breathing, the other concerned with the release of energy from foodstuffs within the cells, or *cellular respiration*. In this chapter, we shall be concerned primarily with the "breathing" kind of respiration. A discussion of cellular respiration is included in Chapter 13, which is concerned in part with the metabolism of foods.

Breathing as respiration can be further subdivided into *external respiration,* during which oxygen leaves the atmosphere and enters the bloodstream, while CO_2 leaves the blood and enters the atmosphere; and *internal respiration,* which involves the exchange of oxygen and CO_2 between the blood and the cells.

Respiratory quotient (R.Q.)

As blood passes through the lungs, it takes up about 5 volumes per cent of oxygen and releases about 4 volumes per cent of carbon dioxide. That is, for every 100 cc of blood moving through the lungs, 5 cc of oxygen are *accepted,* and 4 cc of CO_2 are *given up. The ratio of CO_2 liberation to O_2* (oxygen) *uptake is called the respiratory quotient* (R.Q.), and averages 0.7 to 1.0. Actually, the R.Q. *varies with the diet,* being about 1.0 for a diet rich in carbohydrates, 0.8 for one high in proteins, and 0.7 for a diet high in fat, due to the different energy relationships which result when these three different food substances are metabolized. The respiratory quotient can be expressed in the following manner:

$$R.Q. = \frac{CO_2 \text{ output}}{O_2 \text{ intake}}$$

In order that the student may fully appreciate the mechanisms involved in the two phases of respiration, the following discussion will consist of an integrated consideration of the structure and function of the respiratory organs.

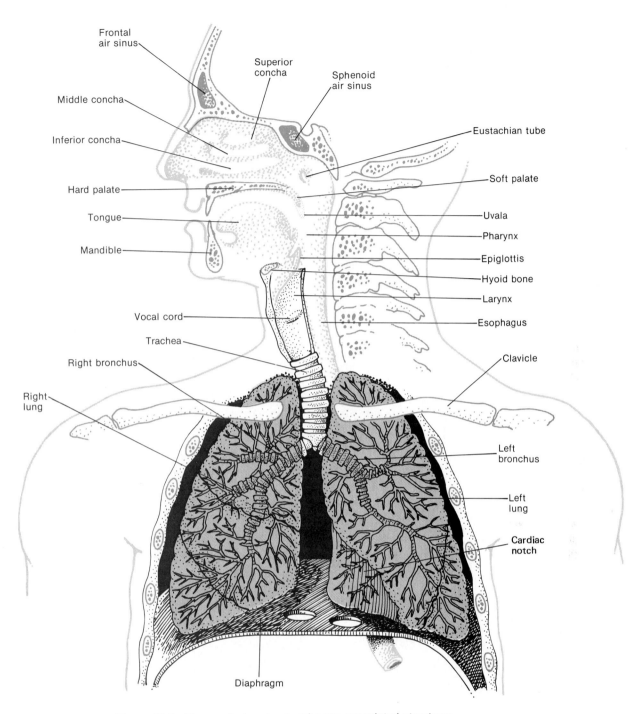

Figure 11-1 The respiratory tract and some associated structures.

Breathing and the respiratory apparatus

Figure 11-1 and Color Plates IV through VII, depicting the *component parts of the respiratory system—nose, pharynx, larynx, trachea, bronchi, lungs,* and *dia-*phragm—should be frequently referred to while reading this chapter.

THE NOSE   The nose consists of two passageways lined with ciliated mucous membrane and separated by a partition made of cartilage and bone, the *septum*. Ciliated mucous membrane is found in most of the airways of the respiratory system, even the bronchioles. Each nasal passageway (*nostril* or *cavity*) is divided into three connecting portions—called the superior, middle, and inferior *meati*—by the superior, inferior, and middle *turbinates* or conchae, which project from the lateral walls of the cavities (Chapter 5). The anterior openings of the nasal passageways are called *external nares,* the posterior openings (which connect with the nasal pharynx), *internal nares.* The floor of the nose (and roof of the mouth) is formed by the palatine and maxillary bones. Failure of these bones to unite in the midline during development results in a condition called *cleft palate.* Individuals with uncorrected cleft palate usually have difficulty in swallowing and speaking.

Besides serving as an airway, the nose warms and moistens incoming air, and its cilia and mucous membranes trap dust and other foreign matter. The nasal mucosa contains the receptors for the sense of smell, and the nasal cavities contribute to the quality of the voice. About 1 quart (qt) of mucus is produced by the nasal mucosa each day, partly as a protective mechanism and partly as a reaction to dust, pollen, and other ma-

terials. Mucus is either eliminated by blowing the nose, or it is swallowed.

Four pairs of *paranasal sinuses* (Fig. 11-2) drain into the nose in the following manner:

1. Above the superior turbinates—sphenoidal sinuses.

2. Into the superior meatus (just below the superior turbinate)—posterior ethmoidal sinuses.

3. Into the middle meatus (just below the middle turbinate)—frontal, maxillary, and anterior ethmoidal sinuses.

THE PHARYNX The pharynx (or "throat") is the tubelike structure that begins just posterior to the nasal cavities and ends at the esophagus. It connects the nose and mouth with the remainder of the respiratory and digestive tracts, and is important in the formation of vowels during phonation. The pharyngeal walls are muscular, and are lined with mucous membrane. The pharynx has three portions:

1. *Nasopharynx* (nasal pharynx). Just behind and continuous with the nasal cavities.

Figure 11-2 The air (paranasal) sinuses of the skull. All drain into the nasal cavity.

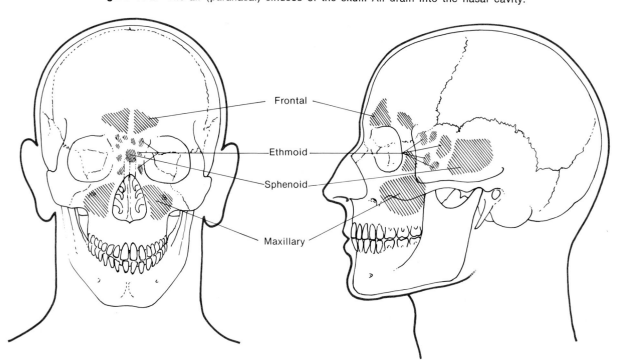

Frontal

Ethmoid

Sphenoid

Maxillary

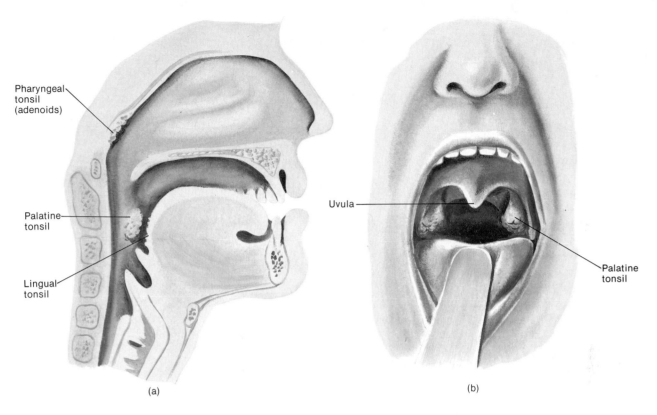

Figure 11-3 The tonsils. (a) Location. (b) Palatine tonsils as seen on physical examination.

2. *Oropharynx* (oral pharynx). Posterior to the oral cavity or mouth.

3. *Laryngopharynx* (laryngeal pharynx). Posterior to the larynx or voice box.

Adjacent portions of the pharynx blend into each other without sharp lines of demarcation. There are seven openings into the pharynx:

1-4. *Nasopharynx.* Right and left *pharyngotympanic* (eustachian) *tubes* and the two *internal nares.*

5. *Oropharynx.* The *fauces* or opening of the mouth into the pharynx.

6-7. *Laryngopharynx.* Openings of the *larynx* and *esophagus* into the pharynx.

Three pairs of lymphoid organs are associated with the pharynx. They are all called *tonsils* (Fig. 11-3).

1. *Pharyngeal tonsils* (adenoids). Located on the posterior wall of the nasopharynx.

2. *Palatine tonsils* (faucial tonsils). Be-

hind and below the pillars of the fauces in the oropharynx.

3. *Lingual tonsils.* At the base of the tongue in the oropharynx.

The tonsils may serve as filters of harmful microorganisms, but chronic infection or inflammation may necessitate their removal. During tonsillectomy the palatine and pharyngeal tonsils are commonly removed, but the lingual tonsils are usually left intact.

THE TRACHEA The trachea or windpipe (Fig. 11-4) extends from the larynx to the level of the fifth thoracic vertebra, where it divides into two *primary bronchi,* one for each lung. The trachea consists of smooth muscle, reinforced with C-shaped rings of cartilage, incomplete posteriorly. The gap at the back of the trachea is bridged by a connective tissue membrane. The esophagus lies directly posterior to the trachea, and as a large food bolus (a mass of food) passes down the esophagus on its way to the stomach, it causes the membrane of the trachea to bulge inwardly. The right and left primary

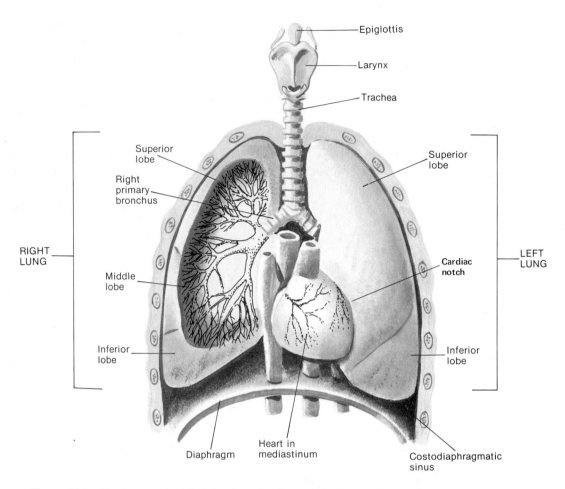

Epiglottis

Larynx

Trachea

Superior
lobe

Right
primary
bronchus

RIGHT
LUNG

Middle
lobe

Inferior
lobe

Superior
lobe

Cardiac
notch

LEFT
LUNG

Inferior
lobe

Diaphragm

Heart in
mediastinum

Costodiaphragmatic
sinus

Figure 11-4 The lungs and related structures in place within the thorax. A portion of the right lung has been cut away to show the branching of the bronchial "tree."

bronchi branch into *secondary bronchi* as they enter the lungs, which in turn branch into *smaller and smaller bronchi,* all with rings of cartilage. Finally, the very smallest bronchi give rise to microscopic branches called *bronchioles,* which are made essentially of *smooth muscle,* without cartilage. The bronchioles end in millions upon millions of microscopic blind or "deadend" air sacs, the *alveoli* (Fig. 11-5). Like the *pulmonary "tree"* of bronchi and bronchioles, the *circulatory tree* of pulmonary blood vessels is very extensive. Each alveolus is surrounded by capillaries, and it is here that the *exhange of oxygen and carbon dioxide* takes place. Clusters of alveoli are called *alveolar sacs;* and each alveolar sac is connected to a bronchiole by a small branch of that bronchiole, the *alveolar duct.*

If heavy mucus—such as that produced by diphtheria or a common cold—or a foreign object is aspirated (sucked into) the trachea, a *tracheotomy* may be performed in order to prevent death by asphyxiation. A small *vertical* incision is made in the tracheal midline, a short distance below the thyroid cartilage, and a metal or plastic tube is inserted in order to establish an airway. The right primary bronchus is shorter and points more directly downward than the left; therefore, an aspirated object that moves all the way down to the bifurcation of the trachea is more likely to pass into the right bronchus than the left. Cilia line the walls of the trachea and bronchi, and they beat or wave constantly, in one direction only—upward, toward the larynx. Normal everyday quantities of mucus and trapped dust particles are moved upward by the cilia, and coughed into the mouth.

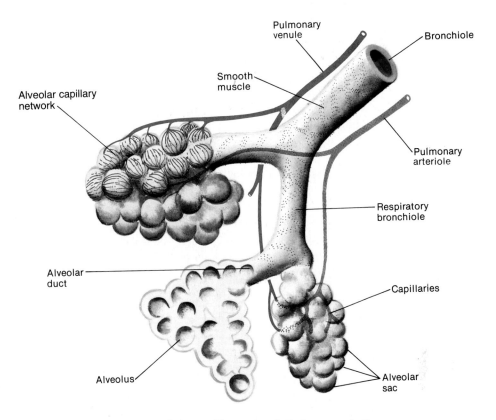

Figure 11-5 The structure of alveoli and the capillary network that surrounds them.

THE LUNGS AND PLEURAE The lungs (Fig. 11-4) are rather cone-shaped, with the *apex* of each directed upward, and the *base* downward, near the diaphragm. The apex of each

Figure 11-6 The pleura. Most of the pleural space is only a potential space, containing a little fluid which prevents the two layers of pleura from rasping as they rub against each other during the movements of breathing.

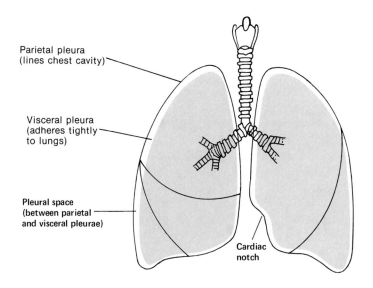

lung reaches *above the level of the first rib,* and it is, therefore, possible to suffer lung damage as a result of a wound in the lower neck region. The lungs literally fill the upper and lateral portions of the chest cavity. The central portion of the thoracic cavity, between the lungs, is called the *mediastinum,* and contains the *heart* and the *roots of its great vessels,* as well as a portion of the *trachea,* the *esophagus, important nerves,* and other structures. The lower borders of the lungs taper downward from the *fifth costal cartilages* at the sternum to approximately the *six to eighth rib at the midaxillary line,* and *tenth rib at a line passed vertically through the approximate center of the scapula.* There is a shallow space below each lung, between it and the diaphragm, called the *phrenicocostal or costodiaphragmatic sinus.* The lungs move downward, their bases occupying these spaces during deep inspiration.

The lungs are covered with a serous membrane called *pleura* (Fig. 11-6), which dips into deep clefts or fissures of the lungs, separating the organs into *lobes.* The right lung has *three* lobes, the left lung only *two*. Each lobe has its own *air and blood supply*. A continuation of the pleura that covers the lungs—more precisely, the *visceral pleura*—lines the walls of the thorax and covers the superior surface of the diaphragm. It is known as *parietal pleura*. The space between the parietal and visceral layers of pleura—the *pleural space*—is in most portions of the thorax only a potential one, containing a little serous fluid to serve as a lubricant to prevent friction and possible *pleuritis or pleurisy*—inflammation of the pleurae—as the two layers rub together during breathing. Each lung lobe is made up of two or more *bronchopulmonary segments* (Fig. 11-7), each with its own blood and air supply. Surgeons take advantage of this fact and remove only as many of these as is deemed necessary when operating upon diseased lungs—instead of taking out a lung lobe or even an entire lung—unless there appears to be no other recourse in saving the patient's life.

In life, lung tissue is not firm to the touch, as it is in the preserved specimens in the laboratory. One advantage of these hardened specimens, however, is that they clearly indicate the positions occupied by the aorta, the heart, and other large structures in relation to the lungs.

The large depressed area on the medial aspect of each lung is called the *hilium*. It is here that the bronchi enter the lungs, as do the blood and lymph vessels and nerves. The right and left pulmonary arteries, themselves branches of the pulmonary trunk, branch and rebranch many times within the lung substance, forming a circulatory tree that eventually supplies every alveolus with capillaries. This system of vessels carries deoxygenated blood, however, which has just returned from the systemic circuit, and, therefore, cannot supply the lung tissue itself with arterial (oxygenated) blood. The lung tissues get their oxygen-enriched blood from branches of two or three *bronchial arteries* (that branch off the back of the aorta) and the *first intercostal artery*, which courses be-

Figure 11-7 The bronchopulmonary segments.

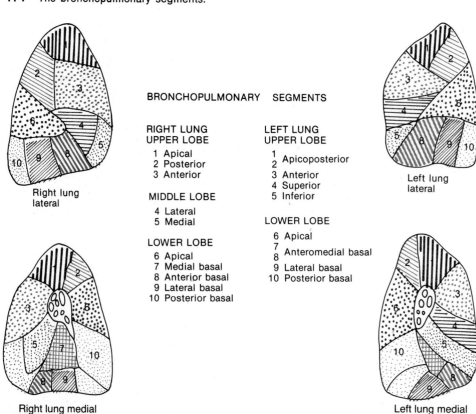

BRONCHOPULMONARY SEGMENTS

RIGHT LUNG
UPPER LOBE

1 Apical
2 Posterior
3 Anterior

MIDDLE LOBE

4 Lateral
5 Medial

LOWER LOBE

6 Apical
7 Medial basal
8 Anterior basal
9 Lateral basal
10 Posterior basal

LEFT LUNG
UPPER LOBE

1
2 Apicoposterior
3 Anterior
4 Superior
5 Inferior

LOWER LOBE

6 Apical
7
8 Anteromedial basal
9 Lateral basal
10 Posterior basal

Right lung
lateral

Left lung
lateral

Right lung medial

Left lung medial

tween the upper two ribs and is also a branch of the aorta. *Bronchial and intercostal veins* return the blood, after it has passed through the lung tissue and given up its oxygen and picked up carbon dioxide, to larger veins, such as the *azygos, hemiazygos,* and *accessory hemiazygos veins,* and eventually the *superior vena cava* and *right atrium.* The pulmonary arteries and their circulatory tree are of course parts of the *pulmonary circulation.* After the blood which entered the lungs in the pulmonary arteries has picked up oxygen and unloaded its carbon dioxide, it returns to the left atrium of the heart in *four pulmonary veins.* From the left atrium the blood moves to the left ventricle and is promptly pumped throughout the body in the *systemic circulation.* The lungs are supplied by the right and left vagus nerves, which carry *parasympathetic fibers* whose impulses bring about *constriction of the bronchi,* and by *sympathetic nerves* that carry impulses that cause *dilation of the bronchi.*

The diaphragm, chief organ of breathing

Breathing consists of two phases—*inspiration,* during which air is taken into the lungs, and *expiration,* during which air leaves the lungs and returns to the atmosphere.

Time was when man thought that the lungs moved air into and out of themselves under their own power; but man has long since learned that this is not true. The thorax is a *closed cavity* with but one opening; and when air enters and leaves the lungs through this opening, it does so mainly because of the action of the large, musculotendinous partition that separates the thoracic from the abdominal cavity: the *diaphragm* (Fig. 11-4). The lungs have no muscles and are completely passive in their actions, responding to pressure changes that occur in the thorax when the diaphragm moves up and down.

PRESSURE RELATIONSHIPS; BOYLE'S LAW
Air—or more precisely, *atmosphere*—exerts a force or *pressure* upon every surface with which it comes in contact. At sea level (760 mm Hg), the pressure of the atmosphere

amounts to 14.7 pounds per square inch (psi). This pressure decreases gradually with increase in altitude, as the atmosphere becomes less dense or "thinner." A well-known law of physics, *Boyle's law,* states that *the pressure of a confined gas—such as air—at a constant temperature, varies inversely with its volume.* That is, the greater the volume of the container, the more widely dispersed will be the elastic molecules of the gas, and the lower its pressure; and conversely.

As the diaphragm moves downward during inspiration, the pressure of the air surrounding the lungs (*intrathoracic pressure*) becomes significantly lower than atmospheric pressure, due to an increase in volume of the thorax (Table 11-1). This relieves pressure on the outside of the lungs, and the pressure within these organs (*intrapulmonic pressure*) also falls. The result is that a partial vacuum is created within the lungs, and air rushes into them from a region of higher pressure (atmospheric) to one of lower pressure. The elastic lungs stretch and expand with this inrush of air. When the diaphragm relaxes and moves back upward, the intrathoracic pressure increases, squeez-

TABLE 11-1

Pressure differences during the respiratory cycle

Phase of cycle	Intrathoracic pressure (mm Hg)	Intrapulmonary pressure (mm Hg)
Beginning of inspiration	−2.5	Atmospheric (760)
During quiet inspiration	−6.0	−2.0
Beginning of expiration	−2.5	−2.0
During quiet expiration	−2.5*	+3.5

* It should be noted that although intrathoracic pressure remains negative during expiration, the elastic recoil of the lungs increases the intrapulmonary pressure to the positive level of approximately +3.5 mm Hg.

ing the lungs so that they expel a good deal of their air. Very briefly, the intrapulmonic pressure must rise slightly above that of the atmosphere, in order that air may leave the lungs. The events just described are those taking place during *one respiratory cycle—* that is, *one inspiration followed by one expiration.* In the average adult, about 16 to 18 such cycles occur each minute at rest. The respiratory rate is much higher in the young, than in the aged, and slightly higher in women than in men. *Excitement, physical exertion,* and *certain diseases and drugs* all either increase or decrease the rate of respiration in certain circumstances.

OTHER RESPIRATORY MUSCLES   It has been stated that the diaphragm is the chief organ in the mechanism of breathing. The diaphragm acts as a suction plunger on inspiration and as a compressing piston on expiration, and in the individual at rest is almost solely responsible for the intake and expulsion of air by the lungs; but other muscles, especially upon exertion, assist in the breathing process. Notable among these are the external intercostal muscles, which help to elevate the ribs and expand the chest during inspiration, and the internal intercostals, which contract to help compress the chest during expiration. During vigorous exercise, even the large pectoralis major muscles help to expand the chest to its greatest diameter, so that as much air as possible may enter the lungs. The serratus anterior, trapezius, and levatores costarum muscles can also help in vigorous inspiration, and the internal oblique, external oblique, transversus abdominis, and rectus abdominis contract rather weakly during expiration. The action of the diaphragm and external intercostal muscles is reflex in nature, and can be overridden voluntarily for only brief periods of time (*try holding your breath for 45 sec*). The reflex is so powerful that it is impossible to stop breathing by merely willing it. It is also impossible for a normal, healthy child to injure himself by holding his breath (as children have occasionally been known to do in order to have their way).

The motor action of the diaphragm follows arrival of impulses over a pair of *phrenic nerves* which take origin as branches of the third and fourth cervical spinal nerves.

The reflexes of breathing; respiratory centers

The continued repetition of the respiratory cycle *depends upon the direct stimulation of, or the reception of afferent impulses by the central nervous system, and upon the subsequent transmission of efferent impulses from the CNS to the diaphragm and other muscles concerned with the breathing mechanism. Stretch receptors* in the *visceral pleura* are stimulated as the lungs expand during inspiration. Impulses initiated by these receptors travel over fibers in the *vagi nerves* to the *medulla.* Located in the medulla and pons are several clusters of neuron cell bodies called *respiratory centers;* these include an *inspiratory center,* an *expiratory center,* and an *apneustic* and *pneumotaxic center* (Fig. 11-8). Impulses arriving in the medulla from the lung stretch receptors *inhibit* the inspiratory center, the diaphragm relaxes due to lack of motor impulses from the medulla, and *expiration* takes place. Following deflation of the lungs, the carbon dioxide concentration of the blood rises rapidly. Neurons of the inspiratory center, being *extremely sensitive to* CO_2 *blood levels,* begin firing, sending impulses to the diaphragm and external intercostal muscles, and *inspiration* takes place. The higher the blood level of CO_2, the more neurons in the inspiratory center that are stimulated, and the deeper and more rapid the breathing. During rest, relatively few neurons in the center are affected, and breathing is slow and shallow; but during strenuous exercise, CO_2 is produced at a rapid rate, and more and more inspiratory center neurons are stimulated. This *automatic inspiration followed by involuntary expiration* is called the *Hering–Breuer reflex.* It is likely that, during quiet respiration, only the inspiratory center is involved, and that the stimulation of the neurons of this center by blood CO_2 and the inhibition of these cells by impulses arriving from the stretch receptors in the pleura accomplish the mechanics required in the respiratory cycle. During increased physical activity, however, the expiratory-center neurons are stimulated, and expiratory muscles (*internal intercostals*) contract, squeezing the thoracic cage and making expiration more forceful. *Chemoreceptors* in the *carotid*

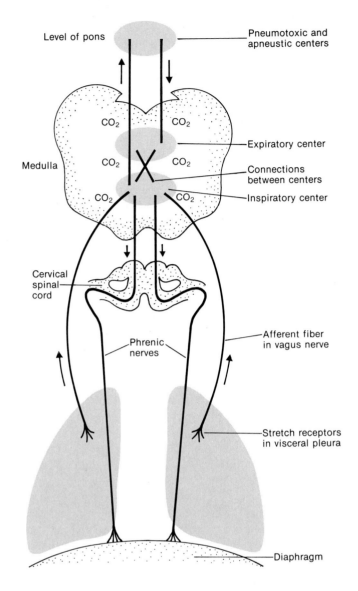

Figure 11-8 Chief nervous connections of the breathing reflex. Ascending arrows indicate direction of afferent impulses; descending arrows indicate efferent impulses.

The labels in the figure read:

Level of pons — Pneumotoxic and apneustic centers

CO_2 CO_2 — Expiratory center

Medulla CO_2 CO_2 — Connections between centers

CO_2 CO_2 — Inspiratory center

Cervical spinal cord

Phrenic nerves — Afferent fiber in vagus nerve

Stretch receptors in visceral pleura

Diaphragm

and *aortic bodies* (Chapter 10) are also thought to send impulses that affect respiration. Impulses are thought to travel from the carotid and aortic bodies to the respiratory centers in response to increased or decreased blood levels of oxygen and carbon dioxide. When oxygen levels get low, or carbon dioxide levels are high, the inspiratory center may be stimulated and the expiratory center depressed, so that breathing is deeper and more rapid. In a reverse situation—higher oxgyen levels and lower carbon dioxide levels—the inspiratory center is not overly stimulated, and breathing is slower and quieter. When the pH of the blood becomes low (increased acidity), the carotid and aortic bodies may send impulses that result in increases in the rate and depth of breathing, impulses that stimulate the inspiratory center.

THE PNEUMOTAXIC AND APNEUSTIC CENTERS
Connected to the neurons of the expiratory and inspiratory centers are neurons of a center located just above the cells of the former two, in the pons. This is the *pneumotaxic center,* a sort of backup mechanism for the Hering–Breuer reflex. For example, if the vagi nerves are cut, the pneumotaxic center can take over, *inhibiting the inspiratory center* (and subsequently, inspiration) and *stimulating the expiratory center,* so that expiration is assured. The pneumotaxic center also comes into play during periods of violent breathing, helping the Hering–Breuer mechanism to bring about forced expiration. The pneumotaxic center is stimulated by impulses arriving from the inspiratory center, at the same time that the latter is sending impulses to the inspiratory muscles. There is evidence that the pneumotaxic center regulates the *rhythm* of normal breathing. This center may, in response to impulses from the inspiratory center, stimulate the expiratory center, which then sends inhibitory impulses to the inspiratory center, resulting in expiration. Inspiration, resulting from the actions of mechanisms previously described, soon follows.

Another collection of neuron cell bodies, the *apneustic center* in the brainstem, seems to act as an *auxiliary inspiratory mechanism.* If an electric shock is applied to this center in an experimental animal, a strong inspiration of up to a half-minute in duration results. It should be pointed out that all centers concerned with the regulation and rhythm of respiration are *paired;* that is, each "center" in reality consists of bilateral clusters of cell bodies in the medulla and pons.

Lung capacities

Various terms are used by physiologists in describing the volume of air in the lungs under various conditions, or at different points of the respiratory cycle. For example, during normal quiet breathing, about 500 cc of air enter the lungs during an inspiration; this is called the *tidal volume.* Even after the strongest expiration that an individual can possibly make, about 1000 cc (1 liter) of air remain in the lungs; this is termed the *residual volume* or *residual air.* The *total lung capacity* is obtained by adding the residual volume to the amount of air that can be taken in during a maximal inspiration, and amounts to about 6 liters. If an individual *expires maximally following a maximal inspiration,* he has demonstrated the *vital capacity* of the lungs. It usually amounts to about 5 liters and remains the same if it is measured as *the volume of air that can be taken in following a maximal expiration.* There are two *reserve volumes* that can be measured. The *inspiratory reserve volume* is the *amount of air that can be breathed in following a quiet inspiration,* and averages 2.5 liters. The *expiratory reserve volume* is the *amount of air that can be exhaled following a quiet expiration,* and averages 2 liters. The *inspiratory capacity,* or *inspiratory air,* amounts to the tidal volume plus the inspiratory reserve volume. Some of the foregoing respiratory measurements can be made by having the subject breathe into a recording device such as a *spirometer,* while others are obtained by simple addition and subtraction of values obtained by spirometric methods. The tidal volume can be obtained, for example, by subtracting the inspiratory reserve volume from the inspiratory capacity; and a new measurement (that is, heretofore unmentioned) can be obtained by adding the residual volume to the expiratory reserve volume; this is called the *functional residual capacity,* and usually amounts to about 3 liters.

Abnormal breathing

Normal respiration is called *eupnea.* Various terms are assigned to the different types of abnormal breathing. *Dyspnea,* for example, means difficult or labored breathing. Some of the other terms include *hyperpnea* (excessively deep breathing), *apnea* (cessation of breathing), and *Cheyne–*

Stokes breathing, which is manifested by alternating periods of hyperpnea and apnea. Many different factors can act to bring on one or another type of abnormal breathing. One of the most common causes of dyspnea is the disease *emphysema;* another is a wound that punctures the chest, allowing air to enter the pleural space (between the parietal and visceral pleurae). This latter condition is called *pneumothorax,* and may result in *atelectasis,* during which the alveoli of the affected area do not expand completely, due to pressure of the entering atmosphere. Because the lungs normally lie in separate pleural cavities, separated by the mediastinum, a pneumothorax on one side of the chest would not affect the lung on the opposite side, unless an opening also existed in both walls of the mediastinum, thus effecting a communication between one pleural cavity and the other.

Hyperpnea naturally follows violent exercise, but it is also present when the lung capacity is diminished, as during the disease emphysema. Hyperpnea makes up one of the phases of Cheyne–Stokes respiration, which is actually an example of a "vicious cycle of pathological respiration," so to speak. During this cycle, a decrease in blood carbon dioxide stimulates the respiratory center so weakly that the center sends fewer and fewer impulses to the respiratory muscles, and breathing slows and even stops for as long as 40 sec. After breathing comes to a halt, the concentration of CO_2 in the blood quickly builds up, and a rapid series of deep breaths results. These breaths are so deep that too much CO_2 is eliminated by the lungs, and so the remaining CO_2 fails to stimulate the respiratory center; thus the cycle is repeated. Causes of Cheyne–Stokes respiration include *congestive heart failure, brain injuries, increased intracranial pressure,* and the *habitual use of narcotics.* It is commonly seen in patients who are in *coma* (irreversible unconsciousness) and can be brought on by variances in hydrogen-ion concentration and/or oxygen level of the blood, as well as by variances in the blood level of CO_2. Hydrogen-ion concentration affects the respiratory center directly, but a decrease in arterial oxygen will stimulate chemoreceptors in the aortic and carotid bodies (clusters of neuron cell bodies inside the aorta and within each common carotid artery near its point of bifurcation), causing impulses to travel from them to the respiratory center and stimulate it so that deep-breathing portion of the Cheyne–Stokes cycle takes place.

Other terms assigned to abnormal types of respiration include *tachypnea* (rapid, shallow breathing); *orthopnea* (dyspnea that is relieved only when the individual is sitting upright); and *polypnea,* a sort of panting that may follow emotional upset. During an attack of polypnea, the individual *hyperventilates;* that is, the depth of breathing is greatly increased. (*Ventilation* is a broad term that refers to the relative efficiency with which air is taken into and expelled from the lungs.) Inhaling carbon dioxide brings on hyperventilation; this phenomenon is sometimes exploited by surgeons as a method of exercising their patients' lungs and to help prevent pneumonia following an operation. One type of hyperventilation occurs during emotional stress. It is often treated by having the patient breathe into a small paper or plastic bag. As the CO_2 level of the blood builds up in excess and the O_2 blood level decreases, a point is reached at which breathing usually returns to normal; however, in some cases, sedation may be required.

The sounds of respiration

During a physical examination, the physician often places his stethoscope over various portions of the thorax. Normally, he expects to hear a rather high-pitched *bronchial sound,* resulting from the passage of air through the trachea and bronchi, and a *vesicular murmur,* which is a "muffled wind" sound. The bronchial sound is heard during both inspiration and expiration, while the murmur is detected during inspiration and at the very beginning of expiration. Diseased respiratory tissues, mucus, or infection materials (such as pus) produce abnormal sounds in the chest, such as *rales* (a sort of rasping sound), *pleural-friction sound* (caused by two dry or inflamed areas of pleura rubbing together), and *wheezing* (best described as a whistle). Fluid in the chest and other abnormal conditions can sometimes be detected

by tapping the thoracic walls, a procedure known as *percussion*. When something is wrong, normal, "hollow" resonance of sound is often replaced by flat or dull resonance, especially during such diseases as pneumonia that cause fluids or solids to accumulate in the lung.

The mechanism of gaseous exchange and the chloride shift

Immediately after being born, an infant takes its first breath. After the lungs once inflate, they *always* contain some air throughout life. Even the most forceful expiration leaves a liter or more of air in the adult lungs. When oxygen enters the alveoli of the lungs as a part of inspired air, it diffuses outward through the thin walls of these tiny sacs and inward through the walls of the surrounding capillaries, thereby entering the bloodstream. Carbon dioxide, on the other hand, diffuses outward through the capillary walls, and inward through the alveolar walls, to be expelled during expiration. The passage of these gases across the membranous walls of the alveoli and capillaries is in accordance with the *law of diffusion;* that is, oxygen moves from a greater concentration of its molecules in the alveoli to a lesser concentration of its molecules in the capillary network; while carbon dioxide moves from a greater concentration of its molecules in the capillaries to one of lesser concentration in the alveolar air.

It must be made clear that the diffusion of gases during respiration gets a great boost from the *pressure* exerted by each gas at the various points of the respiratory process. The following section begins with a consideration of gas pressures, which is followed by a discussion of how pressure affects the movement of oxygen and carbon dioxide through capillary and alveolar membranes.

DALTON'S LAW OF PARTIAL PRESSURE The pressure exerted by any given gas in a liquid or in a mixture of gases is the *partial pressure* of that gas; and the total pressure of the gases in a given solution or mixture of gases is the sum of the partial pressures exerted by all the gases involved.

The partial pressure of any gas in a

mixture varies directly with the concentration of the gas in the mixture and the total pressure of the gases in that mixture. A good example is the calculation of the partial pressure of oxygen (P_{O_2}) in the atmosphere:

$$\left(\begin{array}{c}\text{Concentration of} \\ \text{oxygen in atmosphere}\end{array}\right) = 21\%$$

$$\left(\begin{array}{c}\text{Pressure of atmos-} \\ \text{phere (at sea level)}\end{array}\right) = 760 \text{ mm Hg}$$

$$P_{O_2} \text{ in atmosphere} = 0.21 \times 760$$

$$= 159.6 \text{ mm Hg}$$

Just as the symbol for the partial pressure of oxygen is P_{O_2}, that designating the partial pressure of carbon dioxide is P_{CO_2}. The approximate partial pressures of oxygen and carbon dioxide in the atmosphere, in alveolar air, and in arterial and venous blood are given in Table 11-2.

TABLE 11-2

Partial pressures of oxygen and carbon dioxide (in mm Hg)

	P_{O_2}	P_{CO_2}
Atmosphere	159.6	0.3
Alveolar air	100	40
Arterial blood	100	40
Venous blood	37	46

There is a direct relationship between the quantity of a gas dissolved in a liquid and the partial pressure of the gas; that is, as the amount of the gas in the gas-liquid solution increases, the partial pressure of the gas also increases. The amount of a gas that dissolves in a liquid varies directly with the partial pressure of the gas in the *environment* of the liquid.

Since the blood in pulmonary capillaries is separated from alveolar air only by the thin, highly permeable capillary and alveolar membranes, the alveolar air can be considered to constitute the environment of the blood in these capillaries; and as blood moves through the pulmonary capillaries, diffusion of oxygen and carbon dioxide quickly occurs. Because of this, the partial pressures of oxygen and carbon dioxide in arterial blood and in alveolar air can maintain a dynamic equilibrium.

HOW OXYGEN IS CARRIED IN THE BLOOD As soon as oxygen and carbon dioxide enter the blood, they dissolve in the plasma; but since fluids are able to contain only small quantities of gas in solution, most of the oxygen and carbon dioxide transported by the blood is combined loosely with the hemoglobin of red blood cells. Increasing blood P_{O_2} and decreasing blood P_{CO_2} speeds the rate at which oxygen leaves the plasma and combines with the hemoglobin of red cells; and the reverse situation—a decrease in blood P_{O_2} and an increase in P_{CO_2}—speeds the dissociation of oxygen from hemoglobin. Hemoglobin that is combined with oxygen is called *oxyhemoglobin*, abbreviated HHbO$_2$; while hemoglobin that has unloaded its oxygen to the tissues is *reduced hemoglobin*, HHb. Hemoglobin transporting carbon dioxide is called *carbaminohemoglobin* (HbNH—COOH) or simply *carbohemoglobin*.

About 97% of all the oxygen carried in the blood is transported as oxyhemoglobin. Blood can carry a total of about 20 cc of oxygen in each 100 cc of its volume, at *saturation,* or full capacity. Normally, arterial blood contains some 19 cc of oxygen per 100 cc of blood and is, therefore, about *95% saturated.*

HOW CARBON DIOXIDE IS CARRIED IN THE BLOOD Carbon dioxide is transported in the blood in three ways:

1.   More than half is carried in the plasma as bicarbonate ions.

2.   About one-third of the blood CO_2 combines with the amino (NH_2) group of hemoglobin and forms carbaminohemoglobin, which is carried by the red cells.

3.   A small amount is carried as plasma CO_2—that is, dissolved in the plasma.

An increase in blood P_{CO_2} and a decrease in P_{O_2} speeds carbaminohemoglobin formation, while reversing these conditions has the opposite effect. There are 50 to 80 cc of CO_2 in every 100 cc of venous blood, and about 50 cc of CO_2 per 100 cc of arterial blood.

Exchange of gases in the lungs

Oxygen diffuses from the alveolar air into the blood down a pressure gradient; this gradient exists because the P_{O_2} of alveolar air is greater than that of the blood just entering the alveolar capillaries. This blood is venous, rather than arterial, blood until after it has unloaded its carbon dioxide, picked up oxygen, and is leaving the area of the alveolus. Only then is the conversion complete. The rate at which oxygen diffuses from the alveolus into the blood depends on four factors:

1. The pressure gradient between the oxygen in alveolar air and oxygen in the (venous) blood just entering the alveolar capillaries; that is, the difference between the alveolar P_{O_2} and venous blood P_{O_2}.

2. The total functional surface area of the combined alveolar-capillary membranes.

3. The respiratory minute volume (respirations per minute multiplied by volume of air per inspiration).

4. The degree of alveolar ventilation— the volume of air that actually enters the alveoli during an inspiration.

Here are examples of how each of these factors affects the diffusion of oxygen into the blood:

1. *The Oxygen Pressure Gradient.* At higher altitudes, the atmospheric pressure decreases, thereby causing the P_{O_2} of alveolar air to fall. The rate of oxygen diffusion decreases, and if the altitude is great enough, alveolar air P_{O_2} equals venous blood P_{O_2}, and oxygen diffusion ceases.

2. *The Functional Surface Area of the Alveoli and Pulmonary Capillaries.* A decrease in the surface area through which oxygen may diffuse (as happens in emphysema) decreases the efficiency of oxygen diffusion, and more rapid breathing is necessary in order to compensate.

3. *The Respiratory Minute Volume.* A decrease in the amount of oxygen inspired per minute results in decreased oxygenation of the blood. Certain drugs, notably morphine, are respiratory depressants and slow the rate of breathing.

4. *Alveolar Ventilation.* If the lungs are healthy, the depth of breathing directly affects the amount of alveolar ventilation. Any factor that decreases the depth of breathing, such as drug inhibition of the respiratory center, decreases the amount of this ventilation.

Exchange of gases in the tissues

The exchange of gases in the tissues involves the diffusion of oxygen from the arterial blood of the tissue capillaries into the tissue cells and the diffusion of carbon dioxide from the tissue cells into the venous blood. This exchange, like the exchange of gases in the lungs, is possible because of pressure gradients. The P_{O_2} of arterial blood is about 100 mm Hg, but that of the intercellular fluid through which the oxygen must pass on its way to the cell membrane is only about 37 mm Hg, and that of intracellular fluid, even less.

The P_{CO_2} of the intracellular and intercellular fluids is somewhat greater than that of venous capillaries, so CO_2 leaves the cells and enters the venous circulation.

Increased cellular activity (such as that of muscle cells during exercise) lowers intracellular and intercellular P_{O_2}. This results in an increased oxygen presure gradient between the blood and tissues, and an increased rate of diffusion of oxygen from the tissue capillaries into the tissues. In order words, oxygen utilization is increased. Increased cellular activity also produces increased amounts of carbon dioxide, and the pressure gradient of this gas is also increased, so that more of it is eliminated from the tissues.

The body has *no way of storing oxygen*, and even at rest, some 250 cc of oxygen are used per minute. The liter or so of oxygen that the entire blood volume of the body is capable of holding at saturation can, therefore, be used up in only 4 min at rest. Only 1 min is required to use up the liter during violent physical exercise. It is easy to see why oxygen must constantly be breathed in, in order to maintain blood levels compatible with normal life.

THE CHLORIDE SHIFT The small amount of carbon dioxide that disolves in the blood plasma forms carbonic acid, which in turn dissociates into bicarbonate ions (HCO_3^-) and hydrogen ions (H^+). This is a very slow process; but the same thing happens when CO_2 enters the red cell, almost instantaneously. An enzyme, *carbonic anhydrase*, catalyzes the reaction:

$$CO_2 + H_2O \underset{\text{(in RBC's)}}{\overset{\overset{\text{Carbonic}}{\text{anhydrase}}}{\rightleftharpoons}} \underset{\substack{\text{(carbonic} \\ \text{acid)}}}{H_2CO_3}$$

$$H_2CO_3 \rightleftharpoons HCO_3^- + H^+$$

It will be noted that H^+ ions are also produced in the reaction, and one might think that they could accumulate in excess, thereby bringing on an *acidosis*—an acidic condition of the tissues—due to overproduction of H^+ ions, which would of course lower the pH of the blood. This is prevented from happening by the *buffer action of hemoglobin*. The concentration of bicarbonate ions inside the red cell does quickly rise far above that in the plasma and, obeying the law of diffusion, these ions move from within the red cell through its membrane into the plasma. This tends to leave the red-cell fluid with a *positive charge*—since the diffusing bicarbonate ions are *negative*—and *positively charged potassium ions* remain within the erythrocyte. However, the situation is soon remedied by the diffusion of *negative chloride ions* from the plasma into the red cells, reestablishing its homeostatic *ionic balance*. This movement of chloride ions is known as the *chloride shift*.

Anoxia and hypoxia

True anoxia, which is the complete absence of oxygen in the body tissues, rarely exists—and, of course, *cannot* exist except for extremely short periods of time without the death of the cells in the affected tissues.

Varying degrees of *hypoxia*—low oxygen levels—do occur, however, and are usually classed as one of four general types:

1. *Anoxic Hypoxia.* The oxygen level of arterial blood is low due to insufficient intake.

2. *Anemic Hypoxia.* Due to an inadequate amount of hemoglobin—and, therefore, of oxyhemoglobin.

3. *Histotoxic Hypoxia.* The oxidation-catalyzing action of tissue enzymes is prevented from taking place.

4. *Stagnant Hypoxia.* This results from extremely sluggish flow of blood.

The most common type of hypoxia is of the anoxic variety, and is often due to poor ventilation caused by diseases such as emphysema and by conditions such as *atelectasis* (total or partial collapse of one or both lungs). Atelectasis can result from several different causes, such as *pneumothorax* (air in the pleural space), *hydrothorax* (fluid in the pleural space), and *hemothorax* (blood in the pleural space). In cases of drowning, anoxia is produced either by involuntary contraction of the larynx (*reflex laryngospasm*) or inundation of the airways (trachea and bronchi).

CARBON MONOXIDE POISONING Unfortunately, hemoglobin has over 200 times the affinity for a deadly poisonous gas, *carbon monoxide* (CO), than it does for oxygen. Most fuels used for heating purposes today do not emit this gas; but the exhaust of automobile engines is about 6% carbon monoxide, except when corrective recombustion devices (which burn some of the exhaust fumes) are used. The gas is odorless and, if an automobile engine is operated in an unventilated garage, soon reaches lethal levels of concentration. Carbon monoxide combines with hemoglobin to form *carbonmonoxyhemoglobin* (also called *carboxyhemoglobin*), COHb, which has no affinity for oxygen. When COHb is formed, the amount of oxygen released to the tissues is greatly decreased, and anoxia results. Signs and symptoms of CO poisoning include *nausea and headache,* and *cherry-redness of the nail beds, mucous membranes,* and *skin.* The color is imparted by carboxyhemoglobin.

Hypocapnia and hypercapnia

The term *hypocapnia* means that the blood level of carbon dioxide is very low. This condition is caused by hyperventilation, and can often be remedied by having the patient breathe the air in a small airtight bag for several minutes. Retention of CO_2 in the body is called *hypercapnia,* and brings on *acidosis, mental confusion, diminished sensation, depression of respiration*—and sometimes even *coma,* terminating in *death.* Hypercapnia is fairly common in cases involving *insufficient alveolar ventilation.*

ASPHYXIA Asphyxia, or suffocation, is characterized by anoxia and an increased blood level of carbon dioxide. It is commonly caused by obstruction of the trachea or by the victim being trapped in a burning building or in a closed space, such as a refrigerator or safe, or by drowning. As anoxia develops, so does hypercapnia. The excess CO_2 acts as a stimulant to respiration, and breathing soon becomes extremely violent. There is a corresponding increase in heart rate and blood pressure. After breathing efforts have finally ceased, the heart slows and eventually stops unless the victim is revived (by artificial respiration) within a few minutes.

Effects of variations in barometric pressure on respiration

RESPIRATION AT LOW BAROMETRIC PRESSURES AND HIGH ALTITUDES Barometric pressure (atmospheric pressure) decreases with altitude, and so does the concentration and *partial pressure of oxygen* in the atmosphere (that portion of the total atmospheric pressure exerted by oxygen). The lower the partial pressure exerted by oxygen (P_{O_2}), the smaller the quantity of oxygen that enters the bloodstream from the alveoli; for example, at an altitude of 23,000 ft, only about one-half the hemoglobin of the arterial blood is fully loaded, or saturated, with oxygen. At an altitude of 50,000 ft, the concentration of oxygen in arterial hemoglobin is so low that, any oxygen present will diffuse *from the tissues to the blood* instead of moving in the normal direction (from blood to tissues),

and death takes place very quickly. The oxygen supply of people flying at high altitudes must be supplemented, by means of either a pressurized compartment or individual oxygen containers and masks. The effects of high altitudes and low oxygen concentrations and pressures vary slightly with individuals; in general, it can be said that, at an altitude of some 20,000 ft, a person with no supplementary oxygen supply soon becomes very weak and mentally "befuddled," and there is danger of coma. At about 25,000 ft, a state of coma is reached within a few minutes. Even as low as 12,000 ft, some people develop a sense of *euphoria* (extreme well-being) and drowsiness. The ability to reason logically decreases rapidly above this altitude, and oxygen should be breathed before an "I-don't-care" attitude is inadvertently assumed. When pure oxygen is breathed, it is possible to fly to extremely high altitudes, since the oxygen saturation of hemoglobin is greatly increased thereby. For example, hemoglobin is 100% saturated when pure oxygen is breathed at an altitude of 20,000 ft. If air is breathed at this altitude, the hemoglobin saturation is only a little more than 65%. The height to which a person can ascend and still breathe normally is said to be his *"ceiling."* The ceiling for an aviator not using supplemental oxygen is about 20,000 ft or less, while an individual inhaling pure oxygen can breathe comfortably at 45,000 ft.

RESPIRATION AT HIGH BAROMETRIC PRESSURE; DEEP-SEA DIVING More and more, man is exposing himself to environments of extremely high barometric pressures, both in deep-sea diving and in tunnels constructed under rivers and other bodies of water. Naturally, the higher the pressure of a gas in the environment, the greater the amount of that gas that will diffuse through the alveolar membrane and into the blood. Unless proper precautions are taken, excess dissolved gases in the blood and in other body fluids can produce serious consequences. Even oxygen acts as a poison in environments of high pressure, such as those encountered during deep-sea diving. At sea level, the barometric pressure amounts to 760 mm Hg, or 1 atm. At a depth of only 33 ft, the pressure rises to double that at sea level: 1520 mm Hg, or 2 atm, due to the weight of the water above that depth. At 300 ft, the pressure rises to 10 atm, or 7600 mm Hg. Depths below 200 ft become dangerous for a diver breathing compressed air, due to the fact that at high intrapulmonary pressures (resulting from high pressure in the surrounding medium), large amounts of oxygen diffuse into the blood and dissolve in it, then pass from the blood into the tissues. An extreme oversupply of oxygen in the tissues *drastically upsets cellular metabolism,* and even destroys the cells themselves, especially in the central nervous system. *Oxygen poisoning* in the brain can lead to convulsions, coma, and death. The danger of oxygen poisoning can be lessened (up to a point) by decreasing the amount of oxygen in a diver's air supply in proportion to the depth of the dive.

Nitrogen, an inert gas as far as respiration is concerned, becomes very important when an individual enters a high-pressure environment. Large amounts of nitrogen dissolved in the blood produce an intoxicated state, *nitrogen narcosis* or poisoning. At depths below about 200 ft, the CNS functions as though a general anesthetic has been administered, and the diver may fall asleep following his attack of "drunkenness." Breathing a mixture of helium and oxygen from which nitrogen has been excluded eliminates the possibility of nitrogen poisoning. If ordinary compressed air, with its high proportion of nitrogen, is breathed by a diver or tunnel worker at high pressure, a second danger must be reckoned with, that of "the bends" (*decompression sickness*), discussed in the previous chapter. Decompression sickness occurs if a diver is permitted to ascend to the level of ordinary atmospheric pressure too rapidly, causing nitrogen in the blood to quickly come out of solution and form bubbles which can travel in the bloodstream and severely and permanently damage fiber tracts of the CNS, bringing about mental disturbances and paralysis. If a diver ascends to the surface (or if a tunnel worker is decompressed) very slowly, excess amounts of nitrogen and other gases leave via the lungs during normal expirations rather than forming bubbles and "boiling" in the bloodstream, and the danger of decompression sickness is alleviated. It is possible for an airplane to climb to great heights (approximately 50,000 ft) rapidly enough to bring on decompression sickness, but this is not likely to happen very often, due to the fact that the pilot of such an airplane is usually in a pressurized cabin or wears a pressurized suit.

Actions associated with breathing

Talking, singing, coughing, hiccuping, yawning, sneezing, snoring, crying, sobbing, and *sighing* can all be considered modified forms of breathing or actions associated with respiration. Talking, as a first example, requires first of all the production of sound by the mechanism of passing exhaled air over vocal folds in the larynx (Fig. 11-9). Singing uses this same mechanism. Coughing is a reflex act that usually involves stimulation of the mucous membranes of the respiratory tract by foreign particles or infectious material; it consists of a quick inhalation followed by a violent expiration. Hiccuping is also due to reflex action, and involves contraction of the diaphragm. When the stomach becomes extended by gas or overeating, afferent nerve endings are stimulated by pressure on the diaphragm. Impulses then travel to the respiratory centers in the medulla, and eventually back down the phrenic nerves to the diaphragm, where they cause the contractions we commonly call "hiccups." Yawning consists simply of a deep inspiration followed by long expiration, and helps eliminate excess CO_2. A sneeze is designed to clear the nose, just as a cough clears the throat. The violent expiration of a sneeze is partially routed through the nose, and is commonly due to stimulation of the mucous membranes of the nasal cavities by dust or other irritants. Snoring is best termed "noisy respiration." The noise is produced when the snorer sleeps with his mouth open, causing the uvula (at the back of the roof of the mouth) and other portions of the soft palate to vibrate as air rushes over them during inspiration. Crying and sobbing involve prolonged whines, "keens," or wails, often followed by deep inspiration. Sighing consists mainly of deep, prolonged inspiration followed by prolonged expiration.

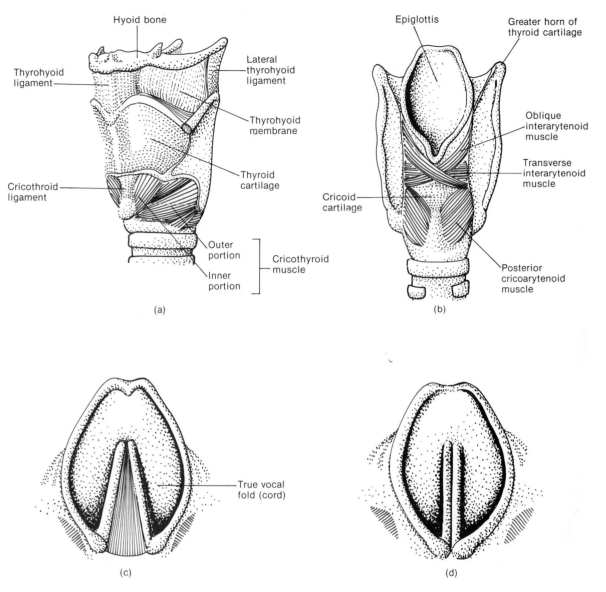

Figure 11-9 The larynx. (a) Anterolateral view. (b) Posterior view. (c) True vocal folds open, or abducted. (d) True vocal folds closed, or adducted.

THE ANATOMY AND PHYSIOLOGY OF THE LARYNX The larynx or "voicebox" is commonly thought of as being used only in the production of sounds, especially those sounds which constitute speech; and although this is indeed the most important single function of the larynx, it is of importance also in the acts of coughing, swallowing, expectorating, breathing, and in protection of those portions of the respiratory tract below the larynx from foreign objects which have "gone down the wrong way" during swallowing. During the acts of speaking and singing, efferent impulses leave the speech centers of the brain and travel to the muscles of the larynx and those of the tongue, lower jaw, and lips, bringing about the complex series of muscle contractions that result in *intelligible speech.* The larynx consists essentially of a framework made up of four large cartilages (a *cricoid, thyroid,* and *two arytenoid cartilages* —the thyroid cartilage is the "Adam's apple"), a pair of *"true" vocal folds* ("cords"), a pair of *"false" vocal folds,* and various *ligaments, muscles,* and *membranes* (Fig. 11-9). During vocalization, the one *transverse arytenoid* and two *cricoarytenoid muscles* adduct the true vocal folds and close the glottis (the space between them). The glottis is opened and the vocal folds abducted by the paired *posterior cricoarytenoid muscles*. The *cricothyroid muscles* tense the vocal folds, while the *thyroarytenoid muscles* relax them. The *more tense* the folds (other factors being equal), the *higher-pitched* will be the sound produced as air rushes between them, and *conversely*. The laryngeal muscles just described are innervated by two branches of the vagus nerve on either side: the *superior laryngeal nerve* and the *recurrent laryngeal nerve*. The superior laryngeal nerve lies close to the *superior thyroid artery;* both must be avoided during surgery involving the thyroid gland.

Age, sex, emotional state, condition of the air sinuses, and the size and other characteristics of an individual's larynx and thorax all seem to have a bearing upon the characteristics of the *voice*. Everyone knows that, even during a cold—when the nasal passages or deeper respiratory tubes may contain excessive amounts of fluids—the voice is often greatly altered. Cancer, or the surgery necessary to eliminate it, can destroy the vocal apparatus. At puberty, the voice of the male typically changes from one of high pitch to one of lower pitch.

Artificial respiration

Every year there is an increasing number of drownings, suffocations, and electrical shocks, all of which can directly bring about a cessation of breathing. In such cases, it is often possible to restore respiratory movements and air exchange by manual or mechanical means, until natural breathing may be resumed. The most efficient manual method of such artificial respiration is called *mouth-to-mouth resuscitation*. Using this method, the operator pinches the victim's nose with one hand (so that air does not escape from it) and the jaw and tongue with the other, and breathes with moderate force into the mouth, thereby forcing air directly into the lungs. The expiration of the operator should take place at a rate of about 12 per minute for adults, and at a slightly faster rate for children. The abdomen should be observed from time to time. If it rises, air is

moving into the stomach instead of the lungs, and the neck should be bent slightly more backward and the tongue pulled farther forward. One should be gentle when employing this method in attempting to revive small children, as there is some danger of rupturing the lung alveoli. If it is not possible to breathe into the mouth (due to a wound, burn, or other cause) but is still possible to close the mouth with the hand, then resuscitation may be given through the nose. Failing this, another manual method of artificial respiration such as the *back-pressure–arm-lift or Nielsen method* may be used. In this method, the patient is placed in the prone position, and the operator lifts the arms, releases them, then presses on the back with both hands. This process is repeated at about the same rate as the expiration rate in the mouth-to-mouth method. All artificial respiration, regardless of the method used, should be continued for as long as the victim has a heartbeat, and for a considerable length of time even though no heartbeat can be detected.

Mechanical respirators are seldom at hand when needed, except in hospitals, where a patient may cease breathing during surgery or for other reasons. A mechanical respirator may be of the type that forces air or pure oxygen into the lungs by means of a pump and mask, or it may be of the *"iron-lung"* type, which alternately increases and decreases the pressure on the external chest and abdominal walls, squeezing and relaxing these areas so that air is forced out of and permitted to enter the lungs. When the respiratory centers are injured by trauma or disease (such as poliomyelitis), mechanical respirators can keep the patient breathing for indefinite periods of time. In dire emergency, breathing may be brought about by stimulating the nerves to the diaphragm (phrenic nerves) electrically, a procedure known as the *electrophrenic method*. During cases involving oxygen therapy, a respirator is not normally used. More commonly, a nasal tube inserted as far as the trachea is connected to a tank or other supply of compressed oxygen, which is slowly released by means of a valve; or the patient is covered by an oxygen tent, in which the air is about 50% oxygen. Oxygen masks are also employed, especially when the therapy is to be applied for only short periods of time. During oxygen therapy, carbon dioxide may be added as a *respiratory stimulant.* Oxygen therapy must be used with caution. If an individual is suffering from failure of his breathing mechanism and has severe hypercapnia, the receptors and nerves that ordinarily send impulses to the respiratory centers may be depressed so much that breathing comes to depend upon afferent impulses from the aortic and carotid bodies. Supplying excess oxygen in such a circumstance may cause the receptors in these bodies to cease sending impulses to the respiratory centers (they send impulses only when the blood oxygen level is relatively low), and complete and permanent cessation of breathing may result. For some reason as yet unknown, the administration of oxygen at levels of 80% or greater for 8 hours or longer produces coughing, inflammation of the respiratory tract, and congestion of the nasal passages. Administering pure oxygen at pressures above 760 mm Hg causes dizziness, *tinnitus* (ringing ears), and—if the pressure is high enough—*convulsions and coma.*

Inhalation anesthetics

We are fortunate enough to be living in a time when it is possible to undergo major surgery in a state of artificially induced "sleep," sensing no pain whatever during the surgery itself. This state of unconsciousness is often produced by a general anesthetic of the inhalation type, such as *ether, cyclopropane,* or *nitrous oxide.* As the anesthetic is inhaled, it quickly diffuses through the alveolar membranes and into the blood, and is carried to the centers of the brain that maintain the state of wakefulness, somehow depresses these centers, and produces unconsciousness.

**OUTLINE
SUMMARY**

1. Phases of respiration
   A. External respiration: transfer of oxygen from the air to the blood, and carbon dioxide from the blood to air
   B. Internal respiration: exchange of oxygen and carbon dioxide between the blood and tissue cells
2. The respiratory quotient (R.Q.): the ratio of CO_2 liberation to O_2 intake

$$R.Q. = \frac{CO_2 \text{ output}}{O_2 \text{ intake}}$$

3. Breathing and the respiratory apparatus
   A. Components of the respiratory system include the nose, pharynx, larynx, trachea, bronchi, lungs, diaphragm and other muscles of respiration
   B. Route of air during inspiration (breathing in): nostrils → nasal pharynx → oral pharynx → larynx → trachea → bronchi → bronchioles → alveoli
   C. The nose
      a. Divided into two passageways by a septum
      b. Passageways or nostrils subdivided into meati
      c. Anterior openings are external nares
      d. Posterior openings are internal nares
      e. Nostrils lined with ciliated mucous membrane, the nasal mucosa
      f. The nose warms, moistens incoming air, traps dust and other foreign matter, and functions in the sense of smell and quality of the voice
      g. Four pairs of paranasal sinuses connect with the nose: sphenoidal, ethmoidal, frontal, and maxillary
   D. The pharynx
      a. Tubelike; begins posterior to nasal cavities, ends at esophagus. Connects nose and mouth with remainder of the respiratory and digestive tracts
      b. Helps form vowels during phonation
      c. Walls are muscular, lined with mucous membrane
      d. Portions of the pharynx include the nasopharynx, oropharynx, and laryngopharynx
      e. Openings into the pharynx include the pharyngotympanic tubes, internal nares, fauces, and larynx and esophagus
      f. The three pairs of tonsils associated with pharynx are called pharyngeal, palatine, and lingual
   E. The trachea
      a. Extends from larynx to level of fifth thoracic vertebra, where it divides into two primary bronchi
      b. Consists of smooth muscle, re-

inforced with C-shaped cartilaginous rings

   c. Lies anterior to the esophagus

F. Bronchi: Primary bronchi branch into secondary bronchi, which branch and rebranch into smaller and smaller bronchi, all with cartilaginous rings. Finally, the smallest bronchi branch into bronchioles, which consist mainly of smooth muscle, without cartilage. Collectively, the air passages within the lungs form a pulmonary "tree." Right primary bronchus is shorter, straighter

G. Alveoli

   a. Consist of highly permeable membrane "grapes," arranged in clusters called alveolar sacs

   b. Connected to bronchioles by alveolar ducts

   c. Surrounded by alveolar capillaries

   d. Function in exchange of gases between air and blood

H. The lungs

   a. Conical: Apex of each reaches above the first rib, base reaches almost to the diaphragm

   b. Consist of distinct lobes and bronchopulmonary segments, each with its own blood and air supply

   c. Hilum is the root of the lung, and the point of entrance of bronchi, blood and lymph vessels, and nerves

I. Mediastinum: the space between the lungs; contains heart, roots of aorta and pulmonary trunk, and portions of the trachea, esophagus, and nerves

J. Pleura: a serous membrane of the respiratory system

   a. Visceral pleura: covers the lungs and sticks tightly to them

   b. Parietal pleura: lines the thoracic cavity, and is continuous with visceral pleura

   c. Pleural space: potential space between parietal and visceral layers of pleura; contains a lubricating serous fluid; pneumothorax is the entrance of air into the pleural space

K. The diaphragm, chief organ of breathing

   a. A musculotendinous structure that separates the thoracic from the abdominal cavity; innervated by a pair of phrenic nerves

   b. Causes air to enter and leave the lungs by increasing and decreasing the intrathoracic volume

   c. Boyle's law (if other factors are kept constant, the pressure of a gas varies inversely with its volume)

   d. Rate of respiration: diaphragm moves up (or down) 16–18 times per minute in the adult, at rest. Affected by age, sex, physical activity, emotional states, etc.

   e. Other respiratory muscles: include the external and internal intercostals, pectoralis major, serratus anterior, trapezius, levatores costarum, internal oblique, external oblique, transversus abdominis, rectus abdominis

L. The reflexes of breathing: depend upon the reception of afferent impulses by the CNS, and transmission of efferent impulses from the CNS to the diaphragm and other muscles of respiration

   a. Respiratory reflex centers include

      1. Inspiratory center

      2. Expiratory center

      3. Apneustic center

      4. Pneumotaxic center

   b. Functions of the respiratory centers

      1. Inspiratory center: sends impulses to diaphragm, causing inspiration, following stimulation of the center by blood CO_2

      2. Expiratory center: during strenuous physical activity, brings about forceful expiration by means of the internal intercostal muscles

      3. Apneustic center: may be an auxiliary inspiratory center

      4. Pneumotaxic center: helps in forceful expiration

   c. Hering–Breuer reflex: automatic inspiration followed by involuntary expiration; depends upon impulses sent from stretch receptors in the visceral pleura to the inspiratory center in the medulla (inhibiting it and causing passive expiration), and subsequent stimulation and activation of the inspiratory center by blood CO_2

   d. Chemoreceptors and pressoreceptors in the carotid and aortic bodies and sinuses (respectively) send impulses which affect the activity of the respiratory centers

M. Lung capacities

   a. Tidal volume: the amount of air that enters the lungs during a normal quiet inspiration; averages 500 cc

   b. Residual volume: the amount of air remaining in the lungs after a maximum expiration; averages 1000 cc

   c. Total lung capacity: the residual volume plus the amount of air that can be taken in during a maximal inspiration; averages 6 liters

d. Vital capacity: a maximal expiration following a maximal inspiration; averages 5 liters
e. Inspiratory reserve volume: the amount of air that can be breathed in following a quiet inspiration; averages 2.5 liters
f. Inspiratory capacity: the tidal volume plus the inspiratory reserve volume
g. Expiratory reserve volume: the amount of air that can be exhaled following a quiet expiration; average 2 liters
h. Functional residual capacity: obtained by adding the residual volume to the expiratory reserve volume; averages 3 liters

N. Abnormal breathing (normal breathing is called eupnea)
a. Dyspnea: breathing that is difficult or labored
b. Hyperpnea: breathing that is excessively deep
c. Apnea: cessation of breathing
d. Cheyne–Stokes breathing: alternating hyperpnea and apnea
e. Tachypnea: rapid, shallow breathing
f. Orthopnea: dyspnea that is relieved only in the upright position
g. Polypnea: panting rapidly and deeply, in hyperventilation

O. The sounds of respiration
a. Bronchial sound: relatively high-pitched; caused by passage of air through trachea and bronchi
b. Vesicular murmur: "muffled wind" sound; a normal sound of air moving through the air passages
c. Rales: an abnormal, rasping sound, produced by pathological conditions in the respiratory system
d. Pleural friction sound: caused by dry areas of pleura rubbing together
e. Wheezing: a "whistle" due to a pathological condition in the chest

4. The mechanism of gaseous exchange and the chloride shift
A. Oxygen transport: oxygen is carried in loose combination with hemoglobin and diffuses from the blood into the tissue cells; carbon dioxide diffuses from tissue cells into the blood
a. Oxyhemoglobin ($HHbO_2$): oxygenated hemoglobin. About 97% of all O_2 carried in the blood is transported in this way, and only 3% is carried in the plasma
b. Reduced hemoglobin (HHb): hemoglobin that has unloaded its O_2
c. Carbaminohemoglobin (HbNH:

COOH): hemoglobin that is transporting CO_2 to the lungs
d. Blood can carry 20 cc O_2 per 100 cc of its volume. Arterial blood usually contains 19 cc O_2 per 100 cc of blood, and is, therefore, 95% saturated
e. There are 50 to 80 cc of CO_2 in every 100 cc of venous blood, but little O_2. Arterial blood carries about 50 cc CO_2 per 100 cc of blood
f. There is no way to store O_2 in the body; and even at rest, an average of 250 cc are used per minute
g. The role of gas pressure in gaseous exchange: diffusion of gases during respiration gets a great boost from the pressure exerted by each gas
h. Dalton's law of partial pressure: the pressure exerted by any given gas in a liquid or in a mixture of gases is the partial pressure of that gas
i. The partial pressure of any gas in a mixture varies directly with the concentration of the gas in the mixture and the total pressure of the gases in that mixture
j. The symbol for the partial pressure of oxygen is P_{O_2}; that for carbon dioxide, P_{CO_2}
k. The partial pressure of a gas dissolved in a liquid varies directly with the quantity of the gas dissolved in the liquid; and the amount of a gas that dissolves in a liquid varies directly with the partial pressure of the gas in the environment of the liquid
l. Increasing blood P_{O_2} and decreasing blood P_{CO_2} speeds the rate at which oxygen leaves the plasma and combines with the hemoglobin of red cells; and a decrease in blood P_{O_2} and an increase in P_{CO_2} accelerates the dissociation of oxygen from hemoglobin

B. Carbon dioxide transport: carbon dioxide is transported in the blood in three ways
a. More than half is carried in the plasma as bicarbonate ions
b. About one-third combines with NH_2 of hemoglobin, forming carbaminohemoglobin, carried by the red cells
c. A small amount is carried dissolved in the plasma

C. Exchange of gases in the lungs: the rate at which oxygen diffuses from the alveolus into the blood depends upon four factors

a. The pressure gradient between the alveolar P_{O_2} and venous blood P_{O_2}

b. The total functional surface area of the alveolar-capillary membranes

c. The respiratory minute volume

d. The degree of alveolar ventilation

D. Exchange of gases in the tissues: is possible because of pressure gradients

  a. The P_{O_2} of arterial blood is about 100 mm Hg, but that of intercellular fluid is only 37 mm Hg, and that of intracellular fluid, even less

  b. The P_{CO_2} of the intracellular and intercellular fluids is somewhat greater than that of venous capillaries, so CO_2 leaves the cells and enters the venous circulation

  c. Increased cellular activity lowers intracellular and intercellular P_{O_2}, increasing the oxygen pressure gradient between the blood and tissues and increases the rate of diffusion of oxygen from tissue capillaries into tissues. Increased cellular activity also produces increased amounts of carbon dioxide

E. The chloride shift: the diffusion of chloride ions from plasma into the red cells, maintaining the ionic balance of their fluid

5. Carbon monoxide poisoning (CO poisoning)

A. Hemoglobin has 200 times the affinity for carbon monoxide than for O_2

B. Carbon monoxide combines with the hemoglobin to form carbonmonoxy hemoglobin, which has no affinity for O_2. When this happens, the amount of O_2 released to the tissues is greatly decreased, and anoxia results

6. Anoxia

A. True anoxia: complete lack of O_2 in the blood or body tissues; rare, except in death

B. Hypoxia: low O_2 levels in the blood or tissues. If severe, usually classed as one of four types

  a. Anoxic hypoxia: low oxygen level of arterial blood due to insufficient intake; the most common form of anoxia

  b. Anemic hypoxia: hypoxia due to inadequate amounts of hemoglobin in the blood

  c. Histotoxic hypoxia: hypoxia due to inactivation of oxidation-catalyzing tissue enzymes

  d. Stagnant hypoxia: due to extremely sluggish blood flow

7. Hypercapnia and hypocapnia

A. Hypercapnia: retention of CO_2, often due to insufficient alveolar ventilation

B. Hypocapnia: low blood level of CO_2; due to hyperventilation

8. Asphyxia or suffocation: characterized by anoxia and elevated CO_2 blood levels; caused by obstruction of the trachea or other portions of the airways

9. Effects of variations in barometric pressure on respiration (barometric pressure at sea level is equal to 760 mm Hg)

A. Respiration at low barometric pressures and high altitudes

  a. At an altitude of 23,000 ft, only one-half the hemoglobin of the arterial blood is fully saturated. At 50,000 ft, O_2 diffuses from the tissues into the blood, instead of in the other direction

  b. At an altitude of 20,000 ft, there is danger of coma, unless supplementary O_2 is provided

B. Respiration at high barometric pressure; deep-sea diving

  a. Even oxygen acts as a poison in environments of high barometric pressure

  b. At a depth of 33 ft, pressure rises to double that of sea level: 1520 mm Hg, or 2 atm. At 300 ft, pressure amounts to 10 atm

  c. High pressure causes large amounts of oxygen to dissolve in the plasma, then pass from the blood into the tissues, upsetting cellular metabolism and killing cells, especially those of the central nervous system

  d. If movement from a region of high pressure to one of low pressure is too rapid, blood nitrogen comes out of solution and forms bubbles which can permanently damage the central nervous system, especially spinal cord tracts and pathways

10. Artificial respiration

A. The number of respiratory arrests due to drownings, suffocations, and electrical shocks is increasing annually

B. The most effective method of restoring respiratory functions is by mouth-to-mouth resuscitation

11. Actions associated with breathing include: talking, singing, coughing, hiccuping, yawning, sneezing, snoring, crying, sobbing, and sighing. Each has its own interrelationships with the anatomy and physiology of the respiratory system. The larynx is of particular importance, due to the fact that this organ is the structure of communication and is a vital part of the main airway to the lungs

1. What body organ is most sensitive to lack of oxygen? What is meant by "gaseous exchange"?

2. Write the formula for the calculation of the respiratory quotient.

3. Mrs. N., aged 54, enters a hospital suffering from difficult, labored breathing. This condition is called what? What is the name of a common disease that can cause it?

4. Make an outline summary of the organs of respiration. Which is more important where breathing is concerned? Where gaseous exchange is concerned?

5. Describe the pleurae and the pleural space. What is the function of the pleurae? What is pleurisy? Pneumothorax?

6. How many lobes are found in each lung? What is the importance of bronchopulmonary segments where lung surgery is concerned?

7. State Boyle's law. Why is it important to the breathing process?

8. Discuss the reflexes of breathing. Can a child (or anyone) deliberately hold his breath until he dies? Why?

9. List and define the various lung capacities. How is the inspiratory capacity calculated?

10. Define: *eupnea, dyspnea, apnea, hyperpnea, polypnea, orthopnea,* and *Cheyne–Stokes breathing.* What is rales, the vesicular murmur, and pleural-friction sound?

11. Discuss the mechanism of gaseous exchange and the chloride shift.

12. Why is it so easy to become a victim of carbon monoxide poisoning, as far as the CO carrying capacity of the blood is concerned?

13. What is asphyxia? Describe the mouth-to-mouth method of artificial respiration. Why is it the most efficient method?

14. At an altitude of 23,000 ft, about how much of the hemoglobin of arterial blood is fully loaded with oxygen?

15. A nurse in a children's hospital finds that one of her young patients has aspirated a piece of candy. If this foreign substance gets as far as the bifurcation of the trachea, which primary bronchus is it most likely to enter? Why?

16. Describe the larynx, or "voice box." What cartilage of this structure forms the "Adam's apple" of men?

17. Approximately where should the trachea be incised in order to perform an emergency (and perhaps lifesaving) tracheotomy? Should the incision be vertical or horizontal with respect to the trachea? Why?

18. Briefly describe the anatomy of the nose. Define septum, external and internal nares, and meati.

19. Describe the paranasal sinuses. What is their chief clinical significance?

20. Describe the pharynx. List the openings into the pharynx, and state where these openings are located.

21. Describe the three pairs of tonsils associated with the pharynx. Which tonsils are removed during tonsillectomy?

22. Discuss the anatomy of the trachea, bronchi, and alveoli. What is meant by the term, "pulmonary tree"?

23. What is the mediastinum, and what does it contain?

24. State Dalton's law of partial pressure. What is the role of pressure in gaseous exchange?

25. What is the symbol for the partial pressure of oxygen? Of carbon dioxide?

26. List three ways in which carbon dioxide is transported in the blood.

27. Discuss the exchange of gases in the lungs, then the exchange of gases in the tissues.

the digestion and absorption of food

ometimes important discoveries in medicine result from accidents. Much knowledge concerning the function of the stomach, for example, was gained following the accidental shooting of an 18-year-old youth named Alexis St. Martin. He suffered a shotgun blast in the upper abdomen, while visiting a trading post on the Canadian–Michigan border one fine June day in 1822. Although his physician, William Beaumont, managed to save the boy's life through quick and diligent surgery, the wound never completely closed, and a *fistula* (abnormal opening leading to the body cavities or organs) extended all the way into the stomach. Knowing a priceless opportunity when he saw it, Beaumont studied the action of the stomach both when it was empty and when various kinds of food and drink were ingested by the patient. The doctor began his observations in 1822 and carried them out intermittently for eight years. For the first time, man knew as fact some of the things that happened to food when it entered the stomach. Although much has been learned about the digestion and absorption of food since the time of Beaumont and St. Martin, man's knowledge of these processes is still incomplete. The main features of **digestion**—*the chemical and physical breakdown of foods into simpler molecular units*—and **absorption**—*the passage of digested foods from the digestive tract into the circulatory system*—will be presented in this chapter in the following manner: first, *the general pathway of food as it moves through the digestive tract will be described;* second, *the organs of the digestive system will be considered separately as functioning units of the entire system;* and third, *the individual processes of digestion, absorption, and elimination will be considered.*

The route of food and drink

Food enters the body—is *ingested*—through the uppermost portion of the digestive tract, the mouth (Fig. 12-1). Here it is chewed and moistened to facilitate swallowing, and an enzyme is added to it to begin its breakdown into smaller particles. Such reduction in particle size is essential because food "as is," even when thoroughly chewed, cannot be absorbed from the intestine into the circulatory system. Food must be altered chemically as well as physically before being absorbed. It does not remain for long in the mouth; it is quickly swallowed (often without thorough chewing) and passes through the pharynx and down the *esophagus* or food tube to the *stomach,* where it is temporarily stored. In this organ, more enzymes and *hydrochloric acid* are added to the food and a certain amount of *mechanical mixing and massage* takes place due to the reflex contraction of smooth-muscle fibers in the stomach wall. After a variable length of time, the partially digested food leaves the stomach and enters the *first 10 in. of the small intestine,* the *duodenum.* Here, secretions of the *liver* and *pancreas* are added, along with a secretion of the *duodenum* itself.

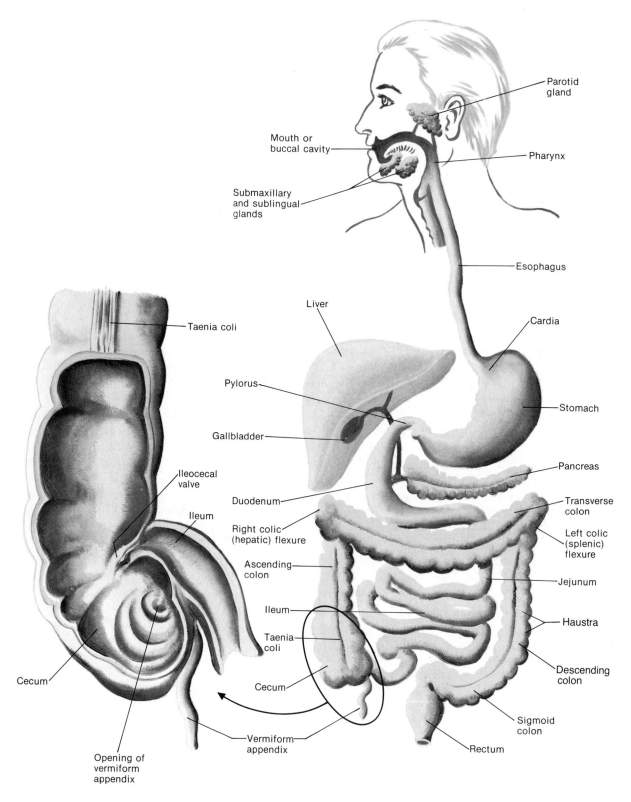

Figure 12-1 The digestive system.

The duodenum is continuous with the next portion of the small intestine, the *jejunum,* which in turn is continuous with the next portion, the *ileum. Intestinal juice* is added as food moves through all portions of the small intestine, and most digestion and absorption takes place within this portion of the digestive tract. After the small intestine has coiled for over 20 ft in the abdomen, the distal end of the ileum joins the first portion of the *large intestine* or *colon.* All unabsorbed food passes into the large intestine as waste, and although absorption of large quantities of *water* and small amounts of other substances occurs in this portion of the digestive tract, the colon serves largely as an organ of *egestion* by eliminating solid wastes from the body.

ANATOMY OF
THE DIGESTIVE SYSTEM

The digestive system or tract includes the mouth, pharynx, esophagus, stomach, and intestines (see Color Plates IV through VIII). The lower portion of the system is known also as the *gastrointestinal* (G.I.)

tract or the *alimentary canal.* The first structure that food encounters on its way through the digestive system is the mouth.

The mouth and pharynx

The mouth or *buccal cavity* has a *roof* (hard and soft palates), *floor* (tongue muscles), and *side walls* (the cheeks). It is lined with mucous membrane, contains taste buds, teeth, and the openings of the parotid, submaxillary, and sublingual salivary glands (Fig. 12-1). The arched soft palate separates the mouth from the nasopharynx on the one hand and the oropharynx on the other. The opening into the oropharynx is called the *fauces,* and the vertical, lateral portions of the soft palate, the *pillars* of the fauces. The upper and lower half-jaws each contain two biting teeth (*incisors*), one tearing tooth (*canine*), two modified grinding teeth (*premolars*), and at least two grinding teeth (*molars*), for a total of 28 teeth (Fig. 12-2). *Third molars* (which appear at about age 17) must be present in order to fulfill the complement of 32 teeth, but often these are abnormally developed and must be extracted. The first deciduous tooth appears at about 6 months of age, and one or two more erupt each month thereafter, until a complete set of twenty "baby teeth" has appeared. Shedding of the deciduous teeth begins at about age 6, and usually ends by age 13.

Taste receptors (*taste buds*) are found mainly on the tongue, but some are also present in the pharynx and roof of the mouth. On the tongue, some of the taste buds are located in slightly raised nipplelike areas called *papillae.* There are three kinds of papillae—*fungiform* on the tip area of the tongue, *filiform* near the center and sides (covering most of the upper surface of the tongue), and *vallate* (or circumvallate) near the back, forming a wide "V." The taste buds in these papillae mediate sensations of *sweetness, saltiness, sourness,* and *bitterness* in the approximate areas outlined in Fig. 12-3. Taste buds are nerve endings that are highly specialized to detect differences in the chemical properties of various foods. Taste pathways involve chiefly the *facial* and *glossopharyngeal nerves* (Chapter 8). It is interesting to note that the sense of taste is virtually non-

Figure 12-2 The mouth and permanent teeth.

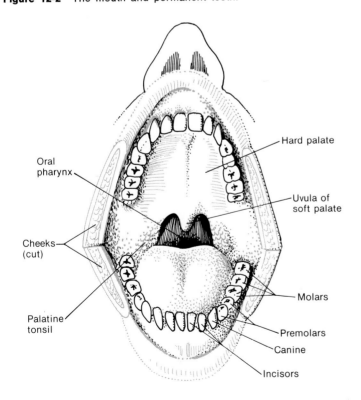

Oral
pharynx

Cheeks
(cut)

Palatine
tonsil

Hard palate

Uvula of
soft palate

Molars

Premolars

Canine

Incisors

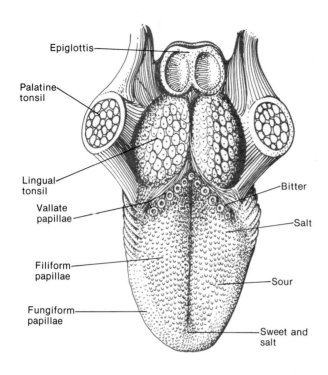

Labels on figure:
Epiglottis
Palatine tonsil
Lingual tonsil
Vallate papillae
Filiform papillae
Fungiform papillae
Bitter
Salt
Sour
Sweet and salt

Figure 12-3 Locations of papillae and areas of taste on the tongue.

existent if its complementary sense, the sense of *smell,* is not functioning properly. If a person is blindfolded and holds his nose, it is almost impossible for him to distinguish between, say, raw chopped potato and raw chopped apple.

The tongue itself consists chiefly of *skeletal muscle, blood vessels,* and *nerves,* and is covered with *mucous membrane.*

SWALLOWING OR DEGLUTITION   After food is chewed and moistened with saliva in the mouth, it must be swallowed. For this purpose, it enters the *oral pharynx,* that region of transition between the posterior portion of the mouth and the upper end of the esophagus. That portion of the pharynx that is involved in swallowing is shown in Fig. 12-4 and Color Plate VIII. It will be noted that the walls of the pharynx consist of layers of *skeletal muscle* lined with *mucous membrane.* During the act of swallowing, the *constrictor muscles of the pharynx contract,* forcing food into the upper portion of the esophagus. Other pharyngeal muscles *raise the pharynx,* cause the epiglottis to *close over the larynx,* and *move* the *soft palate upward, closing off the nasal pharynx.* Simultaneously, the tongue moves backward

and upward, keeping food from reentering the mouth. By these means, there is only one way in which the food can travel: *into the esophagus.* When food begins to leave the mouth, the act of swallowing is a *voluntary* one; but as soon as the food mass or *bolus* moves over the posterior portion of the tongue and stimulates receptors in the walls of the pharynx, swallowing becomes a *purely reflex* act. Contraction of the pharyngeal muscles is followed by contraction of those in the walls of the esophagus, and food is carried to the stomach. Normally, gravity assists in moving food through the esophagus. It is not absolutely essential, however, as can be demonstrated by hanging by the legs from a gym bar and eating or drinking while doing so. Occasionally, food or drink gets past the epiglottis and into the larynx or even down as far as the trachea or bronchi. This can result in infection or even death by asphyxiation. Persons whose pharynxes have been anesthetized for operative purposes temporarily lose the ability to swallow (since the initial impulses of the reflex of swallowing are sent by touch receptors in the pharynx), and should not receive anything by mouth until the swallowing reflex returns. Small children sometimes swallow coins, pins, and other objects that may "go down the wrong way" and enter the respiratory tract.

The esophagus

As soon as food is swallowed, it enters the upper end of the esophagus. This 10-in. tube leading to the stomach at first lies *posterior to the trachea,* then bends to the left and passes *behind the left bronchus* and heart, penetrates the diaphragm, and immediately enters the stomach. It is about 1 in. in diameter and, like the rest of the digestive tract, has *four layers or coats in its walls;* they are, from innermost to outermost (Fig. 12-5): (1) *mucous membrane,* (2) *submucous layer,* (3) *muscular layer,* and (4) *serous layer.* The muscular layer of the esophagus differs from that of the stomach and intestines in that the muscle of the upper one-third of the esophagus is of the *striated type,* that of the middle third is a mixture of *striated and smooth muscle,* and that of the lower third is *smooth muscle alone.* There

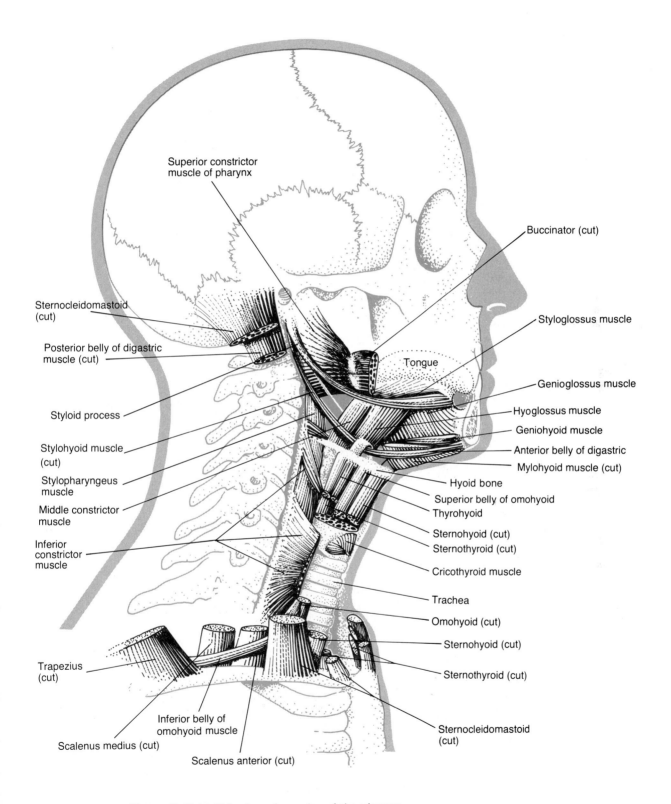

Superior constrictor
muscle of pharynx

Buccinator (cut)

Sternocleidomastoid
(cut)

Styloglossus muscle

Posterior belly of digastric
muscle (cut)

Tongue

Genioglossus muscle

Styloid process

Hyoglossus muscle

Geniohyoid muscle

Stylohyoid muscle
(cut)

Anterior belly of digastric

Mylohyoid muscle (cut)

Stylopharyngeus
muscle

Hyoid bone

Superior belly of omohyoid

Thyrohyoid

Middle constrictor
muscle

Sternohyoid (cut)

Sternothyroid (cut)

Inferior
constrictor
muscle

Cricothyroid muscle

Trachea

Omohyoid (cut)

Sternohyoid (cut)

Trapezius
(cut)

Sternothyroid (cut)

Inferior belly of
omohyoid muscle

Sternocleidomastoid
(cut)

Scalenus medius (cut)

Scalenus anterior (cut)

Figure 12-4(a) Side view of muscles of the pharynx.

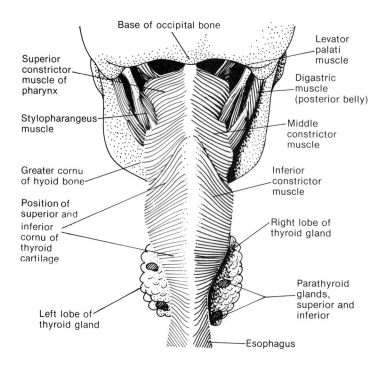

Figure 12-4(b) Posterior view of muscles of the pharynx.

Base of occipital bone

Superior constrictor muscle of pharynx

Stylopharangeus muscle

Greater cornu of hyoid bone

Position of superior and inferior cornu of thyroid cartilage

Left lobe of thyroid gland

Levator palati muscle

Digastric muscle (posterior belly)

Middle constrictor muscle

Inferior constrictor muscle

Right lobe of thyroid gland

Parathyroid glands, superior and inferior

Esophagus

are other notable differences between the structure of the esophagus and that of the stomach and intestines. For example, the outermost layer of the esophagus is *not* a true serous membrane, but is composed of tough *fibrous tissue;* also, the epithelium of the lining of the esophagus is of the *stratified squamous* type, whereas that of the remainder of the tract is *simple columnar—*

Figure 12-5 Microscopic structure of the esophagus, about midway between the mouth and the stomach (cross-section).

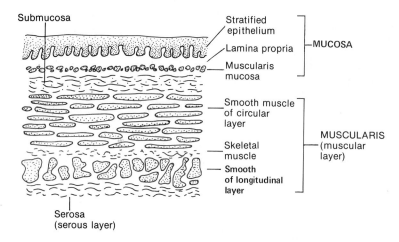

Submucosa

Stratified epithelium

Lamina propria

Muscularis mucosa

MUCOSA

Smooth muscle of circular layer

Skeletal muscle

Smooth of longitudinal layer

MUSCULARIS (muscular layer)

Serosa (serous layer)

except for the *anal region,* where the epithelium is again *stratified squamous.* The muscle fibers in the lower end of the esophagus contract and relax in the manner of a *sphincter* or "purse-string" *valve,* permitting food to enter the stomach within a few seconds of its being swallowed. This *cardiac sphincter valve* (so called because of its location within the cardiac portion of the stomach) is not a true valve and is, therefore, difficult to demonstrate on gross dissection. A mass of swallowed food is often larger than the diameter of a relaxed esophagus, and forces the anterior wall of the food tube to protrude into the membrane that forms the posterior wall of the trachea.

The stomach

The stomach (Figs. 12-6 and 12-9 and Color Plates IV & V) hangs high in the abdomen on the left side, in the *left hypochondriac and epigastric regions.* It is hollow, baglike, and, although it varies in size and shape from one individual to the next, is usually rather J-shaped. It is long and narrow in tall, slender persons, and short and wide in stockier individuals. Examination of Fig. 12-6 shows that a portion of the stomach extends above the level of the entrance of the esophagus; this region is the *fundus,* and in life it is commonly filled with air or gas. That portion of the stomach that is continuous with the esophagus is the *cardia or cardiac region* (again, so called because it is positioned near the heart). A stomach that is distended with food and gas exerts pressure on the heart, even though the two organs are separated by the diaphragm. The right border of the stomach is called the *lesser curvature,* the left border, the *greater curvature.* The distal end of the stomach (that portion that is continuous with the small intestine) is called the *pyloric region,* or *pylorus.* Within it is the *pyloric sphincter valve,* which periodically permits partially digested food to leave the stomach and enter the first portion of the small intestine, the duodenum. Upon dissection, it is easily seen that this is a true sphincter valve. Its fibers are continuous with those of the circular smooth-muscle layer in the wall of the stomach. It is not uncommon in infants for this valve to fail to relax, a condition called *pylorospasm.* Since food

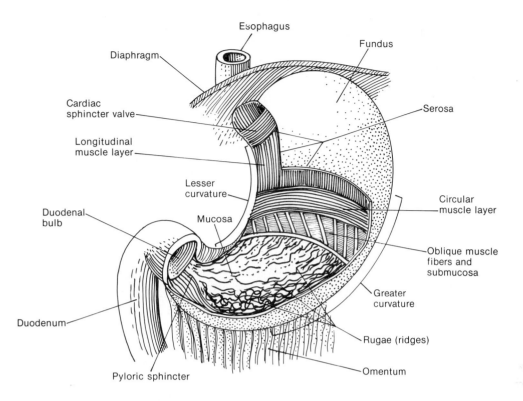

Figure 12-6 Structure of the stomach.

cannot leave the stomach, it does not digest completely and is vomited. Pylorospasm is treated with drugs that relax smooth muscle. More rare than pylorospasm is *pyloric stenosis,* a narrowing of the pyloric opening. This condition may develop at any age. Between the cardia and the pylorus is the largest portion of the stomach, the *body.* Here, food is *temporarily stored* and *partially digested* before moving into the small intestine. The stomach wall has four layers characteristic of the digestive tract in general, except that the *muscular layer* consists of *three thinner layers:* an outer one of fibers that run lengthwise (*longitudinal muscle*), an inner layer of fibers whose course is around the smaller diameter of the organ (*circular muscle*), and a layer of diagonally placed fibers within the circular fibers (*oblique muscle*). The mucous lining of the stomach shows numerous longitudinal folds called *rugae* which disappear when the organ becomes stretched with food.

Located in the mucous membrane that lines the stomach are a very great number of *gastric glands,* consisting of three kinds of cells: (1) *mucous cells* that secrete a watery substance, *mucus,* which has some protein-like material, *mucin,* in it; (2) *chief cells* that secrete *pepsinogen,* an inactive form of the enzyme *pepsin;* and (3) *parietal cells,* which produce *hydrochloric acid.* Also in the mucosa of the stomach are cells that secrete hormones—e.g., *intrinsic factor,* which is necessary for the absorption of vitamin B_{12}. This vitamin is necessary for the formation of sufficient numbers of red blood cells in the bone marrow; and if intrinsic factor ceases to be produced, pernicious anemia results.

The stomach is well supplied with blood by several branches of the *celiac trunk,* itself a branch of the abdominal aorta (Fig. 12-7). Gastric veins carry blood away from the stomach. Some of these gastric veins join the inferior vena cava directly, while others join the portal vein, which in turn enters the substance of the liver (Fig. 12-7). The stomach receives *parasympathetic* nerve fibers via the *vagus nerve* and *sympathetic fibers* that originate in the *sympathetic trunk. Visceral afferent fibers* connecting the stomach with the central nervous system carry impulses which apprise us of certain conditions

331

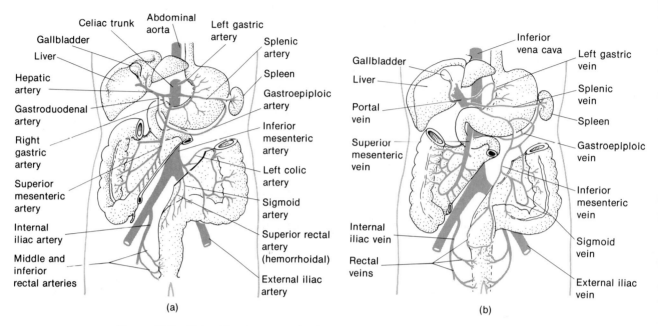

Figure 12-7 Major blood vessels of the digestive organs. (a) Arteries. (b) Veins.

(such as excess gas or indigestion) in the stomach.

FUNCTIONS OF THE STOMACH   The stomach serves as a bag for the temporary storage and partial digestion of food, it churns and breaks up food and mixes the pieces with gastric juice, and it produces intrinsic factor. Alcohol, certain drugs, and moderate amounts of sugar and water are absorbed by the stomach wall.

The small intestine

The stomach becomes the small intestine just distal to the *pyloric sphincter valve* (Fig. 12-1). The first 10 in. of the small intestine comprise the duodenum (Latin: "twelve"), so called because it is about as long as the breadth of 12 fingers. This portion of the small intestine curves sharply to the left, around the *head of the pancreas* and behind the transverse portion of the *large intestine,* then bends forward and downward. At the point of this bend, the small intestine is given the name *jejunum.* The jejunum is about 8 ft long, and is con-

tinuous with the last portion of the small intestine, the *ileum,* which is about 12 ft long. The entire length of the small intestine is approximately 21 ft, but it varies from one individual to another. Its diameter is about 1 in. Small nodules of lymphatic tissue can be seen along the entire length of the small intestine. In some places—particularly along the ileum—nodules are clustered together in groups called *Peyer's patches.* The small intestine has an inner mucous layer, a submucosa, a muscle layer consisting of *inner circular fibers* and *outer longitudinal fibers,* and an outer serous covering called *visceral peritoneum,* which is discussed further in a later section of this chapter. On cross-section, it is seen that most of the inner surface of the small intestine displays circular folds called *plicae circulares* that project into the *lumen,* or central space (Fig. 12-8); however, these folds are not present in the distal one-half of the ileum. The circular folds do not disappear during distension as do the rugae of the stomach, and they serve to greatly increase the inner surface area of the intestine without increasing its overall diameter. Covering the surfaces of the circular folds are millions of near microscopic

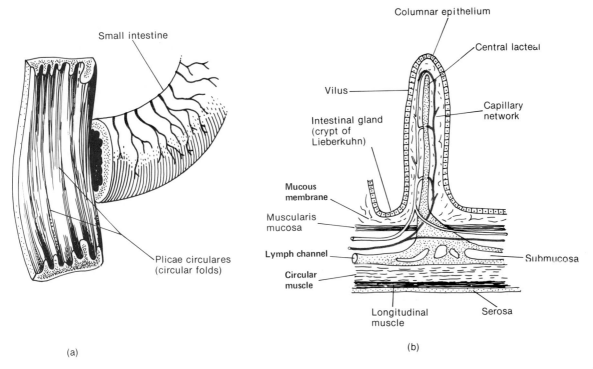

Labels in figure:
Small intestine
Plicae circulares (circular folds)
Columnar epithelium
Central lacteal
Vilus
Capillary network
Intestinal gland (crypt of Lieberkuhn)
Mucous membrane
Muscularis mucosa
Lymph channel
Circular muscle
Submucosa
Longitudinal muscle
Serosa

(a)

(b)

Figure 12-8 Internal structure of the small intestine. (a) Plicae circulares. (b) Structure of a villus.

fingerlike projections called *villi,* which even further increase, by many times, the absorptive surface area of the small intestine. Villi give the lining of the small intestine a velvet-like appearance and texture. The internal structure of a villus is illustrated in Fig. 12-8. Each villus is covered with epithelium and contains a lymph vessel (*lacteal*) and *blood capillaries.* It is easy to see how digested foods can enter the bloodstream or lymphatic system by simply passing through the epithelial cells of the villi and into the blood vessels or lacteals, respectively.

Collections of cells known as the *glands* (or *crypts*) of *Lieberkühn* lie between the villi of the small intestine, and secrete several digestive enzymes. *Brunner's glands,* found in the submucosal layer of the duodenum (but not elsewhere in the small intestine) aid *goblet cells* found in the mucosa to produce mucus. The mucosa of the small intestine, like that of the stomach, has cells that produce hormones.

The small intestine is supplied by the *gastroduodenal and superior mesenteric arteries* (Fig. 12-7). The former is a branch of the *hepatic artery,* itself a branch of the *celiac trunk.* Veins of the small intestine, fed mostly by capillaries of the villi, drain ultimately into the **portal venous system,** which carries blood to the *liver* for processing before being carried to the *inferior vena cava* and the general circulation. The small intestine is innervated by *both divisions of the autonomic nervous system* as well as by *visceral afferent fibers* that connect it with the central nervous system.

FUNCTIONS OF THE SMALL INTESTINE The small intestine completes digestion begun by the stomach and absorbs digested foods into the blood and lymph. Certain hormones—including some that aid in regulating the production of bile, intestinal juice, and pancreatic juice—are secreted by the small intestine.

The large intestine or colon

The diameter of the small intestine is only about an inch or so (hence its name); the diameter of the large intestine is about $2\frac{1}{2}$ times that of the small intestine, and it has a large lumen, but its length is only about 6 ft. The large intestine (Figs. 12-1 and 12-9 and Color Plates IV through VII) begins at the *cecum,* a pouch that extends below the

333

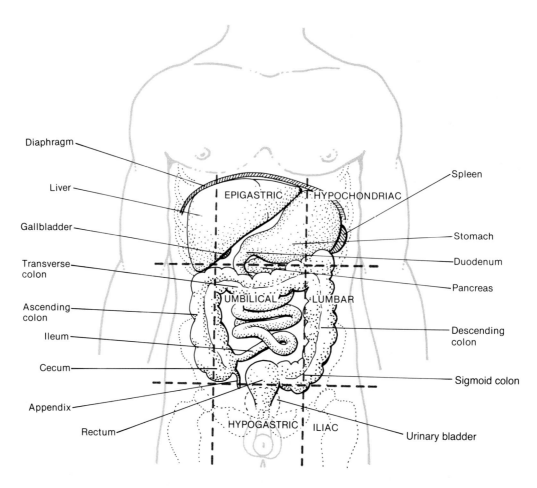

Diaphragm

Liver

Gallbladder

Transverse colon

Ascending colon

Ileum

Cecum

Appendix

Rectum

Spleen

Stomach

Duodenum

Pancreas

Descending colon

Sigmoid colon

Urinary bladder

EPIGASTRIC HYPOCHONDRIAC

UMBILICAL LUMBAR

HYPOGASTRIC ILIAC

Figure 12-9 Positions of the abdominal organs relative to the nine abdominal regions. These are variable. For example, the stomach and transverse colon may hang much lower in some individuals than is shown here.

junction of the ileum with the colon (*ileocecal junction*), in the lower-right portion of the abdomen. The *vermiform appendix* (commonly called simply the appendix) is an outgrowth of the cecum, and although it is usually found extending from the lower-left portion of the pouch, in life it has been found extending in all of the 12 positions of the clock. It may even grow on the posterior aspect of the cecum, in which case it is known as a *retrocecal appendix*. An *ileocecal valve* lets unabsorbed food from the ileum into the cecum from time to time. From the cecum, the large intestine courses upward in the right side of the abdominal cavity as the *ascending colon*. About an inch to the right of the extreme right portion of the duodenum, the large intestine bends sharply to the left, at the *right colic flexure* (*hepatic flexure*). It then runs in a sagging transverse line from right to left across the abdomen,

just beneath the stomach, as the *transverse colon,* and upon reaching the left side of the abdomen, bends abruptly downward at the *left colic flexure* (*splenic flexure*), becoming the *descending colon.* After coursing almost straight downward for several inches, the colon enters the pelvis in an S-shaped bend, the *sigmoid colon.* The last portion of the large intestine extends straight downward a few inches from the sigmoid colon to the external opening or *anus,* and is known as the *rectum.*

The last inch of the rectum is called the *anal canal,* and its opening to the outside, the *anus.* Two sphincter muscles are located at the anus: an internal sphincter of smooth muscle and an external sphincter of striated muscle. The mucous membrane that lines the anal canal is folded vertically, and these vertical folds are known as *rectal columns.* Within each rectal column is an artery and a

334

vein. Enlargements of the veins of the rectal columns are called *hemorrhoids* or *piles.*

The mucous membrane of the large intestine is smooth, and contains *no plicae circulares or villi;* there are, however, numerous *intestinal glands* with abundant *goblet cells,* which secrete no digestive enzymes, but a good deal of *mucus.* The longitudinal muscle layer of the large intestine is modified to form three longitudinal bands, called *taeniae coli,* that can be seen externally on the colon. These bands are shorter than the remainder of the colon, and draw it up into baglike *sacculations* called *haustra.* Small fat-filled sacs of peritoneum, known as *epiploic appendages,* hang along the large intestine.

Both the *superior and inferior mesenteric arteries* contribute to the blood supply of the large intestine. As in the case of the small intestine, blood is drained into veins entering the *portal system of veins,* which carries it to the liver. The large intestine is supplied by *both divisions* of the ANS and *visceral afferent fibers* to the CNS. Both the small and large intestines are richly supplied with *lymph vessels.*

FUNCTIONS OF THE LARGE INTESTINE   The chief functions of the large intestine are the absorption of water and the elimination of solid wastes; however, it is known that moderate quantities of vitamin K and B-complex vitamins are manufactured by bacteria in the large intestine.

*Accessory organs
of the digestive system*

THE LIVER   The most *versatile* organ in the body, the liver is also the *largest.* Situated high in the abdomen on the right side—often reaching the fourth intercostal space—the big gland is usually a surprise to those who see it for the first time. In the average adult, the liver weighs about $3\frac{1}{2}$ lb, and is a dark reddish-brown. The main mass of the organ is concentrated in its right portion, and there is a sharp tapering of its left portion as it extends well across the body midline. Grossly, the liver consists of four lobes: a large *right lobe* and a *left lobe,* with the right being subdivided into a *right lobe proper,* a *quadrate lobe,* and a *caudate lobe* (Fig. 12-10 and Color Plate IV).

The *basic structural and functional unit of the liver* is the *liver lobule* (Fig. 12-11). A lobule is a prismlike or cubelike structure measuring about 1×2 mm, and consists chiefly of sheets of specialized epithelial cells called *hepatic cells,* on section resembling cords. There is considerable branching and anastomosing of the "cords," so the pattern is an irregular one. The liver is very vascular, and the basic blood channel is the *liver or hepatic sinusoid,* of which there are hundreds of thousands in a single liver. Each sinusoid is a sort of capillary with incomplete walls. Blood flows into the liver through the hepatic artery and the portal vein, both of which branch repeatedly into *interlobular arteries* and *interlobular veins.* Blood from these tiny vessels seeps into the sinusoids, then flows to the "hub" of the "wheel" (center of the lobule), where a *central vein* is located. Blood leaves the lobule via the central vein, enters *sublobular veins,* then *hepatic veins,* and finally the *inferior vena cava.* As blood moves through the liver sinusoids, it is filtered by passing through and between large, star-shaped *macrophages* called *Kupffer cells.* These are *phagocytic reticuloendothelial cells* that are important in the body's defense against infection. They can ingest certain microorganisms and foreign matter from the blood that flows through the sinusoids.

FUNCTIONS OF THE LIVER   In times long past, the liver was called the *center of courage, passion, temper, love,* and even the *seat of the soul.* It was believed to produce "yellow bile," which was said to be necessary to good health. Today, we know that the liver is certainly the chemical capital of the body, and that its major functions are these:

1.   The liver produces *bile,* a watery fluid that is important in the emulsification of fats prior to their digestion by enzymes.

2.   Such blood proteins as *fibrinogen* and *prothrombin*—both necessary to the coagulation process—and *globulins* and *albumins* are synthesized in the liver. So is the anticoagulant *heparin.*

3.   The liver converts glucose to glycogen, in a process called *glycogenesis.* Some of this glycogen is then stored and later reconverted to glucose as necessary, in a process called *glycogenolysis.*

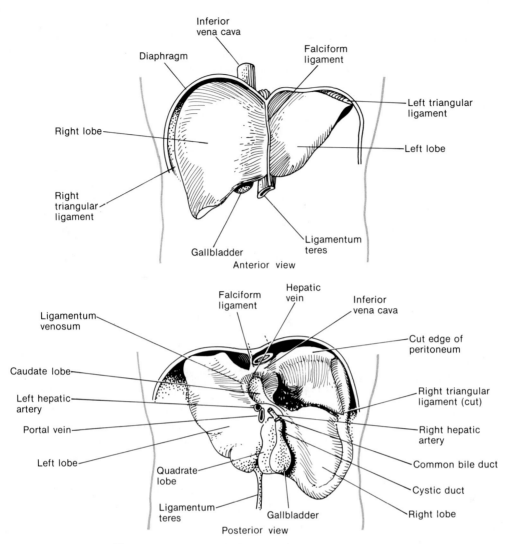

Figure 12-10 Gross anatomy of the liver.

Figure 12-11 Diagrammatic drawing of a liver lobule, the structural and functional unit of the liver.

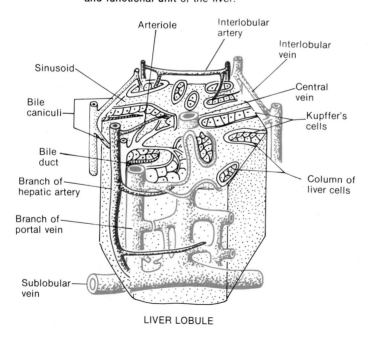

LIVER LOBULE

4. Glucose can be formed from proteins and amino acids, or from glycerol, in the liver. The synthesis of glucose from noncarbohydrate materials is *gluconeogenesis.*

5. The liver is important in the *homeostasis of blood sugar.* If the blood sugar level rises too high (hyperglycemia), as it can in diabetes mellitus, the liver steps up the conversion of glucose to glycogen. Up to a point, this action can offset the hyperglycemia. If the level falls too low (hypoglycemia), as in insulin overdose, the liver *reconverts glycogen to glucose.*

6. A portion of the *metabolism* of all three kinds of foods—proteins, carbohydrates, and lipids—is carried out in the liver. Metabolism consists of the breakdown of certain chemical substances and the buildup of others. The process is discussed in detail in the following chapter.

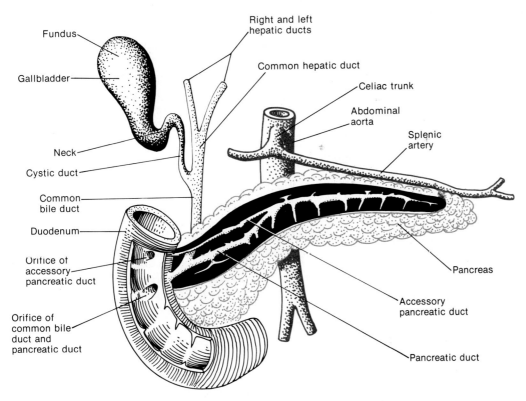

Fundus

Gallbladder

Neck

Cystic duct

Common bile duct

Duodenum

Orifice of accessory pancreatic duct

Orifice of common bile duct and pancreatic duct

Right and left hepatic ducts

Common hepatic duct

Celiac trunk

Abdominal aorta

Splenic artery

Pancreas

Accessory pancreatic duct

Pancreatic duct

Figure 12-12 The gallbladder and pancreas and their systems of ducts. Both empty into the duodenum, often by a common orifice.

7. The liver carries out *hemopoiesis* in the embryo, producing erythrocytes.

8. Toxic nitrogenous wastes, such as ammonia, are changed by the liver into urea, which is not so toxic. This process is called *detoxification*.

9. The liver *stores vitamins A, D, E, and K*—all fat-soluble vitamins—and several water-soluble vitamins such as B_{12}.

10. *Carotene* (from yellow vegetables) *is converted to vitamin A* in the liver.

THE GALLBLADDER (See Figs. 12-1 and 12-12 and Color Plate IV.) The gallbladder is a bulbous sac made of smooth muscle and serous membrane, with a mucosal lining of tall columnar epithelial cells.

It is located on the undersurface of the inferior portion of the liver, near the junction of the right lobe proper with the quadrate lobe. It has three portions—*neck, body,* and *fundus;* the fundus can be seen projecting slightly below the inferior border of the right liver lobe in an opened abdomen. The average gallbladder is 2 cm wide and 8.5 cm long. Its neck is continuous with a slender *cystic duct* which joins it with the *common hepa-*

tic duct of the liver, forming a *common bile duct.* This bile duct enters the duodenum near—and sometimes in conjunction with—the *pancreatic duct.* Bile formed in the liver first enters tiny *interlobular bile ducts,* then increasingly larger ducts, until it flows into one of two relatively large *hepatic ducts,* one serving the right and one the left portion of the liver. Although it is known that some bile passes down the common bile duct and enters the duodenum, most perhaps enters the gallbladder by traveling *up the cystic duct,* where it is *temporarily stored* and concentrated due to the reabsorption of water in the gallbladder walls. At the appropriate time, the gallbladder contracts, sending bile *back down the cystic duct* to the *common bile duct* and into the duodenum, to aid in the emulsification of fats (with water) so that they may be more effectively attacked by digestive enzymes. The release of bile by the gallbladder is dependent upon the presence of fats in the duodenum; a discussion of this mechanism is presented in a later section of this chapter.

Occasionally, the lining of the gallbladder may become inflamed (*cholecystitis*) and the organ may have to be removed (*cholecystectomy*). Bile then travels from the liver directly to the duodenum, through a duct arrangement devised by the surgeon. Obstruction of the hepatic or common bile duct by gallstones or due to other causes is not uncommon. Bile is then absorbed into the blood instead of emptying into the duodenum, and the skin, mucous membranes, and whites of the eyes become yellow due to the deposition of bile pigments, which normally leave the body in the feces. This rather startling sign of duct obstruction is called *obstructive jaundice*. Since the feces do not contain bile pigments, they present a gray or claylike appearance.

THE PANCREAS   (See Fig. 12-12 and Color Plates VI and VII.) Pink and lobulated, the pancreas lies in close anatomical relation to the duodenum and stomach. It has a *head* which is surrounded by the first curve of the duodenum, a *body* that lies behind the stomach, and a tapering *tail* that reaches the spleen. The total length of the gland is about 14 cm. The *duct of Wirsung* or duct of the pancreas empties digestive enzymes into the duodenum near (or sometimes in conjunction with) the common bile duct. The two ducts usually join the duodenum at a common opening, the *ampulla of Vater.* Sometimes, an accessory pancreatic duct, the *duct of Santorini,* joins the head of the pancreas with the duodenum. The pancreas manufactures at least one enzyme for each of the three kinds of food: *proteases,* such as *trypsin* * and *chymotrypsin,* which hydrolyze proteins; *amylases,* which help to break down starches; and *lipases,* which act on fats. *Carboxypeptidase* and other peptidases (which help to finish the breakdown of partially digested proteins called *peptides*), *sodium ions* and *bicarbonate ions* are also produced in the pancreas, most of them by *acinar cells.* The secreted substances collect in small tributary branches of the main pancreatic duct, entering the duodenum as required. All the cells and ducts involved in the production and transmission of the foregoing secretions belong to the *exocrine* portion of the pancreas, which is under both *nervous*

* Digestive enzymes are often secreted as *inactive precursors* (forerunner substances) that become active only after they have entered the intestine. Trypsin is secreted as inactive trypsinogen, chymotrypsin as chymotrypsinogen, etc.

and *hormonal* control. If the *vagus nerve,* which supplies the pancreas, is stimulated, the pancreas secretes a fluid with a high concentration of digestive enzymes. The hormone *secretin,* produced by the duodenal mucosa, stimulates the pancreas to secrete a rather thin, watery fluid poor in enzymes. *Pancreozymin,* another hormone of the duodenal mucosa, causes the pancreas to secrete moderately large quantities of enzymes, especially amylase.

In addition to its exocrine or *ducted* portion, the pancreas also contains *nonducted* or *endocrine* tissue, which pours its secretion directly into the bloodstream via the rich capillary network that ramifies throughout the pancreas. The endocrine portion of the pancreas consists of a multitude of clusters (*islets*) of two different kinds of epithelial cells—designated *alpha cells* and *beta cells*—scattered throughout the substance of the pancreas. Alpha cells secrete a hormone, *glucagon,* while beta cells secrete another hormone—a very important one, *insulin.* Both these hormones help to regulate the blood sugar level, insulin by influencing *carbohydrate metabolism,* and glucagon by speeding the *conversion of liver glycogen to glucose* when conditions warrant. The role of insulin is further discussed in connection with carbohydrate metabolism in the following chapter.

The peritoneum

The visceral organs do not simply flap around loosely inside the abdominal cavity; they are attached to the posterior abdominal wall, and to each other, by double layers of a serous membrane, the *peritoneum* (Fig. 12-13). During embryonic development, the peritoneum began as a large sac, into which the abdominal organs pushed or *invaginated* as they twisted and rotated into their final positions. The result was that the abdomen became lined with—and the organs became covered with—a continuation of the same membrane. Peritoneum that covers visceral organs is called *visceral* peritoneum, and that lining the abdominal cavity is *parietal* peritoneum. In several locations in the abdomen, double folds of peritoneum stick tightly together and are inseparable; these are designated *mesenteries, omenta,* and *ligaments.* In general, a mesentery is a peritoneal duplica-

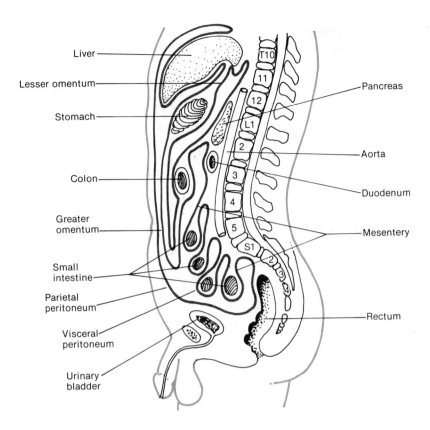

Figure 12-13 The peritoneum.

tion (double fold) that attaches an organ, such as the small intestine, to the posterior abdominal wall; an omentum, such as the *greater and lesser omenta,* attaches the stomach to the intestine; and *ligaments* attach the liver and spleen to the stomach, intestines, and kidneys. These ligaments are not ligaments in the true sense of the word—they do not have the tough fibrous connective tissue found in the ligaments of the skeletal system —but are so designated in order to distinguish them from omenta and mesenteries. The peritoneum provides a *smooth, moist, lubricating surface* so that the abdominal organs may move against each other and against the abdominal wall without appreciable friction. Before the advent of antibiotics, inflammation of the peritoneum—*peritonitis* —was a common complication of *appendicitis,* and often proved fatal. Virtually all the abdominal organs are enveloped in peritoneum—with the notable exception of the kidneys. These latter organs are covered by peritoneum *only anteriorly,* so they lie *behind* the parietal peritoneum; that is, they are *retroperitoneal.*

THE DIGESTIVE PROCESS IN DETAIL

Digestion in the mouth

One of the best ways to learn what goes on during digestion is to trace the course of a mass of food from the moment it enters the mouth and observe what happens to it from that point on. This method was followed in a rather general manner at the beginning of this chapter. Armed with more knowledge concerning the anatomy and functions of the digestive organs, we can now examine the process of digestion in much greater detail. We shall begin by assuming that a bite of food has been taken, and that this food contains protein, carbohydrate, and fat, the three most abundantly eaten food substances. Even before this first bite is taken, *salivary juices* have begun to flow into the mouth, in preparation for the entrance of food. The *sight, smell,* or merely the *thought* of food can initiate this reflex secretion of saliva. After food has entered the mouth, the taste of food—or even food just touching the tongue—further stimulates salivary production. That touch alone is sufficient is amply demonstrated when a substance such as paraffin (which is tasteless) is chewed. *Gastric juice* also begins to flow (in the stomach) when *psychological stimuli,* such as the sight or smell of food, are encountered. The *salivary reflex* depends first upon impulses traveling along neurons in cranial nerves supplying the eyes, nose, and tongue to the *medulla,* then from the medulla to the *salivary glands* via *sympathetic* and *parasympathetic autonomic neurons.* Saliva consists of the digestive enzyme *salivary amylase,* or *ptyalin,* plus such other organic substances as *urea, certain blood proteins,* and a protein-like material that was previously mentioned, *mucin.* Mucin contains a bactericidal enzyme, *lysozyme,* that dissolves bacteria. *Inorganic* substances in saliva include *sodium chloride, potassium chloride, calcium carbonate, sodium bicarbonate, calcium phosphate,* and *sodium phosphate,* all as salts. About 1 liter of saliva, on the average, is secreted each day, and its pH stays fairly close to neutral, although it may become slightly alkaline or slightly acidic from time to time. Salivary amylase does not help much as far as digestion is concerned. Although the enzyme *can convert starch to maltose* (a sugar), very little of it is actually present in saliva, and food is not commonly mixed well with saliva before being swallowed, but rather is often washed down with milk, soft drinks, or other liquids. Thus *little if any chemical digestion takes place in the mouth;* but the *mechanical action* of chewing the food is important, since it is responsible for rendering the food material small enough to be swallowed. Once it has been swallowed, the food mass is known as a *bolus,* and moves by *peristaltic waves* of the esophagus and *gravity* to the stomach. Peristalsis consists of *alternating contractions and relaxations of the smooth muscle of the esophagus* (and stomach and intestines), and is carried out entirely in a reflex manner by the autonomic nervous system, which sends *visceral efferent impulses* to the smooth muscle in the walls of the digestive tract. No digestive enzymes are secreted by the esophagus and, therefore, no digestion takes place there.

It should be noted that some substances —such as *lead, mercury, urea, thiocyanates,* and *sugars*—are sometimes excreted in the saliva, having entered the salivary glands via the circulatory system.

Digestion in the stomach

Both *mechanical* and *chemical* digestive processes take place in the stomach. The mechanical process consists of writhing and churning movements that serve to thoroughly mix the food bolus with the product of the chemical process, *gastric juice.* Gastric juice consists of *mucin, pepsin, hydrochloric acid* (HCl), and *water.* The mucin is produced by *mucous cells,* pepsin by *chief cells,* and HCl by *parietal cells.* These three kinds of cells are located in the mucosa of the stomach, in clusters or aggregations called *gastric glands.* The secretion of gastric juice can be divided into three phases: (1) the *cephalic or psychic phase,* which results from seeing, smelling, or tasting food, or even from the anticipation of eating; (2) the *gastric phase,* brought on by the presence of food in the stomach—certain cells in the stomach wall produce a hormone, *gastrin,* which travels all the way round the circulatory system and back to the gastric glands, stimulating them to secrete; and (3) the *intestinal phase,* which takes place as food enters the duodenum. This third phase, like the gastric phase, is thought to be due to hormone action. The hormone secretin, previously mentioned, produced in the duodenum, enters the circulation directly, so that it soon stimulates the gastric glands.

When a food bolus enters the stomach, gastric juice is thoroughly mixed with it until it becomes a semifluid mass called *chyme.* Slowly, at intervals, chyme is released into the duodenum by the pyloric valve. Food remains in the stomach for lengths of time that vary according to its *chemical makeup* and *physical state* (fluid, solid, or semisolid), the degree of *gastric filling* (that is, how much is eaten before gastric emptying occurs), *emotional factors*—gastric peristalsis often ceases during periods of high tension, for example—and many other factors. A hormone, *enterogastrone,* produced by the intestinal mucosa, is thought to aid in regulating gastric emptying. The average length of time that food stays in the stomach is 3 to 5 hr.

Pepsin is secreted into the stomach in an inactive form, as a precursor, *pepsinogen,* and converted to pepsin by HCl. Pepsin acts to break down (by hydrolysis) proteins into simpler molecular units called *proteoses, peptones,* and *polypeptides.* The HCl in gastric juice, in addition to converting pepsinogen to pepsin, also *curdles milk, causes protein foods to expand and soften,* and *sterilizes the gastric juice* itself. It also causes the pH of gastric juice to be extremely low (about 0.9 to 1.5) and, therefore, highly acidic. About 0.3% of the volume of gastric juice is HCl. Other components of gastric juice (such as mucus) often raise the overall pH of the stomach fluids to about 2.0.

Mucus and saliva (from the mouth) act to prevent the stomach (which is mostly protein) from digesting itself; but in times of stress, an overabundance of HCl may be secreted, and *autodigestion* (self-digestion) of the stomach may occur. The sore or lesion that results is called an *ulcer.* If it is located in the stomach, the lesion is called a *gastric* or *peptic* ulcer. Ulcers often occur in the duodenum, and are then called *duodenal* ulcers.

Cells in the stomach wall secrete *intrinsic factor,* a substance necessary for the absorption of vitamin B_{12}. If an individual is unable to absorb this vitamin, the bone marrow's production of red blood cells is drastically slowed, and *pernicious anemia* results. During this type of anemia, the stomach mucosa ceases to produce HCl and the intrinsic factor. *Achlorhydria,* the absence of HCl in the gastric juice, is a strong indication of pernicious anemia. It should be noted that in infancy, the stomach also produces *rennin,* a substance that curdles milk, thereby causing it to remain in the stomach until pepsin can begin to break down its protein. Hydrochloric acid takes over the function of rennin in children past infancy, and assumes this role for life.

In way of summary regarding gastric digestion, it can be said that *in the stomach a major step is made toward the breakdown of proteins,* but little is accomplished toward the digestion of carbohydrates or of fats (although the stomach does in fact produce small amounts of enzymes which attack all three basic food substances—that is, proteases, carbohydrases, and lipases).

Digestion in the small intestine

Liver bile, pancreatic juice, and the *intestinal juice* itself are all required to carry out proper intestinal digestion. As chyme leaves the stomach and enters the duodenum, liver bile and pancreatic juice pour into this first section of the small intestine. Bile contains salts that quickly *lower the surface tension of fats,* causing them to emulsify. The fats then no longer consist of large lumps, but consist of innumerable tiny particles suspended in the liquid medium of gastric and intestinal juice. Their *surface area* has thus been increased many times, and they are much more easily attacked by the fat-digesting enzymes, *lipases.* Bile also *helps neutralize the pH of chyme, stimulates peristalsis of the small intestine,* and *aids in the absorption of vitamins A, D, E, and K, the fat-soluble vitamins.* The coloring substances of bile—the bile pigments—include *biliverdin* (which is green) and *bilirubin* (reddish-brown). Both are derived indirectly from the *breakdown of hemoglobin* in the liver. During the passage of unabsorbed food through the small and large intestine, *bacterial action* converts the bile pigments into *stercobilin,* which produces the brown color of *feces,* the solid waste that is periodically eliminated from the intestine. Bile salts are mainly the *sodium salts of glycocholic and taurocholic acids. Cholesterol,* a number of a group of compounds known as *sterols,* is found in bile (and, to some extent, in all the body cells and fluids). Certain liver cells and cells lining the gallbladder excrete cholesterol, a component of nervous tissue, and if this excretion is overabundant, the sterol crystallizes into pebblelike bodies we call *gallstones.*

Pancreatic juice contains enzymes that hydrolyze all three kinds of food: a protease, *trypsin;* pancreatic *amylase;* and pancreatic *lipase.* Trypsin is produced as an inactive precursor, *trypsinogen,* and converts to active trypsin upon being mixed with another enzyme, *enterokinase,* present in the intestinal juice. Trypsin helps split the proteoses and peptones resulting from gastric digestion into much smaller *polypeptides,* and breaks down any proteins that have escaped initial breakdown in the stomach. It *does not* convert proteins into their ultimate products, *amino acids,* however. This is done by *enzymes in the intestinal juice.* Pancreatic amylase *hydrolyzes starches,* splitting them into *maltose, glucose,* and *dextrins.* Pancreatic lipase *hydrolyzes emulsified lipids* into *fatty acids* and *glycerol.*

Secretion of pancreatic juice is under *both hormonal and nervous control.* The main source of nervous control, it seems, consists of *autonomic impulses* arriving over branches of the *vagus nerve,* while the hormones *secretin* and *pancreozymin,* released when chyme enters the duodenum, provide the hormonal control. Experiments have proven that the pancreatic secretion produced by vagal stimulation is much thicker and richer in digestive enzymes than that resuling from stimulation by either secretin or pancreozymin.

The intestinal juice or *succus entericus* contains several enzymes, including at least one each of the *amylases, lipases, peptidases, lactases, sucrases,* and *maltases.* The enzyme *enterokinase* is also present, as are the hormones *secretin* and *enterocrinin.* The last hormone causes the intestine to liberate *relatively large quantities* of intestinal juice that is *rich in enzymes.* Amylase, sucrase, lactase, and maltase hydrolyze carbohydrates. The first breaks down *starches,* the second attacks *sucrose* (table sugar), lactase splits *lactose* (milk sugar), and maltaste digests *maltose* (malt sugar). Enterokinase *converts trypsinogen into active trypsin,* and active trypsin plus peptidases split the *proteoses, peptones,* and *polypeptides* resulting from gastric digestion into *amino acids.* The *intestinal glands* (crypts of Lieberkühn) are simple, tubular structures. They are found *between the villi* of the small intestine and *secrete the intestinal juice* and probably all its *enzymes.* Convoluted, branching *duodenal glands* (Brunner's glands), present only in the duodenum, are located in the submucosa.

It is likely that the secretion of intestinal juice is dependent to a large extent upon *stimulation* by the *chemical-breakdown products of the digestion of food* which are liberated during gastric and duodenal digestion. Table 12-1 summarizes the major digestive processes occurring in each of the different portions of the digestive system.

THE ABSORPTION PROCESS

Once food has been converted into a form suitable for entering the bloodstream—that is, when its particles are small enough to pass through the epithelial cells of the intestinal villi—*it passes from the lumen of the intestine,* through the cells of the villi, and *into the rich network of capillaries and lymph vessels that supply the intestines.* The small intestine is supplied by branches of the *gastroduodenal* and *superior mesenteric* arteries; its capillaries become veins that connect with the *portal vein,* which carries blood to the liver for processing. Lymph from the *lacteals* is filtered by *nodes in the mesenteries* before entering the *thoracic duct.*

The smooth muscle of the intestinal wall is supplied by *both sympathetic and parasympathetic efferent fibers,* and impulses traveling over these neurons control the *peristaltic movement of the food mass or bolus* to a large extent. The food mass must be kept moving (at least slowly) or absorption is impaired. During absorption, soluble food substances in the chyme pass through the selectively permeable epithelial cells of the intestinal villi, into the blood and lymph. Absorption takes place at the same time that secretion of intestinal juice is going on, and involves both *simple diffusion* and *active transport.* In some manner as yet poorly understood, the intestinal epithelial cells *utilize energy, perform work,* and *actively assist* in the passage of selected substances (such as *water, salts, vitamins,* and the *breakdown products of digestion*) through their membranes.

Glucose is absorbed by both simple diffusion and active transport, and at least some water and salts appear to utilize active transport. The digestive breakdown products of fats—fatty acids and glycerol—as well as intact fat molecules seem to be absorbed into the lacteals *and* into blood capillaries of the intestinal villi.

TABLE 12-1

**Summary of digestion in
various portions of the digestive system**

Portion of digestive system	Enzymes	Digestive products
Mouth	Salivary amylase	Virtually none in the mouth; some conversion of starches to maltose after swallowing
Esophagus	None	None
Stomach	Pepsin	Conversion of proteins into proteoses, peptones, and polypeptides
Small intestine	Pancreatic protease (trypsin)	Helps intestinal peptidase break down proteoses and peptones of gastric digestion into polypeptides
	Pancreatic amylase	Hydrolyzes starches into maltose, glucose, and dextrins
	Pancreatic lipase	Hydrolyzes emulsified fats into fatty acids and glycerol
	Intestinal amylase	Splits starches into smaller molecular units
	Intestinal sucrase	Hydrolyzes sucrose into glucose plus fructose
	Intestinal lactase	Breaks down lactose into glucose plus galactose
	Intestinal maltase	Breaks down maltose into glucose molecules
	Intestinal peptidase	Helps pancreatic protease split proteoses, peptones, and polypeptides into amino acids

Why is it that certain substances that would seem to be absorbable cannot penetrate the intestinal mucosa? This is a question that science has yet to answer. A case in point is magnesium sulfate, popularly known as Epsom salts. Its molecules are smaller than those of glucose; yet glucose molecules are readily absorbed, while those of magnesium sulfate are not. It is theorized that a sort of "reverse active transport" system acts to *prevent* the absorption of certain substances. The fact that magnesium sulfate is not absorbed is what makes this compound such a powerful cathartic.

Once absorbed materials have *entered the circulation,* they go to the liver, where they are prepared *for use by the tissue cells.* By far the greater amount of absorption takes place in the *small intestine.* Some *drugs,* some *sugar,* a little *water,* and a large amount of *alcohol* can enter the bloodstream by being absorbed in the *stomach,* and large quantities of *water* are absorbed in the *colon.*

Defecation. As semifluid chyme passes through the large intestine and loses much of its water, it becomes a firm, compact mass of *fecal material.* Mucus secreted by the large intestine helps hold the fecal mass together and, at the same time, lubricates the intestine. *Bile pigments,* the cellulose of carbohydrates, connective tissue, fats, *bacteria,* and *intestinal products* (such as mucus) are present in the feces, along with *unabsorbed food.* Once about every 12 hours, the contents of the colon move into the lower portion of the colon, or lower *bowel,* by a series of long contractions called *mass peristalsis*. The ingestion of food will often trigger this reflex. When the feces reaches the rectum, the *urge to defecate* occurs. The act of defecation is *partly reflex* and *partly voluntary* (in very young infants it is purely reflex). The reflex stage begins with *stretch receptors* in the colon. Impulses travel from the distended colon to the *spinal cord and medulla,* and back to the smooth muscle in the *wall of the rectum.* If the urge to defecate is repeatedly ignored, it diminishes or completely disappears, and constipation or *colonic stasis* results. Eating "roughage," such as fruits and vegetables, drinking adequate amounts of water, getting moderate amounts of exercise (at least), and paying regular attention to the urge of nature all help to prevent constipation. In general, *laxatives* and *cathartics* are unnatural aids to defecation, and should be avoided whenever possible. (A laxative is a chemical that promotes relatively gentle bowel movement, while a cathartic usually produces much more vigorous action.) Con-

traction of the abdominal muscles and "bearing down" by holding the breath and thereby increasing the intra-abdominal pressure sometimes helps during elimination.

A good deal of *bacterial decomposition* goes on in the large bowel, but bacteria themselves constitute only a small percentage of the feces. Such gases as *hydrogen sulfide, ammonia, carbon dioxide, methane,* and *hydrogen* are produced as a result of this decomposition or *putrefaction* in the large intestine. Such amines as *skatole* and *indole* (which are waste products of amino acids) and *butyric, acetic,* and *lactic acids* are also produced. Many of these substances—especially indole, skatole, and hydrogen sulfide—impart odors characteristic of fecal matter.

One other significant contribution to health is made by the large intestine. It is known that some of the bacteria that make up the *intestinal flora*—bacterial population—can *manufacture vitamin K* (which is necessary to the normal clotting of blood) and some of the *B-complex vitamins.*

OUTLINE SUMMARY

1. The digestion and absorption of foods
   A. The route of food and drink: mouth, pharynx, esophagus, stomach, small intestine, large intestine
   B. The mouth and pharynx
      a. The mouth or buccal cavity
         1. Has a roof, floor, and side walls
         2. Lined with mucous membrane
         3. Contains the tongue with taste buds, teeth, and openings of three pairs of salivary glands
      b. The pharynx
         1. Nasal pharynx: cavity immediately posterior to the internal openings of the nose
         2. Oral pharynx: cavity between the posterior portion of the mouth and the upper end of the esophagus
      c. Swallowing
         1. Constrictor muscles of pharynx act to force food into the upper portion of the esophagus
         2. Other pharyngeal muscles raise the pharynx, close the epiglottis over the larynx, and close off the nasal pharynx by moving the soft palate upward
         3. The tongue moves backward

   during the above actions, helping constrictor pharyngeal muscles to carry food to the esophagus
         4. As the food bolus stimulates receptors in the pharyngeal wall, the swallowing process changes from a voluntary one to one that is purely reflex
         5. The parotid, sublingual, and submaxillary salivary glands add moisture to food which facilitates swallowing. They also contain a starch-splitting enzyme, salivary amylase
      C. The esophagus: a narrow 10-in. tube leading from the pharynx to the stomach
         a. Has the four main layers present in the remainder of the digestive tract —from inward to outward
            1. Mucous membrane
            2. Submucous layer
            3. Muscular layer
            4. Serous layer
         b. Has a cardiac sphincter "value" near its point of entrance into the stomach
      D. The stomach: is hollow and baglike,

and usually placed in the left hypochondriac and epigastric regions, although the position is variable. It has the following features:

a. Fundus: the bulging upward of a portion of the stomach, above the level of entrance of the esophagus
b. Cardia: the region near the heart
c. Pyloris: continuous with the duodenum, and containing the pyloric sphincter valve
d. Body: largest portion of the stomach
e. Rugae: internal longitudinal folds which disappear when the stomach is distended with food
f. Gastric glands—three kinds of cells
   1. Mucous cells: secrete mucus
   2. Chief cells: secrete pepsinogen
   3. Parietal cells: produce HCl

E. The small intestine: consists of the duodenum, jejunum, and ileum; has internal folds (plicae circulares) which increases the absorptive area, and which are covered with innumerable microscopic villi
a. Duodenum
   1. Continuous with the pylorus of the stomach
   2. About 10 in. long
   3. Receives ducts of the pancreas and gallbladder
   4. Secretes digestive enzymes and hormones
b. Jejunum
   1. About 8 ft long
   2. Continuous proximally with the duodenum and distally with the ileum
c. Ileum
   1. About 12 ft long
   2. Continuous proximally with the jejunum, distally with the large intestine at the ileocecal junction
d. Miscellaneous features of the small intestine
   1. Each villus is covered with epithelium, and contains blood capillaries and a lymph vessel or lacteal
   2. Crypts of Lieberkühn lie between the villi and secrete digestive enzymes
   3. Brunner's glands are found in the submucosa of the duodenum and help goblet cells to produce mucus
   4. Mucosa of the small intestine contains the hormone-producing cells

F. The large intestine
a. Is $2\frac{1}{2}$ in. in diameter, and 6 ft long
b. Begins at the cecum, just below the ileocecal junction
c. Has an outgrowth, the vermiform appendix
d. Has an ileocecal valve (inside the ileocecal junction) which prevents reflex of fecal material from the large intestine into the small intestine
e. Arranged in five portions: ascending, transverse, descending, sigmoid, and rectal. The bend between the ascending and transverse colon is the hepatic flexure; that between the transverse and descending colon, the splenic flexure. The anus is the opening of the rectum
f. Has no plicae circulares or villi, and secretes no digestive enzymes, but does secrete mucus
g. Has longitudinal smooth-muscle fibers arranged in three bands called taeniae coil. These draw the colon up into sacculations called haustra
h. Has epiploic appendages, which are small fat-filled sacs of peritoneum that hang along its border

2. Accessory organs of the digestive system
A. The liver
a. Largest and most versatile organ in the body
b. Has four lobes: a left lobe, and a right lobe that is subdivided into right lobe proper, quadrate lobe, and caudate lobe
c. The structural and functional unit is the liver lobule, consisting chiefly of epithelial cells and a central vein
d. The basic blood channel of the liver is the hepatic sinusoid
e. Flow of blood in the liver: hepatic artery and portal vein → interlobular arteries and interlobular veins → sinusoids → central vein → sublobular veins → hepatic veins → inferior vena cava
f. Kupffer cells filter blood passing through the sinusoids

B. Functions of the liver
a. Production of bile
b. Synthesis of fibrinogen, prothrombin, globulins, albumin, and heparin
c. Glycogenesis, glycogenolysis, and gluconeogenesis
d. Homeostasis of blood sugar
e. Portions of the metabolism of proteins, carbohydrates, and lipids

f. Erythropoiesis (in the embryo)
g. Detoxification
h. Vitamin storage
i. Conversion of carotene to vitamin A
C. The gallbladder
  a. Structure
    1. A bulbous sac about $8\frac{1}{2}$ cm long, lined with tall columnar epithelial cells
    2. Has a neck, body, and fundus, and is positioned on the under surface of the inferior portion of the liver
    3. Its cystic duct joins the common hepatic duct of the liver, forming the common bile duct, which in turn enters the duodenum near or with the pancreatic duct, at the ampulla of Vater
  b. Functions
    1. Temporarily stores bile and concentrates it by absorbing a portion of its water
    2. Releases bile into the duodenum in response to the presence of fats in the duodenum. Bile emulsifies fats, rendering them more digestible
D. The pancreas
  a. Structural features
    1. Head: surrounded by curve of the duodenum
    2. Body: lies behind the stomach
    3. Tail: reaches the spleen
    4. Length: about 14 cm
    5. Its duct, the duct of Wirsung, carries digestive enzymes to the duodenum, and enters the latter structure near or with the common bile duct. An accessory duct (of Santorini) is sometimes present
    6. Tissue—two major types: exocrine or ducted, which produces digestive enzymes; and endocrine or nonducted (islet tissue), which secretes the hormones insulin and glucagon
  b. Pancreatic digestive enzymes
    1. Proteases, such as trypsin and chymotrypsin, secreted as the precursors trypsinogen and chymotrypsinogen
    2. Amylases
    3. Lipases
    4. Peptidases
  c. Cells of the pancreas
    1. Alpha cells: secrete glucagon
    2. Beta cells: secrete insulin
    3. Acinar cells: secrete digestive enzymes

  d. Control of the pancreas
    1. Exocrine portion: both hormonal and nervous control. Vagal stimulation elicits pancreatic fluid rich in digestive enzymes, while the hormones secretin and pancreozymin stimulate the production of thin, watery pancreatic fluid
    2. Endocrine portion: secretion of insulin and glucagon is in response to variations in blood glucose level (chemical control)
3. The peritoneum
  A. Functions: attaches abdominal visceral organs to each other and to the posterior abdominal wall; secretes a serous fluid which permits organs to move against each other with little friction
  B. Divisions
    a. Parietal: lines the abdominal wall
    b. Visceral: adheres tightly to organs
  C. Special terms associated with peritoneum
    a. Mesentery: peritoneum that attaches an organ to the posterior abdominal wall
    b. Omentum: attaches the stomach to the intestine
    c. Ligaments: attach the liver and spleen to the stomach, intestines, and kidneys
    d. Peritonitis: inflammation of the peritoneum
4. The digestive process in detail
  A. Digestion in the mouth
    a. Saliva is secreted in response to the sight, smell, or thought of food, or to the presence of food in the mouth. Secretion is dependent upon sympathetic and parasympathetic autonomic reflexes
    b. Components of saliva
      1. Water (in large amounts)
      2. Salivary amylase
      3. Mucin
      4. Blood proteins
      5. Urea
      6. Sodium chloride
      7. Potassium chloride
      8. Calcium carbonate
      9. Calcium phosphate
      10. Sodium bicarbonate
      11. Sodium phosphate
      12. Miscellaneous substances, such as lead, mercury, thiocyanates, and sugars, all of which are sometimes excreted in saliva
    c. Physical characteristics of saliva
      1. pH: near-neutral
      2. About 1 liter secreted each day

d. Salivary digestion
    1. Of little importance. Saliva prepares food for swallowing, and prevents the mouth from drying out between eating and drinking
    2. Some salivary digestion can occur after food has entered the stomach
B. Digestion in the stomach
    a. Mechanical process—peristalsis: writhing and churning movements that serve to thoroughly mix the food bolus with gastric juice
    b. Chemical process: involves the secretion of gastric juice (mucin, pepsin, HCl, and water) by cells of the gastric glands, and the effects of this juice upon ingested foods
        1. The phases of secretion of gastric juice are called cephalic or psychic, gastric, and intestinal
        2. Pepsin hydrolyzes proteins to proteoses, peptones, and polypeptides
        3. HCl converts pepsinogen into pepsin, curdles milk, and softens protein foods
        4. Some carbohydrase and lipase are also produced in the stomach, but these are of little value in the overall digestive process
        5. Mucin is produced by mucous cells, pepsin (as pepsinogen) by chief cells, and HCl by parietal cells
        6. Stomach cells also produce intrinsic factor, necessary for absorption of vitamin B_{12}
C. Digestion in the small intestine
    a. Bile causes fats to emulsify, stimulates intestinal peristalsis, and aids in the absorption of vitamins A, D, E, and K
    b. Roles of pancreatic-juice components in intestinal digestion
        1. Pancreatic protease, or trypsin: splits proteoses and peptones of gastric digestion into (smaller) polypeptides, and begins the breakdown of proteins that have escaped this action in the stomach
        2. Pancreatic amylase: hydrolyzes starches into maltose, glucose, and dextrins
        3. Pancreatic lipase: splits lipids into fatty acids and glycerol
    c. Intestinal juice contains at least one amylase, lipase, peptidase, lactase, sucrase, and maltase, as well as enterokinase. Their actions are as follows:

1. Amylase: breaks down starches
2. Sucrase: attacks sucrose
3. Lactase: splits lactose
4. Maltase: digests maltose
5. Enterokinase: converts trypsinogen into active trypsin, which in turn attacks proteins
6. Peptidase: splits proteoses, peptones, and polypeptides into amino acids
    d. Secretion of intestinal juice
        1. Performed by cells in the intestinal glands (crypts of Lieberkühn) and duodenal glands
        2. Probably dependent upon stimulation by the chemical breakdown products of gastric and duodenal digestion
5. Absorption
    A. Following digestion, food passes through the cells of the intestinal villi and into the blood and lymph
        a. Food entering the blood travels in the portal vein to the liver for further processing
        b. Fats entering the lacteals are filtered by mesenteric lymph nodes before entering the thoracic duct
    B. Both divisions of the autonomic nervous system maintain peristaltic movements of the small intestine; too little or too much peristalsis impairs absorption
    C. Absorption involves both simple diffusion and active transport
        a. Intestinal epithelial cells utilize energy, perform work, and assist in the absorption of water, salts, vitamins, glucose, and digestive breakdown products, some of which can be absorbed by simple diffusion
        b. Certain drugs, some sugar, some water, and large amounts of alcohol can be absorbed in the stomach
        c. Large quantities of water are absorbed in the colon
    D. Defecation
        a. Following food and water absorption, there is a solid, compact mass of unabsorbed residue called fecal material, which must be eliminated from the large intestine
        b. Intestinal mucus helps hold the fecal mass together, and lubricates the intestine
        c. About every 12 hr, the colonic contents move into the lower bowel by mass peristalsis. This reflex can be triggered by eating. Fecal material in the rectum produces an urge to defecate
        d. The act of defecation is partly re-

flex and partly voluntary (after toilet training)

1. Reflex portion: stretch receptors in the colon set up impulses which travel to the medulla and back to the rectal smooth muscle. Voluntary suppression of this reflex can result in constipation or colonic stasis

2. Voluntary portion: contraction of the abdominal muscles and "bearing down" by holding the breath aids the process of elimination

E. Miscellaneous functions of the large intestine
   a. Bacterial decomposition
   b. Production of vitamin K (necessary to the clotting of blood) and some B-complex vitamins by certain bacteria of the normal intestinal flora

STUDY QUESTIONS AND PROBLEMS

1. Briefly outline the route of food as it moves completely through the digestive system.

2. Mr. E., a successful business man, suffers from a gastric ulcer. This means that his ulcer is located in what organ of the digestive system?

3. Name the three portions of the small intestine, from superior to inferior. Which portion connects with the large intestine?

4. In which does the greater absorption of food take place: the small intestine or large intestine? The greater absorption of water?

5. Name the three pairs of salivary glands and state their locations. How much digestion takes place in the mouth?

6. Describe the four basic layers of the walls of the digestive organs. What kinds of cells are found in the gastric glands?

7. List the chief functions of the liver. Describe the structure of a liver lobule.

8. Mrs. L., a housewife, enters a hospital in order to have a cholecystectomy. Which organ associated with the digestive system will be removed?

9. What kinds of enzymes are produced by the pancreas? Where does the pancreas secrete these enzymes into the digestive tract? What other organ empties a fluid into the digestive tract near to, or in conjunction with, the duct of the pancreas?

10. Briefly describe the peritoneum. What is a mesentery? Omentum? Ligament? What is the term that means inflammation of the peritoneum?

11. List and briefly discuss the phases of gastric secretion. What is chyme? A food bolus?

12. Pepsinogen is said to be a precursor of the enzyme pepsin, which helps to digest protein foods. In your own words, define a *precursor*.

13. What is the approximate pH of gastric juice? Is this pH value acidic, or alkaline (basic)?

14. What four vitamins are classed as fat-soluble?

15. Briefly discuss the control of pancreatic secretion.

16. In what part of the digestive tract does the synthesis of vitamin K take place?

17. Describe the mechanism of defecation. What are the major components of the feces?

18. Why can an amylase be called a carbohydrase?

19. What is the chief reason that magnesium sulfate is such an effective cathartic?

20. List the products of digestion in the stomach, then list those of the small intestine.

metabolism, foods, and nutrition

After they have been absorbed, each of six kinds of foodstuffs utilized by man—*proteins, carbohydrates, lipids, water, minerals,* and *vitamins*—becomes involved in a myriad of biochemical reactions that take place mostly within the body cells. These reactions are known collectively as **metabolism,** and are absolutely essential to the maintenance of a homeostatic state of the body chemistry, which in turn is necessary to good health, and in many cases, to life itself. During metabolism, there is a constant building up and tearing down of substances: compounds are broken down, while others are put together; protoplasm disintegrates, and new protoplasm is synthesized. Energy is used in extracting more energy from foods, and some of it is used to drive vital processes (such as muscle contraction, nerve-impulse transmission, and the synthesis of enzymes and hormones), while much of it is used to maintain a constant body temperature; a great deal of the energy produced by the metabolism of foods is given off as *waste heat.*

Those events of metabolism that are involved in building-up processes are conveniently lumped together under the term *anabolism,* while those concerned with tearing-down processes are grouped as *catabolism.* The most important kind of reaction that occurs during anabolism is the conversion of relatively simple substances into more complex molecules, such as the synthesis of tissue proteins from amino acids. Catabolism, on the other hand, involves the conversion of complex molecules into simpler ones. During catabolic conversion, energy is stored in molecules of adenosine triphosphate. During anabolism, this energy is released. Metabolic processes must go on continuously if an individual is to remain alive and healthy; and in order to insure that these processes will not be interrupted, food must be ingested, digested, and absorbed with regularity; otherwise, the body tissues themselves will be broken down and metabolized, a condition that always results in upset of homeostasis and, if carried too far (as during fasting or starvation), irreparable damage to the liver or central nervous system, or death. *Nutrition* is the process of assimilation of food—that is, the anabolic process of changing food into living tissue. One of the most important ideas considered in this chapter concerns the roles played by each of the basic foodstuffs in the process of nutrition.

Carbohydrates and their metabolism

During catabolism, cells normally oxidize ("burn") carbohydrates as their fuel. Lipids and proteins are utilized only if the carbohydrate supply falls below a certain level.

The most outstanding examples of carbohydrates in the human diet are the sugars and starches. Carbohydrate molecules are made up of carbon, hydrogen, and oxygen, usually with twice as many hydrogen atoms as oxygen atoms in each molecule (the same proportion as in a molecule of water). Carbohydrates can be grouped as *monosaccharides, disaccharides,* and *polysaccharides.* The monosaccharides or simple sugars are easily absorbed in solution. *Glucose* or grape sugar, *fructose* or fruit sugar, and *galactose* are all monosaccharides, and all have the empirical formula $C_6H_{12}O_6$. (Their structural formulas differ, however—see Fig. 13-1.) Galactose is not found free in nature—as are glucose and fructose—but occurs in combination with other sugars in carbohydrate compounds. Glucose (also known as *dextrose*) is the carbohydrate of the circulating blood; thus all other carbohydrates that can be utilized by the body must be converted into glucose before they can be completely metabolized. Any monosaccharide with six carbon atoms in its molecules (such as glucose) is called a *hexose.* Two monosaccharides of extreme importance, *ribose* and *deoxyribose,* have only five carbon atoms in each of their molecules, and are called *pentoses.* They are found in the nucleic acids DNA and RNA and their nucleotides (see Fig. 13-1 and Chapter 2).

Some important disaccharides or "double sugars" are *sucrose, maltose,* and *lactose.* Sucrose is the carbohydrate familiar to all of us as "sugar," and is obtained from sugar cane and sugar beets. Upon hydrolysis, one molecule of a *disaccharide* yields two *monosaccharide molecules.* For example, the hydrolysis of one molecule of sucrose in the intestine produces one molecule of glucose and one molecule of fructose. Each molecule of *maltose,* the principal sugar formed by the action of *amylase* on starch and glycogen, is hydrolyzed to two molecules of glucose. Lactose or milk sugar is found only in the milk of mammals. Cow's milk is about 5% lactose, while the proportion in human milk ranges from 4% to 6% (averaging about the same as cow's milk). Lactose is only slightly sweet to the taste, and when hydrolyzed, yields *galactose* and glucose. Disaccharides have the empirical formula $C_{12}H_{22}O_{11}$.

Polysaccharides, of which the starches and glycogen are the best examples, are carbohydrates consisting of long chains of monosaccharide molecules. Unlike many of the monosaccharides, however, starches are not sweet to the taste. Upon hydrolysis, one molecule of the starch *amylose* yields from 200 to 300 molecules of glucose (Fig. 13-1).

All of the simple carbohydrates absorbed in the small intestine, whether they began as monosaccharides or became such during the hydrolytic processes of digestion, have a half-dozen possible alternative fates awaiting them: (1) *they may enter the circulation as blood sugar** (after being converted to glucose); (2) *they may be converted to glycogen in the liver* and then stored there; (3) *they may be converted to glycogen in skeletal muscles* and utilized in the muscle-contraction process; (4) *they may be changed into lipids* and stored in fat depots (on the mesenteries and beneath the skin) as adipose tissue; (5) *they may be oxidized or "burned"* as sources of quick energy; or (6) if present in excess, or if certain pathological conditions (such as diabetes mellitus) exist, *they may be excreted in the urine.*

THE IMPORTANCE OF CARBOHYDRATES The principal function of carbohydrate is to provide energy in a form which the body can quickly utilize. Like gasoline, coal, oil, or any other fuel, carbohydrate must be oxidized if its stored energy is to be released. When sugars are oxidized, *carbon dioxide, water,* and *kinetic (active) energy* are produced. This can be exemplified by using a chemical equation to represent the oxidation of one gram-molecular weight of glucose:

$$C_6H_{12}O_6 + 6O_2 \rightarrow 6CO_2 + 6H_2O + 683 \text{ Calories **}$$

This oxidation of carbohydrates is carried out within the body cells, and is sometimes called *cellular respiration* or *intermediate metabolism* (Fig. 13-2). Much of the energy released during carbohydrate

---

* The blood glucose level normally amounts to about 80 milligrams per cent (80 mg per 100 ml), but this level may rise briefly to over 115 mg per cent after a meal.

** The unit term *Calories* (abbreviated Cal) represents energy as *kilocalories* (kcal) or "large calories"; 1 Cal is the amount of heat required to raise the temperature of 1000 g of water by 1°C ("one degree centigrade"). The small calorie (cal), spelled with a lower-case "c," is equal to $\frac{1}{1000}$ Calorie (0.001 Cal).

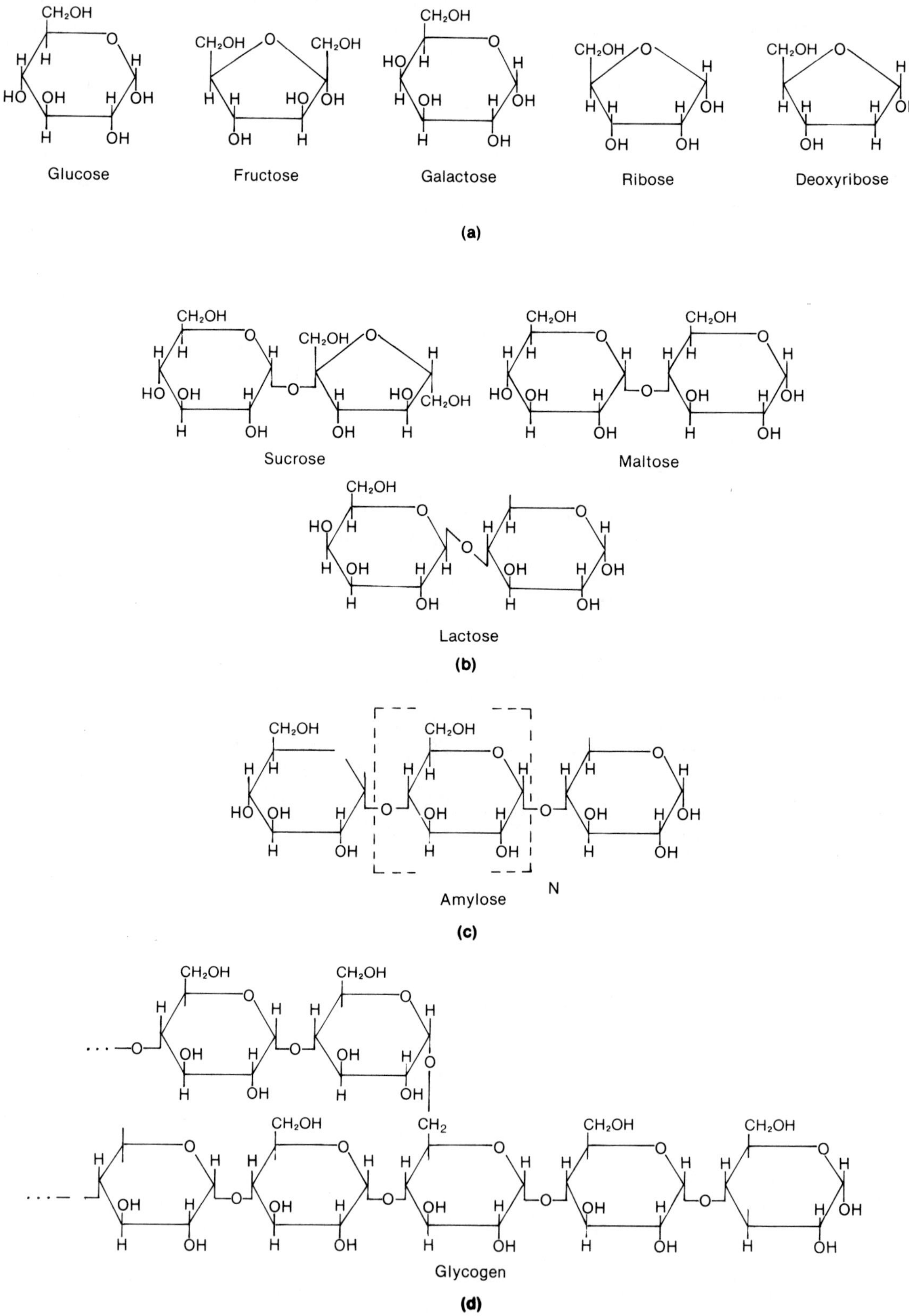

Figure 13-1 Structural formulas of some of the more common carbohydrates.
(a) Five important monosaccharides. (b) Three disaccharides.
(c) Portion of a molecule of the starch, amylose. The lower case n
outside the brackets indicates that the portion within them can be repeated many times.
(d) A portion of a molecule of glycogen, illustrating side-chain branching.

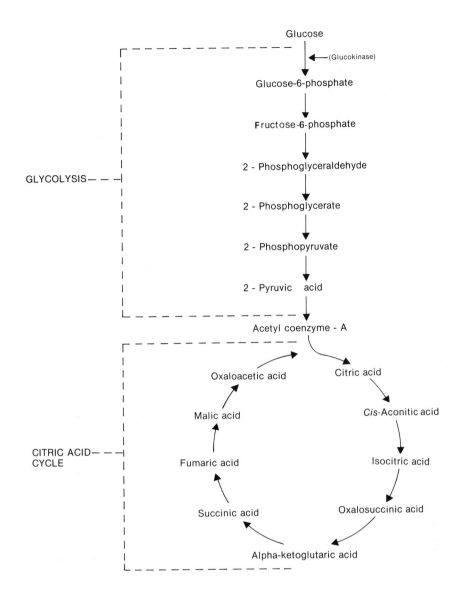

Glucose

(Glucokinase)

Glucose-6-phosphate

Fructose-6-phosphate

2 - Phosphoglyceraldehyde

2 - Phosphoglycerate

2 - Phosphopyruvate

2 - Pyruvic   acid

GLYCOLYSIS

Acetyl coenzyme - A

CITRIC ACID
CYCLE

Oxaloacetic acid

Citric acid

Malic acid

Cis-Aconitic acid

Fumaric acid

Isocitric acid

Succinic acid

Oxalosuccinic acid

Alpha-ketoglutaric acid

Figure 13-2 Glycolysis and the citric acid cycle; cellular intermediate metabolism.

metabolism is stored in the form of high-energy phosphate compounds such as adenosine triphosphate (ATP), and used later for processes requiring energy, such as the process of muscle contraction.

CARBOHYDRATE CATABOLISM During catabolism, cells continuously utilize foods for energy. The catabolic portion of carbohydrate metabolism can be subdivided into two segments or *phases: glycolysis* and the *citric acid* or *Kreb's cycle* (Fig. 13-2). Together, these phases represent intermediate metabolism.

During glycolysis, each molecule of glucose is split into two molecules of *pyruvic acid.* Ten chemical reactions are required for

this to take place. Some of these are shown in Fig. 13-2. Following glycolysis, each pyruvic acid molecule is broken down to form three molecules of carbon dioxide. This occurs during the "turning" of the citric acid cycle, or second phase of carbohydrate catabolism. It will readily be seen that the catabolism of one molecule of glucose produces six molecules of carbon dioxide. The chemical reactions of glycolysis require no oxygen; that is, they are *anaerobic;* however, the citric acid cycle requires six molecules of oxygen for every molecule of glucose oxidized. The equation on p. 351 indicates that each molecule of glucose is oxidized to six molecules of carbon dioxide and six molecules of water. It also indicates that 683 Calories of *energy* are released. The equation represents a summary of all the chemical reactions of carbohydrate catabolism.

Glycolysis is known also as the *Embden-Meyerhof pathway*. It will be noted by examination of Fig. 13-2 that the pathway involves changing glucose to glucose-6-phosphate and then to other compounds before pyruvic acid is finally produced. This reaction is called *phosphorylation,* and is a critical part of carbohydrate catabolism:

Glucose + ATP
(in cytoplasm)

$$\xrightarrow[]{\text{Glucokinase}} \text{Glucose-6-phosphate}$$

It will be noted that an enzyme, glucokinase, is required for the reaction to go to completion. Specific enzymes are necessary for each step of glycolysis and the citric acid cycle to take place. It is this enzyme activity or *biocatalytic action* that enables oxidation to take place at body temperature rather than at the much higher temperature that would be required to burn the food outside the body (where such heat sources as ovens or laboratory burners would be employed). A large number of the enzymes of cellular respiration must themselves be assisted by *coenzymes* (enzyme activators) before they can catalyze a reaction.

More than half the energy extracted from glucose during catabolism is stored in the form of high-energy bonds in ATP. ATP is the real source of immediate energy to the cell, driving the reactions of muscle contraction, tissue protein synthesis, enzyme and hormone manufacture, and others. The breakdown of ATP can be shown as follows:

$$\text{ATP} \xrightarrow[]{\text{Breakdown}} \text{ADP} + \text{Phosphate} + \text{Energy release}$$

Less than 10% of the ATP produced during catabolism is produced during glycolysis; this means that more than 90% of the ATP is produced during the citric acid cycle, the aerobic phase of catabolism. The end products of the cycle are commonly said to be carbon dioxide and water; but it must be borne in mind that ATP is formed and energy is released while this formation of carbon dioxide and water is taking place.

Some of the heat produced during the reactions of catabolism and the other reactions of metabolism serves to prevent the body temperature from dropping too low for enzyme activity; but much is given off as waste heat. Very little carbohydrate is utilized in the synthesis of new protoplasm; most of it is involved in providing energy, through glycolysis and the citric acid cycle.

THE ROLE OF HORMONES IN CARBOHYDRATE METABOLISM   Insulin, produced by the islet cells of the pancreas, is the most important hormone that is involved in the utilization of carbohydrate by the body. To appreciate the role of insulin, we must first recognize that because glucose is the only carbohydrate found in appreciable amounts in the blood, the elevation or lowering of the blood sugar level obviously involves either an increase or decrease in the relative amount of circulating glucose. Insulin somehow speeds the movement of glucose from the blood into the tissue cells, thereby lowering the blood glucose level. Once the glucose is within the cells, insulin may help in the addition of phosphate (*phosphorylation*) during the first steps of glycolysis, by acting as a coenzyme to the enzyme *glucokinase*. If too much insulin enters the bloodstream from the pancreas (or as a result of injecting a diabetic with an overdose), the blood sugar level will drop sharply, to a level far below normal, a condition called *hypoglycemia.* If not enough insulin enters the blood, then the transport of glucose from the blood to the tissue cells slows down, and the blood sugar level may rise too steeply, and *hyperglycemia* exists. If the blood sugar level is very high, glucose will be excreted in the urine; this is known as *glucosuria* or *glycosuria*. A deficiency of insulin secretion by the pancreas is usually due to *diabetes mellitus,* a disease of the islet cells, popularly but erroneously known as "sugar diabetes."

Another hormone that affects the blood sugar level is hydrocortisone, secreted by the adrenal cortex (outer portion of the adrenal gland). This hormone stimulates the liver to convert proteins and fats to carbohydrates (gluconeogenesis), resulting in an increase in the amount of glucose entering the blood. Hydrocortisone could, therefore, be called a hyperglycemic hormone. When the blood sugar level becomes too low, hydrocortisone aids indirectly in maintaining the homeostatic level of around 80 mg of glucose per 100 ml of blood.

Several additional hormones have a hyperglycemic effect upon the glucose in circulating blood, and at least one of these—epinephrine (adrenalin)—is of major importance. Like hydrocortisone, epinephrine is produced by the adrenal gland, but in the central or medullary portion and not, as the former, in the cortex. Other hyperglycemic hormones include thyroid-stimulating hormone (thyrotropin or TSH), adrenocorticotropic hormone (adrenocorticotropin or ACTH), and growth hormone (GH), all of which are secreted by the anterior lobe of the pituitary gland; and glucagon, manufactured by alpha cells of the islet tissue of the pancreas. One hormone other than insulin has a hypoglycemic effect upon the blood glucose: thyroid hormone, secreted by the thyroid gland.

CARBOHYDRATE ANABOLISM   The two phases of carbohydrate anabolism are *glycogenesis* and *fat synthesis*. Glycogenesis is the formation of glycogen (so-called animal starch) from glucose. A number of steps are involved, the first of which is phosphorylation. Each step is catalyzed by a specific enzyme (Fig. 13-3). During glycogenesis, which

occurs mainly in liver and muscle cells, large numbers of glucose molecules are assembled into glycogen molecules. Since glucose is not stored in the liver as such, glycogen in effect is stored glucose. Liver glycogenesis is accelerated by insulin.

Fat synthesis, the second phase of carbohydrate anabolism, involves the assembly of fat molecules from fatty acids and glycerol, and is discussed under fat anabolism.

GLYCOGENOLYSIS AND GLUCONEOGENESIS Although glycogen can be regarded as stored glucose, it is useless unless it can be changed back into glucose when the need arises; and this process, which involves the enzyme-accelerated hydrolysis of glycogen, does indeed go on in liver cells. During glycogenolysis, glycogen is first converted into glucose-1-phosphate, then glucose-6-phosphate, and finally glucose, which passes through the liver cell membrane and into the circulation, where it is carried to cells throughout the body, to be utilized as an energy source. Glycogenolysis takes place in muscle cells as well as in liver cells, but in this case, glycogen is hydrolyzed only to glucose-6-phosphate, and not completely to glucose. Muscle cells do not contain the enzyme phosphatase, which is necessary to bring about the final step in the conversion of glycogen to glucose (Fig. 13-4). Phosphatase is found mostly in liver cells, but it is also present in cells of the intestinal mucosa and kidney tubules.

Gluconeogenesis is the synthesis of glucose from noncarbohydrate materials,

Figure 13-3   Glycogenesis.

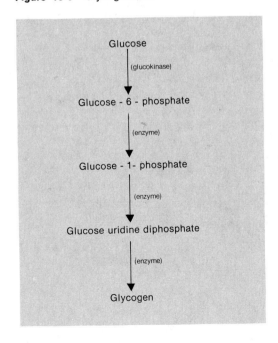

Figure 13-4   Glycogenolysis.

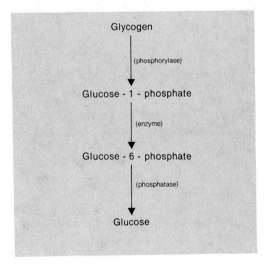

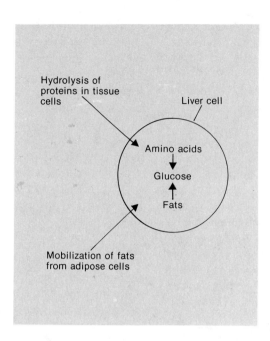

Figure 13-5 Gluconeogenesis.

namely proteins and fats. The process is complicated and is summarized in Fig. 13-5. Like glycogenolysis, gluconeogenesis adds glucose to the blood, thereby helping to maintain the homeostatic balance of blood glucose.

Lipids and their metabolism

The process of fat metabolism is designed primarily to provide energy through oxidation of the fat. Fat produces 9 Cal/g (Calories per gram) when oxidized, over *twice* the energy value of carbohydrate and protein, each of which yields only 4 Cal/g or a little more; but unlike sugars (which can be oxidized very quickly), fats take a roundabout route to catabolism, and are deposited about the body for a time before being utilized as an active energy source. This is not a drawback, however (when not carried to excess), for the deposition of fat serves as a reserve energy source, as well as insulation against cold and as shock-absorbing pads for the kidneys and other visceral organs. Stored fat is in a constant state of flux, with about 50% of all the fat in the body being metabolized and 50% of it synthesized (as new fat) every seven days. During digestion, fats are broken down into fatty acids and glycerol.

LIPID CATABOLISM Fats are catabolized in two phases. The first is known as *ketogenesis,* and the second consists of the citric acid cycle. Ketogenesis takes place mainly in liver cells, and during this process long-chain fatty acid molecules are broken down to short-chain molecules, and *ketone bodies* such as acetone, acetoacetic acid, and betahydroxy butyric acid are formed. Once ketone bodies are formed, they are oxidized in the tissue cells, during the second phase of lipid catabolism, which is the citric acid cycle. The end products of this oxidation—namely, carbon dioxide and water—are the same as for carbohydrates entering the cycle.

Lipid catabolism depends to a great extent on *fat mobilization;* that is, movement of fat from storage depots in the body into the circulating blood, where it is carried to the liver. Glucocorticoids, manufactured by the adrenal cortex, accelerate fat mobilization. In cases of severe malnutrition or starvation, or in such pathological conditions as diabetes mellitus, fat mobilization is high, and ketone bodies may be formed in the liver more rapidly than they can be oxidized in the tissue cells. The result is that the level of ketone bodies in the blood rises above normal, a condition known as *ketosis.*

If the ketone blood level of an individual is high enough, his breath may have a characteristic "fruity" odor, for ketone bodies diffuse out of the blood as it passes through the lung alveoli. Since some of the ketone bodies are acids, an excess of these in the blood can upset the acid-base balance of the body and cause a condition of *acidosis.* This can be fatal because cells of the nervous system and other body tissues cannot survive in a highly acid environment. The presence of relatively small amounts of ketone bodies in the blood is called *ketonemia.* It is only when these chemicals are present in excess that the term ketosis is used. In a true ketosis, ketone bodies can be detected in the urine, a condition known as *ketonuria.*

LIPID ANABOLISM Lipid anabolism occurs in two phases. During the first phase, fat molecules are assembled from the fatty acids and glycerol of digestion (*lipogenesis*). During the second phase, fats are stored as adipose tissue in depots about the body and utilized in the synthesis of new protoplasm (*deposition-synthesis*).

Like carbohydrates and lipids, proteins contain carbon, hydrogen, and oxygen; but unlike sugar and fat molecules, the protein molecule also contains nitrogen and often sulfur. Some proteins also contain phosphorus, copper, iron or manganese. But these elements, although closely associated with the amino acids that make up certain proteins, are *not* constituents of the protein molecule proper; instead, they are attached as prosthetic (additional) groups. During digestion, proteins are ultimately broken down into their component amino acids, which are made up of the first four elements listed above—carbon, hydrogen, nitrogen, and oxygen—and often sulfur and phosphorus. Protein metabolism consists essentially of numerous transformations of amino acids. For example, proteins can be synthesized in the body from amino acids, many of which were taken in as proteins and digested, while other proteins are synthesized from amino acids not present in the diet.

ESSENTIAL AMINO ACIDS   Authorities disagree as to the exact number, but some 8 to 20 different amino acids must be present in the diet for good health. These are called *essential amino acids.* Several more of these *protein building blocks* can be synthesized in the body without having been present in food, and can be called *nonessential amino acids.* Although (if the need arises) proteins can be converted into either carbohydrates or lipids, this does not occur if the diet is adequate. If an individual stays on strictly protein fare for a considerable length of time, it would of course occur; but peak efficiency of body processes would not be maintained, because proteins are needed not only in the *synthesis of new tissue* (especially muscle), but also for the manufacture of enzymes, hormones, antibodies, and other secretions.

PROTEIN CATABOLISM   During digestion, proteins are broken down to amino acids. The metabolism of proteins, therefore, is the metabolism of amino acids. Protein catabolism consists of two phases: *deamination,* during which an amino (NH_2) group splits off from an amino acid molecule, forming *ammonia* and a *keto acid;* and the *oxidation* of this keto acid in the citric acid cycle, forming carbon dioxide and water. Deamination

takes place in liver cells, the oxidation of keto acids in the other body cells. Not all keto acid is oxidized in the citric acid cycle, however. Some stays in cells of the liver, where it is converted to glucose (gluconeogenesis). The ammonia produced during deamination is converted to *urea,* which is excreted in urine. It will be seen that urea is a nitrogenous waste product of protein catabolism. The glucocorticoids tend to accelerate protein catabolism.

PROTEIN ANABOLISM   Protein anabolism and protein synthesis are one and the same. Its importance cannot be overemphasized. Cell replacement (including blood cells), tissue growth and repair, and the production of such substances as plasma proteins, enzymes, and antibodies all depend on protein anabolism. Protein molecules are synthesized from amino-acid molecules in the liver and in other body cells. Amino-acid molecules not undergoing deamination are utilized. The main features of protein synthesis are as follows. Inside a body cell, within the nucleus, a special nucleic acid, *messenger* RNA, is formed under the influence of a gene (which, it will be recalled, is made of DNA—see Chapter 2). The newly formed messenger RNA moves outward, through the nuclear membrane and into the *cytoplasm* of the cell (Fig. 13-6). Here, another nucleic acid, *transfer* RNA, is "waiting." Transfer RNA joins with a specific type of amino-acid molecule, many of which exist freely in the cytoplasm, following the digestion and absorption of proteins. The transfer RNA now moves its newly acquired amino acid to the messenger RNA; because of amino acid molecular configurations ("outlines"), the amino-acid molecules line up in a certain way, forming a specific kind of protein. Each molecule of protein formed by messenger RNA consists of amino acids arranged in the same order. Once the amino acids have linked together to form a molecule of protein (or *peptide*), both types of RNA now leave the new molecule. The messenger RNA is now free to act as a pattern for a new molecule of protein, and the transfer RNA is ready to carry more amino acid to this pattern. Ribosomes play an important role in protein synthesis by moving along the messenger RNA to which the amino-acid molecules have been moved by the transfer RNA,

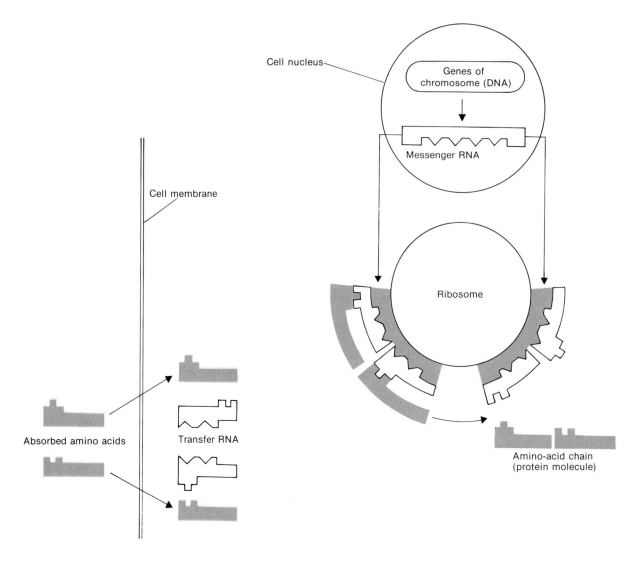

Figure 13-6   Protein synthesis.

and in effect "zipping" these amino acid molecules together. Due to the many possible configurations of DNA and the various RNA molecules, thousands of different cellular enzymes and other proteins can be synthesized. Protein synthesis or anabolism is accelerated by growth hormone and testosterone.

NITROGEN BALANCE   In a healthy body, the amount of nitrogen undergoing anabolism must equal the amount undergoing catabolism; that is, there must be a homeostatic balance of body nitrogen. Since protein foods constitute our only source of nitrogen, this means that the amount of nitrogen in the proteins we eat must equal the amount we

eliminate in the urine, feces, and perspiration.

If the amount of nitrogen excreted exceeds that ingested, a *negative nitrogen balance* is said to exist. During such a state, more tissue protein is catabolized than anabolized, and if uncorrected, this condition will result in atrophy ("wasting") of muscle and other tissues. If protein anabolism exceeds protein catabolism, a state of *positive nitrogen balance* exists. During growth and pregnancy, and during the synthesis of new tissue following a long illness, the body is in a state of positive nitrogen balance.

During negative nitrogen balance, the amount of nitrogen excreted in the urine is greater than that in the proteins consumed;

in the case of a positive nitrogen balance, just the reverse is true.

Metabolism of water, minerals, and vitamins

Protoplasm—and, therefore, cells and tissues—consist chiefly of water. Cells simply cannot live without it, and those which have lost only a little water are susceptible to infection. Although water is not normally thought of as a food, it is a substance that is essential for the growth and repair of body tissues, and under that criterion could be classed as a food, or at least a foodstuff. Water is always one of the metabolites* of the oxidation of proteins, carbohydrates, and lipids (the other being carbon dioxide); it helps form such secretions as saliva, gastric juice, pancreatic juice, intestinal juice, and bile. It makes up large proportions of perspiration and urine. Digestion, absorption, elimination, body temperature regulation, and even circulation and respiration depend a great deal upon water. Metabolic wastes which would otherwise be toxic are greatly diluted by water and excreted in the urine and perspiration.

METABOLIC WATER   Water resulting from the oxidation of proteins, carbohydrates, and lipids is called *metabolic water*. It has been found that during the oxidation of 1 mole (180 g) of glucose, 6 moles (108 g) of water is produced. Appreciably less water is formed during the oxidation of starches, proteins, and lipids. A total of about 375 cc of water is derived from the oxidation of foods each day; this represents about one-tenth the amount of water taken in as liquids.

WATER BALANCE   In health, the homeostatic state that exists between the intake and loss of water is a remarkably good one. The mechanisms of water balance are discussed at length in Chapter 15.

MINERALS   Mineral salts, such as those of sodium, potassium, calcium, and phosphorus are necessary for health and for life itself. Sodium and potassium are essential to the maintenance of water balance and acid–base

---

* A metabolite is any substance produced during metabolism.

balance, and both are important in nerve-impulse transmission. Potassium and calcium are important to efficient heart action and skeletal-muscle contraction, and calcium plays an essential role in sustaining intestinal peristalsis and the growth of body tissues. Calcium and phosphorus are essential to the formation, growth, and maintenance of normal bones and teeth.

VITAMINS   Vitamins are components of enzyme molecules and, like minerals, are substances essential to health and life. Good absorption, normal growth and development, reproduction, resistance to infection, the production of energy, and many other physiological activities are dependent on the presence of adequate amounts of vitamins in the diet.

THE METABOLIC RATE

The relative speed with which food is oxidized in the body is called the *metabolic rate*. Since the speed of anabolism cannot be measured, the term metabolic rate actually refers only to the speed of catabolism, and represents the amount of energy (as heat) released by catabolism per unit of time. The metabolic rate is commonly expressed as Calories (kilocalories) produced per square meter of body surface area per hour, or as "normal," or as a percentage above or below accepted standards.

Factors influencing the metabolic rate

All other things being equal, the rate of metabolism varies with physical activity. For example, if an individual is fed a certain diet one day and is inactive physically, his rate of metabolism will be very slow; but if on another day this same person is given the identical diet as before, but is required to perform physical exercise of a rather strenuous nature, or even in moderate amounts, his metabolic rate will be higher. The speed at which his food is oxidized will be increased with the length and degree of difficulty of the exercise. Other factors that influence the metabolic rate are described in the following paragraphs.

SEX Women have relatively less muscle tissue and more fatty tissue than men, and are often less active physically; therefore, their rate of metabolism is, as a rule, a little lower than that of men.

AGE During the first two years of life, rapid growth processes and physical activity cause the metabolic rate to be greater than during any other time of life. By the time a child has reached the age of seven or eight, his metabolic rate has leveled off considerably, and although it is still relatively high during puberty, it decreases steadily with age. Muscle tissue starts to atrophy with the onset of old age, and the subsequent decrease in muscular activity does much to bring about a sharp drop in the rate of metabolism.

NUTRITIONAL STATE In individuals suffering from malnutrition or starvation, the metabolic rate is significantly lower than otherwise.

DISEASE Glandular diseases, infections, and other pathological states often greatly affect the rate of metabolism. Fever is a manifestation of an extremely high metabolic rate. It is the excess heat that is produced too fast to be handled by the mechanisms that operate to keep the body temperature within the limits of health.

RACE It has been found that the metabolic rate of occidentals is somewhat higher than that of orientals and negroids, while that of Eskimos is higher than either of these groups. In general, the differences in rates of metabolism among races are too small to be significant.

GLANDULAR SECRETIONS The secretions of several of the endocrine glands, especially those of the thyroid and adrenal glands, directly affect the rate of metabolism. Oversecretion of thyroid hormone (hyperthyroidism) causes an elevation of the metabolic rate, while undersecretion (hypothyrodism) produces a subnormal metabolic rate. Elevation of the metabolic rate by oversecretion by the adrenal gland may be temporary, as this gland normally pours greater amounts of its hormone epinephrine into the blood during times of stress.

Determining the metabolic rate

The metabolic rate is commonly determined indirectly, by measuring oxygen consumption at rest. The rate at which oxygen is used up during metabolism is in direct proportion to the rate of metabolism. Such a determination is called the *basal metabolic rate,* or BMR. The BMR was once a useful clinical diagnostic procedure, especially if thyroid or adrenal disease was suspected. The BMR has yielded to a great extent to other tests that are more sophisticated. One of these tests is the *protein-bound iodine* test or PBI, which is described in the following section.

The BMR is determined as follows: prior to the actual testing, the subject is required to fast for at least 12 hr, and is instructed to rest and relax both physically and mentally, the object being to obtain as nearly as possible the minimal metabolic rate. During the testing procedure, the subject lies still and relaxed, and breathes oxygen supplied by the BMR machine. The quantity of oxygen used per unit of time is noted, and the BMR determined by referring to charts showing established standards. The rate is commonly expressed in terms of *Calories per square meter of body-surface area per hour.* For example, an individual with a BMR of 39 requires 39 Calories per square meter of body surface area per hour ($Cal/m^2/hr$). This figure is about average for adult males, but women require only about 37 $Cal/m^2/hr$. The BMR can vary from the average by about 10% and still be considered within the normal range. Thus BMR is often reported clinically as a percentage of the accepted normal, + 10 meaning a basal metabolic rate that is 10% above average, − 10 meaning a rate 10% below average, and so on. Table 13-1 lists average basal metabolic rates according to age and sex.

PROTEIN-BOUND IODINE TEST In recent years, it has become common practive to use a newer procedure, the *protein-bound iodine* (PBI) test, instead of measuring the BMR, in diagnosing suspected thyroid disorder. The percentage of protein-bound iodine in the blood plasma gives a much more direct indication of thyroid function than the BMR,

TABLE 13-1

Average basal metabolic rates *

Age (years)	Males	Females
6	53	51
8	51	48
10	49	46
12	48	43
14	46	41
16	45	39
18	43	37
20–24	41	37
25–29	40	37
30–40	39	36
40–50	38	35
50–60	37	34
60–70	36	34
70–80	34	33

* Rates are expressed as Calories produced per square meter of body surface area per hour.

which measures only total oxygen consumption, and does not single out any organ that may be causing the rate to be significantly higher or lower than normal.

THE BODY TEMPERATURE

Virtually *all* the energy derived from foods during metabolism eventually becomes *heat.* Some 25% of this heat is utilized to maintain the body temperature so necessary for the actions of cellular enzymes, free movements at joints, optimum heart- and skeletal-muscle action, and other processes. Most of the heat generated in the body, however—about 75% of it—is given off as waste energy into the atmosphere.

During rest, the liver, heart, brain, and endocrine glands produce relatively large amounts of heat. The skeletal muscles, which produce about 40% of the body heat even *at rest,* account for even more—about 80% on the average—when we are physically active. Extremely strenuous physical activity for extended periods of time can temporarily raise the body temperature by 5–6°F above the normal average of 98.6°F (37°C). This is true because skeletal muscle comprises about 50% of the entire mass of the body.

At rest, the heat produced by the muscle tonus of a single muscle is not very great; but due to the large number of muscles in the body, and the large proportion of body mass they form, the previously mentioned 40% of the body heat is produced by skeletal muscle.

The maintenance of body temperature within remarkably narrow limits is one of the best examples of *homeostasis* in the study of physiology. In health, the temperature varies by only 1°F or slightly more during the day, unless the body is exposed to extreme heat or cold for long periods of time, or is involved in extremely strenuous and prolonged exercise. In order to maintain this narrow range, the amount of heat utilized or lost by the body must equal the amount of heat produced. That this is a *dynamic* relationship, not a static one, makes constant body temperature such a good example of homeostasis. The production of heat by the body has already been considered. It is now time to examine some of the ways in which the body loses heat.

Heat loss

There are three ways in which the body loses heat to the environment: by *evaporation* (of perspiration), by *radiation,* and by *conduction.* Evaporation is extremely important in the cooling process. Even at rest, a certain amount of perspiration (*insensible perspiration*) is being secreted; and during physical activity, the amount of sweat produced increases by many times. It has been estimated that evaporation of about 150 cc of water per hour would carry away all the heat of basal metabolism. In an extremely hot climate or during strenous physical exercise, up to 1 gallon (gal) of perspiration can be produced per hour, an amount that can carry away 2000 Cal of heat into the surrounding air. This is many times more than that produced at the average basal metabolic rate. Movements of air—*convection currents*—speed heat loss by evaporation and, if the air is still, the reverse is true. About 37% of the body heat is lost by evaporation, if losses in still air and by means of convection currents are combined. Of this percentage, some 22% is normally lost by evaporation in still air alone (most individuals spend far more

361

time in this type of environment). It is a surprise to many to learn that by far the largest portion of body heat—some 60% of it—is lost by radiation. Radiated heat travels in waves of heat energy away from the body and toward nearby walls or other objects. It has long been known that heated objects always radiate heat toward other objects. Even a wall that is heated by steam, electricity, or other means radiates heat-energy waves toward nearby people or objects. This is the principle of radiant heat, sometimes used to heat public buildings. Up to 18% of the body heat can be lost by conduction, or the transfer of heat from the body to an object with which it is in contact, such as a chair or bed or even to the air, the latter without benefit of evaporation. That is, if an individual did not perspire (and, therefore, lost no heat by evaporation) and lost no heat due to radiation, he would still lose a certain amount (the previously mentioned 18%) by means of conduction. Clothing prevents some loss of heat from the body, the exact amount being primarily dependent upon the insulating properties of the material of which the clothing is made. Some materials allow heat to escape readily, and are suitable for use in warm environments; while others trap air, permitting relatively little heat to escape the body. These latter materials are used in making clothing for cold-weather use.

How the body temperature is regulated

The average body temperature is usually given in lay medical writings and even in some textbooks as ranging from 98.0°F to 98.6°F. Actually, there are three places at which the body temperature is commonly read—the mouth, axilla, and rectum—and there are often appreciable differences in readings taken simultaneously in these three regions in the same subject. The *oral temperature* and *axillary temperature* are often nearly identical, but the *rectal temperature* is often as much as 1°F higher than either of the other two. In taking a rectal temperature, the thermometer is better protected from heat loss; this reading is, therefore, considered the most accurate of the three.

Exposure to extremely high or low environmental temperatures for prolonged periods of time can cause the body temperature to rise or fall by 1°F or slightly more, while long periods of strenuous physical activity can bring on a temporary rise of as much as 6°F. Even highly emotional states can bring about *vasodilation* of deep vessels via the sympathetic nervous system and elevate the reading by as much as 1°F. The *hypothalamus* is important in the regulation of temperature. Two centers in this portion of the brain—the so-called *heat-losing* and *heat-gaining centers*—carry out this function. The heat-losing center is located in the anterior portion of the hypothalamus and *lowers* the body temperature; the heat-gaining center is in the posterior hypothalamus and promotes *increases* in temperature. It seems that the heat-losing center and heat-gaining center respond to slight differences in the temperature of the blood flowing through them. If this hypothesis is true, then even a slight lowering of the blood temperature due to prolonged exposure to cold or other causes would stimulate the cold-sensitive cells of the heat-gaining center, which would then send out impulses that bring about actions similar to those induced by the sympathetic division of the autonomic nervous system: *vasoconstriction* (of cutaneous vessels), *shivering,* and *increased rate of metabolism.* When blood vessels of the skin constrict, more warm warm blood is kept internally, to protect the vital organs. Shivering consists of involuntary contractions of skeletal muscles, and the total amount of heat that is produced in this action is significant.

Impulses leaving the heat-gaining center eventually reach a relatively few muscles, bringing about a great increase in their tone. This starts the *stretch reflex,* which causes the muscles to contract. Shortening of the muscles thus affected brings about the stretch reflex in antagonistic muscles, and the muscles in a major portion of the body are soon alternately contracting and relaxing. The overall result: shivering.

The increase in metabolism brought about by stimulation of the heat-gaining center of the hypothalamus results when its sympathetic-type impulses induce the release of the hormone *norepinephrine* into all body tissues. Norepinephrine is a powerful stimulant to cellular metabolism, and the total metabolic rate quickly rises (with an attendant increase in heat production) when it is released by the medullary portion of the adrenal gland (Chapter 9).

We shall assume that when the temperature of the blood becomes too high, cells in the anterior portion of the hypothalamus —the heat-losing center—are stimulated. If this happens, impulses would leave the center, and *vasodilation* of cutaneous vessels, *relaxation of muscles,* and *lowering of the metabolic rate* would occur, effects just the *opposite* of those caused by stimulation of the heat-gaining center. In addition, the *production of perspiration* would be greatly increased. It is obvious that the total effect of these actions is to promote heat loss and lessen the production of heat, thereby lowering the body temperature. An individual whose spinal cord had been severed in the cervical region no longer enjoys reflex control of his body temperature—impulses can no longer reach most of the sweat glands, and the shivering mechanism cannot be activated because impulses cannot reach the skeletal muscles. Since such an injury is permanent, the temperature of the victim's environment must be carefully maintained at all times. If such a patient is taken outside on a warm day, he must not be placed in the sun, as the heat rays of sunlight can raise the body temperature drastically within minutes.

Fever

Elevation of the body temperature well above normal for more than a few minutes is called fever or *pyrexia.* It is often the result of infection, but can also be brought on by lesions or injury to the brain or upper spinal cord, or as an allergenic reaction to such drugs as *adrenalin, thyroxin,* or *ergotoxine,* or to *serum proteins* sometimes used in the manufacture of immunizing agents. The temperature of a patient with fever can rise to 102°F or 103°F, and 104°F is not uncommon. During *heat stroke,* the body temperature can rise to 114°F and above! At first, the heat-stroke victim perspires profusely,

and the plasma volume decreases due to the great loss of water. There follows a decrease in cardiac output and circulation of blood through the skin, so that all perspiration ceases. Without the cooling effect of water evaporation, the body temperature soars, and the victim may lapse into coma. At temperatures around 114°F, cellular enzymes are inactivated and cell proteins are irreversibly coagulated. Death follows quickly.

A somewhat milder, though still serious, form of reaction to high environmental temperature is *heat exhaustion.* This condition is brought on by loss of sodium chloride through excess sweating, and can usually be prevented or remedied by the administration of sodium chloride and water. Symptoms of heat exhaustion include nausea and vomiting, dizziness, hypotension, cramping muscles, pallor, and extreme body weakness and prostration (extreme exhaustion). The body temperature rises to about 101°F.

Fever is due not only to acceleration of the heat-producing mechanisms of the body, but also to failure of the mechanisms involved in cooling the body, although the increased rate of metabolism (and increased heat production) brought on by overactive thyroid glands during hyperthyroidism and by overactive adrenal glands are notable exceptions. There is a daily fluctuation in body temperature of 0.5°F to 1.0°F, with the lowest reading found in the early morning hours and the highest reading in early evening. The temperature of women varies somewhat during the menstrual cycle. At about the time of ovulation, there is a sudden drop of about 1°F, followed by a rise of about 1°F above the normal range. This slight elevation persists until menstruation takes place.

Chills

During the onset of fever, the patient often feels cold, and shivers uncontrollably. Wrapping the patient in extra blankets and attempting to warm him with such implements as hot-water bottles and heating pads do little to make him comfortable, and he is said to be suffering a *chill.* The feeling of cold is due partly to the fact that the heat of fever builds up first within the deeper portions of the body (thereby causing the more peripheral portions to feel cold in comparison) and partly to vasodilation of the vessels in the deeper portions, shunting blood away from the peripheral areas. As the overproduction of heat continues, the body becomes thoroughly warmed, and even the skin feels "hot" to the patient. Cutaneous vessels become dilated, and the face becomes flushed. The skin is dry to the touch, and the chill is terminated.

Fever can often be controlled by the use of aspirin or other drugs. Aspirin apparently exerts its effect on the temperature-regulating areas of the hypothalamus. Curiously, aspirin does not affect the body temperature in health.

Exposure
to cold temperatures

Low external temperatures, like extremely high temperatures, may be injurious or even fatal. An individual who finds himself in a snowstorm, for example, with clothing that is not adequate to retain the body heat, may suffer a drop in body temperature. If this happens, cellular enzyme activity (and, therefore, the rate of metabolism) slows, the rate of breathing decreases, and the amount of oxygen given up by hemoglobin to the body cells diminishes. The desire for sleep may become overpowering, and the victim may become *comatose* (a comalike state) and die. In such cases, ice crystals may form in the cells. In somewhat milder cases, only the cells of portions of the extremities, especially those of the fingers and toes, may die. This condition is called *gangrene,* and may require amputation of the affected parts. The actual freezing of the tissues (which brings about their death) is known as *frostbite.* Gangrene may also be associated with diabetes, arteriosclerosis, typhus, severe burns, tourniquets which have been left on too long, and other factors.

Appetite and thirst

Most people will agree that in order to be enjoyed, food should be pleasing to the taste and to the tactile sense in the mouth (*palatable*) and, if served warm, have a pleasant aroma; in other words, it should be *"appetizing."* We may well ask what appetite is, and consider some of the factors that affect it. In the usual sense, *appetite is the desire to eat when food is present.* A person may have a very strong desire for food, then lose his appetite (*anorexia*) when presented with food served in an unattractive manner or food for which he has no liking. The appetite may also disappear during anger or other emotional upset. Finally, if there is lack of variety in the diet, the appetite may become "jaded," or greatly diminished.

Hunger may be defined as *an intense desire for food.* In the United States, a relatively small percentage of the population knows true hunger, which is experienced only after having missed several meals. We may miss a meal now and then and in our own minds be tremendously hungry, but this is not true hunger. The stimulus giving rise to the sensation of hunger, whether mild or severe, arises in unknown centers of the brain—perhaps in the hypothalamus—apparently following a drop in the blood sugar level, and is projected as impulses to the stomach, which then undergoes contractions periodically. It is these contractions that cause us to "feel hungry" in the region of the stomach. It is a curious fact that man and experimental animals, if permitted to select from a variety of foods, will usually select those which are deficient in essential vitamins and minerals. Man is particularly prone to do this and must pay conscious attention to a balanced diet to remain in optimum health.

In the hypothalamus are two centers possibly concerned with hunger and appetite, sometimes called the *hunger center* and *satiety center.* The hunger center is active until the appetite has been satisfied, when the satiety center takes over. Until the satiety center takes over, an individual is often irritable, feels weak, and may have a headache. Prolonged hunger may even produce nausea. It is a known fact that important decisions are affected by the amount of food in the stomach. Salesmen know that they are more likely to get a large order after dining their prospective customers, and lawyers have found that it is easier to obtain an acquittal if the jury is well fed.

Thirst is the desire for water or such other fluids as tea, beer, or soft drinks. The sensation occurs when the water content of the body is lowered and the mucous membranes of the mouth and pharynx begin to feel dry. Many factors can bring this about, including excessive perspiration, vomiting, diarrhea, low fluid intake, hemorrhage, and excessive urination (as in diabetes). Certain drugs and diseases bring about a decrease in salivary secretion and cause drying of the mouth and thirst. When the water content of the blood is lowered, certain cells in the hypothalamus (*osmoreceptors*) are stimulated, and *antidiuretic hormone* (ADH) is produced by the posterior lobe of the pituitary gland. Traveling in the bloodstream to the kidney, ADH brings about a decrease in the production of urine, thereby contributing to the *homeostatic control of body water volume.*

Caloric requirements and obesity

Depending upon various factors, such as age and physical activity, an individual will normally require enough food to furnish him with 2000 to 8000 Cal each day. In the very young and active, the caloric requirement is high; whereas the aged or inactive need relatively little food in order to meet their daily quota. Table 13-2 lists some average daily caloric requirements of various types of persons and levels of activity.

TABLE 13-2

Typical daily caloric requirements

Condition or age of person	Calories required
Sleeping person	1555
Inactive aged person	1555
Person awake in bed	1860
Sedentary worker*	2400
Moderately active person**	3300
Person doing near-strenuous work†	4500
Person doing strenuous work††	6000–7500
Active young child	6000–7500

* E.g., office clerk or student.
** E.g., person walking leisurely.
† E.g., person mowing lawn.
†† E.g., a lumberjack.

Consistent excessive caloric intake supplies the body with Calories far above the daily requirement, with the result that much of the diet is deposited as fat or adipose tissue. A person with relatively large deposits of fat (that is, too much for his height and body build) is said to be *overweight;* but if fat is present in extremely excessive amounts, the individual is said to be *obese.* Obesity shortens the life span by putting extra work directly on the heart during even mild physical activity (the heart must work harder in order to pump enough blood for the muscles to move the extra weight); by increasing the blood pressure (adipose tissue requires a great blood supply, so many capillaries are formed, thereby increasing the peripheral resistance); by predisposing the obese person to atherosclerosis (fatty deposits in the walls of the blood vessels) and somehow to gallstone formation and such infectious diseases as nephritis (kidney inflammation) and pneumonia.

There are two types of obesity—*exogenous* and *endogenous.* Endogenous obesity is rare, and is the result of glandular disorders, often involving the pituitary, thyroid, adrenals, or gonads; while exogenous obesity is extremely common (especially in the United States) and is caused by **overeating.** Much more food is eaten than is needed for energy, or for normal growth and repair of tissues, with the result that more and more fat is deposited, especially in the adipose layer beneath the skin. The fact that weight is lost when the amount of food that is eaten is decreased has been proven many times during famines throughout the world, and perhaps most dramatically proven in prisoner-of-war camps during World War II. *Weight cannot be lost by exercise alone,* except in insignificant amounts. A person who wishes to lose weight can do so without resorting to drastic diets by simply eating a *balanced* diet of no more than three moderate meals a day. A minimum amount of sugars, starches, and fats should be included in this diet. Food should be taken in *moderate* amounts, and the overweight person must *persist* (for months, a year, or as long as is necessary) until the desired amount of fat is "lost." Some individuals "put on weight" much more easily than others, and must be careful to avoid overeating throughout their lives, or else be overweight. So-called "crash diets" should be avoided, unless followed under the direct supervision of a physician, who may supplement the food intake with vitamin preparations. Enriched dietary foods, such as Metrecal and Sego, are excellent preparations for dieters, but often do not provide the bulk needed in the diet to avoid constipation. Therefore, they should not be used as complete replacement for solid foods. Daily exercise—such as jogging, jumping rope, and calisthenics—*plus* reduction in the total daily caloric food intake will always bring about a decrease in weight over a period of time. Some people are said to be *compulsive eaters,* and ingest excess food because of emotional problems. These individuals, if they find it absolutely impossible to reduce their daily caloric intake, should probably seek the advice of a psychiatrist or psychologist.

ACID–BASE BALANCE

Since the absorption and metabolism of foods cause acids and bases to enter and leave the blood and body cells, homeostatic mechanisms must obviously work continuously to maintain a *balance* between the two classes of substances; otherwise, a condition of *acidosis* or *alkalosis* can result. Acid–base balance depends upon the proper concentration of hydrogen ions in the body fluids. At high hydrogen-ion concentrations, these fluids are *acidic;* at low concentrations, they are *basic.* Normally, the hydrogen-ion concentration of the body fluids is such that the pH of these fluids is about 7.4—very slightly alkaline. In disease or in health, the pH of body fluids rarely falls below 7.0 or rises above 7.8. Acid–base, electrolyte, and fluid balance are partly under the control of the urinary system, which is discussed in the following chapter.

Effects of alcohol, caffeine, and nicotine

Caffeine and alcohol act directly upon the gastric mucosa, stimulating it to produce gastric juice and thereby promoting both appetite and good digestion. Alcohol in *excess,* however, can have a *depressing effect*

upon appetite. Nicotine is said to stimulate the flow of digestive juices. Alcohol seems to promote absorption in some cases, but people who drink to excess often suffer from malnutrition because they tend to eat little, and then only certain types of foods. Even an obese alcoholic may be undernourished. Many people who suffer from *cirrhosis* of the liver are also heavy drinkers. *Delerium tremens* (DT) is the term used to describe a condition brought on by excessive drinking, one in which the drinker suffers from hallucinations and often the belief that others are trying to kill him. Degeneration of cells in the central nervous system is a common result of long periods of excessive alcoholic intake, a condition called *wet brain.* The victim is often delerious, mumbles incoherently, and makes picking motions in the air with his thumb and fingers. The *prognosis* (predicted outcome) is poor. Soon after being absorbed, alcohol acts as a *stimulant,* but later exerts a very definite *depressing effect.* Caffeine and nicotine are both stimulants and act to increase the heart rate and blood pressure. In addition to its effect upon the digestive and circulatory systems, nicotine and tars in tobacco smoke may be contributing factors in cancer of the lung, emphysema, and other diseases of the respiratory system.

Malnutrition

Malnutrition is a syndrome caused by either the *lack of essential foods, minerals, or vitamins,* or the *inability of the body to utilize these substances when they are present in the diet* (due to malabsorption or metabolic disorders). A person can be very plump and apparently well fed and still suffer from malnutrition if he is not eating the proper foods; however, in cases of malnutrition due to lack of food in sufficient quantity, there is always great loss of weight. Adipose tissue is oxidized first, followed by proteins. In many cases of malnutrition, the metabolic rate, blood pressure, and body temperature are reduced, and the victim becomes increasingly susceptible to infection. He is constantly tired and apathetic. Finally, the blood protein level falls, and fluid accumulates in the abdominal region (edema).

1. Metabolism: the sum total of the chemical reactions necessary for the six kinds of foodstuffs (proteins, carbohydrates, lipids, water, minerals, and vitamins) to be utilized by the body
   A. Importance of metabolism
      a. Metabolism is essential to maintenance of homeostasis of the body chemistry
      b. The heat of metabolic reactions is necessary to maintenance of body temperature
      c. The energy of metabolism is used in the synthesis of new protoplasm during growth and tissue repair, in muscle contraction, nerve-impulse transmission, and the secretion of enzymes and hormones
   B. Divisions of metabolism
      a. Anabolism: includes the building-up processes of metabolism, such as protein synthesis
      b. Catabolism: the tearing-down processes of metabolism, during which energy is released. Much of the energy of catabolism is given off as waste heat
   C. Nutrition: the anabolic process of converting food into living body tissue (assimilation)

2. Metabolism of carbohydrates
   A. Carbohydrates: consist of carbon, hydrogen, and oxygen
      a. Grouping of carbohydrates
         1. Monosaccharides: "simple sugars," such as glucose, fructose, galactose, ribose, and deoxyribose
         2. Disaccharides: "double sugars," such as sucrose, maltose, and lactose
         3. Polysaccharides: carbohydrates consisting of long chains of monosaccharide molecules (the starches and glycogen are good examples)
      b. Following absorption, carbohydrates either
         1. Enter the circulation as blood glucose
         2. Are converted into glycogen in the liver and stored there
         3. Are converted into glycogen in skeletal muscles and used in the contraction process
         4. Are converted into fat and stored as adipose tissue
         5. Are oxidized as sources of quick energy
         6. Are excreted in the urine (if they are present in excess, or in such diseases as diabetes mellitus)

   B. The importance of carbohydrates
      a. Chief function: provide the body with a source of quick energy. Oxidation of 1 gram-molecular weight of glucose produces 683 Cal (4 Cal/g)
      b. Cellular respiration (intermediate metabolism): depends upon the oxidation of carbohydrates within the cells
      c. Carbohydrate energy: can be stored as high-energy phosphate compounds, such as ATP
   C. Carbohydrate catabolism: glycolysis and the citric acid cycle
      a. Glycolysis: each glucose molecule is split into two molecules of pyruvic acid. ATP is produced
      b. Citric acid cycle: carbon dioxide, water, and ATP are produced. For each mole of glucose, 683 Cal of energy are released
      c. Enzymes and hormones are important in catabolism
   D. Carbohydrate anabolism: consists of glycogenesis and fat synthesis
      a. Glycogenesis: the formation of glycogen from glucose
         1. Occurs chiefly in liver and muscle cells
         2. Each step catalyzed by a specific enzyme
      b. Fat synthesis: assembly of fat molecules from fatty acids and glycerol
   E. Glycogenolysis and gluconeogenesis
      a. Glycogenolysis: takes place in liver and muscle cells
         1. In the liver, it involves the hydrolysis of glycogen to glucose
         2. In muscle, it involves the hydrolysis of glycogen only to glucose-6-phosphate, not glucose
      b. Gluconeogenesis: the synthesis of glucose from proteins and fats, i.e., proteins and lipids

3. Lipids and their metabolism
   A. Lipids: consist of fatty acids plus glycerol. The chief lipids are the fats, which serve as reserve energy sources, insulation materials, and shock-absorbing pads
      a. Lipid catabolism: consists of ketogenesis and the citric acid cycle
         1. Ketogenesis: occurs mainly in the liver. Long-chain molecules broken down into short ones, and ketone bodies such as acetone, acetoacetic acid, and beta-hydroxy butyric acid are formed

2. Citric acid cycle: ketone bodies are oxidized to carbon dioxide and water
   b. Lipid anabolism: consists of lipogenesis and deposition-synthesis
      1. Lipogenesis: fat molecules are assembled from fatty acids and glycerol
      2. Deposition-synthesis: fats are stored as adipose tissue and utilized in synthesis of new protoplasm

4. Proteins and their metabolism
   A. Proteins: are assembled from amino acids. Molecules often contain nitrogen and sulfur. Proteins are especially important in muscle, enzymes, hormones, and antibodies
      a. Protein catabolism: consists of deamination and the citric acid cycle
         1. Deamination: an amino group splits off from an amino-acid molecule, forming ammonia and a keto acid
         2. Citric acid cycle: the keto acid is oxidized to carbon dioxide and water
      b. Protein anabolism: consists of the synthesis of protein molecules from amino acids within cells and is dependent on different types of ribonucleic acid, RNA
      c. Nitrogen balance: in good health, the amount of nitrogen undergoing anabolism equals that undergoing catabolism
         1. Negative nitrogen balance: amount of nitrogen excreted exceeds that ingested in (protein) food
         2. Positive nitrogen balance: protein anabolism exceeds catabolism, as in growth and pregnancy

5. Metabolism of water, minerals, and vitamins
   A. Water is important as a constituent of protoplasm, in growth and repair of tissues, in such secretions as saliva, gastric juice, pancreatic juice, intestinal juice and bile. Water dilutes toxic wastes and is necessary for good digestion, absorption, elimination, body temperature regulation, circulation, and respiration. About 375 cc of metabolic water is produced by the oxidation of foods each day.
   B. Mineral salts are necessary for life itself.
      a. Sodium: is essential to the maintenance of water and acid–base balance and nerve impulse
      b. Potassium: is necessary for water and acid–base balance, efficient heart and skeletal muscle action, and nerve impulse
      c. Calcium: is important in heart action and skeletal muscle contraction, as well as peristalsis and growth and development of tissues, especially bones and teeth
      d. Phosphorus: is important in the formation, growth, and maintenance of normal bones and teeth
   C. Vitamins: are components of enzyme molecules. They, like minerals, are essential to life. Good absorption, normal growth and development, resistance to infection, energy production, and reproduction depend to a great extent on vitamins

6. The metabolic rate: the relative speed with which food is oxidized in the body; the speed of catabolism, or the amount of heat energy released by catabolism per unit of time
   A. Factors influencing the metabolic rate
      a. Physical activity: rate varies directly with physical activity
      b. Sex: metabolic rate of female is slightly lower than that of male
      c. Age: rate is highest in infancy, levels off at about age 8 and during puberty, and decreases steadily with age
      d. Nutritional state: metabolic rate declines in malnutrition
      e. Disease: can increase or decrease metabolic rate
      f. Glandular secretions: in excess, tend to increase metabolic rate
      g. Race: in general is insignificant
   B. Determination of metabolic rate
      a. Indirectly, by means of oxygen consumption apparatus
      b. Basal metabolic rate (BMR) is determined. For this, subject must fast and attempt to relax both mentally and physically
      c. Results are commonly reported in terms of Calories per square meter of body surface area per hour, or as a percentage of an accepted normal
      d. Protein-bound iodine test: is often used in diagnosis of thyroid disorder, instead of BMR. Percentage of protein-bound iodine in blood plasma is an indication of thyroid function

7. The body temperature: the homeostatic equilibrium between heat production and heat loss
   A. Heat production: carried out by the skeletal muscles, liver, heart, brain, and endocrine glands

B. Heat loss: occurs in three ways
   a. By evaporation of perspiration
   b. By radiation of heat waves into the external environment. Convection currents speed radiation loss
   c. By conduction through objects with which we come in contact
C. Regulation of body temperature: is due primarily to actions of the hypothalamus and autonomic nervouc system
   a. Hypothalamus: has heat-gaining and heat-losing centers. Cooler blood stimulates the heat-gaining center, warmer blood the heat-losing center
   b. Autonomic nervous system: impulses from the hypothalamus travel over the ANS, bringing about vasoconstriction, vasodilation, shivering, and increased or decreased metabolic rate as required. Norepinephrine, released from the adrenal gland under stimulus from the hypothalamus, increases the metabolic rate and, therefore, the production of heat
D. Fever: an abnormally high body temperature, known also as pyrexia
   a. Causes: infection, heat stroke, injury to the CNS, allergenic reactions to serum proteins used in injections, or to such drugs as adrenalin, thyroxin, or ergotoxine
   b. Mechanism: acceleration of the heat-producing processes of the body, as well as failure of the mechanisms involved in cooling the body
E. Chills: cooling of the peripheral portions of the body, resulting from superheating of the central portions during fever. Often accompanied by shivering
F. Exposure to cold temperatures
   a. May produce a drop in body temperature. If so, the metabolic rate slows, breathing slows, and the amount of oxygen given up by hemoglobin to the body cells diminishes. Ice crystals may form within the cells, and frostbite and even gangrene may result

8. Appetite and thirst
   A. Appetite: the desire to eat when food is present. Hunger is an intense desire for food.
      Regulation: via hunger and satiety centers in the hypothalamus
   B. Thirst: the desire for water or other fluids
      Regulation: osmoreceptors in the hypothalamus cause antidiuretic hormone to be produced by the posterior lobe of the pituitary. ADH brings about a decrease in urine production, and therefore a decrease in water loss
9. Caloric requirements and obesity
   A. Range of daily caloric requirement: 6000–7500 or 8000
   B. Requirements vary with age, physical activity, and other factors. Consistent excessive caloric intake supplies the body with Calories far above the daily requirement, with the result that much food is deposited as fat or adipose tissue
   C. Obesity: the presence of body fat in excesive amounts
      a. Endogenous obesity: rare; the result of glandular disorders
      b. Exogenous obesity: common; caused by overeating
   D. Weight loss: can come about by lowering the daily caloric intake. Physical exercise can aid in weight loss by "burning" Calories, but little if any weight can be permanently lost by exercise alone
10. Acid–base balance: homeostatic equilibrium between acidic and basic (alkaline) substances in the blood and tissues. The pH of body fluids normally is about 7.4—slightly alkaline

**STUDY
QUESTIONS
AND
PROBLEMS**

1. List the six kinds of foodstuffs utilized by man.
2. Construct a brief, concise definition of *metabolism.*
3. What are monosaccharides, disaccharides, and polysaccharides? Define and give examples of each.
4. What is hydrolysis?
5. List six fates of the simple carbohydrates absorbed in the small intestine.
6. Write a chemical equation representing the oxidation of 1 gram-molecular weight of glucose.
7. Define the terms *Calorie* and *calorie.* What is a kilocalorie?
8. Write the chemical pathways for glycolysis and the citric acid cycle.
9. Define: *glycogenesis, glycogenolysis,* and *gluconeogenesis.*
10. Discuss the roles of insulin and gluca-

gon in carbohydrate metabolism. What is hypoglycemia? Hyperglycemia? Glucosuria?

11. Discuss ketogenesis and lipid metabolism.

12. A woman, aged 55, is admitted to the hospital. Her breath has a fruitlike odor, and urinalysis reveals the presence of ketone bodies. This ketosis is characteristic of what disease?

13. What are essential amino acids?

14. Briefly discuss the synthesis of protein molecular units (peptides) within the cells.

15. What does the abbreviation *BMR* represent? *PBI?*

16. List the major factors affecting the rate of body metabolism.

17. Normally, an individual will require enough food to supply him with about how many Calories each day?

18. Compare the caloric requirement of the average student with that of a person mowing a lawn.

19. Define: *exogenous obesity* and *endogenous obesity*. Which is more common?

20. Discuss the regulation of body temperature and fever.

21. List the major minerals and vitamins and indicate the importance of each.

the urinary system and its functions

The previous chapters have shown that man is obliged to take food, water, and oxygen into his body if he is to remain alive. It has also been pointed out that the human body must **eliminate wastes** (which would otherwise cause its death), as a part of the vital homeostatic state. It is the *excretion of these wastes,* chiefly by the *urinary system,* that is our primary concern at this time. The urinary system is also important in the homeostasis of fluids, electrolytes, and acids and bases. This role of the urinary system is considered in Chapter 15.

GROSS ANATOMY
OF THE URINARY SYSTEM

The urinary system (Fig. 14-1 and Color Plate VIII) consists of two fairly large bean-shaped organs that form urine, the *kidneys;* a sac for the temporary storage of urine, the *urinary bladder;* a pair of long, tubular *ureters,* connecting the kidneys with the urinary bladder; and a single, shorter tube, the *urethra,* which permits the bladder to periodically empty its contents to the outside.

The kidneys

The kidneys are high in the posterior wall of the abdomen, a few centimeters lateral to the vertebral column, at about the level of the twelfth thoracic and first and second lumbar vertebrae, with the left kidney being situated slightly higher than the right. Each is about 6 cm wide, 12 cm long, and 3 cm thick, and is sheathed in a tough, *fibrous capsule.* During development, the kidneys do not invaginate into the peritoneum (as do the digestive organs), and are covered only anteriorly by this membrane. They are said, therefore, to be *retroperitoneal.* The kidneys can be approached surgically from the back, with a minimum amount of disturbance to the peritoneum and abdominal contents. *Fat pads* cushion the kidneys and help to protect them from the shock of a blow to the body. Atop each kidney sits an *adrenal* (*suprarenal*) *gland,* attached to the kidney only by connective tissue.

The indented medial border of the kidney is called the *hilus.* Here, the *renal artery and vein, lymph vessels, nerves,* and a *ureter* make connection with the organ. The kidney is dark red in color in the living body, and very dense and heavy for its size. The best way to get an idea of the internal gross anatomy of the kidney is to make a *frontal section* of one. Then it can be seen that the organ consists of *two zones:* an outer, granular zone, the *cortex;* and an inner zone, somewhat striated in appearance, the *medulla* (Fig 14-2). The cortex is made up mostly of millions of the (microscopic) functional units of the kidney, *nephrons* (Fig. 14-3). Portions of these nephrons (their *tubules*)

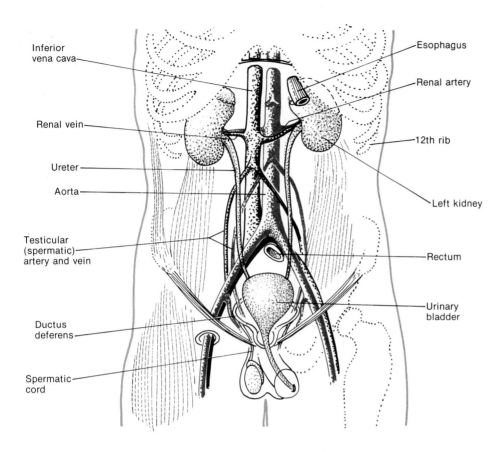

Figure 14-1   Organs of the urinary system and related structures.

Figure 14-2   Frontal section of the kidney showing major anatomical details.

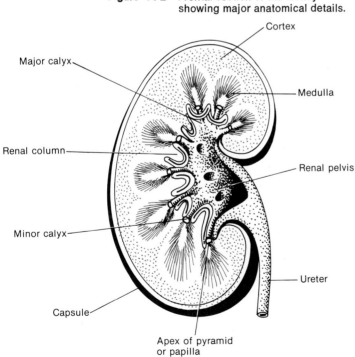

extend into the medullary zone. The substance of the medulla consists chiefly of the triangular areas called *pyramids,* interspersed with inward extensions of cortical material, *renal columns or columns of Bertini.* The pointed tip or apex of each renal pyramid is known as a *renal papilla.*

The upper end of each ureter is enlarged, forming a funnel-shaped structure, the *renal pelvis.* Extensions of the renal pelvis, *calyces,* receive urine from the *papillary ducts* of the nephrons. There are two types of calyces, *major* and *minor,* and normally two or more minor calyces empty into each major calyx, which in turn empties into the renal pelvis.

Nerve fibers enter the kidney along with blood and lymph vessels, and supply the tubules and small vessels of the kidney. Sympathetic fibers originate in the *celiac plexus* (in the abdomen) and numerous afferent endings leading to the central nervous system are also present.

373

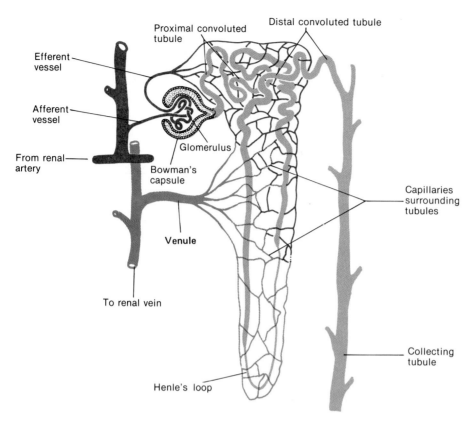

Efferent vessel

Afferent vessel

From renal artery

Proximal convoluted tubule

Distal convoluted tubule

Glomerulus

Bowman's capsule

Venule

To renal vein

Henle's loop

Capillaries surrounding tubules

Collecting tubule

Figure 14-3 Diagrammatic drawing of a nephron, the functional unit of the kidney.

The ureters

Each ureter begins at the kidney as the renal pelvis and courses downward 10 or 12 in. posterior to the parietal peritoneum through the abdominal and pelvic cavities, finally ending in the lower posterior portion of the bladder (Fig. 14-4). The abdominal portion of each ureter crosses the *iliac artery and vein* and *brim of the pelvis.* The ureters enter the bladder at the two posterior angles of a triangle formed by the points of entrance of the ureters and the point of exit of the urethra: the *urinary trigone* (Fig. 14-5). The ureters are lined with a mucosal layer of *transitional epithelium and dense connective tissue.* Outside this is a muscular layer which has *inner longitudinal* and *outer circular fibers;* the outermost coat of the ureter is *fibrous,* and consists of *fibrous connective tissue* as well as *elastic and collagenous fibers.*

Each ureter is only some ⅜ in. in diameter, and if *renal calculi* ("kidney stones") form within the kidney, they may

become lodged in the ureter, distending it and causing severe pain. Blockage of the ureter also causes urine to back up into the renal pelvis and calyces.

The urinary bladder

The bladder is siutated just posterior to the *pubic symphysis.* The *rectum* is directly behind the bladder in the male; in the female, the *uterus and vagina* are posterior to the bladder (Figs. 16-1 and 16-6). Inside the bladder, a fold of mucous membrane at the opening of each ureter prevents urine from refluxing back into the ureters. The urinary bladder, like the ureters, has three coats or layers in its wall. The *muscular layer* is well developed, and its three layers of smooth muscle are known collectively as the *detrusor muscle.* The fibers of the outermost and innermost layer of the detrusor run *longitudinally,* while those of the middle layer course in a *circular direction.* The *mucosal lining* of the bladder is arranged in *rugae,* and parietal peritoneum is reflected

374

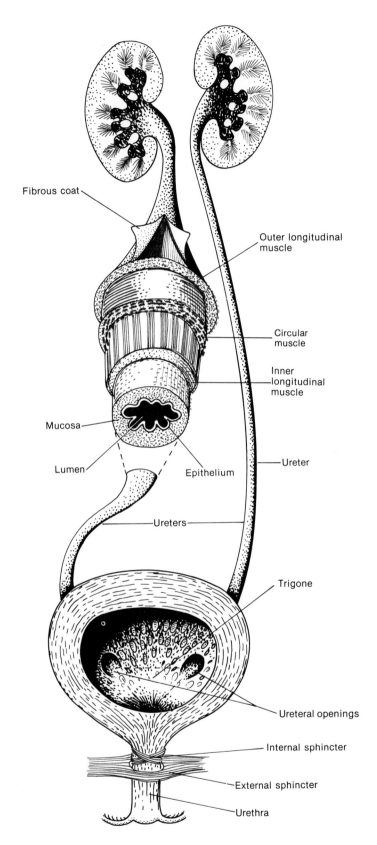

Fibrous coat

Outer longitudinal muscle

Circular muscle

Inner longitudinal muscle

Mucosa

Lumen

Epithelium

Ureter

Ureters

Trigone

Ureteral openings

Internal sphincter

External sphincter

Urethra

Figure 14-4 Sphincter valves of the urethra, trigone of the bladder, and layers of the wall of the ureter.

over its external upper surface. The bladder is richly supplied with blood vessels and lymphatics. Arterial blood is furnished by the *internal iliac arteries,* and venous blood drains into the *internal iliac veins.* Both the sympathetic and parasympathetic divisions of the autonomic nervous system innervate the urinary bladder.

The urethra

The urethra opens into the lower anterior portion of the bladder in the midsaggital plane, and transports urine to the outside. In the male (Fig. 14-5), it carries the reproductive fluid, *semen,* during the ejaculatory phase of sexual intercourse. The male urethra is much longer than that of the female. It averages some 20 to 25 cm in length, and passes through the male copulatory organ, the *penis.* The first portion of the male urethra passes through the *prostate gland,* and is called the *prostatic portion.* The *ejaculatory ducts* (from the testes) *open into the urethra* at this point. The second portion of the male urethra is short—about 1 cm in length—and is known as the *membranous portion.* It passes through the floor of the pelvis, or *urogenital diaphragm,* and quickly becomes the *cavernous* or *penile portion.* This most distal portion of the male urethra lies mostly in the penis, although at its beginning (before it enters the penis), a short section of the cavernous portion is immobile. The diameter of the male urethra varies from one portion to another. It is *narrowest* in the membranous portion, and there are *dilations* in the prostatic and cavernous portions. The openings of the ducts of the *bulbourethral glands* are found in a dilation of the proximal part of the cavernous portion, while prostatic secretion and male sex cells (sperm) enter the prostatic portion. The anatomy of the reproductive structures associated with the male urinary system are discussed in detail in Chapter 16.

The female urethra is only some 3 or 4 cm long. It is attached to the *vagina,* and courses down its anterior surface to the outside, where it opens between the vaginal orifice and glans clitoris as the *urethral orifice* (Fig. 16-5). The female urethra is lined with

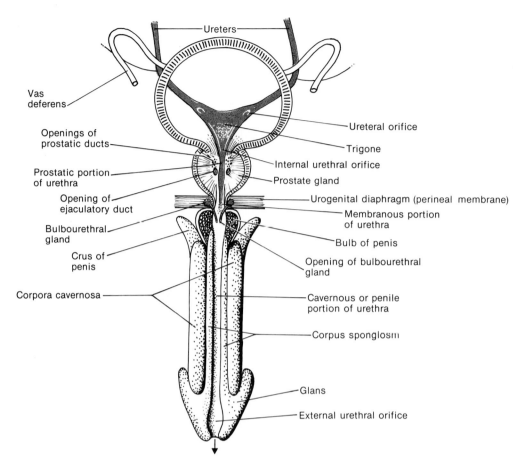

Figure 14-5 The three portions of the male urethra: prostatic, membranous, and penile.

Labels in figure:

Ureters
Vas deferens
Openings of prostatic ducts
Prostatic portion of urethra
Opening of ejaculatory duct
Bulbourethral gland
Crus of penis
Corpora cavernosa
Ureteral orifice
Trigone
Internal urethral orifice
Prostate gland
Urogenital diaphragm (perineal membrane)
Membranous portion of urethra
Bulb of penis
Opening of bulbourethral gland
Cavernous or penile portion of urethra
Corpus spongiosm
Glans
External urethral orifice

a *mucous membrane* and has a *submucous layer,* a thick *muscular layer,* and an *outer fibrous membrane.* The male urethra has a mucosa but no definitive submucosa, and instead of clearly defined muscular and fibrous layers, it has a covering consisting of connective tissue, veins, and groups of smooth-muscle cells. The *tunica albuginea* ("white coat"), a thin sheath of connective tissue, is the outermost layer of the male urethra.

MICROSCOPIC STRUCTURE OF THE KIDNEY

The basic functional and major structural unit of the kidney is the microscopic **nephron,** one of the most complex structures in the body. Most of each nephron lies within the cortical portion of the kidney, with portions extending into the medulla. It is some of these latter portions that collect urine (after it has been formed in the cortical portion of the nephron) and convey it to the minor calyces. Each nephron is an elaborate filtering device that consists of a series of tubules closely associated with a rich network of blood vessels (Fig. 14-3). As blood flows through these vessels, wastes are filtered out of the blood and enter the renal pelvis as *urine,* while large amounts of water, some mineral salts, and other substances never reach the renal pelvis but are reabsorbed into the bloodstream for future use. *All the blood in the body passes through the kidneys in about 5 minutes,* the rate of flow averaging 1000 to 1200 cc per min. The filtration unit of a nephron is the *renal corpuscle,* which consists of a tuft of capillaries (the *glomerulus*) at the end of a tiny branch of the renal artery, the *afferent arteriole* (or *afferent vessel*), surrounded by a double-walled, hollow ball made of epithelium, *Bowman's capsule.* Other important parts of the nephron include the *proximal convoluted tubule, Henle's loop*, the *distal convoluted tubule*, and the *collecting tubule* (Fig. 14-3). The student should note that arterial blood enters the glomerulus and arterial blood leaves the glomerulus; in other words, here is an example of blood leaving the capillaries of a structure and entering arterial vessels, not veins as is usually the case.

THE FORMATION OF URINE

As blood moves through the glomerules, some water and certain dissolved substances pass through the capillary walls and into the cavity of the capsule. From here, they diffuse through the inner layer of capsular epithelial cells, then into the tubule system of the nephron. After having passed through the capsular epithelium that surrounds the glomerulus, the water and other filtered substances are known collectively as *glomerular filtrate*. The filtrate has a composition very similar to that of blood plasma; however, most proteins, colloids, various large molecules, and blood cells cannot diffuse through the capillary walls (or the epithelium of the glomerulus), and so they pass on into the blood vessel leading out of the renal corpuscle, the *efferent vessel* or *efferent arteriole*. The glomerular filtrate first enters a highly tortuous portion of the tubule system, the *proximal convoluted tubule*. From here, it travels from the cortical portion of the kidney to the medullary portion in a continuation of the proximal tubule, the *loop of Henle*. After leaving the loop, it enters that part of the system known as the *distal convoluted tubule*. Once the glomerular filtrate has entered the distal tubule, it moves directly to the *renal papilla* in a *collecting tubule*, and goes from the papilla into a *minor calyx* through one of the 12 or 15 *papillary ducts* found at the tip of each papilla. Leaving the minor calyx, the urine enters a *major calyx*, then the *renal pelvis*, a *ureter*, and is finally stored for a period of time in the *urinary bladder*. Glomerular filtration takes place as a result of the normal pressure of blood as it flows through the kidney, and because of the resistance offered by the small-diameter efferent arteriole of the

glomerulus. The blood pressure in the glomerular vessel is about 65 mm Hg (Fig. 14-6). In the capsule, the pressure of the filtrate surrounding the glomerular vessel is about 12 mm Hg. The osmotic pressure of the blood in the glomerulus is about 30 mm Hg. Both the capsular filtrate pressure and glomerular osmotic pressure work in *opposition* to the blood pressure in the glomerular capillary, so that the *net or effective filtration pressure* (EFP) is only 23 mm Hg [65 — (30 + 12)]. Various factors affect the *rate* of filtration; as examples, *vasoconstriction* of the *glomerular capillary* by the autonomic nervous system or by hormones *increases the filtration rate*, while *vasodilation decreases* it. Imbibing large amounts of liquids dilutes the plasma so that its osmotic pressure is lessened and the net glomerular-filtration pressure is increased. Disease or injury may affect the rate of glomerular filtration. For example, the glomerular blood pressure may fall sharply following severe hemorrhage, with the result that glomerular filtration is slowed.

Antidiuretic hormone (ADH), secreted by the posterior lobe of the hypophysis, acts to control urine output by increasing the permeability of the collecting tubules, or by dilating the vessels surrounding the descending and ascending tubules. In the former instance, *more water leaves the fil-*

Figure 14-6 Pressure affects the rate of glomerular filtration.

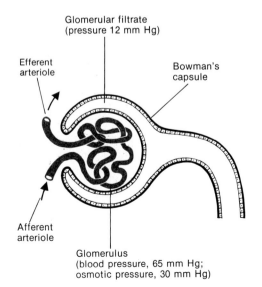

Glomerular filtrate
(pressure 12 mm Hg)

Efferent
arteriole

Bowman's
capsule

Afferent
arteriole

Glomerulus
(blood pressure, 65 mm Hg;
osmotic pressure, 30 mm Hg)

trate, decreasing urine output; in the latter, *water reabsorption is promoted* with subsequent decrease in urine output.

It is possible that *urea, uric acid,* and other substances may be produced by tubule cells and combine with the glomerular filtrate as it moves through the tubules. Urine has a higher concentration of urea than the glomerular filtrate, less water, and normally no sugar. The glomerular filtrate has almost no proteins, but otherwise contains virtually the same substances, and in the same proportions, as blood plasma.

REABSORPTION THROUGH THE TUBULES The convoluted tubules and Henle's loop are enmeshed in a capillary network, connected at its beginning with the efferent arteriole and at its termination with a vein that leads to the *renal vein.* As the glomerular filtrate passes through the tubule system, the bicarbonate ion (HCO_3^-), *sugar, vitamins, amino acids,* the *chlorine salts of calcium, magnesium, sodium,* and *potassium,* and 99% of the *water* in the filtrate are *reabsorbed into the blood* by passing outward through the walls of the tubules and into the capillaries, where they are carried eventually to the renal vein and general circulation. Once in the bloodstream, these substances travel throughout the body to be reused by its cells. Not all substances moving through the renal tubules are reabsorbed at the same rate; in other words, the reabsorption is *selective.* Water is reabsorbed *passively,* proteins by *pinocytosis,* and the remaining substances by *active transport.*

SELECTIVITY AND RENAL THRESHOLDS Substances passing through the renal tubules may be regarded as *high-threshold, low-threshold,* or *nonthreshold,* depending upon whether they are reabsorbed completely, partially, or not at all. Water, glucose, and the salts of calcium, magnesium, sodium, and potassium are all high-threshold substances. Certain phosphates, urea, and uric acid are among the most common low-threshold substances; and creatine and sulfates are not reabsorbed even in limited amounts, so are classed as nonthreshold.

SODIUM AND THE TONICITY OF URINE Recent studies reveal that the filtrate in the proximal tubule is *isotonic* to that in the medullary interstitial fluid, while in the loop of Henle it is strongly *hypertonic,* and again *isotonic* in the distal tubule. Current hypotheses state that sodium and certain other substances move through the wall of the proximal tubule by active transport, creating an *osmotic-pressure gradient* that causes water to move outward also. It is believed that in the descending portion of Henle's loop, sodium moves into the filtrate by simple diffusion, and water moves outward by the same method.

In the ascending portion of Henle's loop, and in the distal convoluted tubule, sodium is actively transported out of the filtrate; there is little or no movement of water until the terminal portion of the distal convoluted tubule.

The filtrate is *isotonic* when it finally gets to the collecting tubule. Here, the surrounding interstitial fluid is *hypertonic,* and water diffuses *out* of the filtrate at a rapid rate, aided by more active transport of sodium in this portion of the tubular system. As a result of this rapid filtration of water, the filtrate becomes highly concentrated, with the result that urine is actually *hypertonic.*

RENAL CLEARANCE It is sometimes desirable clinically to get an idea of the efficiency of glomerular filtration. This is commonly assessed by obtaining a value known as the rate of filtration, or *renal clearance.* A substance such as *inulin or mannitol* is administered intravenously, and the *concentration of the agent appearing in the urine each minute* is determined by direct analysis. It so happens that the rate at which the injected substances appears in the urine is also the rate of glomerular filtration, because inulin and mannitol are not reabsorbed by the renal tubules. They must be injected directly into the bloodstream, however, because they are converted to utilizable carbohydrates by intestinal enzymes. The renal clearance of any given substance is directly proportional to the quantity normally excreted in the urine. The renal clearance of *urea,* for example, is *higher* than that of *glucose,* because some urea is always excreted. Normally, no glucose is present in the urine, so in health its renal clearance is *zero.* It should be mentioned, however, that during periods of emotional stress (as during a difficult college examination, for example) glucose may greatly exceed its normal blood level and "spill over" into the glomerular filtrate in appreciable amounts, simply because the glomerulus cannot handle the extra load. Sugar also appears in the urine in *diabetes mellitus,* a disease that is discussed in a later section of this chapter.

The physical characteristics of urine

A freshly obtained urine specimen is normally transparent, with a yellowish straw *color* imparted by the pigment *urochrome;* but if left standing at room temperature, phosphate precipitates appear following the action of bacteria in the sample and the urine becomes cloudy or *turbid.* The specific gravity of urine is from 1.015 to 1.025, very near the specific gravity of pure water, which is 1.000. Its average normal pH is about 6.0, which is slightly acidic. Various foods, drugs, and disease conditions alter the color, transparency, and pH of urine. The acid wastes of metabolism are present in urine in greater quantities than are the alkaline wastes, illustrating the importance of urine as a homeostatic agent in acid–base balance of the tissues. The selective reabsorption of *ions* by the kidney tubules determines the pH of the urine. The kidneys must constantly contend with changes in the ionic conditions of the blood arising from a variety of causes, but especially from fluctuations in the amount and vigorousness of physical exercise and in the type and quantity of food eaten. Strenuous exercise produces large amounts of perspiration and results in urine that is more concentrated and more acidic than otherwise, because more water is lost in perspiration than normally, and more acid products of metabolism enter the blood during physical effort. Consuming a heavy meal results in a rise in the alkalinity of the blood, because hydrogen ions and chloride ions must be taken from the blood in order that additional hydrochloric acid may be produced to handle the digestion of the extra food. Sometimes this brings about the elimination, in the urine, of alkali in excess of acid, a condition known clinically as the *alkaline tide* of the urine.

The normal constituents of urine

Urinalysis, or the laboratory examination of urine, is a very useful diagnostic procedure. Knowing what should normally be present in urine and in what quantities, the physician or technician can quickly detect abnormal urine. The information thus developed may be indicative of or even constitute conclusive evidence that a particular pathologic condition is present. For example, appreciable amounts of *glucose* or *ketone bodies* indicate possible diabetes mellitus; *blood* in the urine can mean many things, including injured or diseased kidneys or urinary bladder; while *pus* indicates infection somewhere in the urinary tract. Hormones produced by the pituitary gland and reproductive organs are excreted in the urine. Some of these are utilized in tests for pregnancy. Gonadotropic hormones, for example, are produced by the placenta during pregnancy, and the detection of these hormones in the urine is thus indicative of pregnancy.

The composition of normal urine is summarized in Table 14-1, which lists the constituents and the average amount of each that is excreted in the urine during a 24-hr period. The kidneys are the *most important*

TABLE 14-1

The normal constituents of urine

Constituent	Weight (grams per 24 hr)
Water	500–2500 *
Urea	25.0
Sodium chloride	9.0
Potassium chloride	2.5
Sulfuric acid	2.0
Phosphoric acid	1.7
Creatinine	1.0
Ammonia	0.7
Uric acid	0.6
Calcium	0.2
Magnesium	0.2

* Since 1 cc of water weighs 1 g, the weight of water in urine is determined by simply measuring its volume.

organs in the excretion of metabolic wastes. An individual must possess at least a major portion of one kidney in order to live (unless he has access to an artificial kidney). Prolonged lack of one or more of the substances usually found in urine, or the continued presence of substances not usually found therein, indicates a metabolic imbalance. In other words, either the kidneys, or some other homeostatic mechanism, are not functioning properly.

Abnormal constituents of urine

Such proteins as *serum albumin* and *serum globulin,* both present in blood, and such carbohydrates as *glucose* are clinically the most important substances that occur abnormally in urine. The presence of protein above trace amounts is called *proteinuria;* that of carbohydrates, *glycosuria or glucosuria.* Proteinuria may be only temporary, occurring following extreme physical or emotional stress, or even after the ingestion of large amounts of protein food, especially raw eggs. The protein excreted in temporary proteinuria is commonly *albumin.* True proteinuria can be diagnosed by detecting the presence in the urine of *casts*—particles consisting of tubule cells, pus cells, erythrocytes, and albumin. The presence of casts offers conclusive evidence that kidney disease is present. The principal protein excreted during true proteinuria is the same protein excreted in temporary proteinuria—albumin. Other substances sometimes found upon analyzing urine include ketone bodies (such as acetone), dead cells of various kinds, blood, and two chemicals called *mercaptans* (which are normally present in the feces)— *indole* and *skatole.* The presence of ketone bodies is called *ketonuria;* that of blood, *hematuria;* and of pus, *pyuria.*

Urination or micturition

Urine leaves the kidneys and flows into the urinary bladder, aided by intermittent *peristaltic action* of the ureters. Once inside the bladder, the urine can, within limits, be voided at such a time as is convenient. The capacity of the bladder varies among individuals, but a definite urge to void is usually experienced when about 300 cc have collected. When the volume of accumulated urine reaches about 700 cc, the average individual experiences real pain, and will soon be unable to control the *reflex of urination.*

Reflex mechanisms, overridden by voluntary effort, control the emptying of the bladder. When about 300 cc of urine have pooled in the bladder, *stretch receptors* in its walls send impulses over afferent neurons in the pelvic nerves to the sacral level of the spinal cord. Here, connections are made with *parasympathetic efferent fibers* of the same nerves, and motor impulses travel back down the nerves to the *detrusor muscle* of the bladder wall, causing it to contract and expel the urine. (Relaxation of the bladder follows action by the sympathetic nervous system.) As urine passes through the urethra, additional receptors in the walls of that structure are stimulated, resulting in another reflex that augments the first, causing the bladder to contract with even greater force. Still another reflex mechanism brings about the relaxation of the internal sphincter muscle of the urethra, so that the urine can flow freely to the outside.

Termination of urination before complete emptying of the bladder is brought about by voluntary contraction of the external sphincter. This act is not a reflex one, but rather must be learned. The internal sphincter is made of smooth muscle, while that of the external sphincter is striated. Everyone of college age knows that it is possible not only to inhibit the urinary-reflex system, but also to void when the bladder contains only a little urine. This latter act is brought about by contracting the abdominal muscles and fixing the diaphragm so that the *intraabdominal pressure* is increased enough to force urine from the bladder into the urethra, where the reflex mechanism previously discussed takes over. All voluntary control of urination depends upon intact neuron pathways connecting the brain with the bladder, and upon a healthy motor area in the brain. Damage to the motor cortex, spinal cord, or nerves supplying the bladder by either disease or injury can result in *in-*

continence (intermittent, involuntary urination). Incontinence is also common among the aged, whose bladder or urethral sphincter muscles may become flaccid and lose their tone.

Inability to empty the bladder voluntarily is called *retention,* and is commonly caused by prostatitis (inflammation of the prostate gland), childbirth, or surgery of the pelvis. The bladder is drained by inserting a rubber or plastic tube (*catheter*) into the bladder through the urethra *(catheterization).*

Occasionally, an individual is unable to void because the kidneys are not functioning, and the bladder is empty. The term used in this instance is *suppression.*

The amount of urine produced each day varies from person to person and within the same individual on different days or even at different times during a single day. The amount and kind of fluids taken in, the physical activities and emotional state, and the environmental temperature all affect the total amount of urine formed and eliminated. On the average, urine is produced at the rate of about 1 cc per min, or about 0.5 to 2.5 liters per day. When the kidneys are working to capacity, forming nearly 20 cc of urine per minute (as they do when excessively large quantities of fluids are taken in) the individual is in danger of overdiluting his blood, and continued consumption of fluids will do just that. When this happens, a condition of *water intoxication* exists, manifested by nausea and vomiting, lowering of the body temperature, convulsions, coma, and possible death.

Before the age of three, the act of voiding urine is mostly reflex in nature. By about age three, most children can suppress or control the act. A number of children, however, void urine while asleep, even long after the age of three. The medical name for this "bedwetting" is *nocturnal enuresis.* Several drugs have been used from time to time in efforts to control enuresis. One of the most successful of these appears to be the drug *imipramine;* but it is reported that this drug is not very effective in children under six years of age. In any case, the fluid intake of the bedwetter should probably be restricted for several hours prior to going to bed and the child awakened to urinate a few hours after he has gone to sleep. In this way, the child's self-confidence can be built up and his morale boosted, an important step in the management of enuresis.

DIURETIC AGENTS Substances that act to increase the amount of urine formed by the kidneys are known as *diuretic agents* or simply *"diuretics."* Water, milk, coffee, tea, and alcohol are among the most potent and most-often-consumed diuretics. An *antidiuretic hormone,* present in the plasma and secreted by the posterior portion of the pituitary gland, is diluted (and, therefore, inactivated) by drinking relatively large quantities of water or milk, and permits the formation of greater amounts of urine than is usual. The hormone, commonly called ADH, normally promotes the reabsorption of water from the tubules. The caffeine in coffee, tea, and some soft drinks increases the production of urine by somehow decreasing the amount of water reabsorbed through the tubules. The diuretic effect of drinks having a high alcoholic content is well known. In the United States, the percentage of alcohol in beer is so small as to be almost nondiuretic, but the water in the beer acts in the same manner as plain water or the water in milk, coffee, tea, or other beverages: it promotes the production of more urine by diluting ADH and thereby decreasing the rate of reabsorption of water in the tubules.

ARTIFICIAL KIDNEYS In the event a person's kidneys both become nonfunctional or must be removed, a procedure called *dialysis* is performed as a life-saving substitute for the work of the kidneys. Dialysis involves the separation of the solute particles of a true solution (*crystalloid*) from those of a *colloid* by employing a selectively or differentially permeable membrane—one through which the crystalloids can pass, but which bars the passage of colloids. The dialyzing apparatus or "artificial kidney" consists essentially of a coiled tube of selectively permeable material, such as cellophane, immersed in a tank of synthetic extracellular fluid (dialyzing solution) maintained at normal body temperature. Because the blood of the patient is circulated through the tube, the procedure is given the more specific name *hemodialysis.* As the blood moves from one of the patient's

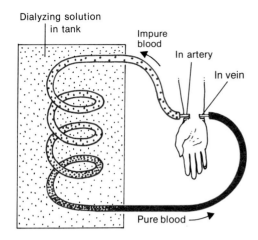

Figure 14-7 Illustration of the principle of an artificial kidney. The impure blood of the patient is pumped from an artery into the dialyzing apparatus, and impurities are removed due to the selective permeability of the coiled tube.

of lesser concentration of their molecules. Virtually all substances of the blood *except protein molecules and red cells* can pass from the blood, through the dialyzing membrane, into the dialyzing solution—including metabolic wastes. Electrolytes can diffuse in *both directions;* acid–base balance is, therefore, maintained.

Large quantities of blood must be pumped through a dialyzing apparatus in order to remove enough waste products to maintain reasonable health, so each dialyzing period requires several hours. The blood must not clot during dialysis, so anticoagulants must be administered to a point at which the patient may be in danger of hemorrhage. In the event that both kidneys are completely nonfunctional or have been removed, the blood must be dialyzed every few days.

arteries through the dialyzing tube and back into one of his veins, erythrocytes and (colloidal) blood proteins are retained in the blood and continue to circulate, while urea, potassium, and certain other crystalloids move through the wall of the dialyzing membrane by simple diffusion and are eliminated when the fluid in the tank is changed. This is a simplification of an actual dialyzing machine (Fig. 14-7), but the principle remains the same, no matter how elaborate the appearance of the apparatus: substances in solution have a natural tendency to diffuse from a region of greater concentration to one

Endocrine action by the kidney

In addition to its primary role of excreting urine, the kidney may also act as an endocrine gland. The hormone *renin* is produced in ischemic kidneys, and may bring about an indirect increase in arterial blood pressure by causing increased production of a substance called *angiotensin,* which causes vasoconstriction. Individuals having renal arteriosclerosis or glomerulonephritis always have renal ischemia to a greater or lesser degree.

OUTLINE SUMMARY

The urinary system: necessary to the elimination of wastes and maintenance of the homeostatic state
1. Gross anatomy of the urinary system
   A. The kidneys
      a. Paired, bean-shaped, 6 cm wide by 12 cm long; covered by a fibrous capsule
      b. Lie high in the posterior abdomen, lateral to the vertebral column; retroperitoneal
      c. Cushioned by pads of fat
         Hilus: the indented medial border

   and point of connection with the ureter, renal blood vessels, lymph vesels, and nerves
      e. Suprarenal gland: loosely attached to the upper medial region
      f. Frontal section—two zones
         1. Cortex: outermost, thinner, granular, consisting chiefly of nephrons
         2. Medulla: inner zone, thicker, striated, made up of pyramids and renal columns
      g. Renal pelvis: the enlarged, funnel-

shaped upper end of a ureter, continuous with the calyces in the kidney

B. The ureters

   a. Begin at the renal pelvis, course retroperitoneally through the abdomen and pelvis, and end in the lower posterior portion of the bladder

   b. Urinary trigone: triangular area formed by connections of the ureters and urethra with the bladder

   c. Histology of the ureter

      1. Lined with transitional epithelium and dense connective tissue

      2. Middle coat: a muscular layer with inner longitudinal and outer circular fibers

      3. Outer coat of fibrous connective tissue and elastic and collagenous fibers

C. Urinary bladder

   a. Lies posterior to the pubic symphysis and anterior to the rectum in the male, anterior to the uterus and vagina in the female

   b. Parietal peritoneum: reflected over the upper surface

   c. Three coats or layers: well developed muscular layer, with three layers of smooth muscle known collectively as the detrusor muscle

      1. Fibers of outer and inner muscular layer run longitudinally

      2. Fibers of middle muscular layer run in a circular direction

   d. Bladder is highly vascular, and is innervated by both sympathtic and parasympathetic divisions of the autonomic nervous system

D. Urethra: opens into the lower anterior portion of the bladder in the midsaggital plane

   a. Male urethra

      1. Carries both urine and semen

      2. Is 20–25 cm long

      3. Passes through the entire length of the penis

      4. Has three portions: prostatic, membranous, and penile or cavernous. It is narrowest in the membranous portion

      5. Prostatic secretion and sperm enter the prostatic portion; secretion of the bulbourethral glands enters the penile portion

      6. Has a mucosa, but no definitive submucosa; has a covering of connective tissue, veins, and groups of smooth

muscle cells, which in turn is covered by a thin sheath of connective tissue, the tunica albuginea

   b. Female urethra

      1. From 3 to 4 cm long

      2. Attached to the vagina

      3. Opens between the vaginal orifice and glans clitoris as the urethral orifice

      4. Lined with mucous membrane, has a submucous layer, thick muscular layer, and outer fibrous membrane

2. Microscopic structure of the kidney

A. The nephron: functional and major structural unit of the kidney. Consists of

   a. Renal corpuscle, consisting of glomerulus and Bowman's capsule

   b. Proximal and distal convoluted tubules and collecting tubules

3. The formation of urine

A. Glomerular filtration: water and other dissolved substances pass out of the glomerular capillaries and into the cavity of Bowman's capsule. This is glomerular filtrate, which is similar to blood plasma but lacks plasma proteins, colloids, blood cells, and various large molecules which cannot diffuse through the membranes

B. Tubular reabsorption: the glomerular filtrate passes through the tubular system and finally into the collecting tubules, which lead to the calyces. During this passage, large amounts of water as well as sugar, vitamins, amino acids, and the chloride salts of calcium, magnesium, sodium, and potassium are reabsorbed by passing outward through the walls of the tubules, and into the capillaries

C. Factors affecting glomerular filtration

   a. Blood pressure in glomerular vessel

   b. Pressure of filtrate surrounding the glomerulus

   c. Osmotic pressure of the glomerular blood

D. Factors affecting tubular reabsorption

   a. Antidiuretic hormone: increases permeability of convoluted tubules, or dilates vessels surrounding the tubules

   b. Simple diffusion, pinocytosis, and active transport

E. Renal thresholds

   a. High-threshold substances: are reabsorbed completely (examples: water, glucose, and the salts of calcium, magnesium, sodium, and potassium)

b. Low-threshold substances: are partially reabsorbed (examples: certain phosphates, urea, and uric acid)

c. Nonthreshold substances: are not reabsorbed (examples: creatinine and sulfates)

F. Sodium and the tonicity of urine: sodium may move through the wall of the proximal tubule by active transport, creating an osmotic pressure gradient that causes water to move outward also

G. Renal clearance: the rate of glomerular filtration; can be determined by injecting a substance such as inulin or mannitol intravenously and noting the rate at which it appears in the urine

4. The physical characteristics of urine
   A. Transparent yellow when fresh, cloudy if left standing
   B. Specific gravity: 1.015 to 1.025, near that of water
   C. Average pH: 6.0
   D. Normal constituents: see Table 14-1
   E. Abnormal constituents:
      a. Serum albumin and serum globulin (proteinuria)
      b. Glucose (glucosuria)
      c. Indole and skatole (mercaptanuria)
      d. Ketone bodies (ketonuria)
      e. Blood (hematuria)
      f. Pus (pyuria)

5. Urination or micturition
   A. Urine travels from the kidney to the bladder by gravity and peristalsis of the ureters. About 0.5 to 2.5 liters is formed each day
   B. Capacity of the bladder varies, but it can hold several hundred cubic centimeters
   C. Phases of urination
      a. Reflex phase: upon accumulation of about 300 cc of urine in the bladder, stretch receptors in its walls send impulses to the sacral spinal cord. Parasympathetic efferent fibers then convey motor impulses to the detrusor muscles of the bladder, which contracts. The presence of urine in the urethra causes the bladder to contract with even greater force, and the sphincter muscles of the urethra to relax
      b. Voluntary phase; brought about by overriding the involuntary phase, and fixing the diaphragm while contracting abdominal muscles
   D. Diuretic agents: substances that act to increase the amount of urine formed by the kidneys. Examples: water, milk, coffee, tea, and alcohol. Antidiuretic hormone, secreted by the posterior pituitary, is diluted when large quantities of fluid are taken in, and larger than normal quantities of urine are formed

6. The endocrine function of the kidney: the kidney may produce renin, which could indirectly bring about an increase in arterial blood pressure

STUDY QUESTIONS AND PROBLEMS

1. What is the role of the urinary system in the maintenance of the homeostatic state?

2. Sketch and label the organs of the urinary system. Which produce urine, and which merely transport it or store it?

3. Describe the gross anatomy of a kidney, including that which can be seen on longitudinal section.

4. Sketch and label a diagram of a nephron, the functional unit of the kidney. In what part of the nephron does filtration take place? Reabsorption of water, glucose, and other substances?

5. Describe the male urethra. In what important way does it differ from the urethra of the female?

6. Briefly outline the formation of urine, and tubular reabsorption.

7. Discuss renal thresholds and renal clearance.

8. List the physical characteristics of urine, as well as the normal constituents and some abnormal constituents of urine.

9. Discuss the act of urination or micturition. When the kidneys are working to capacity, approximately how much urine do they form per minute?

10. What is nocturnal enuresis?

11. List several diuretic agents. What effect do they have on antidiuretic hormone, which is secreted by the posterior lobe of the pituitary gland?

12. Discuss the endocrine action of the kidney.

13. What endocrine gland sits on the upper pole of each kidney? Is this gland associated with the kidney physiologically, or just anatomically?

14. What is meant by the statement that the kidneys are retroperitoneal?

15. What is the urinary trigone, and what three tubular structures are closely associated with it?

16. What is the renal capsule?

fluid, electrolyte, and acid-base balance

To carry out the normal physiological processes, the body must maintain relatively constant levels of water and salts at all times. Also, acids and bases must balance each other to the extent that the pH of body fluids remains near neutral. This chapter is concerned with the homeostasis of fluids, electrolytes, and acids and bases.

FLUID AND ELECTROLYTE BALANCE

It has previously been pointed out that *fluid intake must equal fluid output;* that is, a dynamic balance must exist between the two. Otherwise, serious consequences may result. The body-tissue fluid is chiefly water, which contains small amounts of dissolved salts—such as sodium chloride and potassium salts—and other substances. The kidneys constitute the mechanism that most directly affects the concentration of the body fluids. Water is found in two major locations: (1) within *cells,* as the chief constituent of protoplasm (*intracellular water*); and (2) outside the cells, as *extracellular water.* Extracellular water is found in blood plasma, lymph, cerebrospinal fluid, the aqueous humor of the eye, and as interstitial fluid (tissue fluid). Smaller amounts are found in peritoneal, pleural, pericardial, and synovial fluids. Customarily, the body water is said to occur in three *compartments:* the *intracellular compartment,* the *vascular compartment,* and the *interstitial compartment.* The first is self-explanatory; the second includes the arteries, veins, and capillaries; and the third is represented by the lymph vessels and intercellular, pericardial, pleural, and cerebrospinal fluid spaces. The conditions necessary to a true fluid balance are:

1. The amount of body water must be normal, and must remain dynamically constant; that is, as fast as water is lost, it must be gained.

2. The amount of water in each of the fluid compartments must be normal and remain relatively constant.

About 70% of the body weight is water. Some 40% of the body weight is represented by intracellular water, and 30% by extracellular water. The body's electrolytes are dissolved in body water; therefore fluid balance and electrolyte balance are dependent on each other.

Water loss

Normally, from 2 to 2.5 liters of water is eliminated from the body every 24 hr. This figure is highly variable, because the amount of fluid imbibed, physical activity, humidity, and other factors already mentioned affect it. Most water leaves the body in the urine (about 500-2000 cc daily), and through the skin (500 cc), but about 350 cc is eliminated while breathing out, and 150 cc is included in the feces. Most of the water leaving the body through the skin does so in the perspiration, which is secreted by the sweat glands. A small amount of it is transported by simple outward diffusion of water from the skin cells, and is termed *insensible water loss* or *insensible perspiration*. True perspiration contains salts, whereas insensible water does not.

Since the amount of water lost in the urine each day is so relatively large, it is obvious that the urinary system represents the single most important mechanism in the homeostasis of body water. It is easily noted that when large quantities of fluids are taken in, the amount of urine formed and eliminated increases proportionately, and that when body water is low (following severe exercise and profuse sweating, for example), the kidney output is low, in order that body water may be conserved. The antidiuretic hormone (ADH), secreted by the posterior lobe of the pituitary gland, promotes tubular reabsorption, thereby decreasing the amount of urine formed. *Osmoreceptors* located in the hypothalamus are sensitive to the tonicity of the blood, and send impulses directly to the pituitary when the body water drops to a critical level in the blood, bringing about the secretion of the hormone. It is known also that such other factors as extreme emotional states, severe pain, and strenuous exercise all have their effects upon the secretion of ADH. Extreme nervousness, for example, seems to supress the production of ADH, with the result that urine is produced more rapidly than normally.

Some abnormal conditions that can cause water loss to exceed water gain (and thereby produce a fluid and electrolyte imbalance) include diarrhea, vomiting, and hyperventilation.

Water gain

The great bulk of the body water is acquired by absorption in the large intestine, small intestine, and to a much lesser extent, in the stomach. Milk, coffee, tea, soft drinks, fruit juice, and alcoholic beverages all have their water content, as does solid food—even meat. A small amount of water also enters the fluid compartments as a byproduct of metabolism (metabolic water). Fluid intake is normally regulated to a great extent by the sensation of thirst; however, in the United States people are constantly drinking coffee, tea, soft drinks, and other fluids, and therefore may not often become truly thirsty.

Homeostasis of fluid distribution: constant blood volume

Maintaining a constant amount of blood in the body is important to normal blood pressure, heart action, the transport of oxygen and nutrients to the cells, and the excretion of wastes. Examination of the mechanism of maintaining a constant blood volume gives us some idea of how body fluid distribution is kept in equilibrium.

Two forces tend to move water *out* of the blood—that is, through the capillary membrane and into the interstitial (intercellular) fluid—and two forces tend to move water in the opposite direction—that is, from the interstitial fluid *into* the blood. Obviously, these two pairs of forces must be in dynamic equilibrium in order for a constant blood volume to be maintained. The two forces that tend to move water *out* of the blood and into the interstitial fluid are *capillary blood pressure* and the *osmotic pressure of the interstitial fluid* (remember, osmotic pressure is a *pulling* pressure, whereas blood pressure is a hydrostatic or *pushing* pressure).

The two forces that tend to move water from the interstitial fluid into the blood include the *fluid pressure* (hydrostatic pressure) *of the interstitial fluid* and the *osmotic pressure* (pulling pressure) *of the blood*. In the event of a hemorrhage, there is an immediate decrease in blood volume *and* in blood pressure. Water moves into the blood from the interstitial fluid, and the blood volume increases. If the hemorrhage is not too extensive, normal blood volume will soon be restored; but if the hemorrhage is severe, this mechanism may be inadequate, and the restoration of blood volume may depend on transfusion or the production of new blood by the body over a period of time.

In certain types of kidney disease, blood proteins move from the glomerular capillaries into Bowman's capsule as part of

the glomerular filtrate and, instead of being reabsorbed, are excreted in the urine. When this happens, there is a decrease in blood protein concentration, which brings about a decrease in blood osmotic pressure. The net result is movement of water out of the blood and into the interstitial fluid, a condition called *edema* (Chapter 10).

How electrolytes affect water balance

Sodium and potassium are more important to the homeostasis of body water than any of the other electrolytes found in the body fluids. The permeability of the cell membrane is such that the concentration of sodium within the cells is low, while that of potassium is much greater. In the fluid of the extracellular compartments—especially the blood—the reverse is true. As long as water gain equals water loss, there is no problem; but if one greatly exceeds the other, rapid changes occur. As an example, let us suppose that an individual with normal water homeostasis engages in vigorous exercises for a long enough period of time to perspire excessively, losing a considerable amount of sodium in the process. This sodium comes from the blood and other extracellular fluid, and if enough is lost, water will move from this fluid into the cells, thereby decreasing the blood volume. The blood pressure may drop sharply, and the individual must be given water and sodium chloride in order to prevent collapse of the circulatory system. Under certain circumstances, potassium loss may cause fluid to move out of the tissue cells and into the blood, where much of it is excreted in the urine.

The role of the kidneys in fluid and electrolyte balance

The fastest mechanism for maintaining fluid and electrolyte balance is the mechanism previously described, involving the movement of water from the blood or lymph vessels into the interstitial fluid, or the movement of water from the interstitial fluid into the blood, depending upon the hydrostatic and osmotic pressures of the blood and interstitial fluid in existence at a given time; however, this "fluid-shift" mechanism, rapid though it is, is *not* the most *effective* mechanism available for the maintenance of total fluid and electrolyte balance. This honor goes to the kidneys, whose convoluted tubules absorb water and electrolytes, thus preventing them from being excreted in the urine. Various factors affect the rate at which the absorption of water and electrolytes by the convoluted tubules takes place. Aldosterone, for example, a mineralocorticoid produced by the adrenal cortex, speeds the absorption of sodium ions and some water by the convoluted tubules. The kidneys, by retention or elimination of water and/or ions, play a major role in the maintenance of total fluid and electrolyte balance.

Water movement between interstitial and intracellular fluids

The same basic factors—*hydrostatic and osmotic pressure gradients*—that regulate the movement of water between interstitial fluid and blood or lymph also govern the movement of water between the intracellular fluid and interstitial fluid. In order for water to move in either direction, there must be a pressure gradient, just as is needed for the movement of water between the blood and interstitial fluid.

It so happens that the hydrostatic pressures of interstitial and intracellular fluids do not fluctuate to a great degree; on the other hand, the osmotic pressures of the two show considerable fluctuation. Therefore, it is the osmotic pressures that have the most influence upon the intracellular-interstitial movement of water.

The osmotic pressures of interstitial and intracellular fluids depend a great deal on the concentration of electrolytes dissolved in them—especially the salts of sodium and potassium. The chief electrolyte in intracellular fluid is potassium and in interstitial fluid the chief electrolyte is sodium. A change in the concentration of sodium or potassium salts in either interstitial or intracellular fluid means a change in the osmotic pressure of that fluid and the movement of water in one direction or the other. For example, a decrease in the concentration of sodium in interstitial fluid decreases the osmotic pressure of that fluid; and since the interstitial fluid is now hypotonic to intracellular fluid, water moves from the interstitial fluid into the cells. It can readily be seen that fluid and electrolyte balance are interdependent; one affects the other, and if one becomes imbalanced, so does the other.

The concentration of sodium in interstitial fluid and potassium in intracellular fluid depends on (among other things) the amount of antidiuretic hormone (ADH) and aldosterone produced and released into the bloodstream. ADH regulates the concentration of electrolytes (and therefore the osmotic pressure) of extracellular fluid by controlling the amount of water taken into the blood from the convoluted tubules. Aldosterone acts to regulate the volume of extracellular fluid by controlling the amount of sodium taken into the blood from the convoluted tubules.

ACID–BASE BALANCE

In order for an individual to remain in good health, the pH of his body fluids must remain within narrow limits. It must not rise above 7.8 nor fall below 7.0. Normally, the pH of blood fluctuates between 7.35 and 7.45, a remarkably narrow range. A very slight degree of shift of the pH of body fluids toward the alkaline side is permitted, but no shift to the acid side is long tolerated. Since acids are present in the foods we eat, and acid is produced within the cells themselves (as CO_2), the mechanisms that maintain optimum pH must never fail if health and even life is to continue. Another way of saying this is that *homeostasis of hydrogen ion (H^+) concentration must be maintained in blood and interstitial and intracellular fluids at all times.*

Three mechanisms function to maintain the homeostasis of hydrogen ions in the body fluids: (1) buffer systems of the blood; (2) elimination of CO_2 and H_2O during the expiration phase of breathing; and (3) selective excretion or retention of H^+ by the kidneys. In the discussions to follow, the systems involved in these mechanisms—circulatory,

respiratory, and urinary—will be considered according to their respective roles in acid–base homeostasis.

The role of the circulatory system

Due to the buffers contained in blood, the circulatory system exerts a profound effect on the acid–base balance of the body. A buffer (Chapter 2) may be defined as *a compound which, when added to a solution, prevents drastic changes in pH. Chemically, a buffer usually consists of a weak acid and the salt of that acid, or a weak base and the salt of that base.* Buffers act by replacing strong acids or bases with much weaker acids or bases.*

By virtue of its buffers, blood is able to withstand the blow of a sharp increase in the amount of acid or alkali in the body fluids and so prevent a drastic change in pH. It has been estimated that as much as 1 liter of concentrated hydrochloric acid could be injected directly into the bloodstream of the average adult without fatality; it should be made clear, however, that an individual receiving such an injection would be made quite ill and *could die.* Blood buffers cannot maintain the homeostasis of body-fluid pH for indefinite periods of time; but they are the fastest acting of the body's pH control mechanisms, and up to a point, they are quite remarkable in their ability to keep the pH within a very narrow range. The most important buffers of the blood are as follows:

$\dfrac{\text{NaHCO}_3}{\text{H}_2\text{CO}_3}$ (Sodium bicarbonate buffer)

$\dfrac{\text{Na}_2\text{HPO}_4}{\text{NaH}_2\text{PO}_4}$ (Phosphate buffer)

$\dfrac{\text{Na} \cdot \text{proteinate}}{\text{proteins}}$ (Plasma protein buffer)

$\dfrac{\text{K} \cdot \text{Hb}}{\text{Hb}}$ and $\dfrac{\text{K} \cdot \text{HbO}_2}{\text{HbO}_2}$ (Hemoglobin buffers)

---

* A strong acid is one which in solution yields large numbers of hydrogen ions, while a weak acid yields relatively few hydrogen ions. A strong base in solution yields large numbers of hydroxyl (OH^-) ions, a weak base, relatively few (see Chapter 2).

Hydrogen ions enter the blood constantly, moving into the tissue capillaries. The buffers just described, plus others, act to reduce the number of hydrogen ions added to the blood by converting stronger acids into weaker acids. Here is an example of buffer action: Lactic acid, a product of catabolism, is continually entering the blood, much of it as a product of muscle chemistry. Unbuffered, lactic acid would be free to release hydrogen ions and lactate ions; but upon encountering the NaHCO$_3$ portion of the bicarbonate buffer, lactic acid is changed into weaker carbonic acid, H$_2$CO$_3$, which produces fewer hydrogen ions upon dissociation.

$$\text{H} \cdot \text{lactate} + \text{NaHCO}_3$$
Lactic
acid

$$\longrightarrow \text{Na} \cdot \text{lactate} + \text{H}_2\text{CO}_3$$
Carbonic
acid

The buffering of a base is carried out in a similar manner. The changing of sodium hydroxide, which yields many OH$^-$ (hydroxyl) ions upon dissociation into water, which yields very few OH$^-$, is a good example:

$$\text{NaOH} + \text{H}_2\text{CO}_3 \longrightarrow \text{NaHCO}_3 + \text{H}_2\text{O}$$

The buffer in this instance is the carbonic acid portion of the sodium bicarbonate buffer pair. Sodium bicarbonate is the *most important buffer in the blood.* This compound is always "at ready" in the plasma, acting to convert stronger, more ionizable acids into weaker, less ionizable acids. The sodium bicarbonate buffer is often spoken of as *alkali reserve.*

Just how effective are buffers in the regulation of pH? Most effective, as far as they go. But buffers do not remove hydrogen ions from the body, and they cannot convert all the highly ionizable acids that enter the blood into far less ionizable acids; in other words, buffers cannot maintain homeostasis of blood pH alone. Excess H$^+$ must be eliminated from the body by the respiratory and urinary systems, or acidosis will result.

The role of the respiratory system

As venous blood circulates through the lung capillaries, carbon dioxide diffuses from it through the capillary wall and alveolar membrane and is expelled during each expiration, thus eliminating a substance that would react with water to produce carbonic acid, which in turn would dissociate into hydrogen ions and bicarbonate ions. The elimination of hydrogen ions before they form thus takes place. If for some reason excess hydrogen ions get into the blood and bring about a decrease in pH, the rate and depth of breathing increases reflexly, speeding the removal of CO$_2$. Stimulation of neurons in the respiratory centers by increased concentrations of blood CO$_2$ or fluctuations in blood pH initiates this reflex (Chapter 11). A fall in the pH of arterial blood to about 7.36 will trigger the respiratory center to bring about an increase in the rate and depth of breathing. Another way of considering this is that hyperventilation brings about compensation for blood acidosis; however, it is important to realize that this is an example of a good thing that can be carried too far; because hyperventilation of long duration can eliminate too much H$^+$, resulting in an over-alkaline condition of the blood, or *alkalosis.* This is especially true of individuals who have normal blood pH but who suffer from periods of hyperventilation brought on by emotional problems. Eventually, alkalosis produces *hypoventilation,* which permits the blood to retain more hydrogen ions and subsequent lowering of the blood pH. However, hypoventilation of long duration can lower the blood pH enough to result in acidosis.

The role of the urinary system

The average amounts of various substances normally excreted in the urine each day have already been pointed out (Table 14-1). During the process of urine formation, excess hydrogen ions (that is, a sufficient number of them to prevent the lowering of blood pH) pass into the urine; while sodium ions (which, if present in sufficient number, can raise the pH of the blood) are reabsorbed in the kidney tubules. The number of hydrogen ions sent to the urine and the number of sodium ions reabsorbed depends upon the pH of the arterial blood flowing through the kidneys. If the pH is low—that is, if the blood is becoming too acidic—increasing numbers of hydrogen ions are excreted, while increasing numbers of sodium ions are reabsorbed. If, on the other hand, the blood is becoming too alkaline in reaction, just the reverse is true; now *fewer* hydrogen ions are sent to the urine, and fewer sodium ions are reabsorbed. It is also known that as the number of hydrogen ions in the blood begins to increase, the kidney tubules produce more ammonia (as NH_3) which, together with hydrogen ions (H^+), forms the ammonium ion (NH_4). The ammonium ion then displaces the sodium ion, which is basic, from sodium salts. The sodium ion is now free to be reabsorbed and contribute to the raising of the blood pH.

IMBALANCE OF ACIDS AND BASES

Acidosis

Certain conditions, such as starvation or the ketosis of diabetes mellitus, cause large quantities of acids to enter the bloodstream.

The circulatory, respiratory, and urinary systems—each in its own special way—immediately attempt to compensate for the excess hydrogen ions and to restore acid-base equilibrium. Blood buffers convert highly ionizable acids to less ionizable ones, hyperventilation eliminates more H^+ via the respiratory system, and more acids are excreted by the kidneys. If all these efforts restore the normal pH of the blood, *compensated acidosis* exists; but if these three mechanisms fail and the pH decreases in spite of them, *uncompensated acidosis* is the result. Since the respiratory center is stimulated by low blood pH, hyperventilation is a strong indication of acidosis.

Alkalosis

Alkalosis is not so common as acidosis, but excessive vomiting, prolonged hyperventilation, and intake of relatively large amounts of alkaline drugs can cause alkalosis. The amount of blood carbonic acid increases, hypoventilation takes place, and the kidneys excrete smaller amounts of acid, in a combined attempt to restore acid-base balance. If the attempt is successful, the alkalosis is said to be compensated; if the attempt is not successful, the alkalosis is uncompensated.

OUTLINE SUMMARY

1. Fluid balance: fluid intake must equal fluid output
   A. Locations of body water
      a. Within the cells (in intracellular fluid)
      b. Outside the cells (extracellular fluid, as interstitial fluid, and in plasma, lymph, cerebrospinal fluid, the aqueous humor of the eye, pericardial, peritoneal, and pleural spaces, and synovial cavities)
   B. Compartments of body water
      a. Intracellular: in cell protoplasm
      b. Vascular: in blood vessels
      c. Interstitial: in lymph vessels and in intercellular, pericardial, pleural, and cerebrospinal spaces
   C. Conditions necessary to a true fluid balance
      a. Amount of body water must be normal and dynamically constant
      b. Amount of water in each fluid compartment must be normal and relatively constant
   D. Relationship between fluid balance and electrolyte balance: the body's electrolytes are dissolved in water; therefore fluid balance and electrolyte balance are interdependent
   E. Water loss: amounts to 2–2.5 liters every 24 hr by the following routes
      a. Urine (1500 cc)
      b. Skin (500 cc)
      c. Breathing (350 cc)
      d. Feces (150 cc)
   F. Some factors affecting water loss
      a. Antidiuretic hormone, secreted by the posterior pituitary, promotes

tubular reabsorption, decreasing the amount of urine formed. This is in response to impulses from osmoreceptors in the hypothalamus
   b. Emotional stress, severe pain, and strenuous exercise all have effects on secretion of ADH
G. Water gain—from two sources
   a. By absorption in the large intestine, small intestine, and stomach
   b. As a byproduct of metabolism
2. Homeostasis of fluid distribution
   A. Maintenance of a constant blood volume
      a. Important to normal blood pressure, heart action, oxygen-nutrient transport, excretion of wastes
      b. Forces tending to move water out of the blood
         1. Capillary blood pressure
         2. Osmotic pressure of interstitial fluid
      c. Forces tending to move water into the blood
         1. Hydrostatic pressure of interstitial fluid
         2. Osmotic pressure of blood
   B. Two major effects of electrolytes on fluid distribution
      a. Following excess sodium loss during exercise, water may move from extracellular fluid into cells
      b. Potassium loss may cause fluid to move out of tissue cells and into the blood; it is then excreted in the urine
   C. The role of the kidneys in fluid and electrolyte balance
      a. Fastest mechanism for maintaining fluid and electrolyte balance: the "fluid shift." But this is not the most effective mechanism available
      b. Selective absorption of water and electrolytes by the kidney tubules is most effective mechanism
      c. Various factors affect the rate of absorption of water and electrolytes by convoluted tubules; for example, aldosterone speeds absorption of $Na+$
   D. Water movement between interstitial and intracellular fluids
      a. Regulated by hydrostatic and osmotic pressures. There must be a pressure gradient in order for movement to take place
      b. Osmotic pressures have the most influence on intracellular-interstitial movement of water
      c. Osmotic pressures depend largely on concentration of electrolytes dissolved in them. The chief electrolyte in intracellular fluid is potassium, that of interstitial fluid, sodium

   d. Concentration of sodium in interstitial fluid and potassium in intracellular fluid depends largely on the amount of ADH and aldosterone produced and released into the blood. ADH regulates the concentration of electrolytes of extracellular fluid by controlling the amount of water absorbed by the convoluted tubules; aldosterone regulates the volume of extracellular fluid by controlling the amount of sodium absorbed by the convoluted tubules
3. Acid–base balance
   A. Ranges of pH
      a. The pH must not rise above 7.8 nor fall below 7.0
      b. Normal pH of blood is between 7.35 and 7.45
   B. Mechanisms that function to maintain homeostasis of $H+$ concentration
      a. Buffer systems of the blood
      b. Elimination of CO_2 and H_2O during expiration
      c. Selective excretion or retention of $H+$ by the kidneys
   C. Role of the circulatory system
      a. Buffers are compounds that prevent drastic changes in the pH of a solution. Buffers usually consist of a weak acid and its salt, or a weak base and its salt
      b. Buffers convert stronger (highly ionizable) acids into weaker (less ionizable) acids, and stronger bases into weaker bases
      c. Four important blood buffers are the bicarbonate, phosphate, plasma protein, and hemoglobin buffers
      d. Buffers are fast, but not completely effective, as they cannot remove $H+$ or $OH-$ from the body. Excess ions must be eliminated by the respiratory and urinary systems
   D. Role of the respiratory system
      a. Expiration removes CO_2, which would react with water, producing carbonic acid. Carbonic acid produces hydrogen ions and bicarbonate ions upon dissociation
      b. A fall in arterial blood pH to about 7.36 triggers the respiratory center to increase rate and depth of breathing. This can go on long enough to produce alkalosis and hypoventilation. Hyperventilation is a good indication of acidosis
   E. Role of the urinary system
      a. Usually, large amounts of hydrogen ions are excreted, while sodium ions are absorbed by the tubules
      b. If blood becomes too alkaline, fewer hydrogen ions are excreted,

and more sodium ions are excreted by not being absorbed

   c. As the number of H+ in the blood increases, the tubules produce more ammonia (as NH_3), which combines with H+, forming the ammonium ion (NH_4). The ammonium ion then displaces the sodium ion from its sodium salts, and this ion is absorbed as a contribution to raising blood pH

F. Imbalance of acids and bases

   a. Acidosis: excessive numbers of hydrogen ions in the blood or tissue fluids

      1. Compensated acidosis: an acidosis during which the circulatory, respiratory, and urinary systems have been able to restore homeostasis of blood pH

      2. Uncompensated acidosis: one that has overcome the three mechanisms that are usually able to maintain normal blood pH. The blood becomes acid in reaction

   b. Alkalosis: excessive numbers of hydroxyl ions in the blood or tissue fluids, or insufficient numbers of hydrogen ions in the blood or tissue fluids. Not so common as acidosis, but can be caused by excessive vomiting, prolonged hyperventilation, and intake of large amounts of alkaline drugs. In compensated alkalosis the normal pH of the blood is restored, while in uncompensated alkalosis, it is not. In an attempt to compensate for alkalosis, the circulatory system utilizes acid salt buffers, the respiratory system eliminates less CO_2 (by hypoventilation), and the urinary system excretes more sodium and retains more hydrogen ions

STUDY QUESTIONS AND PROBLEMS

1. Briefly discuss what is meant by fluid balance.

2. What are the conditions necessary to a true fluid balance?

3. Why are fluid balance and electrolyte balance dependent on each other?

4. What pituitary hormone influences urine production by the kidneys?

5. State the two categories of water gain.

6. List the two forces that move water into the blood, and the two forces that move water out of the blood.

7. In the event of a severe hemorrhage, in which direction does water move: into the blood from the interstitial fluid, or out of the blood into the interstitial fluid? Explain your answer.

8. What is edema and what is the mechanism that brings it about?

9. How does sodium affect water balance?

10. Which is the most effective in maintaining fluid balance: the "fluid-shift" mechanism or the urinary system? Explain.

11. What is the effect of aldosterone on the absorption of sodium ions by the convoluted tubules?

12. What kind of "pressure" has the most influence on the intracellular-interstitial movement of water?

13. What is the chief electrolyte in intracellular fluid? In interstitial fluid?

14. Compare the roles of the circulatory, respiratory, and urinary systems in maintaining or regulating the acid-base balance of the body.

15. Describe the "compartments" of body water.

16. What is the normal pH range of the blood?

17. Define a buffer, and describe the mechanism used by buffers in order to help maintain acid–base balance.

18. List the names of the four most important blood buffers.

19. Mrs. C., who was admitted to the hospital, is a diabetic. She suffers from hyperventilation. What is the acid-base condition on Mrs. C.'s blood? How do you know this?

20. Why is hypoventilation associated with alkalosis?

21. What is "compensated" acidosis? "Uncompensated acidosis?"

22. List some possible causes of alkalosis.

reproduction and development: pregnancy and childbirth

To survive as a species, human beings must **reproduce,** or bring forth their own kind. Today, the rate at which we carry out this process is so great that we may be forced to curtail it by one means or another or face starvation. Death from lack of food is already commonplace in many countries of the world.

Incredible as it may seem to many of us, there are millions of people living on earth today who have no idea of "where babies come from." For centuries, the whole matter of reproduction of offspring has been shrouded in mystery, and for many people it still is. When, at last, man began to realize that "some substance" from both the male and the female united before the formation of a new individual could take place within the body of the mother, the first step toward the understanding of the reproductive process was made. Our present-day knowledge of reproduction has been worked out during the last 40 years or so.

A brief explanation of human reproduction, without detail, is a fairly simple one: The male, by means of his copulatory organ, the *penis,* injects his sex cells, *sperm,* into the *vagina,* which is the copulatory organ of the female. If pregnancy is to take place, one of these sperm cells must unite with a female sex cell, or *ovum* (egg cell). If this happens, *fertilization* has occurred, and the newly fertilized egg, or *zygote,* will grow and develop into an *embryo* and then a *fetus* before birth takes place approximately nine months later. A more complete understanding of the processes involved in reproduction and childbirth demands detailed consideration of the reproductive systems of both male and female. It is to the anatomy and physiology of these systems that we now turn our attention.

THE MALE REPRODUCTIVE SYSTEM

The external reproductive structures of both the male and female are known as the *genital organs* or *external genitalia.* The external genitalia of the male include the penis and the *testes* within their saclike *scrotum.* The remaining male reproductive structures include the *epididymis, vas deferens* (ductus deferens), *seminal vesicles, prostate gland,* and *bulbourethral glands* (Fig. 16-1).

THE PENIS   The penis is firmly anchored to the rami of the pubic and ischial bones on either side by deep fascia and muscles of the region, and is covered with skin continuous with that of the scrotum. The organ varies in size from one individual to the next, but averages about 6 in. in length and 1 in. in diameter when in a state of *erection*—that is, engorged with blood to the point of firmness, as it is just prior to sexual intercourse (*coitus* or *copulation*) or often before emptying the bladder after a night's sleep. The penis consists mainly of three elongated rods or *columns* of specialized *erectile tissue*—also called *cavernous tissue* —which contains a large number of blood

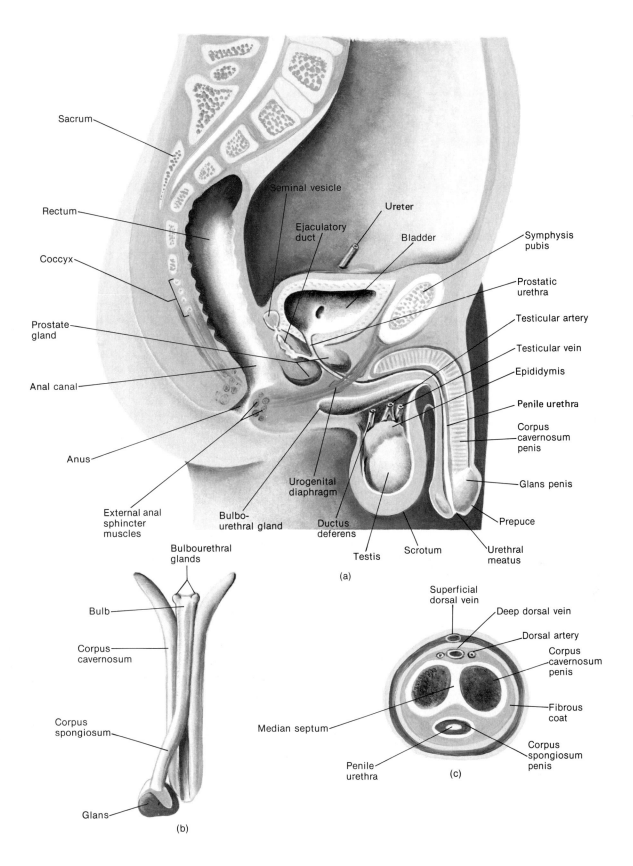

Sacrum

Rectum

Coccyx

Prostate
gland

Anal canal

Anus

External anal
sphincter
muscles

Bulbo-
urethral gland

Seminal vesicle

Ejaculatory
duct

Ureter

Bladder

Symphysis
pubis

Prostatic
urethra

Testicular artery

Testicular vein

Epididymis

Penile urethra

Corpus
cavernosum
penis

Glans penis

Prepuce

Urogenital
diaphragm

Ductus
deferens

Testis

Scrotum

Urethral
meatus

(a)

Bulbourethral
glands

Bulb

Corpus
cavernosum

Corpus
spongiosum

Glans

(b)

Superficial
dorsal vein

Deep dorsal vein

Dorsal artery

Corpus
cavernosum
penis

Fibrous
coat

Median septum

Penile
urethra

Corpus
spongiosum
penis

(c)

Figure 16-1 The male reproductive system. (a) Sagittal section through the pelvis. (b) Structure of the penis. (c) Cross-section through the penis.

spaces that fill with blood when a man is sexually excited, producing erection. The completion of sexual intercourse, cold temperature, and pain return the penis to its normally flaccid (limp) condition. The upper two columns of penile erectile tissue are called the *corpora cavernosa penis,* while the lower column is the *corpus cavernosum urethrae,* or *corpus spongiosum.* This lower portion contains the urethra, which serves as a common passageway for urine and sperm cells. The caplike end of the penis is known as the *glans.* When the organ is in the flaccid state, the glans is covered by the *prepuce or foreskin,* a rather loose fold of the skin over the penis. A cheeselike substance, *smegma,* is secreted by small *preputial glands* around the base of the glans penis and deep surface of the prepuce. The prepuce is often cut around or *circumcised* shortly after birth, so that the region around the base of the glans may be more easily kept clean. The penis is highly vascular, and its blood vessels are supplied by both divisions of the autonomic nervous system. A rich supply of tactile receptors make the organ extremely sensitive during copulation.

Figure 16-2 Structure of the testis and epididymis.

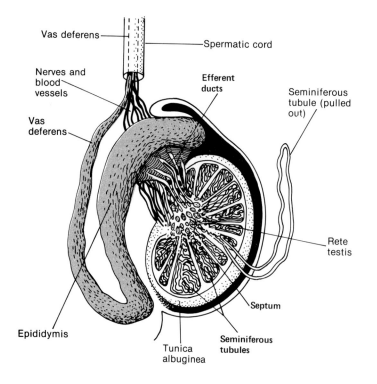

Vas deferens

Spermatic cord

Nerves and blood vessels

Efferent ducts

Seminiferous tubule (pulled out)

Vas deferens

Rete testis

Epididymis

Septum

Tunica albuginea

Seminiferous tubules

THE SCROTUM The testes are suspended in a sac, the scrotum, which is constructed of skin continuous with that over the abdomen, two different sets of muscle fibers, and fascia. The scrotum is divided into right and left compartments by a partition or *septum,* indicated externally by a line, the *median raphe.* Each compartment contains one testis. The muscles of the scrotum include the *dartos layer or tunica dartos,* which consists of smooth-muscle fibers, and the *cremaster muscle,* a skeletal muscle that originates on the lower border of the internal oblique muscle. If the scrotum is exposed to cold temperatures, the fibers of the dartos layer contract, causing the scrotal wall to become wrinkled and to squeeze the testes upward toward the warmth of the pelvis. The cremaster muscle assists in this action by contracting and shortening the length of the entire scrotum. This reflex action is important to the protection of sperm cells, which cannot survive for long in an environment where the temperature is either too cold or too warm. Normally, the testes descend from the abdomen into the scrotum before birth. If they do not, no viable (living) sperm are produced; that is, the individual is *sterile,* due to the effect of the higher temperature within the abdomen. Such an individual is called a *cryptorchid,* and his condition, *cryptorchidism.*

THE TESTIS AND THE EPIDIDYMIS (See Fig. 16-2.) The testes or gonads are appropriately called the *primary sex organs of the male,* because sperm formation, *spermatogenesis,* takes places within the special epithelium of these organs. Within their interstitial cells (cells of Leydig), the testes produce the male sex hormone *testosterone* (androgen), which greatly influences the development of secondary sex characteristics of the male, including the appearance of a beard, growth of hair in the axillary and pubic regions, development of a deeper voice than the female (due to enlargement of the larynx), and assumption of a typical male body form (broad shoulders, narrow hips, relatively coarse facial features). Testosterone is also necessary for the normal development of the penis, scrotum, epididymis, seminal vesicles, and prostate gland; and the hormone influences protein anabolism and the growth of bone. Erection—and in fact the entire male sex drive or *libido*—are usually absent without it. Secondary sex characteristics are normally completely developed (in both male and female) at about the age of puberty (10 to 14 for girls, 14 to 16 for boys).

The production of testosterone is regulated by interstitial cell stimulating hormone (ICSH) of the anterior pituitary. When the blood level of testosterone reaches normal, the production of ICSH is quickly inhibited, in a typical feedback relationship.

Each testis is shaped somewhat like a flattened egg, and is about 3 or 4 cm long. The interior is divided into several compartments by a number of *fibrous septa*. Each compartment contains a long coiled *seminiferous tubule*, also called a *convoluted tubule*. These tubules are lined with a layer of highly specialized cells called the *germinal epithelium*, and it is within this layer that sperm cells are formed. The seminiferous tubules all lead to a structure that is connected to the upper posterior portion of the testis by a number of *efferent ductules*, the *epididymis*. The epididymis consists essentially of a convoluted tubule, small in diameter, but about 20 ft long. As more and more sperm are formed in the testis, some are forced upward into the epididymis, where they become *motile*—that is, they acquire the ability to move under their own power. After the sperm have passed through the epididymis, they enter a long duct, the *vas deferens*.

THE VAS DEFERENS AND THE SEMINAL VESICLES Coursing first upward and anteriorly within the spermatic cord, each vas deferens bends posteriorly just above the pubic bone, passes lateral to the urinary bladder, then bends downward to the prostate gland. The *spermatic cord* consists of a vas deferens, blood vessels, lymph vessels, and nerves to the testis, all bound together by fascia and covered (from superficial to deep) by *external spermatic fascia, fibers of the cremaster muscle,* and *internal spermatic fascia*. As it enters the substance of the prostate, each vas deferens joins the *ejaculatory duct of a seminal vesicle,* just posterior to the urinary bladder. Each seminal vesicle opens by means of its ejaculatory duct into the

urethra as this latter structure passes through the prostate as the *prostatic portion* of the urethra. The seminal vesicles are small sacs that are divided internally into tiny *lobules*. A slightly alkaline fluid produced by the vesicles becomes a part of the *seminal fluid,* or *semen,* that carries sperm through the urethra during sexual intercourse. The remainder of the semen consists of prostatic secretion and sperm cells.

THE PROSTATE GLAND Lying below the urinary bladder and just anterior to the rectum, the prostate gland is easily located during physical examination. It is about the size of a walnut and somewhat pear-shaped, and can be palpated from within the rectum. The prostate consists of *glandular, connective,* and *smooth-muscle tissues,* and like the seminal vesicles secretes an alkaline fluid that makes up a portion of the semen and helps to neutralize the acidity of any urine that might be present in the urethra during the expulsion of semen, or *ejaculation*. The prostatic secretion enters the urethra by means of numerous tiny *pores* that open into the urethra. The prostate is fairly large (about 4 cm in diameter), and often becomes troublesome in old age. In *prostatitis* (inflammation of the prostate), for example, it may become so enlarged that urination is difficult or impossible, since the swelling of the gland squeezes its portion of the urethra closed. Treatment may or may not include removal of the prostate (*prostatectomy*). The prostate seems to be a favored site of cancer.

THE BULBOURETHRAL OR COWPER'S GLANDS Just as the urethra is about to enter the penis (after it has passed through the prostate), a pair of small, teardrop-shaped structures, the *bulbourethral (Cowper's) glands,* join it, one on either side and below the urethra. These glands are yellowish in color, and often described as being about the size of peas. Their secretion is slightly alkaline, and is produced during sexual stimulation even if ejaculation does not take place. Since most of this secretion appears on the surface near the anterior end of the penis before intercourse, it is thought that its chief purpose is to act as a lubricant for the glans penis; but since it is alkaline in reaction, it obviously also helps the secretions of the seminal vesicles and prostate in neutralizing any urine in the urethra (urine is acidic, and would, therefore, kill sperm cells passing through).

EJACULATION   Ejaculation or *seminal emission* is the rather forceful expulsion of semen. Ideally, this takes place during sexual intercourse, but also occurs reflexly during sleep (*nocturnal emission*). Before ejaculation occurs, erection must take place. The penis becomes firm and elongated due to the movement of blood into the organ at a much faster rate than it can move out. Erection follows sexual excitement, which may be either psychological, physical, or a combination of both. The presence of a member of the female gender is the most powerful stimulus to erection. Erection is always due to reflex mechanisms, even though these mechanisms may be set to work consciously as well as unconsciously. The hypothalamus sends autonomic impulses to the penis via the spinal cord and sacral spinal nerves, in response to psychic or physical stimulation. Erection resulting from postponement of urination is due to a reflex initiated by pressure of the distended urinary bladder on the prostate gland. In both cases, afferent impulses are received by the hypothalamus or perhaps merely by the sacral region of the spinal cord, and efferent impulses are sent back to the penis, bringing about dilation of its arteries and blood sinuses, so that engorgement with blood results. After erection, the friction of the copulatory act stimulates the numerous nerve endings in the glans, and impulses travel to the thalamus and cerebral cortex. The physical pleasure and mental elation registered in these areas of the brain serve to activate a second reflex mechanism, that of ejaculation itself. During this act, the vas deferens, seminal vesicles, and prostate gland all contract, sending the semen with its sperm cells into the vagina. Almost at once, excess blood flows away from the penis and it resumes its normal flaccid condition. Ejaculation plus the feelings of intense pleasure associated with it comprise the *male orgasm,* or *climax.* The penis and clitoris are homologous organs, and the *female orgasm* is achieved largely through stimulation of the clitoris. Normally, sperm cells are extremely motile, and following ejaculation they employ their long tails to begin "swimming" upward toward the uterus and uterine tubes, where fertilization of an ovum may or may not take place.

Approximately 300 million sperm cells are present in the average 3-cc ejaculation, thus helping to ensure fertilization if an egg cell is present in the oviduct or uterus at the time of intercourse. Even though sperm are so minute as to be microscopic, they can "swim" from the vagina to the upper end of the uterine tube in about half an hour.

THE FORMATION OF SPERM CELLS: SPERMATOGENESIS   The male *sex cell* or *gamete*— the sperm—is more properly called a *spermatozoon* (pl. spermatozoa). Sperm cells are formed in the seminiferous tubules of the testes, in the germinal epithelium. During the early stages of its formation, each sperm has the full complement or *diploid number* of chromosomes, which contain the genes, the determinants of all hereditary traits. This number of chromosomes must be reduced by one-half—that is, to the *haploid number*—before maturation of the sperm is complete, so that if and when it unites with an egg cell (which at maturity also bears the haploid number of chromosomes), the resulting fertilized egg—the *zygote*—will bear the normal, diploid number of chromosomes. A schematic drawing of this *reduction division,* called *miosis,* is shown in Fig. 16-3. It will be noted that the first cells produced by the germinal epithelium of the seminiferous tubules are called *primary spermatocytes.* Each of these cells contains the full diploid number of chromosomes, but then undergoes two miotic divisions in rapid succession, with the result that only one-half the original number of chromosomes is present after the second miotic division has taken place. The cells are now called *spermatids,* each of which undergoes several changes during a process of *metamorphosis* and becomes a sperm. In summary, it can be said that each primary spermatocyte, containing 46 chromosomes, eventually becomes four spermatozoa, each containing only 23 chromosomes and ready to unite with a mature ovum that also contains 23 chromosomes. One of the chromosomes in each mature sperm or egg cell is a *sex chromosome,* designated X or Y (Fig. 16-3). The remainder of the chromosomes

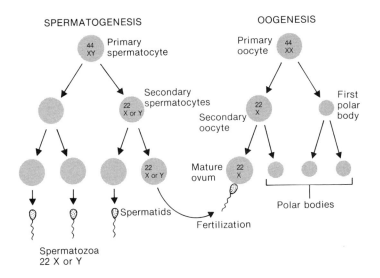

GAMETOGENESIS

SPERMATOGENESIS   OOGENESIS

44 XY Primary spermatocyte

Primary oocyte 44 XX

Secondary spermatocytes 22 X or Y

Secondary oocyte 22 X

First polar body

Mature ovum 22 X

22 X or Y Spermatids

Fertilization

Polar bodies

Spermatozoa
22 X or Y

Figure 16-3 Gametogenesis; spermatogenesis on the left, oogenesis on the right. Each primary spermatocyte has 44 autosomal chromosomes plus an X and Y sex chromosome. After reduction division (miosis), spermatozoa have only 22 autosomes and an X- or Y-chromosome. Ova never have a Y-chromosome, because this type is never present in the primary oocyte. During fertilization, a sperm unites with an egg cell, and 44 autosomes are present in the resulting zygote. If both sex chromosomes are of the X type, the offspring will be a female; but if the fertilization sperm cell carries a Y-chromosome, a male results.

are called *autosomes.* Each of the chromosomes in both sperm and egg bear only one gene for each trait; in other words, a chromosome in the sperm will bear one gene for hair color, for example, while a chromosome in the egg cell will also bear one gene for hair color. If fertilization takes place, the color of the hair of the offspring will be determined by the influence these two genes have upon each other. If one gene is for a certain hair color and the other gene is for another, then one gene may *dominate* the other, and the potential color carried by the second gene will not appear in the offspring. If both genes are for the same hair color, however, that color will probably be manifested in the offspring. This is an oversimplification of a basic principle of heredity involving *dominance and recessiveness of genes.*

THE INGUINAL CANAL   The inguinal canal is a passageway that courses obliquely through the lower portion of the anterior abdominal wall (Fig. 16-4). The canal is about 4 cm long; in the male, the spermatic cord and the internal spermatic vessels and fibers of the cremaster muscle pass through it. The inguinal canal is formed by complicated folds of the inguinal ligament, fascia, and aponeuroses of the external and internal abdominal oblique and transversus abdominis muscles.

The inguinal region is a weak point in the abdominal wall, and sometimes a loop of intestine protrudes through the inguinal canal as a result of this weakness or following excessive muscular strain (as in lifting a heavy weight), producing an *inguinal hernia* or "rupture."

THE FEMALE REPRODUCTIVE SYSTEM

External structures, or genitalia

THE PERINEUM   Both the male and the female have a *perineum;* but due to its extreme importance during childbirth, that of the female will be described, and the male perineum compared to it by means of an illustration (Fig. 16-5). The perineum is a region located at the *pelvic outlet,* and includes all structures between the pubic symphysis and coccyx. Clinically, the term *obstetrical perineum* is used to denote that part of the perineum between the vagina and anus. This portion may be torn during childbirth. The perineum consists of the muscles and fascia of the pelvic floor and the external urogenital organs and anus. When the thighs are abducted, the perineum assumes a diamond shape; and a line drawn between the ischial tuberosities divides this diamond into an *anterior* or *urogenital triangle,* which includes the mons pubis, labia majora and minora, glans clitoris, vestibule, and hymen, known collectively as the *vulva;* and a *posterior* or *anal triangle,* which includes the anus. The mons pubis is a rounded area over the symphysis pubis, and is much more prominent in women than in men. It is sometimes referred to as the *mons veneris,* which means "mound of Venus." The *labia majora*

401

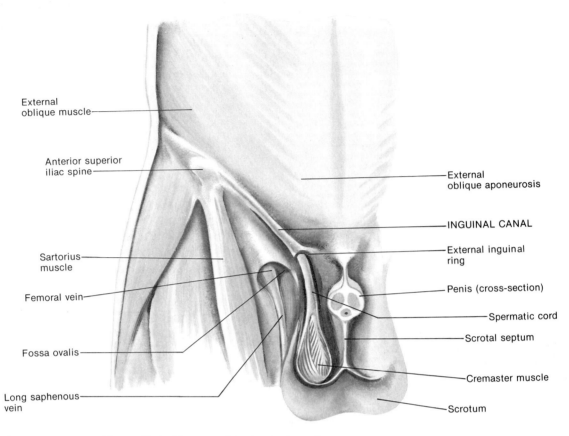

Figure 16-4 Structure of the inguinal canal.

Figure 16-5 The perineum. (a) Female. (b) Male.

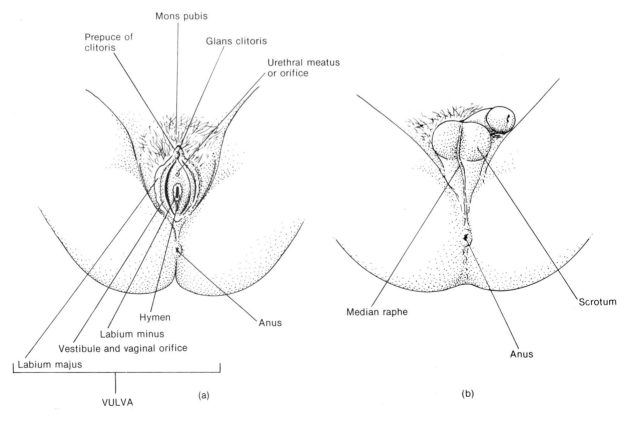

(a)

VULVA

(b)

(sing., labium majus) are very large, fleshy, liplike structures bounding the other parts of the vulva. They and the mons pubis are, by the age of sexual maturity or puberty, covered with pubic hair, just as is the comparable area of the male perineum. The *labia minora* (sing., labium minus) are much smaller than the labia majora, and surround the remaining structures of the vulva. The *glans clitoris* is positioned at the point of junction of the labia minora anteriorly. It is a small organ consisting of erectile tissue, and is homologous to the penis of the male. It is very small, and does not contain the urethra as does the penis. Tissues in the walls of the vestibule and the nipples of the female breasts also contain erectile tissue. The *vestibule* is simply the space between the labia minora. The opening of the vagina (*vaginal orifice*), opening of the urethra (*urethral orifice or meatus*), the openings of the vestibular glands, and the hymen are all contained within the vestibule. Numerous minute *paraurethral glands,* or *glands of Skene,* homologous to the prostate of the male, are present around the urethral orifice. On either side of the vaginal orifice is a *greater vestibular gland,* or *Bartholin's gland.* These glands are homologous to the bulbourethral glands of the male. All of the glands of the female perineum secrete a mucuslike substance which may serve as a lubricant during sexual intercourse. The hymen is a thin mucous membrane that stretches across the opening of the vagina. It may be complete or *imperforate,* completely separating the vagina from the vestibule; or it may be incomplete or *partial;* or it may be *entirely absent.* Although it is true that the hymen is normally ruptured during the female's first copulation, the presence or absence of a hymen does not necessarily indicate virginity or nonvirginity.

Internal structures

The internal structures of the female reproductive system, or internal organs of reproduction, are the *vagina, uterus, uterine tubes* or *oviducts* (also called Fallopian tubes), and *ovaries* (Figs. 16-6 and 16-7).

THE VAGINA Serving as the female copulatory organ by receiving the penis during coition, the vagina also makes up a portion of the *birth canal* during *parturition* or childbirth. It is a tubular structure, consisting chiefly of smooth muscle lined with mucous membrane. A skeletal-muscle sphincter is found at its entrance. The vagina is only about 5 in. deep, and is posterior to the bladder and anterior to the rectum. Before intial coitus, the vaginal orifice is only a few centimeters in diameter, but becomes significantly larger following a number of periods of sexual intercourse. The vagina is greatly stretched during childbirth, and its orifice is even more enlarged, returning to a diameter of about 3 or 4 times that of the virginal vagina. The vagina is continuous superiorly with the *cervix* or "neck" of the uterus.

THE UTERUS Positioned above the urinary bladder and anterior to the colon is the pear-shaped uterus or "womb." In the nongravid (nonpregnant) state, its muscular walls or *myometrium* are extremely thick, and its cavity almost nonexistent. During the later stages of pregnancy, however, the uterine walls are stretched until they are relatively thin, and the cavity is surprisingly large. Before pregnancy, the uterus is only about 3 in. long by 2 in. wide, and is flattened from front to back. The upper, larger portion is called the *body,* while the lower, narrow portion that is continuous with the vaginal canal is termed the cervix or neck. The extreme uppermost portion of the uterus bulges higher than the points of entrance of the uterine tubes, and is called the *fundus.* The fundus of the uterus and all of its body except a small area on the lower anterior surface is covered with peritoneum. None of the cervix is covered with peritoneum, however. The nonpregnant uterus normally tilts forward about 90 degrees with respect to the vagina (*anteversion*). Backward tilting of the organ is abnormal and is called *retroversion.* In addition to its opening into the vagina or external orifice (*external os*), the uterus has two other openings, one at each of its upper lateral aspects: the *orifices of the uterine tubes,* which lead to the ovaries. The point at which the upper end of the cervical canal meets the lower portion of the uterine cavity is called the internal orifice (*internal os*) of the uterus. During pregnancy, the smooth-

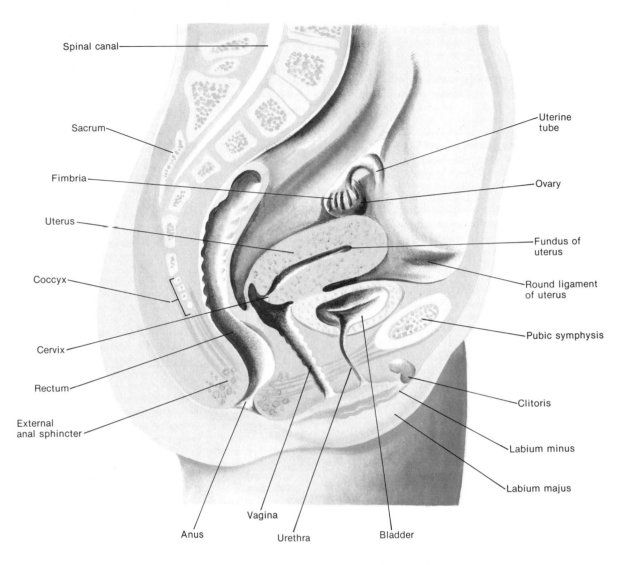

Spinal canal

Sacrum

Fimbria

Uterus

Coccyx

Cervix

Rectum

External
anal sphincter

Uterine
tube

Ovary

Fundus of
uterus

Round ligament
of uterus

Pubic symphysis

Clitoris

Labium minus

Labium majus

Anus

Vagina

Urethra

Bladder

Figure 16-6 Sagittal section through the female pelvis,
showing organs of the reproductive system.

muscle fibers of the uterus increase both in number and in length. There is no striated muscle in the uterus, and the smooth muscle is arranged in bundles, divided by connective tissue. The bundles are further arranged into three layers. The cavity of the uterus is lined with columnar epithelium, here called *endometrium.* It is abundantly supplied with glands of the mucous type. It is the endometrium that undergoes such dramatic cyclic changes during *ovulation* and *menstruation,* discussed in a later section of this chapter.

The uterus is held securely in place in the pelvic cavity by a number of *ligaments* and *peritoneal folds* which are also called ligaments. The most important ligaments of

the uterus are the *broad ligaments,* attaching the lateral aspects of the uterus to the walls of the pelvis, and the *round ligaments,* extending from the upper lateral angles through the inguinal canals. After coursing through the inguinal canals, the round ligaments extend for some distance in folds along the anterior borders of the broad ligaments. Both the broad ligaments and the round ligaments are covered by peritoneum.

The uterus is well supplied with blood vessels and nerves. Branches of two large arteries, the *internal iliac* and *ovarian,* anastomose time and again to ramify throughout the organ. The internal iliac is a branch of the common iliac, which is a branch of the

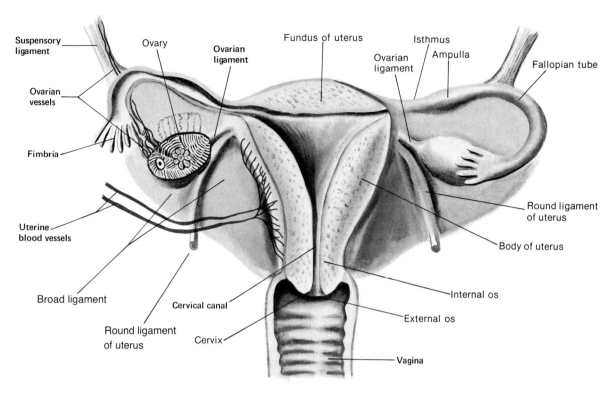

Figure 16-7 Details of the uterus, ovary, and associated structures.

aorta; while the ovarian branches directly off the aorta. The nerve supply of the uterus includes both afferent and efferent fibers. The former reach the spinal cord only via the eleventh and twelfth thoracic spinal nerves, while the latter originate in two plexuses—the hypogastric and ovarian—and in the third and fourth sacral nerves. The uterus is a necessary organ during menstruation, pregnancy, and childbirth.

THE UTERINE TUBES Extending laterally from the superior lateral angles of the uterus are the uterine tubes, also known as *Fallopian tubes,* or *oviducts.* Each uterine tube is about 10 cm long, and is suspended by a fold of peritoneum—the *mesosalpinx,* which is actually a portion of the broad ligament of the uterus. The rather constricted medial end of the uterine tube is called the *isthmus,* while the funnel-shaped lateral end is called the *infundibulum.* The opening or *ostium* of the infundibulum is surrounded by fingerlike *fimbriae,* only one of which is attached to the ovary. It is unfortunate that the infundibulum is not more firmly attached to the ovary, as it is possible for an ovum to fail to enter the infundibulum and be fertilized by a sperm

actually within the abdominal cavity instead of within the uterine tube or uterus. In the event this takes place, as occasionally it does, an *ectopic pregnancy*—one outside the uterus—is said to occur. Furthermore, this "gap" between infundibulum and ovary is a potential route for the *spread of infection* from the uterus or its tubes to the peritoneal cavity. The infundibulum is thought to move toward the ovary somewhat during release of a mature ovum, helping to lessen the chances of an ectopic pregnancy.

The uterine tube is muscular and lined with a mucous membrane consisting mainly of simple columnar epithelium. Some of these epithelial cells secrete mucus, while others are ciliated, the direction of their stroke being toward the uterus. The walls of the uterine tubes are thick, and the lining is folded longitudinally, with the result that the lumen is small and irregular in outline (Fig. 16-7). Fertilization usually takes place within one of the uterine tubes.

THE OVARIES The ovaries or *primary sex organs of the female* are about 3 cm long, and are about the size and shape of large almonds. They lie one on either lateral ab-

405

dominal wall, below and medial to the infundibulum of the uterine tubes, and behind the broad ligaments of the uterus. An *ovarian ligament* attaches the ovary to the upper lateral portion of the uterus. The ovary produces the female gametes—ova—and secretes hormones; so (like the testis) it is said to have a dual function, one *cytogenic* (cell-producing), the other *endocrinic* (hormone-producing). Blood vessels enter the ovary at its *hilus,* in the manner of the lungs and kidneys. The substance of the ovary is divided into a relatively thin, outer *cortex,* covered with a layer of columnar cells, the germinal epithelium; and a less dense, less compact *medulla,* the *stroma* of which consists of connective tissue, blood vessels, spindle-like cells, and *hollow,* spherical vesicles called *follicles.* The development of ova takes place within the follicles, which in turn originate in the germinal epithelium and migrate inward toward the central portion of the ovary. The hormones FSH (*follicle-stimulating hormone*) and LH (*lutenizing hormone*), both produced in the anterior lobe of the pituitary gland, reach the ovary in the bloodstream and bring about the development of the ova. Approximately every 28 days, one follicle with its mature ovum migrates outward to the periphery of the ovary and breaks through the surface, during a process called *ovulation.* This process begins at puberty and continues until the cessation of menstruation, or menopause, which occurs usually in middle age. Normally, a woman produces some 400 ova during her lifetime, with the two ovaries possibly alternating in the production.

The reproductive cycle of the female

Ovulation and menstruation alternate throughout the productive sex life of the female, and both have usually ceased by age 50. Both processes are under hormonal control. *Estrogens,* a group of hormones secreted by the ovary, and *follicle-stimulating hormone* (FSH) are involved. Ovulation usually occurs on or about the fourteenth day of the average 28-day cycle—that is, at the midpoint of the cycle. During the first 14 days

of the cycle, three important physiological processes take place: (1) FSH stimulates a follicle in an ovary, bringing about its maturation into a *vesicular (Graafian) follicle* (while it is stimulating the follicle, FSH is also promoting the secretion of estrogens by the ovary); (2) estrogens promote the rapid growth of cells in the endometrium, thus preparing the lining of the uterus for possible implantation of a fertilized egg cell—in other words, a pregnancy; and (3) an ovum must develop within the mature follicle; during this process, called *oögenesis,* the ovum undergoes miosis, and the normal diploid chromosome number of 46 is reduced by one-half, just as was that of the sperm cells during spermatogenesis. These two processes, *spermatogenesis* and *oögenesis,* are both divisions of *gametogenesis,* which simply means gamete formation. Once a mature egg has been expelled, its follicle undergoes some rather dramatic changes. Under the influence of luteinizing and luteotropic hormones secreted by the anterior pituitary, the cells comprising the follicle enlarge and take on an accumulation of yellow, fatty material (because of its yellowish appearance, the follicle is now called a *corpus luteum* or "yellow body"). After about two weeks, the corpus luteum degenerates and the anterior pituitary again secretes FSH, stimulating the growth of more follicles. The corpus luteum produces progesterone which, during a pregnancy, is important in preventing premature expulsion (*miscarriage*) of an embryo.

THE FORMATION OF OVA   Egg cells, or ova, are formed in much the same way that spermatozoa are formed. *Primary oöcytes* grow in the germinal epithelium of the ovary. Only one *ovum* develops from each primary oöcyte, however, and one-half the chromosomes that were present in the primary oöcyte are lost in small *polar bodies,* which soon degenerate (Fig. 16-3). This is in contrast to spermatogenesis, which produces four spermatozoa from every primary spermatocyte.

THE MENSTRUAL CYCLE AND BIRTH CONTROL It has long been known that women are more "fertile" at certain periods of the female reproductive cycle than during the remainder of the cycle; that is, during this "fertile" period, a pregnancy is more likely to result from coitus than at others. Since ovulation occurs at approximately the middle of the cycle—on about the fourteenth day—this is the ideal time for fertilization ("conception") to take place. In other words, *most women reach the high point of their fertility at about midway between one menstruation and the next.* This period of fertility is a short one, because an egg cell that has been released from an ovary lives only a day or two at the most, and if a sperm cell does not reach it within this time, fertilization cannot occur. In order to use a knowledge of the menstrual cycle as an aid to birth control, accurate records should be kept of all menstruations, and their relative degree of regularity noted. If a woman menstruates almost exactly every 28 days, and does not ordinarily start several days early or several days late, then awareness of the menstrual cycle can be very useful in birth control. Since ovulation does not occur until the end of the second week of the normal female cycle, coitus during the *first week following menstruation* (the week before ovulation) would not bring about fertilization; and since the ovum lives for only one or two days if not fertilized, *the week just prior to menstruation* is also a period of relative "safety." It should be borne in mind that this "rhythm method" of birth control is not infallible, as any irregularity in the menstrual cycle can result in a miscalculation and pregnancy. Birth control is discussed further on p. 418.

THE PROCESS OF MENSTRUATION   Approximately every 28 days, the cells of the outer layers of the endometrial lining of the uterus die and slough away, and the tiny blood vessels supplying this tissue rupture, producing a moderate amount of bleeding. This natural, cyclic cleansing of the uterus is called *menstruation,* and follows the cessation of production of two hormones (estrogen and progesterone) by the ovary. After a period of from three to five days, production of these hormones again begins, menstruation ceases, and the layers of cells that line the uterus again begin building up. An average of about 5 cc of blood, plus a quantity of dead cells and serous fluid, are lost during each menstrual "period." Menstruation is interrupted during pregnancy and lactation, due to hyposecretion or complete cessation of secretion of the ovarian hormones.

PREGNANCY AND CHILDBIRTH

Fertilization

Research has indicated that as soon as a sperm enters the female reproductive tract, it lives for only one day—or, at the most, two—even though it may remain in the tract for as long as two weeks before degenerating. The average 3-cc ejaculation contains some 300 million spermatozoa, and semen containing fewer than 60 million per cc is considered sterile. With 300 million sperm cells headed toward one ovum—and assuming that the ovum is mature, viable ("alive"), and waiting in the uterine tube—fertilization would seem virtually assured; but many things can happen to the sperm as they leave the male reproductive system. Some may die from the acidity of the male urethra or that of the vagina, in spite of the neutralizing fluids previously discussed; some do not survive the relatively high temperature of the female abdomen; while still others never complete the (for them) long trip from the vagina to the uterine tube. Using their tails, viable sperm move upward in the female reproductive tract at the rate of about 1 or 2 mm per minute, and can reach the uterine tube in about half an hour. Sperm cells contain an enzyme, *hyaluronidase;* with the aid of this enzyme, a sperm may reach the ovum, penetrate the membrane of this cell, and enter its protoplasm. The ovum is many times larger than the sperm, and the latter is soon "dissolved" within it. Fertilization has taken place, and the new cell is now a *zygote.* Remarkably, *only one sperm is permitted to fertilize an ovum.* The exact instant that a sperm penetrates an ovum, the membrane of the latter changes in such a manner that no other sperm may enter. It is likely that most ova do not undergo the second miotic division until after the sperm has entered the egg; in fact, it is believed by many physiologists that only the entrance of the sperm triggers this final stage of maturation of the ovum, and that ova that are not fertilized never reach this stage. Just prior to fertilization, the nuclei of the egg and sperm contain the haploid number of chromosomes, and are called by the special name *pronuclei.* When the male and female pronuclei unite, the diploid number of chromosomes is achieved, and fertilization is complete.

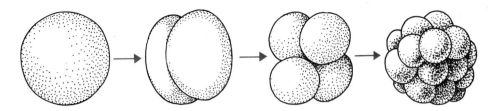

Figure 16-8   Segmentation and formation of the morula.

Embryology

SEGMENTATION   Immediately following fertilization, the zygote begins to divide *mitotically* into smaller and smaller cells that are incompletely separated. The external furrow-

Figure 16-9   Early implantation. (a) Implantation of the blastocyst. (b) Development of the umbilical cord and extraembryonic membranes.

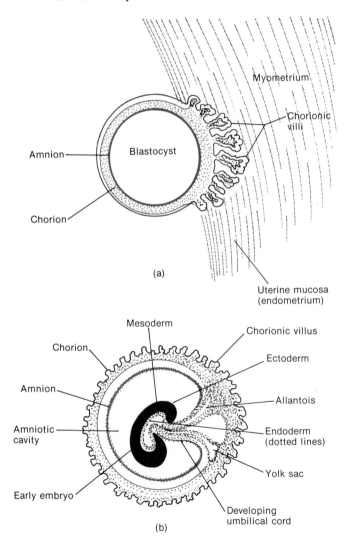

ing that is a part of this process is called *cleavage,* and it continues at a rapid pace until a ball of 32 smaller cells called a *morula* is produced (Fig. 16-8). Cleavage begins when the zygote divides into two cells, and continues in multiples of 4: 4, 8, 16, 32, 64, and so on, until the cleavage process is complete, and hundreds of tiny cells have been produced. While cleavage is progressing, a cavity known as the *blastocoele* is developing within the morula; when this is completed, the mass of cells is no longer called a morula, but a *blastocyst.* The blastocyst consists of an *inner cell mass,* which will become the *embryo,* and a single *outer layer of cells,* the *trophoblast,* which will eventually become a part of the *placenta,* a structure that attaches the developing baby to the uterine wall and indirectly supplies it with oxygen and nutrition during pregnancy. During formation of the blastocyst, the ball of cells is being moved toward the uterus by the action of cilia in the uterine tube.

IMPLANTATION   Usually within ten days after the onset of cleavage, the blastocyst reaches the endometrium of the uterus and begins to embed itself there. Two membranes have developed around the blastocyst, and one of these, the *chorion,* sends fingerlike projections called *chrionic villi* deep into the uterine mucosa (Fig. 16-9). The other membrane is called the *amnion,* which, filled with protective fluid, will hold the embryo and subsequently, the *fetus.*

Germ layers and their derivatives; differentiation

For a short time, the developing organism exists as a hollow ball, its walls consisting essentially of a single layer of cells. Soon, however, certain cells on the border of the yolk sac roll into a tube, in a process called *gastrulation*. When this process is complete, the entire mass is known as a *gastrula*. In conjunction with gastrulation, the process of *differentiation* begins in earnest. There is rapid movement and specialization of cells, until three distinct layers are formed. From outside inward, these layers are named *ectoderm, mesoderm,* and *endoderm*. The cells of these three **primary germ layers,** as they are called, soon begin to differentiate into the cells of the different kinds of tissues, which in turn form the various organs of the body. The changing of the primary cells into highly specialized tissues is called *histogenesis,* while the changes in shape and organization of the "body" and its parts is *morphogenesis.* In general, the cells of the *ectoderm* become the *epidermis of the skin, hair, nails, the nervous system, lens of the eye,* and *enamel of the teeth;* these are thus termed *ectodermal in origin*. The *mesoderm* gives rise to *skeletal, smooth,* and *cardiac muscle; connective tissues; peritoneum;* and *linings of the urinary and reproductive systems*. The *endoderm* becomes the *lining of the digestive tract* and its associated glands, and the *lining of the trachea and bronchi* and *portions of the urinary and reproductive systems*. The linings of *all* systems are of *epithelium* of one kind or another.

The extraembryonic membranes

Not all the cells of the rapidly growing embryonic mass help in forming the actual embryo. Cells of the extreme outer portion of this mass become *extraembryonic or fetal membranes* and associated structures that provide for the protection, nutrition, respiration, and excretion of the embryo—and subsequently, the fetus*—until the time of birth. These very essential structures include the *yolk sac, amnion, chorion,* and *allantois,* all of which are *fundamental fetal membranes;* and the *placenta* and *umbilical cord*.

---

* The unborn infant is termed an *embryo* during the first two months of intrauterine life. During the remaining seven months before birth, the unborn infant is called a *fetus*.

The placenta—or "afterbirth" as it is commonly called (Fig. 16-10)—develops from the combining of portions of the chorion, allantois, and endometrium. The umbilical cord develops in conjunction with the placenta, and serves as a connecting cable between the *fetus* and the *placenta*. There is *no direct connection between the circulatory systems of the mother and embryo* (or fetus); but both the placenta and pregnant uterus are extremely vascular, and the exchange of nutrients (e.g., food and oxygen) and of wastes (such as carbon dioxide and urea) takes place by *diffusion* between the capillaries of these organs. The *umbilical arteries and veins,* present in the umbilical cord, make direct connection with the circulatory system of the embryo (Fig. 16-11).

The yolk sac begins to shrink and degenerate by the time it has grown to about 5 mm in diameter, about the sixth week following fertilization. A remnant of it can usually be seen at birth, near the point at which the umbilical cord enters the placenta. The human yolk sac does not store yolk, as does the yolk sac of lower animals, but blood vessels develop within its covering and serve in the early nutrition of the embryo. The amnion is thin, tough, transparent, and without blood vessels. It is filled with clear, watery *amniotic fluid*. The embryo is completely surrounded by this fluid and is protected from mechanical injury by it. Just before birth (or sometimes, earlier) the amniotic membrane ruptures, and the pregnant woman is said to have "spilled her water" or to have "broken her water." The relatively thick chorion, by means of its villi, is important to the nutrition and elimination of wastes of the embryo; it forms much of the placenta. The allantois helps in excretion of wastes in the early embryo, and helps the chorion and lining of the uterus in formation of the placenta.

At full growth, the placenta averages 8 in. in diameter and about 1 in. in thickness. It makes up the major portion of the last material to be expelled during childbirth (hence "afterbirth"). Most bacteria cannot pass from the mother to the fetus because they are filtered out by the placenta; but certain viruses can pass through, as can some

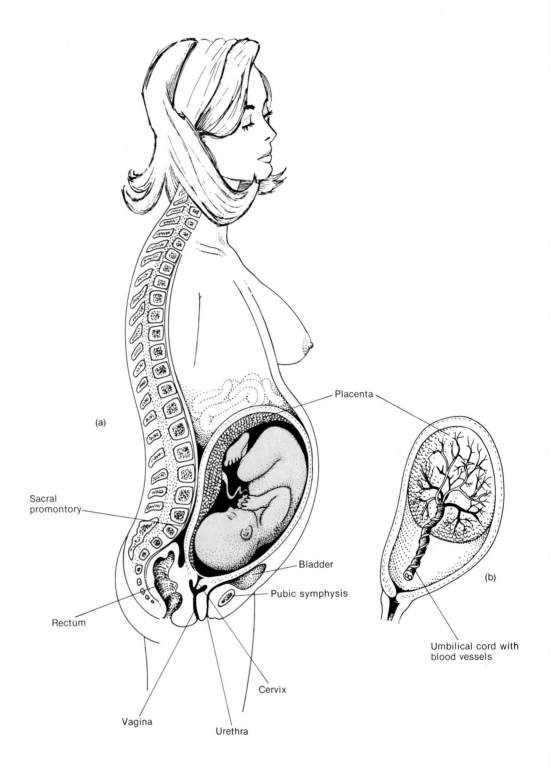

Placenta

Sacral
promontory

Rectum

Bladder

Pubic symphysis

(a)

(b)

Cervix

Vagina

Urethra

Umbilical cord with
blood vessels

Figure 16-10 Near full-term pregnancy.
  (a) Normal position of fetus within the uterus.
  (b) Fetal side of the placenta, with umbilical cord.

changes take place within the circulatory system of the infant, and the remaining stub of the umbilical cord degenerates, producing the *umbilicus* or "belly button." A weakness of the abdominal wall sometimes exists at the umbilicus, and a portion of the intestine may protrude through this region, creating an *umbilical hernia.*

The term of pregnancy

The actual birth of a child is an act that culminates a long series of events that begins with fertilization of an ovum by a sperm. Any discussion of childbirth must include consideration of the terms *pregnancy, parturition,* and *lactation.* A state of pregnancy is said to exist when the zygote becomes firmly implanted in the uterine wall. The approximate date of birth can be determined by ascertaining the first day of the last menstrual period (menstruation ceases during pregnancy) and counting ahead 280 days. The fetus remains within the uterus about 270 days, but this period often varies by several days or even a few weeks in either direction. If birth occurs more than a few weeks before the full term of 270-odd days, the infant may be placed in a *controlled-environment apparatus,* or "incubator," and given special nursing care until fully developed. Under these conditions, such variable factors as air temperature, humidity, and oxygen content of the atmosphere can be kept within ranges that provide the premature infant with maximum chances of survival. The time elapsing between fertilization and birth is customarily divided into *three prenatal periods,* as follows:

THE PERIOD OF THE OVUM (PRE-EMBRYONIC PERIOD) This period begins with fertilization and lasts until implantation begins about ten days later. As previously stated, segmentation takes place during this time, and the three primary germ layers are laid down. The extraembryonic tissues, which will become the fetal membranes and associated structures, are also established.

THE PERIOD OF THE EMBRYO (See Fig. 16-12.) Beginning after the zygote has become

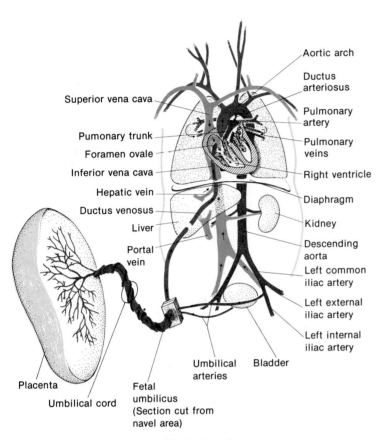

Figure 16-11 Embryonic and fetal circulation.

disease organisms carried by the mother's blood, most notably *Treponema pallidum,* the causative organism of syphilis. *Congenital syphilis* is the term used to describe the condition of an infant born with the disease. The placenta secretes estrogens, progesterone, and gonadotropic hormones.

The umbilical cord is about 23 in. long and $\frac{1}{2}$ in. in diameter. It is made up of a portion of the yolk sac, two umbilical arteries, one umbilical vein, and miscellaneous tissues. At birth, it is expelled from the uterus along with the placenta, and is ligated and cut near the umbilicus. As exchange of wastes and nutrients is no longer possible between mother and fetus (via the placenta), appropriate morphological

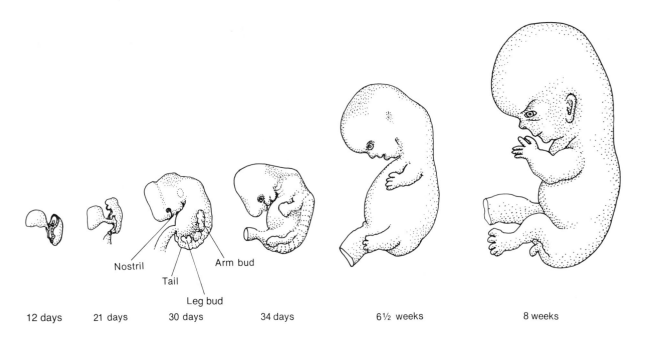

Nostril

Tail

Arm bud

Leg bud

| 12 days | 21 days | 30 days | 34 days | 6½ weeks | 8 weeks |

Figure 16-12 Appearance of the embryo at various time periods.

implanted at about the end of the second week and extending to near the end of the second month—approximately 50 days—this period includes many dramatic changes in the developing organism. It is during this time that differentiation of cells into tissues —and finally, organs themselves—begins, and the embryo takes on some of the features of a human infant. The trunk "unbends" to some extent, the facial features become better demarked, a tail grows and then disappears, the umbilical cord develops, and the external genital organs, limbs, bones, and muscular and nervous systems are all fairly well differentiated.

THE PERIOD OF THE FETUS This is the *longest* period of development. It begins on the first day of the third month, and includes the last seven months of pregnancy. During the period of the fetus (that is, during fetal life) many outstanding changes take place. Some of these are as follows:

1. *Third Month.* Growth of the trunk and limbs is more rapid than that of the head, with the result that the head appears relatively smaller than previously. The nails and external sex organs can be seen. Bone begins to form in centers throughout the body.

2. *Fourth Month.* Bones can be distinguished as such, but are still incomplete. The eyes, ears, nose, and mouth are fairly well formed. Hair grows on the head and begins to appear on the rest of the body. The fetus now "looks like a human."

3. *Fifth Month.* The bone marrow develops, and blood begins to form within it. The entire body is now covered with a coat of fine hair called *lanugo.*

4. *Sixth and Seventh Months.* The head is relatively large in proportion to the trunk (this has been so since about the 6th week) and to some extent will remain so until about the twentieth year. However, the body, although somewhat wrinkled, is in general better proportioned than in previous months.

5. *Eighth Month.* During this month, the testes descend from the abdomen into the scrotum (if the fetus is a male), and some adipose tissue accumulates beneath the skin, helping to smooth out some of the wrinkles of the sixth and seventh months. If born prematurely at this point, the fetus can usually survive without incubation or other special care, and is said to have arrived at the *age of viability.*

6. *Ninth Month.* During this month, the nails grow to full length, the lanugo falls away, and overall growth plus more deposition of adipose tissue brings the fetus to a

plump weight of approximately 7 pounds. After the ninth month, the fetus has reached full term and can usually be born without complications.

Changes in the mother during pregnancy

The maternal changes during pregnancy begin with the cessation of menstruation. As the fetus grows, the cells of the uterus multiply and grow longer, in order that the organ may enlarge at the same rate as the fetus. By the fourth month, the uterus and its fetus have become too big for the pelvis, and begin to grow upward into the abdomen, pushing the visceral organs out of their normal positions. The anterior abdominal wall gradually becomes stretched so that it protrudes greatly to help make additional room. While the uterus is growing, its arteries are branching and rebranching, so that its walls become even more vascular than usual. By the end of the eighth month of pregnancy, the top of the uterus has risen to the level of the xiphoid process, and the mother may lean backward when she stands or walks to compensate for the weight of the abdomen. The general body contour is altered and may never again return fully to its dimensions before the first pregnancy. The feet and ankles may swell, and the eyes and face may become puffy. Urination may become more frequent due to pressure on the bladder.

During the early stages of pregnancy, the mother may experience periods of nausea, often upon arising; hence the term "morning sickness." During the fifth month, the *fetal heart sounds* can be heard by the physician or nurse, and the mother feels "life" within her as the fetus shifts position from time to time. As the fetal bones develop, more and more calcium is required, and the mother may be given supplementary amounts of this mineral element in order to prevent a deficiency. The mother's blood pressure may tend to rise, and should be checked regularly. The kidneys must excrete continually increasing amounts of nitrogenous wastes in order to prevent a *toxemia*. Periodic urine analysis will determine whether or not there is any renal failure. Changes in the breasts,

followed by lactation or milk production, are described in a later section of this chapter.

Parturition or childbirth (labor)

Near the end of pregnancy, some 280 days after the onset of the last previous menstrual period, the fetus is at *full term* and ready to be expelled. This expulsion depends upon rhythmic contractions of the uterus and is known as *parturition, childbirth,* or *labor.* The last term is much more often used than the other two. Labor lasts about 16 to 17 hours at the first pregnancy, and 11 or 12 hours during subsequent births. During labor, the head of the fetus stretches the cervix of the uterus, and this action is thought to initiate reflexes which bring about contractions of the fundus. Contractions of the fundus and walls of the uterus then push the fetus downward, stretching the cervix even more, thus creating a *cycle of contractions* that is repeated over and over until the fetus is expelled. Two factors are thought to bring about contractions of the uterus: (1) pressure of the body of the fetus against the uterine walls; and (2) a decrease in the secretion of progesterone and an increase in the secretion of estrogens (both by the placenta), and a possible increase in the secretion of the hormone oxytocin by the pituitary. In other words, two types of factors may be involved in initiating and maintaining contractions—mechanical and chemical—and are possibly of equal importance in the overall mechanism of labor. The process of labor can be divided into three phases or stages, which will now be described (Fig. 16-13).

THE FIRST STAGE OF LABOR Labor *begins* with dilation of the cervix. This occurs as contractions of the uterus move the fetus downward, causing "labor pains" to be felt. As the amniotic sac that surrounds the fetus is forced into the cervix, it dilates the cervical canal, but eventually bursts and releases its fluid. An average of 6 hours' time elapses during dilation.

THE SECOND STAGE OF LABOR Following dilation of the cervix, contractions become more and more frequent and labor pains more severe, and several hours later, the

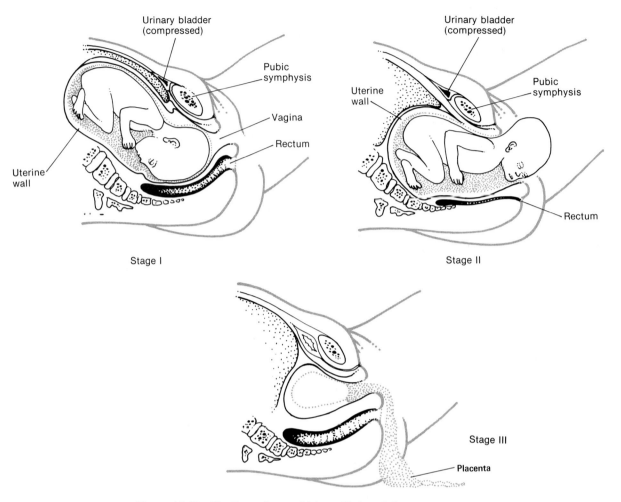

Figure 16-13   The three stages of labor: dilation, delivery, and expulsion of the placenta (see text for discussion).

infant is delivered. During the latter part of the second stage, the mother is instructed to assist in delivery by "bearing down," as though she were attempting to defecate or urinate. This tenses the abdominal muscles and aids in the actual expulsion of the fetus. Contractions of the uterus continue for a short time following delivery, but soon cease. During a normal delivery, the head of the infant emerges first, and even though the vagina can stretch to several times its ordinary size, the perineum may be torn as the head passes through. This may often be prevented by incising the perineum (*episiotomy*), then suturing the edges of the incision together after parturition is complete. After expulsion, the fetus is called an *infant*. The newborn infant is induced to breathe; then he is cleaned, and the umbilical cord is ligated and severed near the abdomen. At

this point, the placenta remains in the uterus of the mother.

After a time— perhaps 30 minutes, perhaps hours after the birth of the infant—the uterus again begins to contract, serving to expel the placenta and constrict uterine blood vessels, preventing possibly fatal hemorrhage. The third stage of labor can often be speeded by permitting the infant to suckle his mother's breast as soon as possible following parturition. Following the completion of labor, extrauterine life (life outside the uterus, and therefore, outside the mother's body) begins.

Abnormal deliveries

Normally, the first part of a fetus to emerge from the birth canal is the head, but occasionally the buttocks get into the cervix first. This is called *breech presentation.* Even an arm, leg, or shoulder may be presented first, though such cases are fairly rare. An abnormal presentation can cause the head to clamp the umbilical vessels against the walls of the birth canal and deprive the fetus of oxygenated blood. The obstetrician (physician who specializes in childbirth) may attempt to turn the emerging fetus within the birth canal in order to prevent this. On occasion, he may judge the mother's pelvis to be too narrow for safe delivery, in which case he may elect to deliver the baby by *cesarean section*—through incision of the abdominal and uterine walls.

The mammary glands and lactation

Lying mainly within the superficial fascia of the front of the thorax, the *mammary* or milk glands develop as modifications of skin glands resembling apocrine sweat glands. The mammaries of the female de-velop to a much greater extent than those of the male, mainly due to the deposition of fat after puberty in the female; but even the female glands do not fully develop internally until pregnancy and childbirth. The area covered by the mammary is shown in Fig. 16-14. The circular, wrinkled, pigmented area found in the skin over the mammary is called the *areola,* while the elevated area in the center of the areola is the *nipple.* The areola is usually pinkish in color until pregnancy, when it turns a dark brown or red, never to regain its original hue. In the nipples can be seen the 10 or 15 openings of the *lactiferous ducts* (milk ducts) of the mammary. Each duct leads to a *lobe of glandular tissue* lying deeper within the gland. Each lobe is made up of several smaller *lobules,* which in turn are composed of still smaller sacs, *alveoli.* The milk-producing cells, or *gland cells,* of the mammary make up the walls of the alveoli, and are of the cuboidal to low columnar type. Following childbirth, they are stimulated to produce milk (lactate) by *prolactin,* a hormone of the anterior lobe of the pituitary. Prolactin also acts to maintain milk

Figure 16-14 The mammary gland. (a) Normal position of mammaries of a young sexually mature female. (b) Structure of the mammary gland.

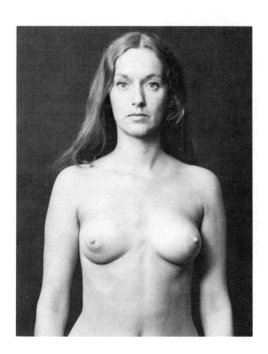

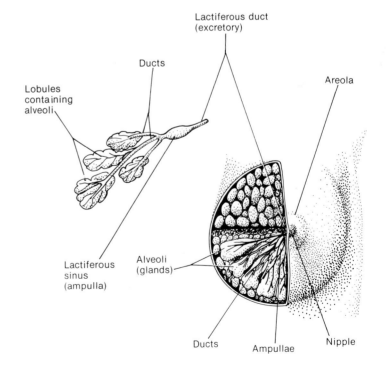

(b)

production for as long as the mammary is nursed by the infant, up to a period of several months. If nursing is completely discontinued, there is soon some degeneration of cells and other regressive changes in the glandular tissue, and the secretion of milk (lactation) comes to an end. The mammary gland has a rich blood supply, even richer during lactation. Arterial sources include the internal mammary, thoracic branches of the axillary, and branches of the intercostal arteries of the region (third, fourth, and fifth). Numerous lymph vessels drain chiefly into the axillary nodes. A cancer of the breast can *metastasize* (spread) through the lymphatics and involve the pectoral muscles or muscles of the upper arm. The nerve supply of the mammary is derived from cutaneous branches of the fourth, fifth, and sixth thoracic spinal nerves.

LACTATION   Once a fertilized ovum has become implanted in the uterus, the mammary tissues of the breasts develop, and by the time pregnancy has terminated in childbirth, secretion of a watery, yellowish fluid called *colostrum* has begun. Colostrum is rich in proteins and may contain chemical substances which afford the newborn infant a certain degree of protection against the common microorganisms he is likely to encounter until immunological agents are formed within his own blood during his first few months of extrauterine life. The production of colostrum ceases two or three days following parturition, at which time the secretion of true milk—lactation—begins. During lactation, milk is continually secreted, at the rate of from 500 to 1000 cc per day. This milk must be taken from the breast, either by the suckling infant or by means of a breast pump; otherwise, milk production will cease and the mammary tissue will shrink, undergoing a process called *involution*. Normally, the mammary glands will secrete milk for at least eight or nine months. By this time, the infant has usually been started on prepared baby foods, supplemented with an occasional bottle of "formula." Today, in the United States, few women "breast-feed" their babies, except for perhaps a few days. Often, the mother's milk is not of sufficient quality to feed. Cow's milk, commonly condensed and canned, is used as the basic ingredient for a feeding formula which may also include dextrose in the form of table syrup, sucrose (table sugar), or other carbohydrate. The mother's milk contains ample quantities of the proteins *lactalbumin* and *casein,* plus an easily digested sugar, *lactose,* as well as *calcium phosphate,* small amounts of *vitamins* and *electrolytes,* sufficient *cholesterol, phospholipids, butterfat,* and other lipoid substances, but is conspicuously lacking in *iron.* Enough iron has been stored in the liver of a newborn infant to carry out the production of hemoglobin for approximately two months. If care is not taken to see that iron is present in the baby's diet after this two-month period, there is imminent danger of anemia. Human milk is about 88.5% water, cow's milk about 87.0%.

Life after birth

If all vital processes (circulation, respiration, etc.) of the newborn are being carried out, extrauterine life begins and continues for as long as they do. *Five periods* comprise the life of a human organism after it arrives in the world:

1.   *The Period of the Newborn.* This lasts through the second week following birth.

2.   *The Period of Infancy.* This period begins at the end of the period of the newborn and lasts until the baby stands alone and walks, usually around the twelfth month.

3.   *The Period of Childhood.* This begins at the end of the first year and lasts until sexual maturity (puberty). In girls, this is reached at approximately age 14; in boys, at about age 16.

4.   *The Period of Adolescence.* Once puberty has been reached, young people are classed as adolescents until they "grow up," or reach a sort of plateau mentally and physically. Actually, adolescence is a very arbitrary term, and an impossible one to define accurately. Girls are said to end their adolescent period at about age 19, boys at 21.

5.   *The Period of Maturity.* Once an individual leaves the period of adolescence, he is classed as living in the period of maturity, and remains in this period until old age or

senility. It should be emphasized that there are no sharp divisions or demarcations between one period of extrauterine life and the next; the fact is that they blend together and overlap to a great extent. It has often been said that probably no person is completely mature, and that everyone has his adolescent or childlike qualities, no matter what his age may be. It goes without saying that in some there are more outstanding manifestations of these qualities than in others.

Tests for pregnancy

Many tests have been devised to confirm a pregnancy that has been indicated by a missed menstrual period. The most commonly employed tests for pregnancy belong to one of two categories: *biologic* tests or *immunologic* tests.

1. *Biologic Tests.* These are the most widely used of pregnancy tests. They depend on the presence of the hormone *chorionic gonadotropin* in either the urine or blood of the pregnant patient. The buildup of chorionic gonadotropin to a level sufficient for testing requires about 40 days, and this period must immediately follow the last menstruation. The embryo has now been implanted for three weeks. The hormone produces a specific effect when the urine or blood of the patient is injected into a laboratory animal.

Two commonly employed biologic tests are the *Aschheim-Zondek* and the *toad test.* In the Aschheim-Zondek (A-Z) test, 0.4 cc of urine from the patient is injected subcutaneously into a laboratory mouse twice a day for three days. Four days after the first injection, the ovaries of the mouse are removed and examined. Ruptured follicles and the presence of corpora lutei are indicative of pregnancy. Although this test is almost 100% accurate, the relatively long time required for its completion is a definite disadvantage.

In one kind of toad test, 1 ml of the patient's urine is injected into the dorsal lymph sac of a female South African clawed toad. If eggs are deposited 8–16 hr after injection, the test is considered positive. The same test may be performed by using a male toad, and noting when sperm are deposited.

The reliability of biologic tests as a group is about 95%.

2. *Immunologic Tests.* Tests depend on antigen-antibody reactions. One example is the *urine chorionic gonadotropin* (UCG) *slide* test. Here urine, antiserum, and latex are mixed on a microscope slide. Agglutination of the mixture into tiny clumps indicates the presence of chorionic gonadotropin in amounts characteristic of pregnancy. This test is said to be extremely accurate and can be performed in about 2 min.

Determination of sex

At one stage in their development, each ovum and sperm cell has 23 *pairs* of chromosomes, instead of the 23 single chromosomes which they will have after miosis has taken place. One pair of the original 23 are known as *sex chromosomes.* The sex chromosomes of the ovum are alike, and are designated X-chromosomes; those of the undeveloped spermatozoon can be either alike or different. If they are alike, they are X-chromosomes; but if they are unlike, one member of the pair is an X-chromosome, and the other is a Y-chromosome. Following miosis, each mature sperm cell is left with either an X- or Y-chromosome, while each mature ovum can have only an X-chromosome. During fertilization, if the sperm that unites with the egg carries an X-chromosome, the offspring will be a *female;* if, on the other hand, the fertilizing sperm carries a Y-chromosome, the offspring will be a *male.* In other words, it is the male gamete that determines the sex of the offspring.

Twins and other multiple births

Ordinarily, the human female produces a single offspring each time she becomes pregnant; occasionally, however, two or even more zygotes result from one fertilization. Twins can be either of two types: *fraternal* or *dizygotic twins,* which result from the production and fertilization of two separate ova; and *identical* or *monozygotic twins,* resulting from the division of a single fertilized ovum very early in development. Most cases of twinning—about 75%—are of the fraternal type; these twins may be of *the same or opposite sexes,* and each usually has his or her own extraembryonic membranes. Often, the members of such a twin pair do not greatly resemble each other. Identical twins are *always of the same sex* and usually look very much alike. The fingerprints of one member of such a twin pair are mirror images of those of the other pair.

Triplets, quadruplets, and quintuplets are occasionally born, but such cases are extremely rare. They may result from the splitting and resplitting of one fertilized ovum, from separate fertilized ova, or by combinations of both. There is strong evidence to indicate that certain drugs given in an attempt to increase the fertility of a woman may heighten the probability of a multiple birth.

Birth control

The size of a family may be intentionally limited in a number of different ways: the woman may take birth-control pills, such as those which consist chiefly of estrogenlike compounds, thus inhibiting ovulation; either she or her husband may use mechanical appliances, some of which prevent the entrance of sperm into the vagina, while others prevent the passage of sperm any further than the cervix; the previously discussed "rhythm method" may be employed; or there may be surgical sterilization of either the man or woman. In sterilization procedures, one of the marital partners is made nonfertile— "sterilized"—by a physician. There are two ways in which this procedure may be carried out: the vasa deferentia of the man may be ligated and cut, through a small incision in the scrotum, in an operation called *vasectomy;* or the uterine tubes of the woman may be ligated and/or cut. The latter operation is of course more complex and is accompanied by somewhat greater risk. Vasectomy can be performed in a few minutes under local anesthetic, and requires no hospitalization. Sperm cells are still formed after the operation, but they degenerate and are reabsorbed in the tissues and blood, since they can no longer reach the penis. Since the sperm comprise only about $\frac{1}{1000}$ or less of the total volume of semen, their absence is undetectable during ejaculation.

Occasionally, a woman will be forced to have her ovaries, her uterus, or both removed as a life-saving measure, in which case she is automatically left sterile. Removal of the entire uterus is *complete hysterectomy;* removal of only the cervix, *partial hysterectomy.* It is, of course, entirely possible for a woman with only one ovary and the uterus to become pregnant.

ABORTION The "last-resort" method of birth control, abortion entails the deliberate interruption of a pregnancy. It is a surgical procedure which ideally should be performed within a few weeks after the onset of pregnancy. It involves *dilation and curettage* (scraping) of the uterus ("D-and-C operation"), and the patient must be carefully watched for signs of infection or hemorrhage. An abortion may be performed in order to save the mother's life, or for other reasons. The operation is at present a subject of controversy, with various groups on the one hand urging repeal of all laws prohibiting it, and others voicing disapproval under any and all circumstances. Still others favor abortion only under certain conditions, such as when the pregnancy endangers the life of the mother.

OUTLINE SUMMARY

Reproduction: a natural biological process, necessary to survival of the species
1. The male reproductive system
   A. External genitalia: penis and testes
   B. Other reproductive structures: epididymis, vas deferens, seminal vesicles, prostate gland, and bulbourethral glands
   C. The penis
      a. Consists chiefly of three elongated rods of erectile tissue
         1. Two corpora cavernosa penis

2. One corpus cavernosum urethra
b. Other features of the penis
    1. It is anchored to the rami of pubic and ischial bones
    2. It is capable of becoming firm and enlarged (erect) by being engorged with blood
    3. The glans penis is its anterior end
    4. A foreskin or prepuce covers the glans in the nonerect state
    5. Its vessels are innervated by both divisions of the autonomic nervous system, and the organ tissue itself is well supplied with tactile receptors and afferent neurons
D. The scrotum
a. Structural features
    1. A sac made of skin, two sets of muscle fibers, and fascia
    2. Divided into two compartments by a septum
    3. Muscles: include the dartos layer (smooth muscle), which contracts and raises the testes toward the abdomen in cold environments, and cremaster (skeletal)
E. The testes
a. Primary sex organs: manufacture sperm
b. Produce testosterone, responsible for development of secondary sex characteristics and reproductive structures
c. Size: 3–4 cm long; egg-shaped
d. Interior: divided into compartments, each containing a seminiferous tubule, by septa
e. Tubules: lined with germinal epithelium, in which sperm cells are formed
F. The epididymis
a. Located on the upper posterior portion of the testis, and connected to the seminiferous tubules by efferent ductules, and on its other end to the vas deferens
b. Consists of a convoluted tubule about 20 ft long
c. Is the site where sperm become motile
G. The vas deferens and seminal vesicles
a. Vas deferens
    1. The duct through which the sperm travels from testis to penis
    2. Bound up in the spermatic cord along with the blood and lymph vessels and nerves to the testes

    3. Enters the prostate and joins duct of the seminal vesicle
b. Seminal vesicles
    1. Small sacs, divided internally into lobules
    2. Open into the prostatic urethra
    3. Produce an alkaline fluid, which, along with prostatic secretion and sperm cells, constitute most of the seminal fluid
H. The prostate gland
a. Located below the urinary bladder, anterior to the rectum
b. Pear-shaped, about the size of a walnut
c. Consists of glandular, connective, and smooth-muscle tissues
d. Secretes an alkaline fluid that is a portion of the semen
e. Opens into the urethra by means of pores
f. May become inflamed, enlarged, or both, and interfere with urination; may also become cancerous
I. The bulbourethral glands
a. Small, teardrop-shaped, positioned below the urethra and prostate
b. Produces an alkaline, mucuslike secretion which may help lubricate the penis during intercourse
2. Ejaculation: the forceful expulsion of semen; occurs during sexual intercourse and during sleep (nocturnal emission)
A. Erection: must occur prior to ejaculation; follows sexual excitement
a. After erection, the friction of copulation stimulates nerve endings in the glans, which send impulses to the thalamus and cerebral cortex
b. Physical pleasure activates a second reflex mechanism, producing ejaculation
c. During ejaculation, the vas deferens, seminal vesicles, and prostate contract and send semen into the vagina
d. Ejaculation and accompanying feelings of pleasure constitute the orgasm
e. Ejaculated sperm cells immediately begin swimming upward toward the uterus
f. About 300 million sperm cells are present in an average ejaculation. They can travel from the vagina to the upper end of a uterine tube in about half an hour
3. Spermatogenesis: formation of sperm cells
A. Spermatogenesis takes place in the germinal epithelium of the seminiferous tubules
B. Early in development, each sperm has the diploid number of chromosomes

C. During development, the diploid number of 46 chromosomes is reduced to the haploid number of 23, in a process called miosis

4. The inguinal canal
   A. Courses obliquely through the lower abdominal wall; is about 4 cm long
   B. Contains the spermatic cord, internal spermatic vessels, and fibers of the cremaster muscle
   C. Formed by folds of the inguinal ligament, fascia, aponeuroses of the external and internal abdominal oblique and transversus abdominis muscles
   D. Sometimes the site of inguinal hernia

5. The female reproductive system
   A. External genitalia
      a. Perineum: a diamond-shaped area between the pubic symphysis and coccyx; present in both sexes, but clinically more important in the female. The obstetrical perineum is that portion of the perineum between the vagina and anus
      b. Structure of the perineum: consists of muscles and fascia of the pelvic floor and the external sex organs
      c. Regions of the perineum
         1. Urogenital triangle: region anterior to a line drawn between the ischial tuberosities, and includes the mons pubis, labia majora and minora, glans clitoris, vestibule, and hymen—known collectively as the vulva
         2. Anal triangle: region posterior to the urogenital triangle; contains the anus
      d. Individual structures of the vulva
         1. Mons pubis: rounded eminence over the pubic symphysis
         2. Labia majora: large, fleshy structures bounding the other parts of the vulva
         3. Labia minora: smaller "lips," within the labia majora
         4. Glans clitoris: small erectile organ, homologous to the penis
         5. Vestibule: space between the labia minora
         6. Hymen: thin mucous membrane stretching across the opening of the vagina
      e. Other structures in the perineum
         1. Vaginal orifice: opening of the vagina
         2. Urethral orifice: opening of the urethra
         3. Vestibular glands: glands that open into the vestibule
         4. Paraurethral glands: located around the urethral orifice

5. Greater vestibular glands: located one on either side of the vaginal orifice
(Note: all the above glands secrete a mucous-type substance which may serve as a lubricant during copulation)
   B. Internal structures: vagina, uterus, uterine tubes, and ovaries
      a. Vagina
         1. The female copulatory organ
         2. A portion of the birth canal
         3. Tubular in shape, about 5 in. deep; lies posterior to the bladder, anterior to the rectum
         4. Made of smooth muscle lined with mucous membrane
         5. Continuous superiorly with the cervix of the uterus
      b. Uterus
         1. The womb; pear-shaped, 3 in. long by 2 in. wide; lies above the bladder, and anterior to the colon
         2. Muscular walls (myometrium) are very thick, and entirely smooth muscle; endometrium is the columnar epithelial lining
         3. Has a body, fundus, and cervix
         4. Normally tilts forward about 90 degrees with respect to the vagina
         5. Orifices of uterine tubes: open into upper lateral portions of the uterus
         6. Internal orifice: point at which the upper end of the cervix meets the uterine cavity
         7. Ligaments of the uterus include
            Broad ligaments: attach the lateral aspects of the uterus to the pelvic walls
            Round ligaments: extend from the upper lateral angles through the inguinal canals
         8. Blood supply: branches of the internal iliac and ovarian arteries
         9. Innervation: includes autonomic and afferent fibers
      c. Uterine tubes
         1. Extend from upper lateral portions of the uterus and curve to reach the ovaries
         2. About 10 cm long, suspended by the mesosalpinx
         3. Isthmus: the constricted medial end of the uterine tube
         4. Infundibulum: the funnel-shaped lateral end of the uterine tube; has a rather flimsy connection (at one point) with the ovary, making an ectopic pregnancy possible

5. Tubes: muscular and lined with simple columnar epithelium; some cells ciliated, others secrete mucus; thick walls, folded longitudinally

d. Ovaries
1. About the size and shape of large almonds; lie below and medial to the infundibulum of the uterine tubes; primary sex organs of the female
2. Ovarian ligament: attaches each ovary to the upper lateral portion of the uterus
3. Like the testes, the function is both cytogenic (cell-producing) and endocrinic (hormone-producing). The cells are the female gametes or ova
4. Each ovary has a hilus, similar to the hilus or hilum of the lungs and kidneys
5. The cortex is the thin outer portion of the ovary; it is covered with a layer of columnar cells, the germinal epithelium
6. The medulla has a stroma consisting of connective tissue, blood vessels, spindle cells, and follicles
7. Two hormones of the anterior pituitary—FSH and LH—bring about development of the ova
8. Ovulation continues until middle age, and some 400 ova are produced during that time

6. Female reproductive cycle
A. Alternating ovulation and menstruation throughout productive sex life
a. Ovulation occurs on or about the fourteenth day of the average 28-day cycle
b. Important physiological processes of the first 14 days of the cycle
1. FSH stimulates the maturation of a follicle and promotes ovarian secretion of estrogens
2. Estrogens promote the rapid growth of cells in the endometrium
3. Oögenesis occurs
4. Luteinizing and luteotropic hormones of the anterior pituitary bring about the development of a corpus luteum

B. The menstrual cycle and birth control
a. The ideal time for fertilization is approximately at mid-cycle, when ovulation occurs
b. Periods of relative "safety" include the week just prior to and immediately following menstruation

c. Menstruation
1. About every 28 days, the outer layers of the endometrium die and slough away. This is a natural, cyclic cleansing process
2. Menstruation follows cessation of production of estrogen and progesterone by the ovary
3. When these hormones are again produced (within 3 to 5 days), menstruation ceases

7. Pregnancy and childbirth
A. Fertilization
a. A sperm reaches an ovum and, with the aid of hyaluronidase, penetrates the ovarian membrane. Only one sperm may enter
b. The fertilized egg is called a zygote
c. The haploid number of chromosomes of the sperm combine with the haploid number of chromosomes of the egg, producing a diploid number

B. Embryology
a. Segmentation: the zygote divides mitotically, forming in succession a morula and blastocyst
b. Implantation: within 20 days after the onset of cleavage, the blastocyst embeds itself in the endometrium. One of the membranes that have developed around the blastocyst is the chorion; it sends chorionic villi deep into the mucosa
c. Differentiation
1. Gastrulation occurs
2. Three primary germ layers (ectoderm, mesoderm, and endoderm) are formed
3. Cells of primary germ layers differentiate into the various body tissues
d. Extraembryonic membranes: provide for protection, nutrition, respiration, and excretion of the embryo and fetus until birth. They include
1. Yolk sac
2. Amnion
3. Chorion
4. Allantois
e. Placenta or "afterbirth"
1. Consists of portions of the chorion, allantois, and endometrium
2. Provides an organ of exchange for nutrients and wastes between mother and embryo or fetus
f. Umbilical cord
1. About 2 ft long and ½ in. in diameter

2. Connects the placenta with the developing infant

C. The term of pregnancy—about 270 days
   a. Period of the ovum: begins at the fertilization and lasts until implantation (about 10 days)
   b. Period of embryo: begins after implantation is complete (about the end of the second week) and extends until the end of the second month (about 50 days)
   c. Period of the fetus: begins on the first day of the third month, and includes the last 7 months of pregnancy

D. Changes in the mother during pregnancy
   a. By the fourth month, the fetus is big enough to push the visceral organs out of their normal position
   b. By the end of the eighth month, the mother may lean backward to compensate for the weight of the abdomen. The general body contour is altered
   c. Other possible changes in the mother include
      1. Swelling of feet and ankles
      2. Puffy appearance of eyes and face
      3. Frequent urination due to pressure on the bladder
      4. "Morning sickness"
      5. Detection of fetal heart sounds (fifth month)
      6. Feeling movement of the fetus
      7. Lowering of calcium levels unless supplemented
      8. Increase in arterial blood pressure
      9. Enlargement of breasts and development of milk-producing tissues
      10. Increase in excretion of nitrogenous wastes

E. Parturition or childbirth
   a. Depends upon rhythmic contractions of the uterus (labor) when the fetus is at full term
   b. Lasts 16 to 17 hr at the first pregnancy, and 11 to 12 hr during subsequent births
   c. Two factors may bring about contraction of the uterus
      1. Pressure of the fetus against uterine walls
      2. A decrease in secretion of progesterone, an increase in secretion of estrogens, and an increase in the secretion of oxytocin by the pituitary
   d. The three stages of labor
      1. First stage: the cervix dilates, and labor pains are felt; the amniotic sac bursts
      2. Second stage: contractions become more and more frequent and severe until the infant is born, normally head first
      3. Third stage: some time after parturition the uterus again contracts, expelling the placenta; uterine blood vessels constrict
   e. Abnormal deliveries: may include breech, arm, or leg presentation, and may necessitate cesarean section

8. The mammary glands and lactation
   A. Mammary glands
      a. Lie within the superficial fascia of the front of the thorax
      b. Are modified skin glands
      c. Areola: the pigmented area around the nipple
      d. Lactiferous ducts: open into the nipples
      e. Glandular tissue: consists of lobes, lobules, alveoli, and gland cells of cuboidal or low columnar type
      f. Arterial supply of the mammary includes the internal mammary (internal thoracic) artery and branches of the axillary artery and the third, fourth, and fifth intercostals
      g. Lymph vessels: drain to the axillary nodes
      h. Innervation of the mammary: by cutaneous branches of the fourth, fifth, and sixth thoracic spinal nerves
   B. Lactation
      a. Following implantation of a fertilized ovum, the mammary tissues develop
      b. By the time pregnancy has reached full term, secretion of colostrum has begun
      c. Following childbirth, the milk-producing cells of the mammaries are stimulated to produce milk by prolactin (from the anterior pituitary). This hormone maintains milk production for as long as the mammary is nursed, up to a period of several months
      d. Long-term discontinuation of nursing results in some degeneration of cells, and regressive changes in glandular tissue, so that milk production ceases
      e. During lactation, milk is secreted at the rate of 500–1000 cc per day; milk can be produced for at least 8 or 9 months

f. Human milk is nutritious, but lacks iron
9. Life after birth: the five periods of extra-uterine life are periods of the newborn, infancy, childhood, adolescence, and maturity
10. Some of the most common tests for pregnancy
   A. Biologic tests
      a. Aschheim-Zondek (A-Z) test
      b. Toad test
   B. Immunologic tests. Urine chorionic gonadotropin (UCG) slide test
11. Determination of sex: the male gamete determines the sex. If both sex chromosomes of the sperm are of the X type, the offspring will be female; but if one sex chromosome of the sperm is of the Y type, the offspring will be male (the egg cell contains only X-chromosomes)

12. Twins and other multiple births
   A. Two types of twins
      a. Fraternal or dizygotic: results from the production and fertilization of two separate ova
      b. Identical or monozygotic: result from the division of a single fertilized ovum very early in development
   B. Triplets, quadruplets, and quintuplets are also produced by the methods outlined above
13. Birth control: may be accomplished by a variety of methods, such as
   A. Birth-control drugs
   B. Appliances worn by husband or wife
   C. The rhythm method
   D. Sterilization of either husband or wife
   E. Abortion—the "last-resort" method of birth control

STUDY QUESTIONS AND PROBLEMS

1. What is the primary function of the reproductive system?
2. Without great detail, explain the essential steps in reproduction.
3. Compare the external genitalia of the male with those of the female. In what ways are they adapted to the reproductive process?
4. Describe the unique structure of the penis. What is the disadvantage of using the urethra for both urine and male sex cells, as far as reproduction is concerned?
5. Exactly where are spermatozoa formed in the testes? What term is given to that portion of gametogenesis that involves the formation of sperm?
6. List the secondary sex characteristics of the male. What hormone brings about the development of these characteristics?
7. Describe the prostate gland, its function, and its relationship (sometimes unfortunate) to the male urethra.
8. Describe the reflex that brings about ejaculation. About how many sperm cells are present in each one?
9. Mr. D. told a fellow patient that he was suffering from an inguinal hernia. What did Mr. D. mean by this term?
10. Where is the perineum? Describe the structures of the female perineum. Why is the female perineum so important clinically?

11. Describe the internal organs of the female reproductive system. What are the functions of the vagina? The ovaries? The uterus? What is meant by the statement, "The function of the ovaries, like that of the testes, is both cytogenic and endocrinic"?
12. Discuss ovulation. How many mature ova does the average woman produce during a lifetime?
13. Discuss the menstrual cycle. Why is it important that this cycle proceed on a regular, undisturbed schedule (except during pregnancy and after menopause)?
14. Briefly discuss fertilization, segmentation, and implantation. List the three germ layers and their major derivatives.
15. Describe the extraembryonic membranes and the umbilical cord. How does the exchange of gases and nutrients take place between mother and developing fetus?
16. List and briefly discuss the periods of the term of pregnancy.
17. Discuss lactation.
18. Why is birth control becoming increasingly important today?
19. Describe two methods for diagnosing pregnancy. What are the two main categories of pregnancy tests?
20. What are the primary sex organs of the male? Of the female?

weights and measures

THE METRIC SYSTEM

Length

1 meter (m) = 39.37 inches (in.)
= 3.281 feet (ft)
1 centimeter (cm) = 0.01 m
= 0.3937 in.
(1 in. = 2.54 cm)
1 millimeter (mm) = 0.1 cm = 0.001 m
1 micron (μ) = 0.001 mm = 0.00004 in.
1 millimicron (mμ) = 0.001 μ
1 Angstrom unit (Å) = 0.0001 μ

Area

6.45 square centimeters (cm^2)
= 1 square inch (sq. in. or in.^{2})

Weight

1 gram (g or gm) = 0.03527 ounce (oz)
= 0.0022 pound (lb)
(The weight of 1 cubic centimeter or 1 milliliter of distilled water at its maximum density, which it reaches at 4° centigrade)
1 dekagram = 10 g
1 hectogram = 100 g
1 kilogram (kg) = 1000 g = 2.2 lb
1 decigram = 0.1 g
1 centigram (cg) = 0.01 g
1 milligram (mg) = 0.001 g

1 microgram (γ) = 0.001 mg
= 0.000001 g
454 g = 1 lb
1 oz = 28.4 g

Volume

1 cubic centimeter (cc) = 1 milliliter (ml)
1 milliliter = 0.0610 cubic inch
(cu in. or in.^{3})
1 liter = 1000 cc
= 0.2643 U.S. gallon (gal)
= 1$^+$ quarts (qt)
1 liter = 0.220 Imperial gal

APOTHECARIES' SYSTEM

Weight

1 scruple = 20 grains (gr)
1 dram (dr) = 60 gr
1 ounce (oz) = 480 gr
= 8 dr
1 pound = 5760 gr
= 12 oz

Volume

1 fluid dram (fl dr) = 60 minims
1 fl oz = 480 minims
1 pint (pt) = 7680 minims
= 16 fl oz
1 quart (qt) = 2 pt
1 gallon (gal) = 4 qt

HOUSEHOLD MEASURES

(Equivalents are approximate.)

$$1 \text{ teaspoon (tsp)} = 4 \text{ cc}$$
$$= 1 \text{ fluid dram (fl dr)}$$
$$1 \text{ tablespoon (tbsp)} = 15 \text{ cc} = \tfrac{1}{2} \text{ fl oz}$$
$$= 3.75 \text{ tsp}$$
$$1 \text{ cup} = 240 \text{ cc} = 8 \text{ fl oz} = \tfrac{1}{2} \text{ pt}$$

TEMPERATURE

Zero degrees on the centigrade (Celsius) scale is the freezing point of water, and is equivalent to 32° on the Fahrenheit scale. The boiling point on the centigrade scale is 100°; that on the Fahrenheit scale, 212°. One degree Fahrenheit is $\tfrac{5}{9}$ degree centigrade. Calculations for conversion from one temperature scale to the other are as follows:

From centigrade to Fahrenheit:

$$°F = (°C \times \tfrac{9}{5}) + 32 \quad (\tfrac{9}{5} = 1.8)$$

From Fahrenheit to centigrade:

$$°C = (°F - 32) \times \tfrac{5}{9} \quad (\tfrac{5}{9} = 0.5556)$$

Absolute zero: the temperature at which all molecular motion ceases, that is —273.18°C or —459.72°F.

ENERGY

Calorie (Cal): the amount of heat required to raise the temperature of 1 kg of water 1°C—e.g., from 15° to 16°C—also known as a "large calorie" or kilocalorie (kcal). One "small calorie" (cal) is the amount of heat required to raise the temperature of 1 g of water 1°C.

$$1 \text{ cal} = 0.001 \text{ Cal}$$
$$= 252 \text{ British Thermal Units (BTU)}$$

NORMAL CLINICAL VALUES

Urine

Average amount (24 hr): 1500–2000 cc
Reaction to litmus: slightly acid (pH 6.0)
Specific gravity: 1.005–1.022
Color: pale straw to amber

Constituents in 24-hr specimen:

Urea	20.0–30.0 g
Uric acid	0.6–0.75 g
Total nitrogen	10.0–16.0 g
Ammonia	0.5–15.0 g
Chlorides	10.0–15.0 g
Phosphate	2.0–4.0 g
Total sulfur	1.0–3.0 g
Creatinine	0.3–0.45 g
17-Ketosteroids:	
adult men	5.0–27.0 mg/24 hr
adult women	5.0–15.0 mg/24 hr
Total solids	50.0–70.0 g

(Total acidity is equivalent to 400–600 cc of 0.1 N-sodium hydroxide)

Blood

Volume	4,000–6,000 cc
% of body weight	7–9%
pH	7.35–7.45
Erythrocytes/mm³	4,500,000–5,000,000
Reticulocytes	0.8–1.0%
Leucocytes/mm³:	5,000–10,000
Neutrophils	60–70%
Eosinophils	1–3%
Basophils	0.25–0.5%
Lymphocytes	25–33%
Monocytes	2–6%
Platelets/mm³	200,000–400,000
Hemoglobin/100 cc	14–16 g
Hematocrit:	
In men	40–54%
In women	37–47%
Color index	0.9–1.1
Volume index	0.9–1.1
Mean corpuscular volume	80–94 μ3
Mean corpuscular hemoglobin:	
volume	27–32 $\mu\mu$g
concentration	32–38%
Bleeding time	1–3 min
Coagulation time	6–12 min
Clot retraction time:	
beginning	1 hr
complete	24 hr
C-Reactive protein precipitation	<1 mm
Prothrombin time (quick)	10–15 sec

Blood grouping
(using anti-A and anti-B sera)

Group O: no agglutination with either serum

Group A: agglutination with anti-A serum only

Group B: agglutination with anti-B serum only

Group AB: agglutination with both sera

Rh factor, using anti-Rh (anti-D) serum:
  Rh+ (positive): agglutination
  Rh− (negative): no agglutination

Cerebrospinal fluid

Volume:	approximately 130 cc
Color:	clear, colorless
Specific gravity	1.003–1.008

Reaction to litmus	alkaline
Protein	15–45 mg/100 cc
Glucose	40–60 mg/100 cc
Chloride (as NaCl)	710–750 mg/100 cc
Phosphate (inorganic)	1–2 mg/100 cc
Calcium	4.5–5.5 mg/100 cc
Cells	0–10 mm^3
Pressure	5.0–7.5 mm Hg

Gastric contents

Total acidity	50–100 degrees *
Free HCl	25–50 degrees
Combined HCl	10–15 degrees
Organic acids and acids salts	4–5 degrees

* Degrees are equivalent to the number of cc of 0.1 N-sodium hydroxide required to neutralize 100 cc of gastric contents.

glossary

Abortion: the termination of a pregnancy before fetal viability has been reached.

Acapnia: diminished carbon dioxide content of the blood.

Achlorhydria: lack of hydrochloric acid in gastric juice.

Acidosis: a condition in which acid is present in the blood in proportionally greater amounts than base.

Acuity: sharpness or clearness, especially of the visual sense.

Adenoids: the pharyngeal tonsils.

Adhesion: the abnormal joining of two surfaces, especially after surgery.

Adolescence: period between the age of puberty and adulthood.

Aerobic: reacting chemically or growing only in the presence of molecular oxygen.

Albuminuria: the presence of albumin in the urine.

Aldehyde: member of a class of substances derived from primary alcohols by oxidation and containing the CHO group.

Alkaline reserve: the entire amount of alkaline salts present in the body fluids, mainly sodium bicarbonate; known also as *alkali reserve*.

Alkalosis: a condition in which alkali or base, especially bicarbonate, is present in the blood in proportionally greater amounts than acid.

Alveolus: a small cavity or sac, such as a tooth socket or microscopic air sac of the lung, respectively.

Ameboid movement: movement by the extension of cell cytoplasm as pseudopodia ("false feet") in the manner of the single-celled organism *Ameba*. This manner of locomotion is often utilized by leucocytes.

Amenorrhea: absence or abnormal cessation of menustration.

Ampulla: a saclike dilation of a canal, tube, or duct.

Amyl Nitrite: a volatile organic compound used in cases of angina pectoris. It is a vasodilator and cardiac stimulant.

Anabolism: the constructive phase of metabolism, during which protoplasm and such other complex compounds as hormones are synthesized from simpler substances, within the cell.

Anaerobic: chemical reaction or growth without benefit of molecular oxygen.

Analgesia: loss or absence of sensitivity to pain.

Anaphylactic: serving to decrease the immunity or susceptibility to an infection instead of increasing it; may be due to the introduction of a foreign protein into the body following an infection. See also *anaphylaxis*.

Anaphylaxis: an unusual or exaggerated reaction of the body tissues to a foreign protein or other substance, sometimes following sensitization produced by the injection of agents prepared with horse serum.

Anastomosis: a connection between blood vessels without an intervening capillary network; also, a surgical connection of blood vessels or other body parts, such as the intestines.

Anesthesia: loss of feeling or sensation.

Aneurysm: a blood-filled, saclike dilation of the wall of an artery or vein.

Angina: any disease or condition typified by choking, suffocative pain. Angina pectoris is the most familiar example.

Anisocytosis: inequality in the size of erythrocytes.

Ankylosis: the fusion of the bones of a joint, with resultant immobility.

Anorexia: loss of appetite or of the desire for food.

Anoxemia: a diminished supply of oxygen in the blood.

Anoxia: reduction of the oxygen supply to the body tissues.

Antibody: a chemical substance produced in the body in response to the introduction of an antigen, such as the toxin produced by a disease organism. It may inactivate the antigen.

Antigen: any substance which, when introduced into the body, brings about the formation of antibodies which react against it.

Antiseptic: any substance that will inhibit the growth of microorganisms, preventing decay or putrefaction.

Antrum: a cavity or chamber within a bone or visceral organ, such as the pyloric antrum of the stomach.

Aperture: an opening, in some instances called an *orifice*.

Apex: the pointed portion of a conical structure, as in the apex of the lung or heart.

Aphasia: loss of the ability to speak language, or sometimes to understand the spoken word.

Apnea: the transient cessation of breathing, due to temporary interruption of the breathing impulse.

Apoplexy: a cerebral hemorrhage or cerebral thrombus and the effects produced by either, such as paralysis, coma, and death.

Appendage: an attached part, such as the upper and lower extremities.

Aqueduct: a channel or canal for the transport of a fluid; e.g., the cerebral aqueduct, which connects the third and fourth ventricles of the central nervous system and transports cerebrospinal fluid.

Areola: the pigmented area around the nipple of the breast; also, any minute space within a body tissue.

Arthrosis: an articulation or joint.

Ascites: an accumulation of serous fluid within the abdominal or peritoneal cavity.

Asphyxia: loss of consciousness due to inadequate oxygen supply; suffocation.

Aspiration: the removal of fluids or gases by suction; also, the accidental inhalation of an object into the trachea.

Astereognosis: loss of the ability to recognize the form of an object by touch.

Asthenia: weakness of the body or a body part.

Ataxia: loss of coordination by the skeletal muscles, especially those of locomotion.

Atresia: absence or closure of a normal body opening.

Atrophy: diminution or wasting away of a body part, especially a skeletal muscle.

Atropine: an alkaloid drug that inhibits the action of the parasympathetic division of the autonomic nervous system.

Ausculation: listening to sounds within the body, as when determining blood pressure or while conducting other diagnostic procedures.

Axial: pertaining to the central portion or axis of the body or a body part, as in the axial skeleton, or axis of a long bone.

Benign: not a threat to life; nonmalignant.

Bifurcate: forked, or divided into two, like the "arms" on a Y.

Bilateral: found on both sides of the body or a body part.

Bolus: a rounded mass of food that has been swallowed.

Buccal: pertaining to the mouth, but especially the cheeks.

Buffer: any substance which tends to resist a change in pH (acidity or alkalinity) when acid or base is added. Buffers of the blood are of particular importance, as they help to prevent acidosis or alkalosis.

Bursa: a connective tissue sac, lined with synovial membrane and containing synovial fluid. Bursae are found around joints, providing cushions over which tendons can slide without contacting bone.

Cachexia: a profound and marked state of general ill health and malnutrition.

Caffeine: an alkaloid substance obtained from the tea leaves or coffee beans. It is a cardiac stimulant.

Calculus: a "stone" formed in the gallbladder or urinary system. It may consist of cholesterol or calcareous substances.

Calorie: a unit of heat. One calorie is the amount of heat required to raise the temperature of 1 g of water from 15° to 16°C, and is called a small calorie; 1 *Calorie* (or 1 *kilocalorie*) is the amount of heat required to raise the temperature of 1 kg of water from 15° to 16°C.

Canal: a relatively narrow passage or tubular channel.

Cancellous: a latticelike, reticular, or spongy structure.

Cancer: a malignant tumor or neoplasm, made up chiefly of epithelial cells.

Carbaminohemoglobin: the compound formed by the union of carbon dioxide with hemoglobin.

Carcinoma: a neoplastic growth or cancer, consisting of epithelial cells, and having the ability to metastasize or spread.

Caries: decay of a tooth or bone.

Casein: the principal protein found in milk.

Cast: a mold of a body part, such as a bronchial tube, formed of solid but plastic effused matter or exudate. Also, the placing of a body part in an immobilizing device, such as a plaster cast; or a small particle in urine.

Castration: removal of the primary sex organs (gonads).

Catabolism: the "tearing-down" process of metabolism, during which complex substances are converted into simpler compounds within the cells.

Catalyst: a substance that affects the speed of a chemical reaction, but does not become a part of the final product.

Cataract: opacity of the crystalline lens of the eye.

Caudal: pertaining to a position or direction away from the head, as in the caudal end of the spinal cord.

Cephalic: pertaining to a position or direction toward the head; the opposite of caudal.

Cerumen: waxlike secretion of the external ear.

Cervix: a neck, such as the cervix or neck of the uterus.

Cesarean section: surgical removal of a fetus through an incision in the abdominal wall and uterus.

Cheilosis: a condition marked by lesions on the lips and angles of the mouth, characteristic of riboflavin deficiency.

Chemoreceptor: a nervous-system receptor that is stimulated by chemical substances. The taste cells of the tongue are examples.

Chemotherapy: treatment of disease by means of various chemicals.

Chiasm: an X-shaped crossing, such as that of optic-nerve fibers connecting with the medial half of each retina.

Cholecystectomy: surgical removal of the gallbladder.

Chondrification: the formation of cartilage during growth and development.

Choroid: skinlike.

Chromatin: the hereditary or genetic substance; divides into chromosomes during mitosis, and is made mostly of DNA.

Chromosome: a rodlike body of chromatin, seen in the cell nucleus during mitosis (nuclear division).

Chyle: the milky fluid absorbed by the lacteals and transported to the thoracic duct. It consists of lymph and emulsified fat.

Chyme: the semifluid, creamy mass produced by the digestion of food in the stomach. It enters the small intestine for further digestion.

Cilia: minute, hairlike processes found on the free surfaces of certain body cells, such as those lining the trachea and bronchi.

Circadian: daily, as in circadian rhythms or biological clocks.

Cocaine: an alkaloid drug made from cocoa leaves. It is used as a local anesthetic, narcotic, and dilator of the pupil (mydriatic).

Coenzyme: a nonprotein substance that activates an enzyme.

Collagen: the chief structural protein of skin and connective tissue.

Collateral: accessory to, a branch of, or running parallel to.

Colloid: a state of matter in which one phase is dispersed within the other, with the particles of the dispersed phase being larger than those of a true solution (crystalloid), but still submicroscopic in size (1 to 100 millimicrons).

Colostomy: creation of an opening into the colon, thereby forming a new anal aperture.

Colostrum: the first milk secreted following childbirth.

Coma: profound unconsciousness, from which arousal is unlikely.

Commissure: groups of nerve fibers connecting opposite corresponding portions of the central nervous system.

Congenital: existing at or previous to birth.

Contraction: a shortening, especially of a muscle.

Contralateral: situated on or pertaining to the opposite side of the body or a body part.

Convoluted: twisting, turning, or coiled.

Corium: a term meaning the true skin or dermis.

Coronal: crownlike. The *coronary* arteries and their branches surround the heart like a crown.

Corpus: the body as a whole, or the main portion of a body organ.

Cortex: the outer portion of an organ, the inner portion of which is often called the medulla, as in the kidney and adrenal gland.

Costal: pertaining to one or more ribs.

Crenation: the shriveling of a cell due to the passage of its fluid into the surrounding medium; most commonly demonstrated when erythrocytes are placed in a solution which is hypertonic to their intracellular fluid. Crenation is also known as *plasmolysis*.

Cruciate: shaped like a cross.

Crypt: a small, tubelike depression opening on a free surface.

Crystalloid: a true solution. The particles of the solute are smaller than those of a colloid, and can often pass through a cell membrane.

Curare: an extract of the *Strychmas* plant. It paralyzes muscles by acting at the motor end plates.

Cutaneous: pertaining to the skin.

Cyanosis: A dark, bluish appearance of the skin, lips, and nails due to inadequate oxygenation of the blood.

Cystoscopy: examination of the interior of the urinary bladder by means of a cystoscope.

Deamination: a chemical reaction in which the amino group is split off the amino acid.

Debilitating: contributing to loss of strength.

Decussation: crossing of a band of nerve fibers from one side of the central nervous system to the other.

Defecation: expulsion of fecal matter from the bowel.

Deglutition: swallowing.

Dehydration: loss of water from the body cells and tissues.

Dentate: sawtoothed or having toothlike projections.

Dentin: that portion of a tooth beneath the enamel.

Dentition: the number, shape, and arrangement of the teeth; also, the process of teething.

Diagnosis: the process of identifying a disease from its signs and symptoms. A *differential diagnosis* is made by comparing a case with other diseases producing similar signs and symptoms.

Dialysis: the separation of crystalloids from colloids in solution by using a selectively permeable membrane. Crystalloids pass through rapidly, colloids slowly or not at all. This principle is utilized in the artificial kidney.

Diapedesis: the wriggling of leucocytes through the walls of blood vessels, particularly capillaries.

Diffusion: the passage of a liquid or gas from a region of greater concentration of its molecules to a region of lesser concentration of its molecules. Of particular importance in physiology is the diffusion of substances through cell membranes.

Digitalis: a cardiac stimulant, produced from the dried leaves of the foxglove plant.

Diopter: the refractive power of a lens with a focal length of 1 meter.

Diplopia: double vision, the condition in which a single object appears as two.

Diurnal: occurring daily.

Diverticulum: an outpouching from a main tubular structure or organ cavity.

Dropsy: edema; accumulation of fluid in a body cavity, especially the abdomen.

Duct: a tube for the passage of secretions or excretions.

Dyspnea: difficult or labored breathing.

Dystrophy: a degenerative disease of the body tissues, particularly the skeletal muscles; also, defective or faulty nutrition.

Ectopic: located in an abnormal place; for example, an ectopic pregnancy is one in which the fertilized egg does not become implanted in the uterus, but may lodge in the abdominal cavity outside the uterus.

Edema: accumulation of fluid in various locations, such as the abdomen, lungs, and extremeties.

Effector: a structure, such as a muscle or gland, which carries out a particular function when stimulated by a nerve impulse.

Effusion: the escape of blood or lymph from their respective vessels into the tissues or a body cavity.

Electrocardiogram: a graphic record of the electrical activity of the heart muscle.

Electroencephalogram: a graphic record of the electrical activity of the brain ("brain waves").

Electrolyte: a substance which dissociates (ionizes) in solution and is then able to conduct an electric current.

Electron: the negatively charged particle of an atom.

Elimination: the act of expelling something from the body, especially fecal matter.

Embolism: occlusion of a blood vessel by a transported clot or embolus.

Embryo: term applied to a developing human organism up to the age of two months; after that, the term *fetus* is used.

Emesis: the act of vomiting.

Emphysema: the distension and rupture of pulmonary alveoli and the presence of air in the intra-alveolar tissue.

Empirical: pertaining to the simplest form, such as the empirical formula of a compound; also, referring to a skill that is based upon experience.

Empyema: pus in a body cavity, especially the pleural cavity.

Encephalon: the brain.

Endocrine: ductless, as in the endocrine glands.

Energy: the capacity for doing work.

Enuresis: involuntary urination after the age of three years.

Enzyme: an organic catalyst, made in a cell.

Epinephrine: hormone produced by the adrenal medulla; known also as *adrenalin*.

Epistaxis: nosebleed.

Erectile: capable of erection, as in the erectile tissues of the penis, clitoris, and mammary glands.

Etiology: the study of the causes of disease.

Eupnea: normal breathing.

Evagination: an outpouching of some body part or organ.

Eversion: turning the soles of the feet so that they face outwardly; also, the turning inside out of any structure.

Excoriation: any superficial loss of tissue, such as that produced when scratching the skin.

Exocrine: ducted; e.g., the exocrine glands pour their secretions into ducts, unlike endocrine glands, which have no ducts.

Exophthalmos: protrusion of the eyeballs, as seen in severe exophthalmic goiter.

Extravasation: the escape of blood or lymph from a vessel into the tissues.

Extrinsic: originating outside the body part upon which it acts, as in the extrinsic muscles of the eye.

Exudate: any substance deposited in or on a tissue by either a normal body process or disease.

Facilitation: the state of excitability produced in nerve tissue during the transmission of an impulse.

Fascia: a sheet of connective tissue just under the skin (superficial fascia) or investing the skeletal muscles (deep fascia).

Fasciculus: a small bundle of nerve fibers or muscle cells.

Febrile: pertaining to fever.

Fetus: the name given to a developing human organism after the second month of pregnancy.

Fiber: an elongated, threadlike structure, such as a muscle fiber or nerve fiber.

Filiform: thread-shaped.

Filtration: the passage of a liquid through a filtering device.

Fissure: a relatively deep cleft or groove, such as the fissures of the brain. Some are abnormal, such as fissures of the skin.

Fistula: an abnormal opening, often leading from the body surface to an internal organ.

Flaccid: limp, flabby, or soft.

Follicle: a small secretory or excretory sac-like structure.

Foramen: an opening or hole in a body part, especially a bone.

Fossa: a depression or pit, especially in a bone.

Fovea: a cup-shaped fossa, such as the fovea centralis of the eye.

Frenulum: a small fold of mucous membrane or skin that acts to limit the movement of an organ, as in the frenulum of the tongue.

Fusiform: spindle-, cigar-, or torpedo-shaped; tapered at both ends.

Gangrene: tissue death (necrosis) with putrefaction.

Gel: a jellylike or semisolid colloid.

Gene: the unit of heredity; located in the chromosome, and made mostly of DNA.

Genu: refers to the knee, or a bend in certain other body parts.

Gestation: pregnancy.

Glossal: pertaining to the tongue.

Gonad: a primary sex organ, either testis or ovary.

Groin: the lower anterior portion of the abdominal wall.

Hallucination: a sensation not based upon reality.

Hematuria: the presence of blood in the urine.

Hemiparesis: muscular weakness of one side of the body.

Hemiplegia: paralysis of one side of the body.

Hemostasis: checking of flow of blood through any part of the body; also, the arrest of hemorrhage.

Hepar: referring to the liver.

Hernia: protrusion of a portion of an organ (such as the intestine) through an abnormal opening (especially in a weak place in the body wall, such as the inguinal-canal region).

Homeostasis: that state of dynamic physiologic equilibrium that must be maintained in good health.

Homogenous: of uniform consistency throughout.

Homologous: of similar structure and embryological origin, but not necesarily of similar function.

Hordeolum: inflammation of a sebaceous gland of the eyelid, commonly known as a "sty."

Hormone: the secretion of a ductless gland or other endocrine tissue.

Hyaluronidase: an enzyme that promotes the breakdown of hyaluronic acid.

Hydrolysis: chemical breakdown by the addition of water; often must be accelerated by enzymes.

Hydrostatic: pertaining to a liquid in a state of equilibrium.

Hyperemia: excess blood in any part of the body.

Hyperopia: farsightedness.

Hyperplasia: the abnormal increase in the number of normal cells of a given kind in a tissue.

Hyperpnea: abnormally rapid breathing, with exaggerated respiratory movements; panting.

Hypertrophy: abnormal enlargement of an organ (such as the heart or liver) due to increase in the size of its cells.

Hypochondriac: the upper lateral region of the abdomen; also, an individual who constantly takes medication, often needlessly.

Hypodermic: under the skin, as in a hypodermic injection.

Hypoxia: deficiency of oxygen in the inspired air; low oxygen level or content of inspired air.

Impermeable: pertaining to a barrier (such as a cell membrane) which does not permit the passage of certain fluids or gases. If it is *impermeable* to certain substances but *permeable* to others, on the whole it is *selectively permeable.*

Impulse: a wave of excitation passing over a nerve, muscle, or other body tissue; a sudden uncontrollable determination to act.

Inflammation: a series of reactions in tissues produced by microorganisms or other irritants, marked by redness of the affected area. There is an influx of erythrocytes with exudation of plasma and leucocytes.

Inguinal: pertaining to the region between the abdomen and the thigh; the groin.

Inhalation: the inspiration of air or other gases into the lungs.

Inhibition: restraint of a process by an overriding mechanism.

Innominate: having no name, or anonymous; e.g., the brachiocephalic artery or veins were formerly known as the innominate artery and veins, respectively.

In situ: located in place; also, in the normal place.

Insulin: a hormone produced in the islet cells of the pancreas; helps to regulate carbohydrate metabolism.

Intercellular: situated between the cells of a given tissue.

Intercostal: situated between the ribs, as in an intercostal space, or intercostal muscles, nerves, or blood vessels.

Internuncial: a connection between two other structures, as in an internuncial neuron.

Interstitial: within a tissue; intercellular (between cells).

Intracellular: within a cell.

Intravascular: within the blood vessels or lymph vessels.

Intrinsic: referring to a structure originating within the organ it serves; e.g., the intrinsic muscles of the eye dilate and constrict the pupil and change the shape of the lens.

Intussusception: the invagination or infolding of one portion of the intestine into another portion; also, growth of an organism from within, as opposed to growth of nonliving materials, such as mineral deposits by lamination or accretion.

Invagination: the pushing of the wall of a hollow organ into the cavity of that organ.

Inversion: the turning inward or other reversal of the normal relationship of a body part.

In vitro: "in glass"; also, in the broad sense, in the laboratory.

In vivo: within the living body.

Involuntary: performed independently of will; due to reflex.

Involution: degenerative—or at least retrograde—change; return of an hypertrophied organ to smaller (and perhaps normal) size.

Ion: an atom or group of atoms bearing a positive or negative electrical charge.

Ipsilateral: pertaining to the same side of the body or a body organ; also called *homolateral.*

Irritability: responsiveness or excitability of a tissue; an outstanding property of all living protoplasm.

Ischemia: a local and temporarily inadequate blood supply, often due to vasoconstriction in the region affected.

Isotonic: two solutions having the same concentration of solute and solvent and, therefore, identical osmotic qualities; also, a muscle contraction that involves no change in tonus.

Isotope: a chemical element having the same atomic number as another, but a different atomic weight. Several isotopes, such as those of carbon, nitrogen, sodium, potassium, phosphorus, chlorine, and iodine, can be made radioactive and then used in diagnostic procedures and therapy.

Keratin: a sulfur-containing protein, the principal constituent of hair and nails.

Ketone: any compound containing the carbonyl group, CO. Acetone is a good example.

Ketosis: excessive amounts of ketone bodies in the blood and tissues.

Kinesthetic: pertaining to stereognosis or proprioception; the knowledge of position of body parts in space.

Labium: a lip or lip-shaped structure, such as the labium majus and labium minus of the female reproductive system.

Lacrimal: pertaining to the tears or tear-producing apparatus.

Lactation: the production of milk by the mammary glands.

Lactose: milk sugar; found in mother's milk and cow's milk.

Lacuna: a small hollow, depression, or pit.

Lamella: a thin layer or plate, as of bone.

Lamina: a thin, flat layer in a portion of tissue consisting of layers of cells. Also, a flat plate; e.g., the laminae of vertebrae.

Lecithin: an aminophosphatide found in egg yolk, semen, and nervous and other tissues.

Lesion: any pathological or traumatic destruction of an area or part of the body.

Leukemia: a disease of the blood-forming tissues, marked by increase in the number of leucocytes (leucocytosis) and enlargement and proliferation of the lymphoid tissues, including the spleen.

Loin: the posterolateral portion of the trunk, between the lower ribs and the top of the pelvis.

Lumen: the internal space of a tubular structure, such as the intestine and blood vessels.

Macroscopic: large enough to be seen without a microscope.

Malaise: an overall feeling of bodily weakness, discomfort, or distress, sometimes the first sign of infection.

Malignant: lethal, deadly, as in a malignant tumor or cancer.

Manometer: an instrument for measuring the pressure of liquids or gases.

Mass: a quantity of substance made up of cohesive particles, such as a fecal mass; also, the weight of an object, or a quantity of substance.

Mastication: the act of chewing food.

Meatus: a passage or channel, such as the external auditory meatus.

Membrane: a thin layer of tissue that covers a surface, or divides a space or organ.

Mesial: positioned in or near the middle; median.

Mesothelium: a layer of squamous epithelial cells that covers the surface of all serous membranes.

Metabolism: the sum total of the chemical processes of nutrition (see also *anabolism* and *catabolism*).

Metastasis: the spreading of disease from one portion of the body to another.

Microscopic: small enough to be visible only with the aid of a microscope.

Micturition: urination; the act of voiding urine.

Miosis (Meiosis): The reduction cell division of gametogenesis, during which the chromosomes of the egg and sperm are decreased in number from 46 to 23, or in other words, from the diploid to the haploid number.

Mitosis: division of the nucleus during the process of ordinary cell division.

Monovular: derived from or pertaining to a single ovum.

Morbid: pertaining to or affected by disease.

Moribund: in a dying state or condition.

Morphine: the principal narcotic derived from opium; it has analgesic and hypnotic properties.

Multiparous: having given birth to two or more viable offspring.

Myopia: nearsightedness.

Narcosis: a state of stupor or unconsciousness produced by a narcotic drug.

Necrosis: death of tissue in a localized area.

Nuchal: pertaining to the posterior of the neck.

Nulliparous: having never given birth to a viable offspring.

Nystagmus: rhythmic oscillation of the eyeballs, either horizontal, vertical, or rotatory.

Oögenesis: the process of formation of ova or egg cells. It is one of the two divisions of gametogenesis, the other being *spermatogenesis,* or the formation of spermatozoa.

Orifice: name given to certain of the apertures and openings of the body.

Os: bone.

Osmosis: the diffusion of water through a selectively premeable membrane.

Osseous: bony or bonelike.

Ossification: the process of bone formation, or the replacement of cartilage by bony material.

Ostium: a small opening, such as the one in the distal end of the uterine tube.

Oxidation: the combining of oxygen with food substances in the cells; also, the gain of positive charges by an atom through the loss of electrons.

Oximeter: a galvanometer, modified to measure the oxygen saturation of hemoglobin in the circulating blood.

Palliative: affording bodily ease or relief, but not cure.

Palpation: examination by touch or feel, as in palpating the pulse, breasts, liver, or spleen.

Palpitation: ventricular systole so forcible as to be sensed by the individual.

Papilla: a small nipple-shaped elevation or projection.

Paralysis: loss of power of contractility of a muscle, due to injury or disease of the muscle or its nerve supply.

Paresthesia: an abnormal or perverted sensation, such as burning or prickling.

Parietal: pertaining to the walls of a cavity.

Parturition: labor, or the act of giving birth.

Pennate: featherlike, feather-shaped.

Peripheral: situated away from the central portion of the body.

Peroneal: pertaining to the lateral side of the leg.

Perspiration: the excretion of sweat; sweating.

pH: symbol used in expressing concentration of hydrogen ions in a solution. The pH *number* is the logarithm of the reciprocal of the hydrogen-ion concentration.

Phagocyte: a cell (such as a leucocyte or macrophage) which ingests foreign particles, microorganisms, and other cells.

Phagocytosis: the engulfing of other cells, microorganisms, or foreign particles by phagocytes.

Physiotherapy: treatment of diseases, especially those involving body motion, by the use of exercise, heat, water, air, and light.

Pilocarpine: an alkaloid substance that stimulates the parasympathetic division of the autonomic nervous system.

Pilomotor: pertaining to or causing the movement of hair.

Plantar: pertaining to the sole of the foot.

Plasmolysis: shrinking of a cell due to loss of water from osmotic action. In the case of erythrocytes, this is called *crenation*.

Polymer: a high-molecular-weight compound formed by the linking together of simpler molecules.

Potential: difference in electrical charges on the inner and outer surfaces of a cell membrane.

Presbyopia: farsightedness due to old age.

Pressor: a substance or a reflex which produces vasoconstriction and, therefore, an increase in arterial blood pressure.

Prognosis: a prediction of the probable outcome of an illness.

Prolapse: the collapse or falling of an organ, such as the uterus.

Proliferation: the reproduction or duplication of similar forms, especially of cells.

Psychogenic: originating in the mind; psychic.

Psychosomatic: pertaining to physical conditions having psychological causes.

Puberty: the age of sexual maturity.

Pus: a fluid containing leucocytes and cellular debris; produced by infection and inflammation.

Racemose: resembling a bunch of grapes on their stalk.

Rachitic: related to rickets, or affected by that disease.

Receptor: a sensory nerve ending which responds to stimuli.

Reflection: the rebounding of a ray of light from a surface which it does not penetrate. Also, the incising and pulling away of skin.

Reflex: a predictable, involuntary response to a stimulus.

Refraction: the bending of light rays as they pass from one medium (such as air) into another medium of different density (such as the cornea and lens of the eye).

Reguritation: the return of food from the stomach into the mouth. The amount may be small, or it may be large, as in vomiting. Also, the backflow of blood through inadequately closed heart valves.

Reticulum: a network; e.g., a protoplasmic network within cells.

Retroversion: the bending of the uterus or other organ backward.

Rh factor: an antigen first discovered in the red blood cells of the rhesus monkey. An individual whose blood has this antigen is "Rh-positive"; one who does not, "Rh-negative."

Rigidity: stiffness or inflexibility.

Rostral: cephalad, cranial, or toward the head.

Sarcoma: a tumor that arises from connective or nonepithelial tissue, often malignant.

Sebum: the secretion of sebaceous ("oil") glands.

Semen: the ejaculatory fluid, consisting of sperm cells and secretions of the prostate and bulbourethral glands and seminal vesicles.

Senescence: the normal process of growing old.

Serotonin: a compound, 5-hydroxytryptamine, found in blood and having an action similar to that of epinephrine, but more powerful.

Serous: fluid-producing, as in the serous membranes of the thorax and abdomen (pleura and peritoneum, respectively); also, pertaining to or resembling serum.

Sinus: a hollow space in a bone or other organ or tissue; a channel for the transport of blood.

Sinusoid: sinuslike; also, a vascular space in the liver, spleen, or other organ.

Somatic: pertaining to the nonvisceral portions of the body, such as the skeleton and skeletal muscles.

Spasm: a sudden, violent, involuntary contraction of a muscle or group of muscles; such an action involving other structures, such as the digestive organs, excretory ducts, or glands.

Spasticity: the state of being spastic; pertains especially to skeletal muscles.

Spermatogenesis: the process of formation of sperm cells or male gametes, also known as male sex cells, spermatozoa, or simply sperm. It is one of the two divisions of gametogenesis, the other being oögenesis, or formation of ova (egg cells).

Sphincter: a circular or ringlike muscle surrounding a body orifice; e.g., the anal sphincter muscle.

Splanchnic: pertaining to the viscera, as in the splanchnic nerves.

Stasis: a stoppage of the flow of blood or other body fluid.

Stenosis: narrowing of an opening, duct, or canal; e.g., mitral stenosis is a narrowing of the opening of the left atrioventricular (mitral) valve.

Sterility: inability to produce young; infertility.

Stimulus: any chemical or physical change, in the internal or external environment, that produces a response.

Stratum: a layer.

Stricture: the abnormal narrowing of a passage, such as a canal, duct, or the intestine.

Stroma: the material which forms the ground substance, matrix, or framework of a cell, tissue, or organ.

Subcutaneous: located beneath the skin.

Sulcus: a relatively shallow groove or furrow, such as the central sulcus of the cerebrum.

Susceptibility: the degree of proneness to infection; liability to infection. An individual may be highly or moderately susceptible or nonsusceptible at any given time.

Syncytium: a multinucleate mass of protoplasm, such as a striated muscle cell.

Syndrome: a collective group of signs and symptoms which are typical of a particular disease.

Synovial: of or pertaining to the viscous fluid, secreted by synovial membranes, which lubricates joints.

Syringomyelia: the presence of abnormal fluid-filled cavities in the spinal cord.

Tactile: pertaining to the sensation of touch or "feel."

Tension: the condition of being stretched, or the act of stretching.

Tetanus: steady contraction of a muscle without twitching; also, the acute infectious disease known as "lockjaw," manifested by tonic contractions of certain muscles.

Tetany: a syndrome which includes forcible flexion of the wrist and ankle joints, muscle cramps, and convulsions; it is caused by abnormal calcium metabolism, and occurs in hypoparathyroidism.

Therapy: the treatment of disease.

Thrombophlebitis: formation of an intravascular thrombus or clot following inflammation of the wall of a vein.

Thrombosis: formation of an intravascular blood clot in the living individual.

Thrombus: a stationary intravascular clot.

a ringing or humming sound in the auditory apparatus.

Titer: the amount of a chemical substance required to produce a reaction with a certain volume of another chemical substance.

Toxic: pertaining to a poison, or harmful to the body as a poison.

Trabecula: a connective-tissue septum that extends from a capsule into the main substance of an organ.

Transudation: the passage of a fluid, such as serum, through a membrane.

Trauma: a wound or injury.

Trigone: a triangular area, particularly that formed by the openings of the ureters and urethra into the urinary bladder.

Tube: an elongated, hollow, cylindrical structure.

Unilateral: denoting that a certain organ or point is located on only one side of the body.

Urticaria: raised, itching, white patches on the skin; commonly called "nettle-rash" or "hives."

Valence: the combining power of an element or radical.

Varicocele: dilation or enlargement of the veins of the spermatic cord.

Vermiform: worm-shaped, as in the vermiform appendix.

Vertigo: giddiness or dizziness.

Vesicle: a small, fluid-filled, saclike structure.

Viscera: the internal organs of the body.

Viscosity: resistance to flow by a fluid substance.

Volvulus: intestinal obstruction due to twisting of the bowel.

Zymogen: a substance which is converted into an enzyme upon coming into contact with a coenzyme.

selected references

Note   *Since new editions of the follow-ing textbooks are constantly being published, neither the number of the edition nor the year of publication has been included in the list. The student is urged to always ask for the latest edition when visiting the library or bookstore.*

Anatomy

CUNNINGHAM, D. J., *Textbook of Anatomy.* New York: Oxford University Press, Inc.

Goss, C. M., ed., *Gray's Anatomy of the Human Body.* Philadelphia: Lea & Febiger.

HAMILTON, W. J., *Textbook of Human Anatomy.* New York: St. Martin's Press, Inc.

MORRIS, H., *Human Anatomy.* New York: Blakiston Co.

WISCHNITZER, Saul, *Outline of Human Anatomy.* New York: McGraw-Hill Book Company.

Physiology

BEST, C. H. and N. B. TAYLOR, *Physiological Basis of Medical Practice.* Baltimore: The Williams & Wilkins Co.

GUYTON, A. C., *Textbook of Medical Physiology.* Philadelphia: W. B. Saunders Co.

LANGLEY, L. L., *Outline of Physiology.* New York: McGraw-Hill Book Company.

MITCHELL, P. H., *Textbook of General Physiology.* New York: McGraw-Hill Book Company.

PACE, D. M. and B. W. McCASHLAND, *College Physiology.* New York: Thomas Y. Crowell Company.

Anatomy and physiology

BEST, C. H. and N. B. TAYLOR, *The Human Body: Its Anatomy and Physiology.* 4th ed. New York: Holt, Rinehart & Winston, Inc.

STEEN, E. B. and A. MONTAGU, *Anatomy and Physiology* (2 vols.), College Outline Series. New York: Barnes & Noble.

index

* Asterisk indicates that this entry appears in text and table on cited page.

Bronchus, right, and aspirated objects, 304
Brunner's glands, 333, 342
Buccal cavity (*see* Mouth)
Buccinator muscle, 108 (Table 6–3) *
Budding of nerve cells, 199
Buffer(s):
  and acid-base balance, 390
  bicarbonate, 287
  blood, 287, 288, 390
  definition, 390
Bulbourethral glands, 396, 399
Bundle of His, 266
Bursae, 79
Buttocks, 2
Butyric acid, 344

C

C. O. (*see* Cardiac output)
Caffeine, effects of, 366
Calcaneus bone, 77
Calcium:
  carbonate in bone, 49
  and clotting, 283
  hydroxide in bone, 49
Calculi, renal, 374
Callouses, 43
Caloric requirements, 365 (Table 13–2) *
Calorie, definition, 351
Calvaria, 55
Calyces, 373
Canal:
  alimentary, 9
  central, of bone, 49
  definition, 54
  Haversian, 49
  inguinal, 73, 401
  medullary, 47
  neural, 63
  of Schlemm, 210
  vertebral, 8, 63, 65
Canaliculi, 49
Cancer:
  breast, 291
  metastasis, 291
  of prostate, 399
  and smoking, 366
Canine teeth, 84, 327
Cannon, Walter B., 14
Canthus, of eye, 211
Capillaries:
  alveolar, 249
  and diffusion, 249
  lymph, 289
  pulmonary, functional surface area, 313
  structure, 249
Capillary:
  "bed," 249
  definition, 249
  pressure, 275
Capitate bone, 72
Capitulum, 69
Capsule of kidney, 372
Carbohydrates, 351–356
  fates after absorption, 351
  groups, 351
  in human diet, 350
  hydrolysis, 351
  metabolism, 350, 351, 353, 355, 356
  oxidation and energy release, 351
  phosphorylated, 353
  and protoplasm synthesis, 354
  in urine, 380
Carbon dioxide:
  blood level, and heart rate, 270
  effect on respiratory centers, 308
  elimination, 300
  as metabolite, 359

Carbon dioxide (*cont.*)
  method of transport, 312, 313
  output, 300
  respiratory stimulant, 319
  retention, 315
Carbon monoxide:
  and anoxia, 314
  attraction to hemoglobin, 314
  and automobile exhaust, 314
  poisoning, 314
Carbonmonoxyhemoglobin, 314
Carboxyhemoglobin, 314
Carboxypeptidase, 338
Carbuncles, 43
Cardia of stomach, 330
Cardiac:
  arrest, 284
  cycle, 265, 270
  dynamics, and blood pressure, 271–276
  muscle, 32
  nerves, 265
  output, 271
    and blood pressure, 273
    factors affecting, 272
    region of stomach, 330
    sphincter valve, 330
Cardioaccelerator center, 270
Carotene, conversion to vitamin A, 337
Carotid artery:
  external, 259
  and pulse, 258
Carotid bodies:
  and heart rate, 270
  and respiration, 309
Carotid sinus reflex, 185
Carotid sinuses and respiration, 309
Carpals, 70–72
Carpus, 70
Carrier:
  enzymes and molecules, 25
  substances, and nerve impulse, 149
Carsickness, 223, 224
Cartilage, 30, 47, 51
  articular, 47
  costal, 67
  flexibility, 51
  kinds or classes, 52
  of larynx, 317
  and nutrients, 52
Caruncle, 211
Castration, and secondary sex characteristics, 240
Casts, in urine, 380
Catabolism, 350
Cataract, 216
Catecholamines, 237
Cathartics, 343, 344
Catheterization, 381
Cauda equina, 65, 164, 171
Caudal anesthesia, 65
Caudate nucleus, 163
Cavernous:
  sinus, 263
  tissue, 396
Cavities of body, 8, 9
Cavity:
  abdominal, 9
  buccal, 9
  cecum, 333
  cranial, 8
  spinal, 8
  thoracic, 9
Celiac:
  ganglion, 186
  trunk, 255, 331
Cell(s), 9, 16–28 (*see also specific types of cells*)
  acidophil, of adenohypophysis, 230
  ameloblasts, 85
  appearance and function, 18

Cell(s) (*cont.*)
  basophil, of adenohypophysis, 230
  bone, 30
  bone-forming, 47, 50
  cartilage, 30
  cornified, 39
  cytoplasm, 21
  effect of dehydration on, 32
  division, 27
    reduction type, 400
  idealized, 19
  inclusions, 21–23
  major parts, 19
  membrane, 19, 25
    muscle, 91
  muscle, 32
    response to stimuli, 94
  of nervous tissue, 146
  nucleus, 19
  number in newborn, 17
  odontoblasts, 85
  organelles, 21, 22
  organized into living matter, 17
  parts, 19
  plasma, 290
  reticular, 49
  sex, 396
  size and shape, 18
  visible to unaided eye, 18
Cellular respiration, 351
Celom, 9
Cementing substance, 49, 50
Cementum of teeth, 85
Center of gravity, 77
Central:
  artery to retina, 210
  canal, of spinal cord, 165, 193
  nervous system, 151, 152, 165
    blood supply, 196–199
    venous drainage, 198
  sulcus (of Rolando), 155
  vein,
    of liver, 335
    to retina, 210
Centrifugal force, 224
Centrioles, 21, 22
Centrum of vertebrae, 62
Cephalic vein, 262
Cerebellar arteries, 258
Cerebellum, 159
  function, 159
  nuclei, 159
  peduncles, 159
Cerebral:
  aqueduct (of Sylvius), 161, 193
  arteries, 198, 259
  cortex, 148, 157
    association areas, 199
  hemispheres, 153–155
  peduncles, 161
  vascular accident, 285
Cerebrospinal fluid, 65, 191, 196
  formation and circulation, 193, 196
  function, 193
Cerebrum:
  acoustic center, 223
  anatomy, 152–157
  frontal lobe, 157
  functions of lobes, 157
  lobes, 155
  methods of study, 157
Cerumen, 39, 223
Ceruminous glands, 223
Cervical:
  plexus, 173
  rib, 67
  spinal nerves, 171
Cervix:
  dilation, 413
  of uterus, 403

P

Pacemaker of heart, 266
Pain:
  conscious awareness, 157
  headache, 182, 183
  migraine, 183
  phantom, 182
  of psychological origin, 182
  referred, 182
Palate:
  cleft, 302
  hard, 55, 327
  soft, 327
Palatine:
  bones, 55
  tonsils, 303
Palmaris longus muscle, 122, 124 (Table 6–12)
Palpation, 6
Palpebrae, 211
Palpebral fissure, 211
Polypeptides, 342
Pancreas, 238–240, 338
  acinar cells, 338
  alpha cells, 338
  beta cells, 338
  body, 338
  and carbohydrate metabolism, 338
  endocrine function, 238, 239, 338
  exocrine portion, 338
    nervous and hormonal control, 338
  head, 338
  and homeostasis of blood glucose, 240
  hormones, 239
  hypersecretion of insulin, 240
  ion production, 338
  islet tissue cells, 238
  regulation of endocrine secretion, 240
  relationships, 332
  tail, 338
Pancreatic:
  amylase, 341, 342
  ducts, 337, 338
  enzymes, 338, 341
  juice:
    hormonal and nervous control, 342
    and intestinal digestion, 341
  lipase, 341, 342
  protease, 341
  secretion:
    and autonomic impulses, 342
    and vagal stimulation, 338
Pancreosymin, 241
  and pancreatic secretion, 338, 342
Papillae:
  dermal, 38
  renal, 373
  of tongue, 218, 327
Papillary muscles, 253
Parasympathetic:
  supply to heart, 265
  and heart rate, 272
Parasympathicotonia, 188
Parathormone:
  actions, 235
  regulation of secretion, 235
  and tetany, 236
Parathyroid glands, 235
  and calcium-phosphorus metabolism, 235
  chief cells, 235
  location and structure, 235
  oxyphil cells, 235
  and plasma calcium, 282
  principal cells, 235
  regulation of secretion, 235
Paraurethral glands, 403
Parietal:
  bones, 55

Parietal (*cont.*)
  cells of stomach, 331, 340
Parietooccipital fissure, 155
Parotid gland, and facial nerve, 170
Parturition, 403, 411, 413, 415
Passive transport, 25
Patella, 77
Patellar:
  reflex, 184
  tendon, 134
Patent:
  ductus arteriosus, 265
  foramen ovale, 265
Pathogenic bacteria, 41
Pathway(s):
  ascending, 180
  corticospinal, 181
  descending, 181
  Embden-Meyerhof, 353
  enteroceptive, 179
  exteroceptive, 179
  final common, 181
  for hearing, 221, 222
  mapping, in spinal cord, 180
  nervous system, 147, 179–181
    motor, 181
    and reflex actions, 179
    for sense of smell, 219
    sensory, 179
    spinal reflex, 183
    for taste, 218
    and thalamus, 181
    visual, 212
Pavlov, Ivan, 186
PBI (protein-bound-iodine test), 360
Pectoral region, 2
Pectoralis major muscle, 117 (Table 6–7), 120 (Table 6–10)
Pectoralis minor muscle, 117, 118 (Table 6–9)
Pedicles of vertebrae, 63
Pelvic:
  girdle:
    component parts, 73
    function, 73
  inlet, 75
  outlet, 75, 401
Pelvis:
  articulated, 75
  brim, 75
  clinical divisions, 75
  component parts, 73
  contents, 73
  false, 75
  female, clinical importance, 75
  landmarks and measurements, 75
  sex differences, 75
Penis, 396, 398
  innervation, 398
Pentose, 21
Pepsin, 331, 341
  of gastric juice, 340
  hydrolytic action, 341
Pepsinogen, 331, 341
Peptidases, 338
Peptides, 338, 357
Peptones, 341, 342
Percussion, 311
Pericardial space, 252
Pericardium:
  parietal, 252
  visceral, 252
Perichondrium, 52
Pericranium, 39
Perilymph, 222
Perimysium, 91
Perineum:
  anterior (urogenital) triangle, 401
  comparison of male and female, 402 (Figure 16–5)

Perineum (*cont.*)
  during childbirth, 401, 414
  obstetrical, 401
  posterior (anal) triangle, 401
Period(s):
  of the embryo, 411
  of extrauterine life, 416
  of the fetus, 412
  of the ovum, 411
Periodontal disease (pyorrhea), 86
Periosteum, 47
  of scalp, 39
Peripheral:
  nervous system, 151, 165–179
    classes of nerves, 165
    component parts, 152, 165
  resistance, and blood pressure, 272
Peristalsis, 340
  mass, 344
  nervous control, 342
Peritoneum, 338, 339
  function, 339
  and kidneys, 339, 372
  parietal, 338
  visceral, 332, 338
Peritonitis, 339
Permeability, 23, 25, 26
  theories, 25
Pernicious anemia, 279
Peroneal vein, 262
Peroneus tertius muscle, 134 (Table 6–17) *
Personality, 159
Perspiration, 39
  composition, 41
  and heat loss, 361
  odorous, 41
Petrosal sinuses, 263
Peyer's patches, 290, 332
pH:
  of body fluids, 366
  of blood, and heart rate, 270
  of gastric juice, 341
Phagocytic cells, of liver, 335
Phagocytosis, 26, 27, 281
Phalanges:
  of fingers, 72
  of toes, 79
Phantom:
  limb, 182
  pain, 182
Pharmacology of the autonomic nervous system, 190
Pharyngeal tonsils, 303
Pharyngotympanic (Eustachian) tube, 52, 221, 303
Pharynx:
  laryngeal, 303
  muscle action during swallowing, 328
  nasal, 302, 327
  openings, 303
  oral, 303, 327
  and phonation, 302
Phenylhydrazine, and taste, 218
Phosphatase, and glycogenolysis, 355
Phosphorylation, 353
Phrenic:
  arteries, 255
  nerves, 173, 308
Phrenicocostal sinus, 305
Physical activity, and heart rate, 270
Physiograph, 95
Physiology:
  definition, 12
  fundamental concepts, 13
  of heart, 265–272
  of sleep, 200
Pia mater, 192
  of spinal cord, 163
PIF (*see* Prolactin, inhibiting factor)

Turbinates, 302
"Tweenbrain" (*see* Diencephalon)
Twins:
fraternal (dizygotic), 417
identical (monozygotic), 417
Tympanic membrane, 59, 221

U

Ulcer:
duodenal, 341
gastric (peptic), 341
of skin, 43
Ulcerations, 43, 86
Ulna, 70
Ulnar nerve, 173
Umbilical:
area, 7
arteries and veins, 264, 409
cord, 264, 409, 411
hernia, 411
Umbilicus, 264, 411
Underbite, 86
Unit membrane, 19
Uracil, 21
Urea, from ammonia, 357
Ureters, 374
Urethra:
female, 375
layers, 375, 376
male, 375, 376, 399
Urethral orifice, 403
Urinalysis, 379
Urinary:
bladder, 374
system, 371–385
and acid-base balance, 391, 392
functions, 13, 372, 391
trigone, 34
Urination, 380, 381
and prostatitis, 399
Urine:
abnormal constitutents, 380
in acid-base balance, 379
alkaline tide, 379
and blood, 380
formation, 377, 378, 381, 388
normal constituents, 379 (Table 14–1)*
physical characteristics, 379
and pregnancy tests, 379
retention, 381
Urochrome, 379
Urogenital diaphragm, 375
Urticaria, 43
Uterine:
cavity, 403
tubes, 403, 405
Uterus, 403–405
anteversion, 403
blood supply, 404
cervix, 403
endometrium, 404
functions, 405
innervation, 404
ligaments, 404
and peritoneum, 403, 404
retroversion, 403
Utricle, 222
Uvula, 316

V

Vacuoles, 21, 22
Vagina, 396, 403
and coitus, 403

Vagina (*cont.*)
size and relationships, 403
Vaginal orifice, 403
Vagus nerve, 160, 165, 169 (Table 7–1), 170
dorsal motor nucleus, 171
and heart, 265
and taste, 171
Valve(s):
of heart, 253
actions, 271
ileocecal, 334
of inferior vena cava, 265
of lymph vessels, 289
"purse-string," 330
sphincter, of anus, 330
of veins, 259, 275
Vas deferens, 396, 399
Vasectomy, 418
Vasoconstriction, and bleeding, 283
Vasoconstrictor center of medulla, 273
Vasodilator center of medulla, 273
Vastus intermedius muscle, 133 (Table 6–16), 134
Vastus lateralis muscle, 133 (Table 6–16), 134
Vastus medialis muscle, 133 (Table 6–16), 134
Vater, ampulla of, 338
Veins, 249, 250, 259, 262 (*see also specific veins*)
of brain and meninges, 261
definition, 249
of head, 261
and injection, 262
of lower extremity, 262
major, 259
microscopic structure, 249
spinal, 199
of thorax, 262
of upper extremity, 262
valves, 259
Vena cavae, 249, 259, 262, 269, 307, 335
Venous:
circulation, 246, 259–262
drainage of brain, 263
pressure, 275
sinuses, of CNS, 198, 199
stasis, 284
Ventilation, alveolar, 313, 315
Ventricles:
of brain, 160, 161, 193
of heart, 252, 268
Ventricular filling, importance, 272
Venules, 249
Vermiform appendix, 334
Vermis, 159
Vertebra prominens, 65
Vertebrae:
comparison in portions of vertebral column, 63, 64
features common to most, 62
Vertebrae:
arteries, 63, 64, 196, 255, and 258
canal, 63, 65
column, 61–63, 65
curvatures, normal and abnormal, 62
foramen, 62
functions, 62
movements, 110, 112 (Table 6–5)
veins, 259, 261
Vertical plane, 5
Vertigo, 223, 224
Vesicular murmur, 311
Vessels (*see* Arteries, Veins, Arterioles, Venules, Capillaries, Lymph vessels)
Vestibular:
ganglion, 170
glands, 403

Vestibular (*cont.*)
membrane, 221
nerve, 170
Vestibule:
of ear, 222
of female reproductive system, 401, 403
Villi of small intestine, 333
Villus, intestinal, typical, 333
Virginity, and hyman, 403
Viscera, 9
Visceral:
motor:
endings, 151
pathways, 181
sensations, 181
Vision:
acuity, 217
binocular, 215
blindness, inherited, 217
color, 212
defects, 215–217 (*see also specific disorders*)
detailed, 217
impulses of, 212
monocular, 215
physiology of, 212
stereoscopic image, 214
tunnel, 217
twilight, 212
Visual:
cortex, 208
fields, 215
image, 212
pathway, 208, 212
pigments, and vitamin A, 212
purple, 217
reflex, 168
sense, 208–217
Vital capacity, 310
Vitamin(s):
A, and rhodopsin, 217
B-complex, 344
and large intestine, 335
B$_{12}$, and intrinsic factor, 331, 341
deficiencies, and gum disease, 86
fat-soluble, 337, 341
importance to body processes, 359
K, and coagulation, 282, 284
deficiency, and hemorrhage, 284
and large intestine, 335, 344
metabolism, 359
storage, in liver, 337
water-soluble, 337
Vitreous:
body, 208
chamber, of eye, 208
humor, 208
Vocal:
apparatus, 317, 318
folds ("cords"), 317
Vocalization, 317, 318
Voice, 318
Voicebox (*see* Larynx)
Vomer, 55
Vomiting, and motion sickness, 224
Vulva, components, 401 (*see also specific parts*)

W

Wakefulness:
and cerebral cortex, 200
and hypothalamus, 162
and thalamus, 162
Walking, 139
Wallerian degeneration, 199
Warmup, 97